D0990139

THE MAPPING OF AMERICA

THE

OF

MAPPING AMERICA

Seymour I. Schwartz
and Ralph E. Ehrenberg

This edition published in 2001 by

WELLFLEET PRESS
A division of Book Sales, Inc.
114 Northfield Avenue
Edison, New Jersey 08837

Published by arrangement with Dr. Seymour I. Schwartz

Editors: Patricia Egan and Reginald Gay
Designer: Philip Grushkin
Picture Editor: Lois Brown

Library of Congress Cataloging in Publication Data

Schwartz, Seymour I. 1928-
The mapping of America.

Bibliography: p. 352
Includes index.
I. Cartography—North America—History.
I. Ehrenberg, Ralph E., 1937- joint author.
II. Title.

GA40I.S38 912'.7 79-24113

ISBN: 0-7858-1319-5

Originally published by Harry N. Abrams, Incorporated, New York.

Printed and bound in Spain by Bookprint, S.L., Barcelona

CONTENTS

PART TWO

SINCE 1800 Ralph E. Ehrenberg

NOTE ON THE CAPTIONS FOR MAPS

Unless otherwise noted, maps are on paper. Manuscript maps are drawn in pen and ink, unless specified otherwise. In dimensions, height precedes width.

To Ruth
who opened my eyes to the
fascination of old maps
S. I. S.

To Tessa
R. E. E.

PREFACE

THIS BOOK on American cartography, which draws from a broad spectrum of scholarly studies, has been written for the general reader. It has two major purposes. One objective is to present a detailed, analytic history of the mapping of North America, emphasizing that area which comprises the United States. A second and equally important objective is to demonstrate that a map is often more than a visual record of boundaries; it may also be an expressive work of art. The earliest maps are far more artistic than factual and utilize a variety of graphic mediums. Manuscript maps are in pen and ink techniques, often embellished with watercolor, oil paint, and gold leaf. The printed maps range from simple woodcuts to elegant copper engravings on handmade paper and even on silk. Maps of the nineteenth and twentieth centuries are characteristic examples of lithography, cerography, photography allied with graphics, and even computer technology. Thus this series of important historical documents reveals a metamorphosis from artistry to science.

Two major periods are considered—the first extending from 1500 to 1800 and the second from 1800 to the present. The year 1500 was selected as an appropriate starting point for two reasons: fifteenth-century fanciful and imaginative maps, which were primarily products of rumor and speculation, are not pertinent to a serious historical examination, and early prototype maps that scholars are convinced existed have not been uncovered. The first 300 years of American cartography extend from the discovery of a new continent through the early years of a newly formed nation. The earliest maps of this period, those of the sixteenth century, reflect the explorations along the eastern coastline, then the expeditions into the interior and the initial efforts of setting up colonies. In the seventeenth century permanent colonization is finally successful, and maps now define internal boundaries, embryonic communities, and protective forts. Maps of the eighteenth century concentrate on battles, first in allegiance to an English or a European crown and then in the struggle for independence. The maps at the end of the eighteenth century exhibit a brief respite from battle: the boundaries of individual states are more precisely defined and the beginnings of an aggressive westward expansion are evident.

The second period of American cartography, that including the nineteenth and twentieth centuries, shows an acceleration in westward expansion. The blank spaces in the interior of the continent are filled in as uncharted areas are organized into territories and as territories later are divided into states. Rivers and mountain ranges are more accurately located and man-made avenues of transportation appear, including canals, post roads, highways, and railroad systems. Small settlements expand and amalgamate into large urban areas. Changes in appearance of these maps parallel and reflect social, political, and technological progress. The cartographic precision achieved in the modern age of mapping is a vivid expression of American industry and the application of its technology.

Many of these maps present cogent evidence that the defining of an idea graphically does not necessarily establish it as absolute and incontrovertible fact. The historian Henry Wagner has suggested that "there is nothing that has such an air of verisimilitude as a map," but delighted skeptics have unmasked as myths many seemingly unequivocal truths. The focus of this first essay in the comprehensive mapping of North America is to show cartographic progression, both as historical statement and as artistic development. Maps that first expressed significant geographic and political changes and established the basis for subsequent maps are illustrated and discussed in detail. These maps highlight America's heritage by providing a graphic picture of the nation and an illustrated chronicle of its evolution.

SEYMOUR I. SCHWARTZ

ACKNOWLEDGMENTS

THE CALIBER of the first seven chapters was notably increased by the efforts of four people. Reginald Gay's editorial contributions significantly enhanced the text, James Hudak's skill is evident in the quality of reproduction of the many photographs he supplied, and Lois Brown's selection of ancillary illustrations added a new dimension to the book. Beyond this, special citation must be made of the very considerable role of Wendy Cowles Husser, whose interest and care extended over the entire project. She served as researcher, editorial assistant, and gentle prodder with a pleasantness and equanimity that eased my task.

SEYMOUR I. SCHWARTZ

IN THE PREPARATION of the last three chapters I have relied upon the interpretive and informative works of that trinity of scholars to whom all historians of modern American cartography are indebted—Walter W. Ristow, Herman R. Friis, and Carl I. Wheat. Ristow has provided the foundation for the study of commercial cartography through his extensive writings based on the vast map holdings of the Geography and Map Division of the Library of Congress, with which he was associated for more than thirty years. Friis, former director of the Cartographic Records Branch of the National Archives, has contributed numerous articles and books describing the important role of the Federal government in mapping and charting the United States. Finally, Carl Wheat, lawyer by profession and cartophile by preference, synthesized the cartography of western exploration in his monumental five-volume work, *Mapping the Transmississippi West.*

Since most of the maps reproduced in this section are based upon original maps in the National Archives and the Library of Congress, I am indebted to the cartographic reference staffs of both institutions. Dr. Ronald Grim, Raymond Cotton, and Linda Cullember of the National Archives, and Richard Stephenson, Andrew Modelski, Gary Fitzpatrick, James Flatness, and Patrick Dempsey of the Library of Congress were most helpful. Dr. Herman Viola of the Smithsonian Institution provided both encouragement and assistance. Finally, I am particularly grateful to Patricia Egan, Senior Editor at Harry N. Abrams, Inc., for her careful and insightful editing of the manuscript.

RALPH E. EHRENBERG

PART ONE

1500-1800

SEYMOUR I. SCHWARTZ

1. *Mapping a New Continent– The First Decade*

In past days I wrote very fully to you of my return from the new countries... and it is lawful to call it a new world, because none of these countries were known to our ancestors, and to all who hear about them they will be entirely new.

AMERIGO VESPUCCI
Mundus Novus (1503), published letter to Lorenzo de' Medici

1500-1510

THE MAPPING of North America was built upon the foundations of a heritage that originated in classical times and extended through the medieval era. Marco Polo's travels at the end of the thirteenth century opened up land routes between the East and the West, and as the result of the subsequent monopoly of these routes by the Italian maritime states, the ocean nations on the fringe of Europe looked to sea routes to satisfy their own motives. By the fifteenth century there were notable advances in the design of ships, which greatly improved their sailing qualities. Before the middle of the century the Portuguese were fitting out caravels, fast-sailing vessels that were able to withstand the stresses of ocean travel, and with the emergence of these weatherly ships, navigators could venture on longer oceanic voyages with some confidence of a return. Navigation methods were also being improved at the time, and a pilot could begin to determine latitude with more assurance.

The development of the science of navigation in the fifteenth century, which greatly increased the range of sea voyages, profoundly affected the content and form of maps, as did other advances, especially the new printing process with its application to the cartographer's work. The period of late medieval monastic cartography also coincided with the rediscovery of Ptolemy's *Geographia*. The celebrated Greco-Egyptian mathematician, astronomer, and geographer, Claudius Ptolemaeus, who flourished in the second century of the Christian era, is generally credited with the origin of scientific cartography. It is debatable whether Ptolemy drew any maps himself, and from the second to the fifteenth century the maps associated with him were known only to Arab geographers. But with the translation into Latin of Arabic works in the early fifteenth century and the consequent knowledge of Ptolemy among Western scientists, Ptolemy's concepts and the maps based on them then dominated European mapping for over a hundred years. During the period of the great geographical discoveries the *Geographia* was the canonical work in the field of cartography.

Geographic concepts of the world on the eve of the discovery of the Americas by Cristoforo Colombo were best expressed on the 1492 globe of the German cosmographer Martin Behaim, which is now in the Germanisches Museum in Nuremberg. Although it showed the extent of available geographic knowledge at the end of the fifteenth century, the globe could not have had a direct influence on Columbus. Behaim produced it in Nuremberg, and therefore Columbus could not have seen it, but it is reasonable to assume that he had consulted one of its prototypes. It was natural that Columbus should seek the backing of Portugal for his "Enterprise of the Indies," as he called his persistent and determined dream of reaching land by sailing west. Portugal had taken the lead in the technical achievements at the end of the century, and Lisbon was to become the maritime center during the golden age of Portuguese exploration. The search for a sea route to Cathay (China) and the Indies became the overriding motive behind the voyages and this inspired two major enterprises of the great age of discovery—the opening of a seaway into the Indian Ocean and the discovery of America. Columbus was repeatedly rebuffed in his scheme, first at the court of John II and then at the court of Ferdinand and Isabella of Spain. Perhaps as a consequence of political confidence that the Spanish monarchs gained from conquering the Moorish kingdom of Granada, Ferdinand and Isabella decided to risk the venture.

Columbus's first and second voyages antedated the discovery of the continent itself. Sailing under the Spanish flag, Columbus made landfall on the island of Guanahaní (renamed San Salvador by the Spaniards) in the Bahamas on October 12, 1492. When he reached Cuba, Columbus believed he had arrived at Cipango,

Woodcut of a caravel similar to the Santa Maria, *from the Basel 1493 edition of Columbus's official report of his first voyage*

the name used by Marco Polo for Japan, which he described as an island east of Cathay. Columbus made his second voyage in 1493–96, and during that trip, in 1494, he had the crew affix their names to an affidavit stating that Cuba was a peninsula of Asia. His third voyage led to the discovery in 1498 of South America; in 1502–03, during his fourth and final voyage, his ships traveled along the coast of Central America, from Honduras to Panama.

Columbus and his brother Bartolomeo were both chart makers, and of the maps that Columbus drew on his four voyages to America only one has survived. This sole extant cartographic record of his voyages is a sketch of the northwest coast of the Caribbean island of Hispaniola made in December 1493 on his first voyage. This map, now in the collection of the duke of Alba in Spain, includes two names that still exist as placenames: St. Nicolas Cape and the island of Tortuga, so designated for its turtle shape.

Europeans accepted the premise that Columbus had discovered a westerly route to the Indies. For over a half century Portugal had been dispatching expeditions in the search for an easterly route to the Indies and finally was successful in 1487 when Bartolomeu Dias rounded the southern tip of Africa and entered the Indian Ocean heading toward the Indies. Portugal coveted control of the East Indian islands, potential sources for the spice trade, and moved to safeguard its interests. On September 26, 1493, Pope Alexander VI issued a bull dividing the non-Christian world into two zones of influence, granting right of domain to Spain and Portugal respectively on either side of a line of demarcation. On June 7, 1494, a treaty was signed by Portugal and Spain at Tordesillas establishing this line at a meridian 370 leagues (roughly 1,175 miles) west of the Cape Verde Islands. East of this meridian all discoveries, even those made by Spanish ships, would belong to Portugal, and west of it they would belong to Spain. Except for the large area in South America that is now Brazil, the continental New World was entirely on the Spanish side.

Discounting the romantic and unauthenticated tales of Saint Brendan and the Irish monks, who purportedly discovered America between A.D. 400 and 600, and also the Norsemen's visit to Vinland between A.D. 800 and 1400, it is the English who must be credited with the modern discovery of North America. Giovanni Caboto (John Cabot), an Italian navigator sailing under patent from Henry VII of England, set forth from Bristol in 1497 in the ship *Mathew* and made the first North American landfall on June 24 of that year. It is not known whether he landed on what is presently Cape Breton Island, or on Newfoundland, but, like Columbus, apparently he believed he had reached Cathay. He embarked on a second voyage, in 1498, and although he and his four ships disappeared without a trace, the English at the time asserted that his ships had ranged as far south as Florida.

The naming of North America actually resulted from the voyages to South America. Whether Amerigo Vespucci, whose name became affixed to two continents, sailed to South America as early as 1497 has been disputed by many historians; yet there is little doubt that he made such a voyage in 1499, under the flag of Spain. In the same year the Portuguese king, Manuel I, granted to João Fernandes—a small landed proprietor [lavrador] living in the Azores—a patent to search for lands in that part of the world assigned to the Portuguese. Fernandes landed at what is now Cape Farewell, Greenland, in 1500, which accounts for the name Tiera del Lavrador. Thus Labrador, a prominent North American placename, was first delegated to part of Greenland; later it was transferred to the region of its present location on the continent in order to thwart the attempt of Martin Frobisher—the English explorer who first sought a Northwest Passage in 1576—to name that region West England.

Woodcut from Columbus's official report of his first voyage

Completing our consideration of exploration that contributed to the first decade of the mapping of North America were the voyages of the Corte Real brothers, who sailed for the king of Portugal. Gaspar Corte Real's expedition in 1500 resulted in the name Terra Verde, which designated Newfoundland on many of the early maps. He suffered the fate of many of the daring early explorers: he disappeared during a second journey to the newly discovered continent, and Miguel Corte Real, who in May 1502 followed his brother to North America, met a similar end.

The maps of North America that were produced in the first decade of the sixteenth century were crude, imprecise, and at times erroneous representations of the newly discovered land. The major European powers, first Spain and Portugal and later England, were embarking on programs of expansion and felt that establishing their claims on a document like a map would attest to their validity. By the beginning of the sixteenth century cartography was still an inexact science and was limited by the contemporary state of navigation and survey. Latitude was determined by trigonometric methods, not always accurately, and there was no method of deciding longitude at sea. The accuracy and scope of maps of the North American continent during this first decade were specifically restricted and compromised by the fact that these pictorial descriptions were based on fewer than half a dozen voyages of exploration.

To which map should priority as the cartographic genesis of North America be ascribed? The "Vinland Map," anonymously donated to Yale University in 1965, supposedly executed in 1440, was briefly credited with this primacy. The geographic areas that may have represented specific areas of North America include Labrador or Baffin Land (Helluland on the map), Newfoundland or Nova Scotia (Markland), and Cape Cod or Nantucket Sound or perhaps even the Maine coast (Vinland). These romantic associations were dispelled in the 1970s by microanalysis, which suggests that the ink contained a high concentration of titanium dioxide (anatase), a compound characteristic of commercial pigments first produced in the 1920s.

Henry Harrisse, the renowned French historian and carto-

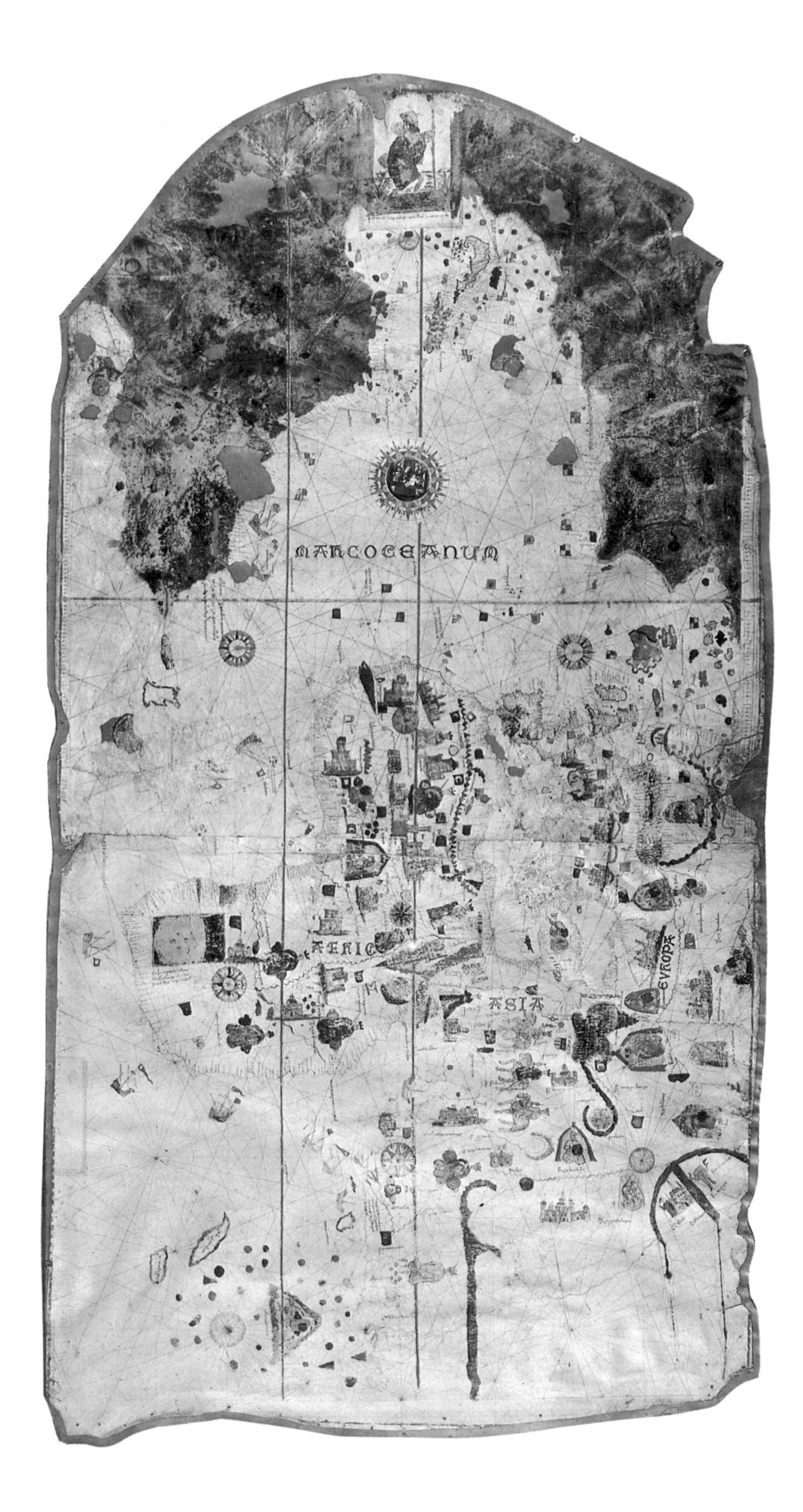

PLATE 1: Juan de la Cosa. "Portolan World Chart." 1500. Manuscript on oxhide, pen and ink and watercolor; 180 × 96 cm. Museo Naval, Madrid. *The earliest extant map showing any part of the continent of North America. The phrases "mar descubierta por yngleses" [sea discovered by the English] and "cavo de ynglaterra" [cape of England] indicate evidence of the Cabots' voyages in 1497 and 1498; the map is the only authentic cartographic record of John Cabot's expedition in 1497, when he made discovery of North America. Eleven Spanish and five English standards are drawn on the map, and the extension to the west implies that the new discoveries were still assumed to be connected to Asia.*

(opposite) PLATE 2: Cartographer unknown. "Cantino Planisphere." 1502. Manuscript on vellum, pen and ink and watercolor with gilt; 101 × 220 cm. Biblioteca Estense, Modena. *This double planisphere is the first sea chart of the sixteenth century that can be precisely dated. It ignores English voyages and reflects the Portuguese view, placing Newfoundland east (therefore on the Portuguese side) of the papal demarcation line established in 1494. Gaspar Corte Real is credited with discovering Newfoundland. First map to present Florida as a peninsula.*

graphic scholar who wrote the first great scholarly book on the mapping of the New World (*The Discovery of North America*, London, 1892), lists several maps believed to have been executed before 1500, but not one of these has been discovered. This leaves for Juan de la Cosa's portolan world chart (*Plate 1*) the distinction of being the earliest document generally regarded as portraying any part of the continent of North America. Yet both its authorship and date of execution continue to be contested.

As is true of many significant historical documents, the discovery and disposition of this one also involved dramatic coincidence. While browsing in a Paris bric-a-brac shop in 1832, Baron Walckenaer, the Dutch ambassador to France, came upon an intriguing map drawn on oxhide and bearing the signature of Juan de la Cosa and the date 1500. The ambassador surmised its importance and brought it to the attention of the German naturalist and traveler Alexander von Humboldt, who authenticated it after extensive study. Following Walckenaer's death, the map was auctioned in 1853; Henry Stevens, one of the first collectors of Americana in the United States, bid the equivalent of $200 for the map, but lost it to the queen of Spain, who bid approximately $8 more, and eventually it became the major attraction of the Museo Naval in Madrid.

The identity of the mapmaker is uncertain. Most scholars identify the name Juan de la Cosa, written on the parchment, with the great Basque cartographer who traveled on Columbus's first and second voyages—the owner and mate of the *Santa María* and one of the signers of Columbus's affidavit affirming that Cuba was part of Asia. Yet there are others who claim that its author was another Juan de la Cosa—a sailor who served on the *Niña* only during Columbus's second voyage. The inscribed date of 1500 is also under contention, since it is apparent that the Western Hemisphere portion was executed later than the European. The map could not have been drawn much before 1500 because it incorporates Cabot's voyage of 1497. It is now generally

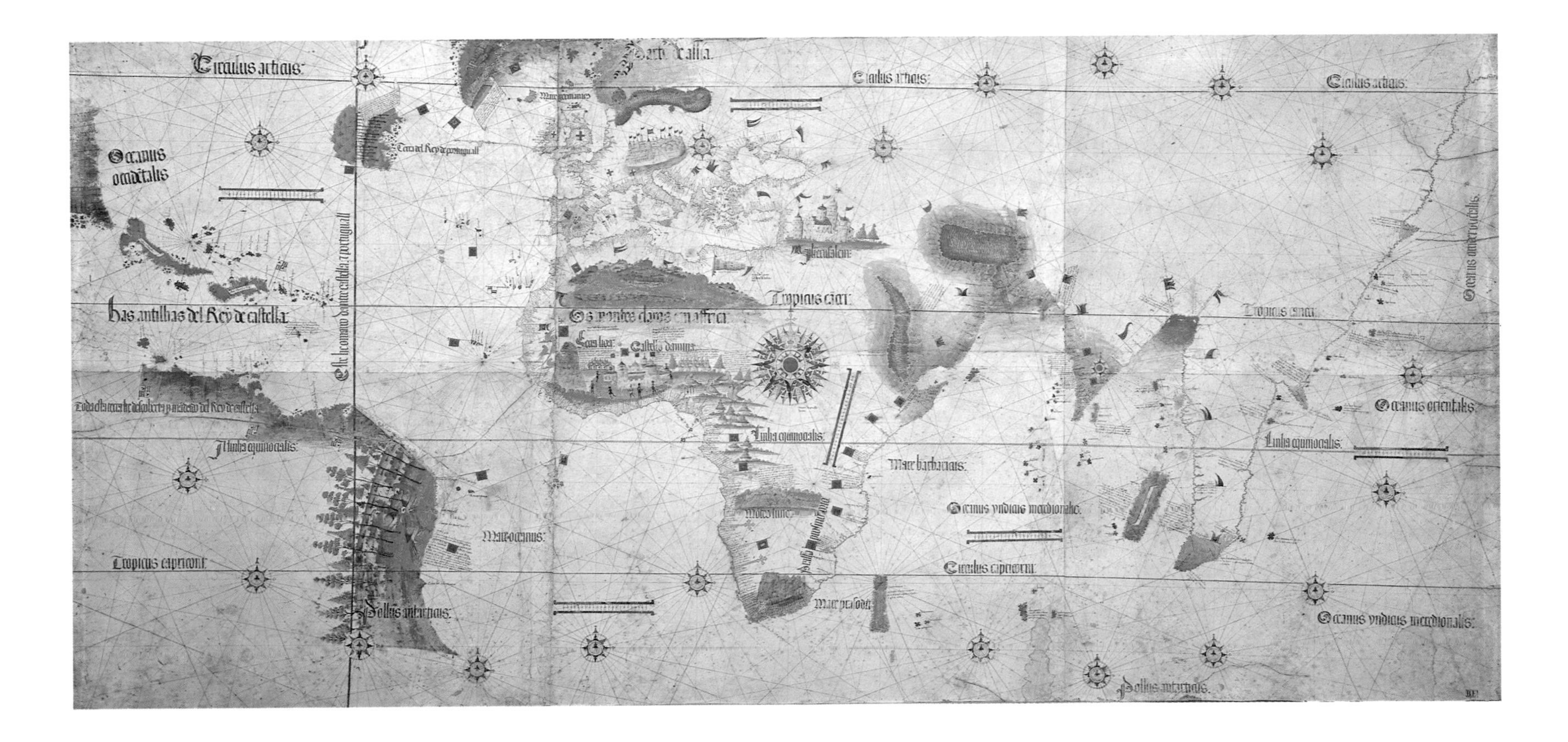

thought that the map was not completed before 1505, perhaps not until 1509. It has even been suggested that the Cosa map is actually an early copy of an original 1500 map.

Measuring 180 by 96 cm, this elegantly colored map is classified as a portolan, or sailing chart, after the style of maps drawn in Spain and Italy during the fourteenth and fifteenth centuries. The portolans, at first drawn on parchment, came into use in the thirteenth century and were made by seamen for the use of seamen. The term is properly restricted to charts that give sailing directions and generally disregard the interior of landmasses, emphasizing coasts, currents, harbors, shoals, and winds. The charts also display a system of lines emanating from the centers of compass roses, navigational aids first placed on sailing charts in the Middle Ages to designate points of the compass. Although they are lines of direction, there was no contemporary explanation for this system.

The absence of latitude and longitude and the style of projection on the Cosa map does not allow for easy identification of specific areas. On the other hand, it does proffer a chronicle of Columbus's voyages. It is the first map on which Cuba is so named, Columbus having referred to it as Iuna or Juana, paying homage to Doña Juana Infanta, Queen Isabella's daughter. Since Cuba is shown as an island, which is at variance with Columbus's concept, the map perhaps reflects the results of a voyage Amerigo Vespucci purportedly made in 1497. The significance of the map, however, relates to the North American continent. Placed along the northeastern coastline of America are five English standards. The phrases "mar descubierta por yngleses" [sea discovered by the English] and "cavo de ynglaterra" [cape of England] are irrefutable evidences of John Cabot's explorations. It has even been conjectured that the Cosa map may have been copied from an undiscovered Cabot map.

The North American continent displays twenty inscriptions, including seven capes, a river, an island, and a lake. The names are not significant since they had no influence on later place-names and are not found on subsequent maps. They were probably specific inventions of the cartographer, a common practice at the time. The map's North American geography cannot be precisely ascertained, and although there is a consensus among historians that the present Labrador–Newfoundland areas are depicted, it has even been suggested that the Gulf of Maine, the Cape Cod peninsula, and New York's Lower Bay are also de-

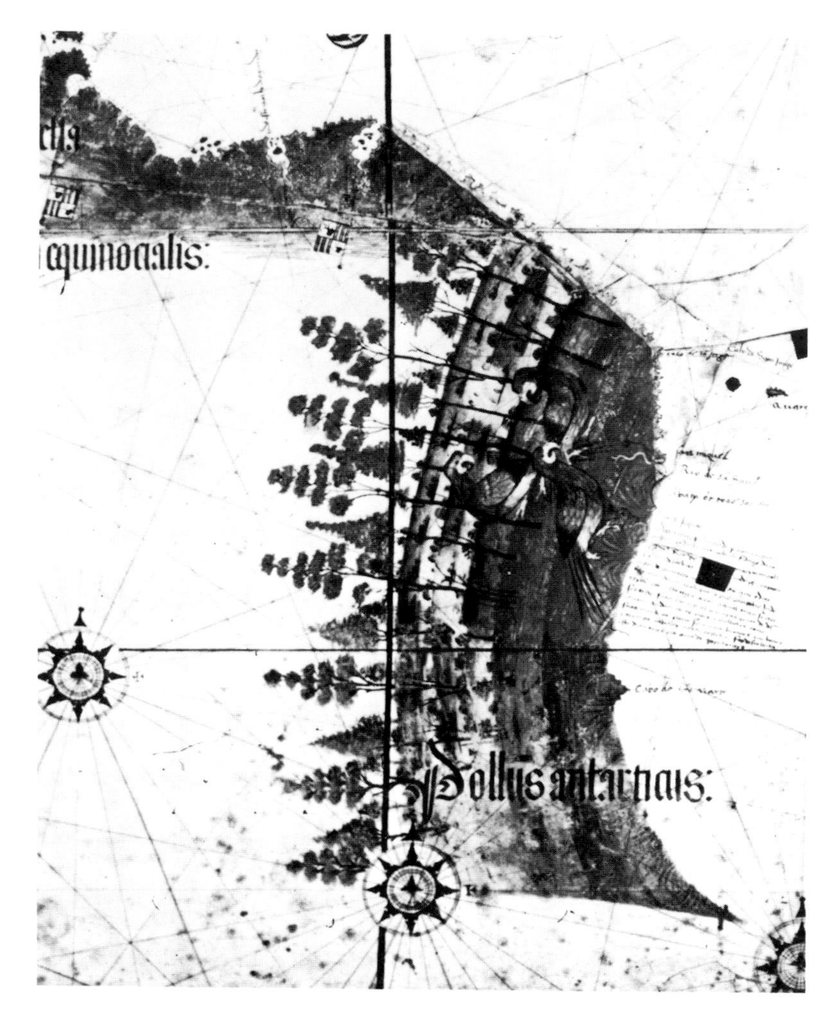

Detail from the 1502 "Cantino Planisphere" (see Plate 2)

lineated. Although the Cosa map stands at the summit of historical listings as the first map of North America, it apparently was not available to other contemporary cartographers and had little influence on subsequent mapping of the continent.

The date of 1502 for the world map known as the "Cantino Planisphere" (*Plate 2*) has been definitely authenticated, and therefore certain historians designate the Cantino map, over that of Cosa, as the earliest extant representation of the new continent. This mappemonde (the general term for a medieval world map; also known as mappa mundi) is undoubtedly the earliest Portuguese map portraying North America. Alberto Cantino was the envoy representing Ercole d'Este, duke of Ferrara, at the court of Portugal, and he was in Lisbon when two of Gaspar Corte Real's ships returned from North America in October 1501. Describing the Corte Real voyages, Cantino wrote to the duke in a letter dated October 17, 1501 (cited in Henry Harrisse's *Les Corte Real et Leurs Voyages au Nouveau-Monde*, Paris, 1883): "The land which was found was considered to be large, well watered, and covered with great pine trees and varied fruits. The land abounded with large deer, wolves, foxes, tiger, and sables, and as many falcons as there were sparrows in Italy." Fifty-seven Beothuk Indians, kidnaped from a tribe living in Newfoundland and shipped to the king at Lisbon, provided the basis, in the same letter, for a description of the inhabitants, who apparently were gentle in demeanor and somewhat taller than the average European of the time. The hair of the men was long, and their faces were marked with impressive ornamental designs. The women were described as having small breasts, beautiful bodies, and pleasant faces. The natives were "quite naked except for their privy parts, which they covered with a skin from the deer."

To supplement this letter, Cantino sent the duke a beautiful world map, which Cantino had commissioned from a cartographer in Lisbon. He was forced to send it clandestinely to Italy since the Portuguese king had placed an embargo on charts displaying the new discoveries. The subsequent history of this map is intriguing in itself. It remained in the ducal archives at Ferrara until 1592, when the entire ducal collection was transferred to Modena at the order of Pope Clement VIII, who relieved Cesare d'Este of his duchy. When the palace was looted by republicans in 1859 the map disappeared, but it was rediscovered in 1870 by the librarian of the Biblioteca Estense in Modena, who espied it being used as a screen in a butcher shop, reclaimed it, and returned it to the library. Measuring 100.5 by 220 cm, the map is a planisphere (that is, the representation of a sphere or a part of a sphere on a plane surface), and it is drawn in pen and ink on vellum with added color and gilt. Although Gaspar Corte Real found relics of the Cabot voyage in Newfoundland in 1501, it is obvious that this planisphere was oriented politically toward the Portuguese point of view, totally ignoring the English voyages.

Terra del Rey de Portuguall, the name representing Newfoundland, is placed east of its actual location. The placement was probably a political expedient, the implication being that Newfoundland was on the Portuguese side of the the papal line established in 1494. The east and south coasts of Newfoundland, from the Strait of Belle Isle to Placentia, would indicate that Gaspar Corte Real had sent home an accurate chart of the capes and bays of that island. The map gives a relatively accurate description of Greenland appropriately covered with ice but erroneously shown as a portion of Asia. Portuguese flags are placed on Greenland and Newfoundland. The west coast of Newfoundland is vague because it was still uncharted. An inscription on this island reads in translation: "This land was discovered by order of the very high and excellent prince, king of Portugual, D. Manuel, and the man who discovered it was Gaspar de Corte Real, gen-

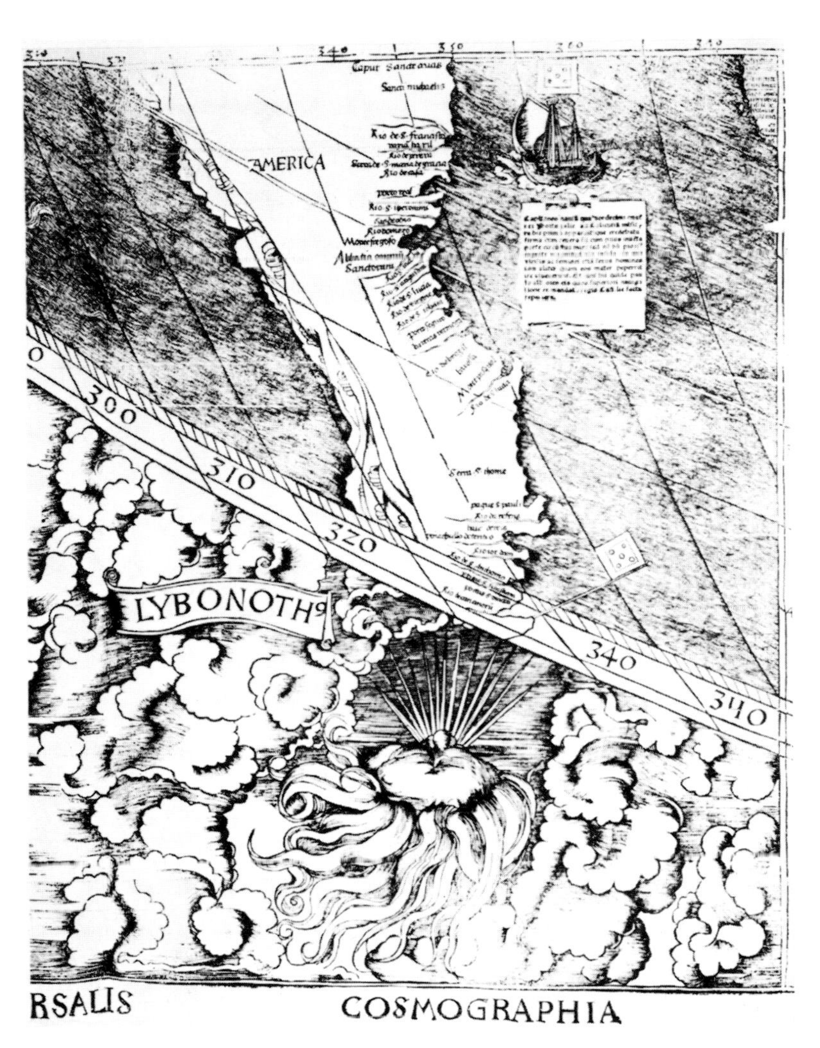

First appearance of the name "America" on a map (see Plate 4)

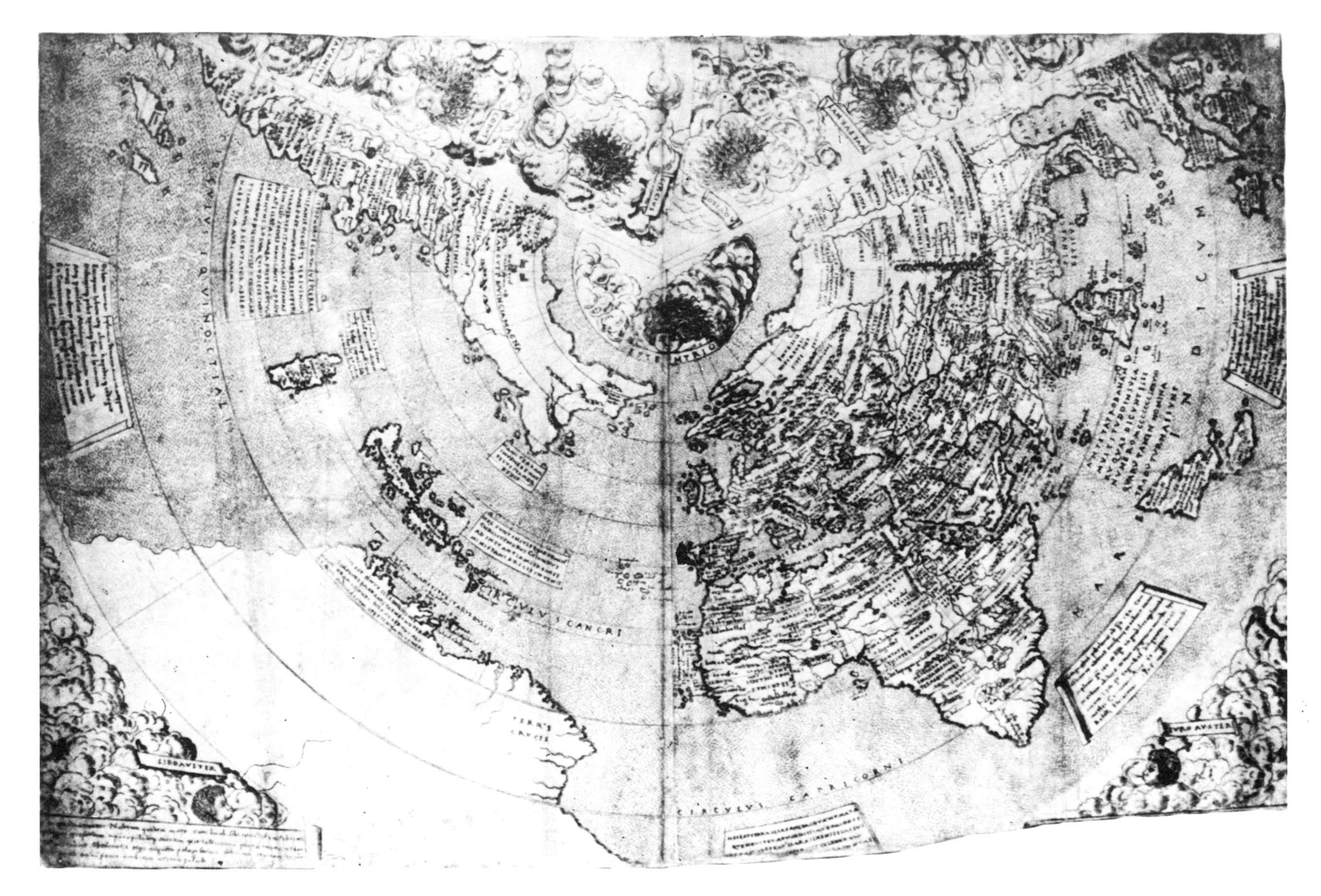

PLATE 3: Giovanni Matteo Contarini and Francesco Roselli. "A Map of the World." 1506. Engraving, 43 × 63 cm. Map Department, British Library, London. *Wide sea separates Columbus's discoveries from Newfoundland and Labrador, which are connected with Cathay (Asia). Omission of coastline to the west of Cuba is offered as evidence that the cartographer thought Columbus had reached Asia. Added evidence is found in inscription off the coast of Asia stating that Columbus sailed to Ciamba (the Orient). Explorations by the Corte Reals are referred to in a Latin statement, translated: "The seamen of the king of Portugal discovered this land."*

(opposite) PLATE 4: Martin Waldseemüller. "Universalis Cosmographia." 1507. Woodcut, 137 × 244 cm. Castle of Wolfegg, Württemberg. *Woodcut world map made of twelve wood blocks and compiled from the tradition of Ptolemy and the voyages of Amerigo Vespucci, for whom the continents are named. Waldseemüller was the earliest cartographer to sketch Columbus's western discoveries as an unambiguous and distinct new continent. First large map to show both Spanish and Portuguese discoveries. Inset (center, upper right) clearly shows the continuity between North and South America. Earliest known map with the name "America" for the New World.*

tleman of the court of said king; he who discovered it sent a ship with men and women who belonged to that land, and he went off with the other ship and never returned but was lost." The Cantino map is the first to show a peninsula in the Florida region, and, unlike the Cosa map, its concepts and delineations were copied for the next twenty-five years. The placenames, all of which are Portuguese, did not persist.

In 1892 an undated manuscript map representing the entire world as known in 1504 was found in the Archives du Service Hydrographique de la Marine in Paris. Measuring 115 by 225 cm, it was the work of the Genoese cartographer Nicolas de Canerio and probably drawn in Portugal in 1504. The geographic configurations and nomenclature are similar to the Cantino map, but a new feature, extremely important in later mapping, is its regular scale of latitude. Newfoundland, as on the Cantino map, is an island unconnected with the Florida landmass. The area, here unnamed, is again placed incorrectly in terms of longitude. A large body of open water leads to Asia (designated as Cathay). The corruption of placenames on earlier maps is also evident on this one: for the first time the name Lago del Ladro [lake of the thief] is given, a name that crops up later, on the 1508 Johannes Ruysch map "Vniversalior Cogniti Orbis Tabvla" (*see Plate 6*), as Lago del Oro [lake of gold].

Between 1504 and 1510 an attractive and little-known map, dubbed the "Oliveriana Mappemonde" was produced in Florence. This anonymous manuscript world map is now in the Bib-

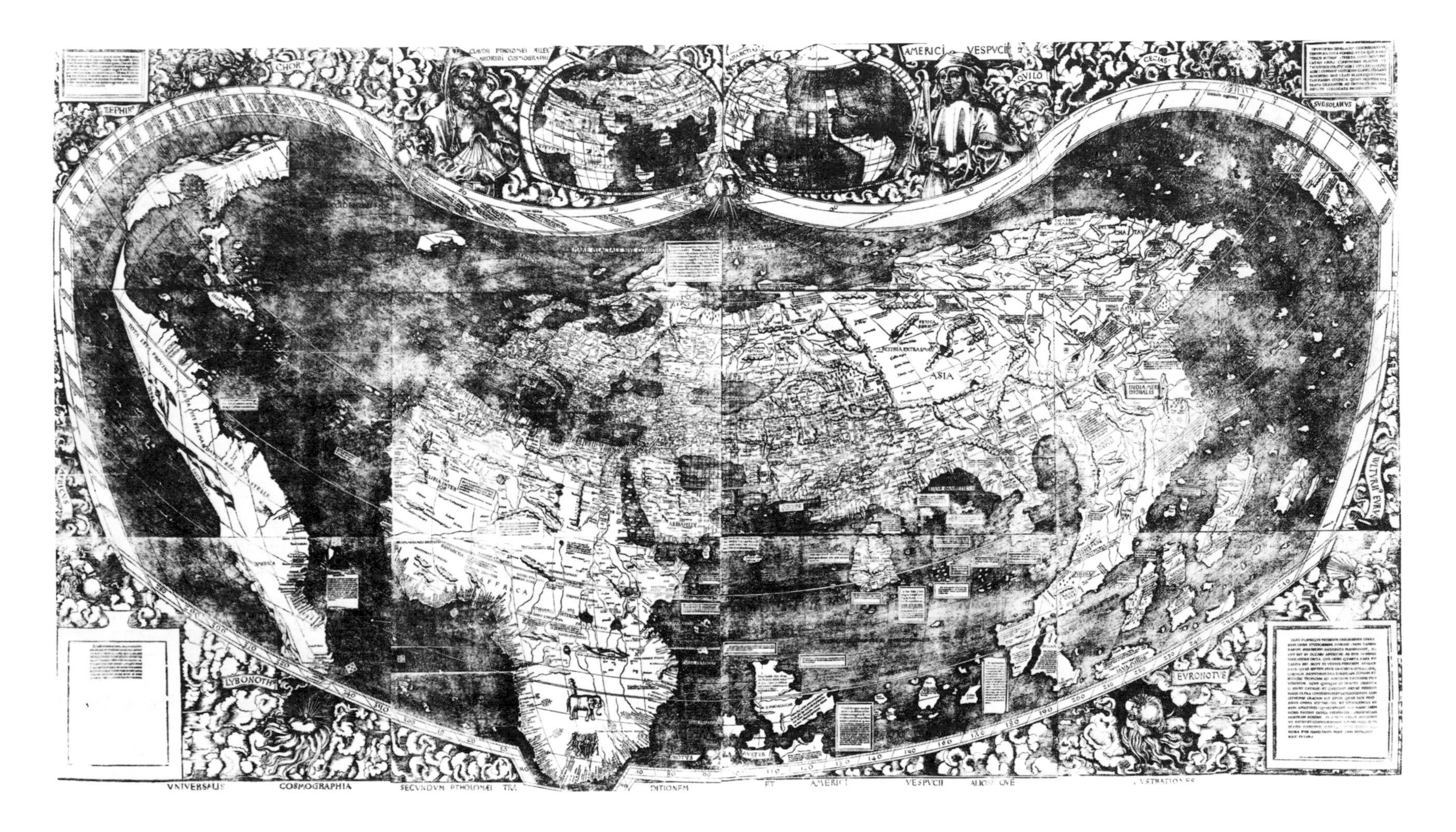

One of the earliest depictions of American Indians, apparently drawn from hearsay; Germany, c. 1505.

lioteca Oliveriana in Pesaro. It has been conjectured that it is a copy of an early map by Amerigo Vespucci and subsequently may have inspired Verrazano's search for a northern strait. Of primary interest is its representation of part of the northern portion of the New World, with three large landmasses in the North Atlantic. Cuba is shown, and to the north of Cuba is a coast that was intended as an eastern promontory of Asia. To the east of this Asian promontory is a landmass inscribed as Cava de Corte [cape of Corte; that is, Gaspar Corte Real], and Greenland appears as a large island. South of Greenland there is a second large island, called Insula de Labardor; it may be a reduplication of Greenland itself. Named in the area of Newfoundland are Cavo del Marco, Bonaventura, Rivo de los Bacalaos [river of cod], Rivo de Bosas, and Cavo de la Spera (an early map appearance of Cape Spear).

Chronologically the next map of North America is the 1506 engraved "A Map of the World" by the Italian cartographers Giovanni Matteo Contarini and Francesco Roselli (*Plate 3*); it was designed by Contarini and engraved by Roselli. Although it was unknown before 1922 when the only extant copy was purchased by the British Museum Library (now incorporated into the British Library), its existence was predicted during the 1880s by Henry Harrisse, who was convinced that an Italian map must have been a progenitor of Johannes Ruysch's 1508 map (*see Plate 6*), which was known in Harrisse's time. The Contarini-Roselli map, though not the missing prototype, furnishes salient evidence that one existed, for this map, the earliest printed document to show North America, has the same unusual fanlike form of projection as the Ruysch world map. Roselli, who was the first specialized Europan map printer and dealer, used a rolling press for printing from copperplates rather than the earlier screw press. Contarini came from a family of considerable inportance in Venice, but except that he designed this map, little else is known about his life.

The map represents an intermediary stage between the old Ptolemaic system and modern world geography. The Old World is represented by Europe, Africa, and most of Asia within the 180 degrees of longitude known to Ptolemy. Its western portion illustrates the conceptions of Columbus, but rejects his assertion that on his first voyage he reached Cipango and the coast of Cathay. It also reflects the discoveries of John Cabot and Gaspar Corte Real in the north. Although there are similarities between this engraved map and the manuscript maps of Cosa, Cantino, and Canerio, not one of them is followed closely. A wide sea passage divides the northern discoveries of the English and Portuguese from those of the Spanish in South America. This is the first known map that attempts to express a relationship between John Cabot's and Gaspar Corte Real's discoveries and the Far East; the northern part of the North American continent is a large northeastern extension of Asia and not a separate continent. Beginning at what is probably present Newfoundland, the landmass runs almost due west to Cathay. An inscription, referring to the North American continent, reads: "Hanc terram invenere naute Lusitanor [um] Regis" [The seamen of the king of Portugal discovered this land]. In the West Indies there is no continental land west of Cuba; Contarini apparently had no conception of any landmass separating the Atlantic Ocean from the Pacific. Contarini states in an inscription that Columbus, after leaving the West Indies, sailed to the land of Ciamba; that is, the Chamba described by Marco Polo on his return from Indochina. All North American placenames on the manuscript maps described earlier in this chapter reappear on this one.

The noteworthy Martin Waldseemüller map of 1507, "Universalis Cosmographia" (*Plate 4*), earns its reputation because it was the first map to include the name America. Its importance also rests on its exhibition of contemporary geography, which is radically different from all earlier maps. It was extremely popular in its day and the author states that 1,000 copies were sold, but they had all disappeared until 1901 when Joseph Fischer, a Jesuit scholar working in the library of Prince Waldburg-Wolfegg in Württemberg, uncovered a copy. He found in an old book, placed there incidentally, twelve sheets made from separate woodcuts, which when placed together comprised one map impression measuring 137 by 244 cm. Although this map does not contain a cartographer's name or a date, both the authorship and the date are established by Waldseemüller's references to it on his 1516 map, "Carta Marina Navigatoria Portugallen Navigationes," and in his book *Cosmographiae Introductio* (Strasbourg, 1507).

The map was obviously of grand proportions and was the first one that reflected both the Spanish and the Portuguese discoveries. Yet Waldseemüller's main intent was to display the information gained from Amerigo Vespucci's voyages. Vespucci was highly regarded for his knowledge and experience in navigation, and later, in 1508, was the first one to be appointed to the prestigious position of pilot major in Spain's official Casa de Contratación de las Indias [Board of Trade for the Indies] in Seville; not only was he in technical control of the Casa, he was also in charge of the Padròn Real, the official map on which new dis-

Inset from Waldseemüller's 1507 map (see Plate 4) clearly shows the continuity between North and South America

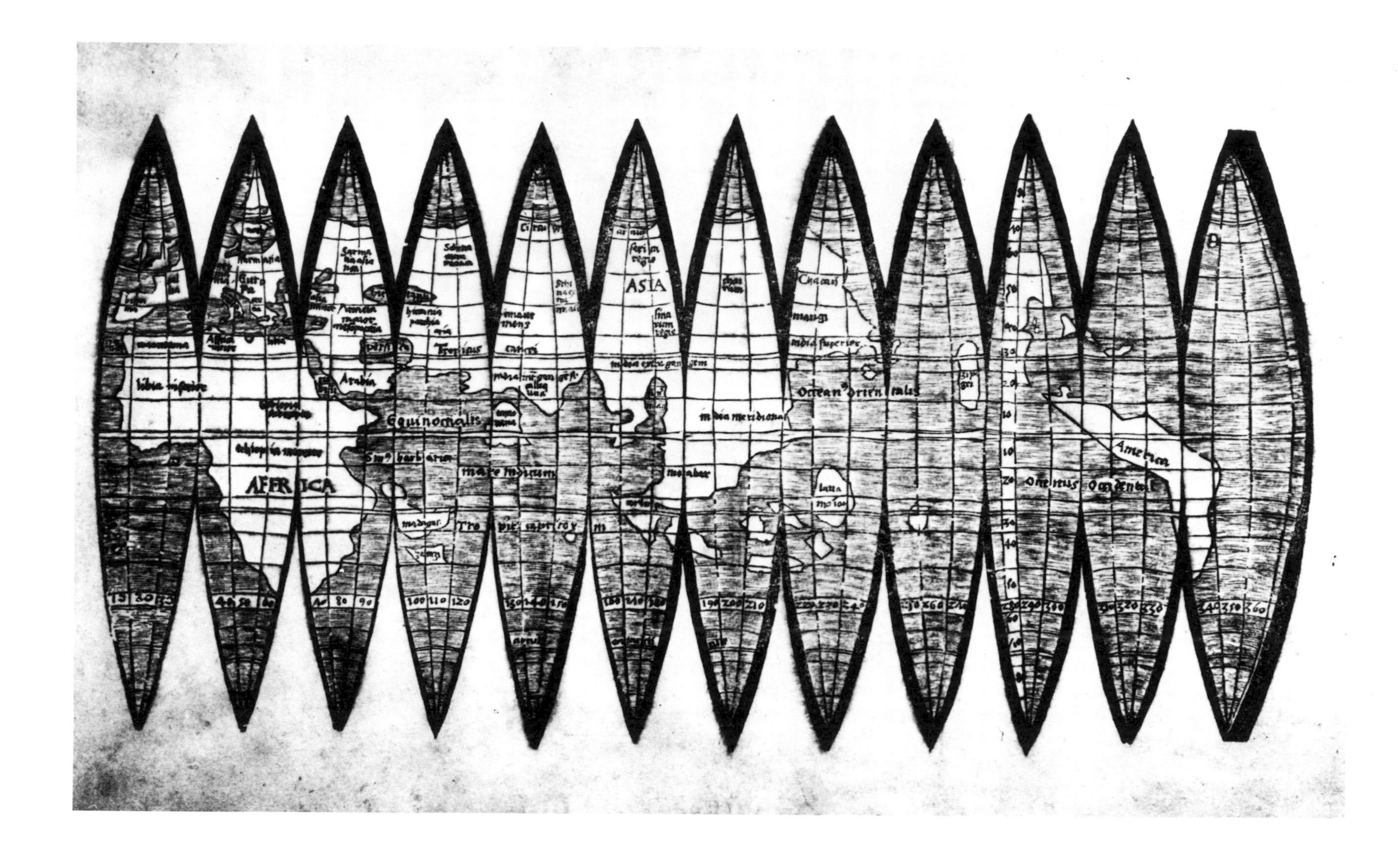

coveries were recorded as soon as the information reached Seville, which was begun by Juan de la Cosa. As in previous maps, land is shown west of Cuba on the Waldseemüller map, but its distinguishing feature is the long, attenuated form given to the whole of America. The western coast is rolled back to indicate uncharted territory, and Asia is separated from the continent by a wide gap. There is a space between North and South America on the main map, but this is contracted to a narrow strait on the small inset map (on the right at the top), where an isthmus links the two continents.

Martin Waldseemüller was a highly regarded German cartographer and artist working at St.-Dié in the Vosges Mountains in northeastern France, and his 1507 map was probably contracted for the duke of Lorraine. It was apparent that Waldseemüller placed an early confidence in Vespucci's work. Vespucci had evolved a system for computing nearly exact longitude, previously determined by dead reckoning, and he had accepted South America as a new continent rather than as part of Asia. This was a new geographical concept and radically altered cosmography at the time. In the part of the text of *Cosmographiae Introductio* describing the map, Waldseemüller wrote, "Now truly these parts [Europe, Africa, Asia] have been more widely ex-

(opposite) PLATE 5: Martin Waldseemüller. "Globe Gore." 1507. Woodcut, 25 × 38 cm. James Ford Bell Collection, University of Minnesota, Minneapolis. *The name America, honoring the explorer Amerigo Vespucci, appears on South America, which is shown as an island.*

PLATE 6: Johannes Ruysch. "Vniversalior Cogniti Orbis Tabvla." 1508. Engraving, 41 × 61 cm. Private collection. *First modern world map added to Ptolemy's* Geographia. *Newfoundland (Terra Nova on the map) is the irregular peninsula extending from Asia. Columbus's discoveries are definitively separated from Asia by a body of water, whereas those of Cabot show continuity with Asia. Published in Rome in the 1508 edition of Ptolemy's* Geographia.

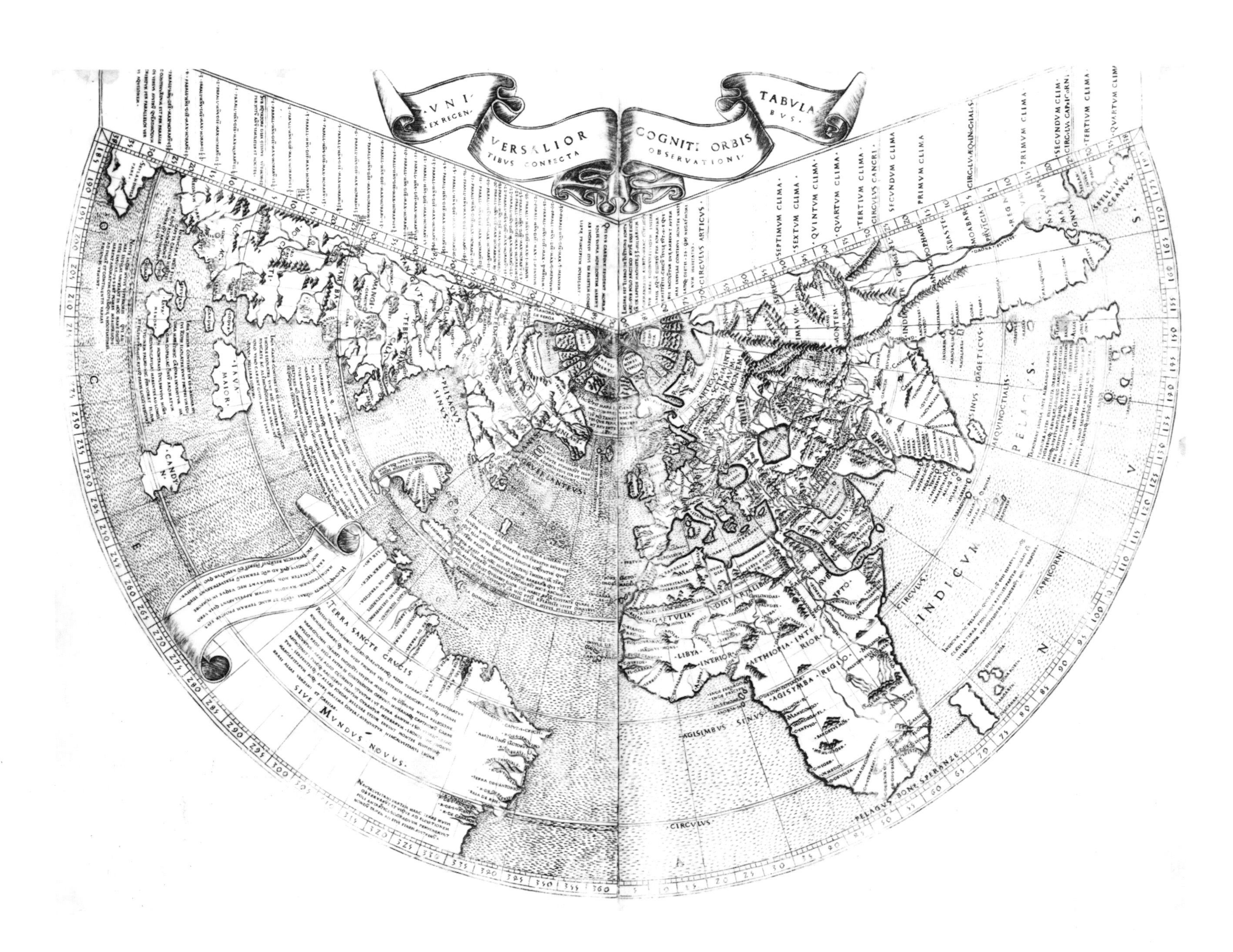

Drawings of an opossum and cannibals from Waldseemüller's 1516 "Carta Marina" are obviously based on hearsay

plored, and another, fourth, part has been discovered by Americus Vespucius (as will appear in what follows), and I do not see why anyone should rightly forbid naming it Amerige—land of Americus, as it were, after its discoverer Americus, a man of acute genius—or America, since both Europe and Asia have received their names from women. Its position and the manners and customs of its people may be clearly learned from the twice-two voyages of Americus that follow." Deciding later that Vespucci was not deserving of the honor, Waldseemüller deleted the name America from his 1516 map, but since he did not replace it with another, the name persisted, to become a salient example of the efficacy of the printed word. The import of the one name was at once appreciated by Prince Waldburg-Wolfegg, who placed a value of $300,000 on the map.

Waldseemüller's text *Cosmographiae Introductio* also describes a small globe; two copies of its gores (flattened spherical triangles joined at the equator) have survived (*Plate 5*). By 1892, when Henry Harrisse wrote *The Discovery of North America*, such a globe or set of gores had not yet been discovered, but he noted, with an air of expectation, in his classic text: "If there is very little prospect of ever discovering one of those globes, we may yet hope to find the set of gores which served to make them, printed on a single sheet; as within the last few years several series of that kind have come to light."

The remaining map in this chapter covering the first decade of the cartographic history of North America is the 1508 engraved "Vniversalior Cogniti Orbis Tabvla" (*Plate 6*) by the German-Dutch cartographer and astronomer Johannes Ruysch. It is important in several respects, one being its relationship to Ptolemaic geography; it is the first modern world map added to Ptolemy's *Geographia*. Modernization of maps occurred when Ptolemy's outlines of the Mediterranean countries were improved and the orientation of the countries was corrected. Marine charts, rather than ancient concepts, were utilized for plotting these new maps. But the transformation on maps depicting North America was gradual, first combining the old geography with the new in the 1506 Contarini-Roselli map and in 1508 in the Ruysch map. After Ruysch the Ptolemaic conception essentially disappeared.

The map first appeared in the 1508 edition of the *Geographia*, published in Rome, but has also been found in the 1507 edition as a later insert. Although extremely rare, it is the oldest map of North America still collectible since a number of copies are extant. Except for the fact that Ruysch was born in Antwerp of German parentage and that he died in 1533, little else is known about him. Certain scholars believe that he sailed on Cabot's voyages from England to America, but historical consensus has him participating in one of the Bristol-Portuguese syndicate expeditions of 1501–5 rather than those of Cabot. Ruysch's map is the first printed map of America by a cartographer who had been to the New World.

The map, which is a copperplate engraving occupying two facing pages in the *Geographia*, is a planisphere on a conical projection, with its apex at the north pole, similar to the Contarini-Roselli map. In each half the arc swings to 180° longitude, with 0° longitude placed on the line dividing the two halves. This line passes just west of Ireland and Africa. It is the first printed map on which the Portuguese discoveries along the coast of Africa were displayed. Africa itself is appropriately represented as a peninsula, and its southern point is placed at approximately the correct latitude. India was drawn as a triangular peninsula for the first time.

Its major importance relates to the New World. Ruysch pictures the northern extremity of the North American continent as a continuous coastline from Greenland to Newfoundland, merging on its western extremity with Cathay. For the first time Greenland (Gruenlant on the map) is no longer connected to Europe by a polar continent. The name Terra Nova is applied to Newfoundland, which is now west of the line of papal demarcation and out of the Portuguese domain. Newfoundland appears as a large peninsula extending from the Asian mainland rather than as the archipelago of most maps of the first half of the sixteenth century.

The name Baccalauras, an island off the coast of Terra Nova, is another early appearance of the Portuguese word for cod fish—*baccallaos*. Present Cape Race, the Cavo de Ynglaterra on Juan de la Cosa's portolan (*see Plate 1*), is given as C. de Portogesi. None of the northern names appears on previous or subsequent maps. Ruysch's representation of the West Indies is confusing. The

Stradanus's allegorical presentation of the discovery of America showing Amerigo Vespucci in Brazil; engraving by Théodore de Bry, late sixteenth century

names derived partly from the narrative of Michele de Cuneo, who sailed with Columbus and chronicled the second voyage. Cuba is not named, but on the west coast of an unnamed land, suggestive of Cuba, is the statement "Huc usque naves Ferdinandi Regis Hispanie venerut" [As far as this the ships of Ferdinand, king of Spain, have come]. An interesting inscription in the vicinity of Greenland reads "Hic compassus navium non tenet nec naves quae ferum tenent revertere valent" [Here the ship's compass loses its property, and no vessel with iron on board is able to get away].

This map, which shows the northern part of the New World as an extension of the east coast of Cathay, the North Atlantic and North Pacific oceans as one body of water, and the discoveries of Columbus separated from China by a wide ocean, is considered a landmark in cartography, but in fact it had little influence on the development of subsequent maps.

2. *A Rough Draft of the Atlantic and Gulf Coastlines*

My intention on this voyage was to reach Cathay and the extreme eastern coast of Asia, but I did not expect to find such an obstacle of new land as I have found.... The ancients... believed that our Western Ocean was joined to the Eastern Ocean of India without any land in between.... Land has been found by modern man which was unknown to the ancients, another world with respect to the one they knew, which appears to be larger than our Europe, than Africa, and almost larger than Asia, if we estimate its size correctly; I shall give Your Majesty a concise account of it.

GIOVANNI DA VERRAZANO
From July 8, 1524, citation in the Cèllere Codex

1510-1550

THE PICTORIAL representation of the coastline of a vast continent was an evolutionary process. The mysteries of the unknown shores may have been forbidding even to the sturdy and adventurous navigators of the fifteenth and sixteenth centuries, but the inchoate ideal of accuracy, besides the obvious exigencies of navigation, led eventually to some verisimilitude. Some of the earliest maps may appear as not much more than crude likenesses, especially when compared with modern sophisticated cartographic methods.

The maps produced between 1510 and 1550 were still based on a small but increased number of explorations. Those of the second and third decades of the century did not incorporate new discoveries. They merely mirrored those voyages described in Chapter 1, thus exposing a cartographic lag in representing the vast uncharted regions. England at the time was not a serious contender in the political struggle for land and wealth. France vigorously entered the competition for the purported wealth of the new continent, while Spain exploited the footholds it had already established in the Western Hemisphere, using Puerto Rico, Cuba, and Mexico as nuclei for expansion.

It was not until mid-century that significant alterations on the maps of the New World occurred. Spanish explorations in the south and west, coupled with French incursions along the Atlantic coast and in Canada, resulted in the beginning of an accurate estimation of the American coastline.

The 1511 portolan atlas of the Genoese cartographer Vesconte de Maggiolo (or Maiollo) is significant historically as the earliest Italian delineation of the northern part of the New World. In the same year a woodcut cordiform (heart-shaped) world map, following the Cantino prototype (*see Plate 2*) and outlining Cuba correctly, was published in Ptolemy's *Geographia*. Another 1511 (or 1512) map, showing both Cuba and Española (Hispaniola), is credited to Peter Martyr (Pietro Martire d'Anghiera), an Italian humanist and historian who wrote extensively about the early explorations; this was the first map of the New World printed in Spain. Peter Martyr, who was teaching at the Spanish court, was well placed to hear about the new discoveries. His map of the West Indies was suppressed in Spain—it included landfalls not previously made public and their locations may have been too accurate. In 1512 a woodcut mappemonde by Jan ze Stobnicy (Joannes de Stobnicza) was published in Krakow (*Plate 7*). A cartographer, philosopher, and apparently a Franciscan friar, Jan was noted for his work on metaphysics and occupied the chair of cosmography and natural sciences at the university in Krakow. Only one extant copy of his map, which appeared in his *Introductio in Ptholomei Cosmographiam*, is known, now in the Österreichische Nationalbibliothek in Vienna. Historians had for years agreed that this was the first map example of a continuous coastline between North and South America, but the presentation is so similar to the inset map on the large 1507 Waldseemüller map (*see Plate 4*) that it is now judged a plagiarism.

In the most significant edition of Ptolemy's *Geographia* of the sixteenth century, published in Strasbourg in 1513, there are two maps that are important in the history of Western Hemisphere cartography. Probably drawn by Waldseemüller, they employ the same nomenclature as the 1504 Canerio map and show the northeast coast of North America and the coast of South America as one continuous coastline. A comment in the accompanying text gives the source of one of the maps, "Orbus Typus Universalis," as "the admiral," probably a reference to Columbus. The other map, "Tabula Terre Nove" (*Plate 8*), exhibits a greater portion of the Western Hemisphere; it includes Cuba as well as a landmass to the west of Cuba, abutting the edge of the map so that there is no indication of a western coast.

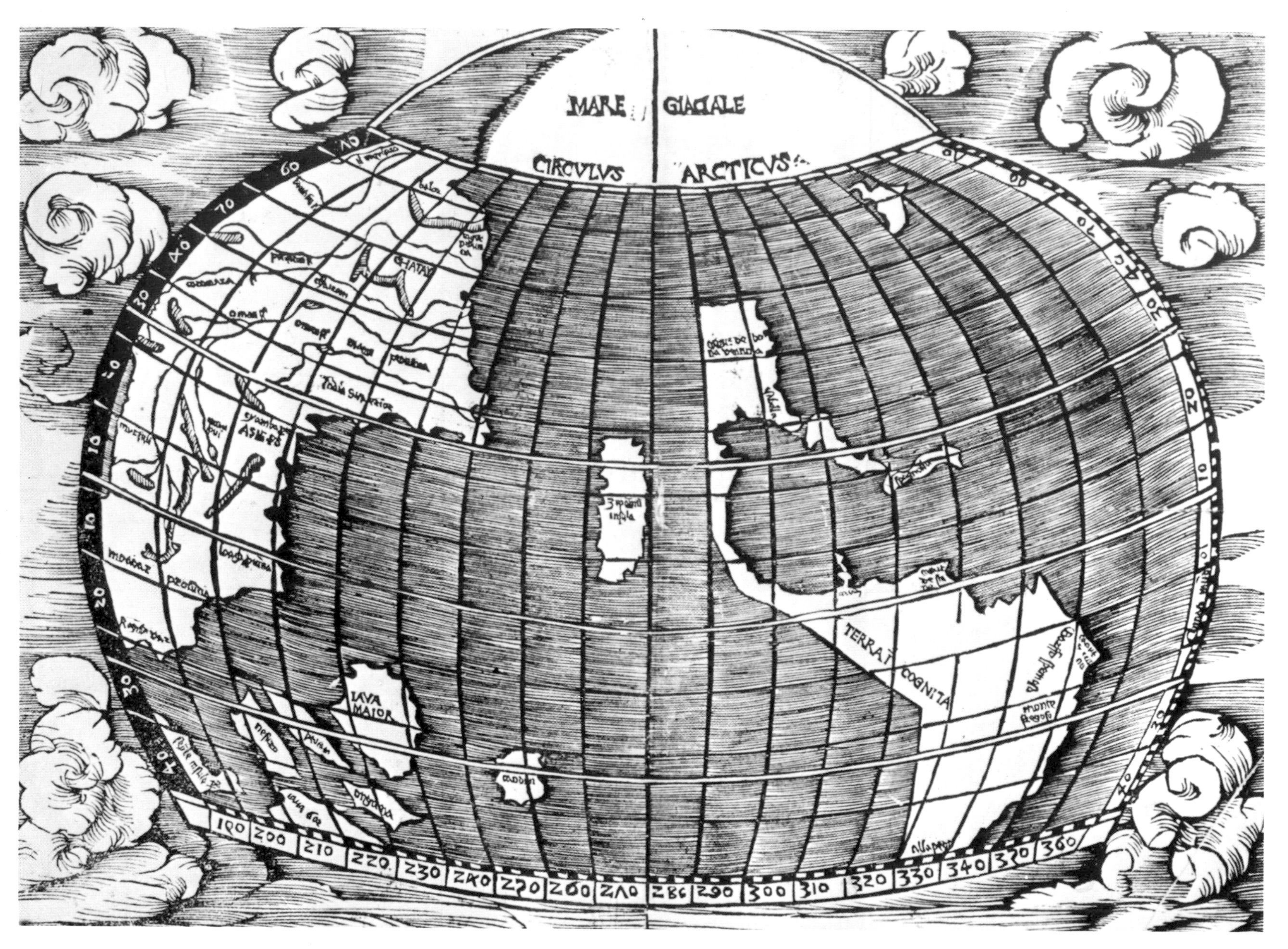

PLATE 7: Jan ze Stobnicy. "Mappemonde." 1512. Woodcut, 27 × 38 cm. Österreichische Nationalbibliothek, Vienna. *For a time this map was regarded as the first to show a continuous coastline between the two continents, but it represents a plagiarism from the insets on Martin Waldseemüller's 1507 world map (see Plate 4). From Jan ze Stobnicy's* Introductio in Ptholomei Cosmographiam *(Krakow, 1512).*

Gregory Reisch's encyclopedia *Margarita Philosophica Nova* (Strasbourg, 1515) includes a woodcut map showing a landmass quite similar to Waldseemüller's 1513 "Tabula Terre Nove," but the Florida area is named Zoana Mela, an error extracted from Peter Martyr's *Libretto de Tutta la Navigation de Re de Spagna* (Venice, 1504). A 1515 globe by the German mathematician, astronomer, and geographer Johannes Schöner, in the Landesbibliothek in Weimar, presented the two continental masses of

Title page from Hulsius's Kurtze Warhofflige, *Nuremberg, 1603, showing Magellan's ship,* Victoria

North and South America separated by a sea. The name America appears only on the southern region. Another globe, also ascribed to the year 1515, is the "Paris Globe" (*Plate 9*). This diminutive sphere, now in the Bibliothèque Nationale in Paris, is quite similar to the Schöner globe. The name America appears four times, but most striking is its placement, for the first time, on the North American continent. The first printed map that applied the name America to both the North American and the South American continents was drawn in 1538 by Gerard Mercator and published in the same year (*see Plate 16B*).

Waldseemüller's world map of 1516, the twelve-sheet woodcut "Carta Marina Navigatoria Portugallen Navigationes," the only copy of which is in the archives of the castle of Wolfegg, is similar to his "Tabula Terre Nove" of three years before insofar as the area representing North America is at the western border of the map and is defined by the phrase "Terra de Cuba Asie Partis" [land of Cuba as a part of Asia]. This inscription connotes a regression, which perpetuates Columbus's concept of a connection between the land he discovered and Asia.

The first voyage of the sixteenth century's second decade that influenced mapping occurred in 1513. Juan Ponce de León, an explorer of exemplary qualifications who had accompanied Columbus on his second voyage, had subsequently conquered and ruled Puerto Rico. In 1513, with a license for discovery issued by the king of Spain, Ponce de León sailed from Puerto Rico, and in April, during the Easter feast (*Pascua Florida* in Spanish), he sighted land which he erroneously believed was part of an island, naming it La Florida. The name Florida was applied to the entire southeastern portion of North America on many maps until early in the eighteenth century. The neighboring island, Bimini, had appeared on maps shortly after 1510.

As he sailed along the east coast of his new discovery, Ponce de León passed a cape that he named Cabo de las Corrientes for the strong currents in that area; the Spanish renamed it Cape Canaveral [*cañaveral* is Spanish for cane brake], which is the oldest persisting European placename in the United States. On the same voyage he discovered and reported on the strong current that is known today as the Gulf Stream. Sailing west past the Florida Keys, he landed in the area of Pensacola. In 1521, on his second voyage from Puerto Rico, he was ambushed by Indians in the region of Tampa Bay and sustained fatal wounds.

The next voyage of historical and cartographical consequence to the southeastern coastal region of North America was carried out in 1519 by Alonso Álvarez de Pineda at the behest of Francisco

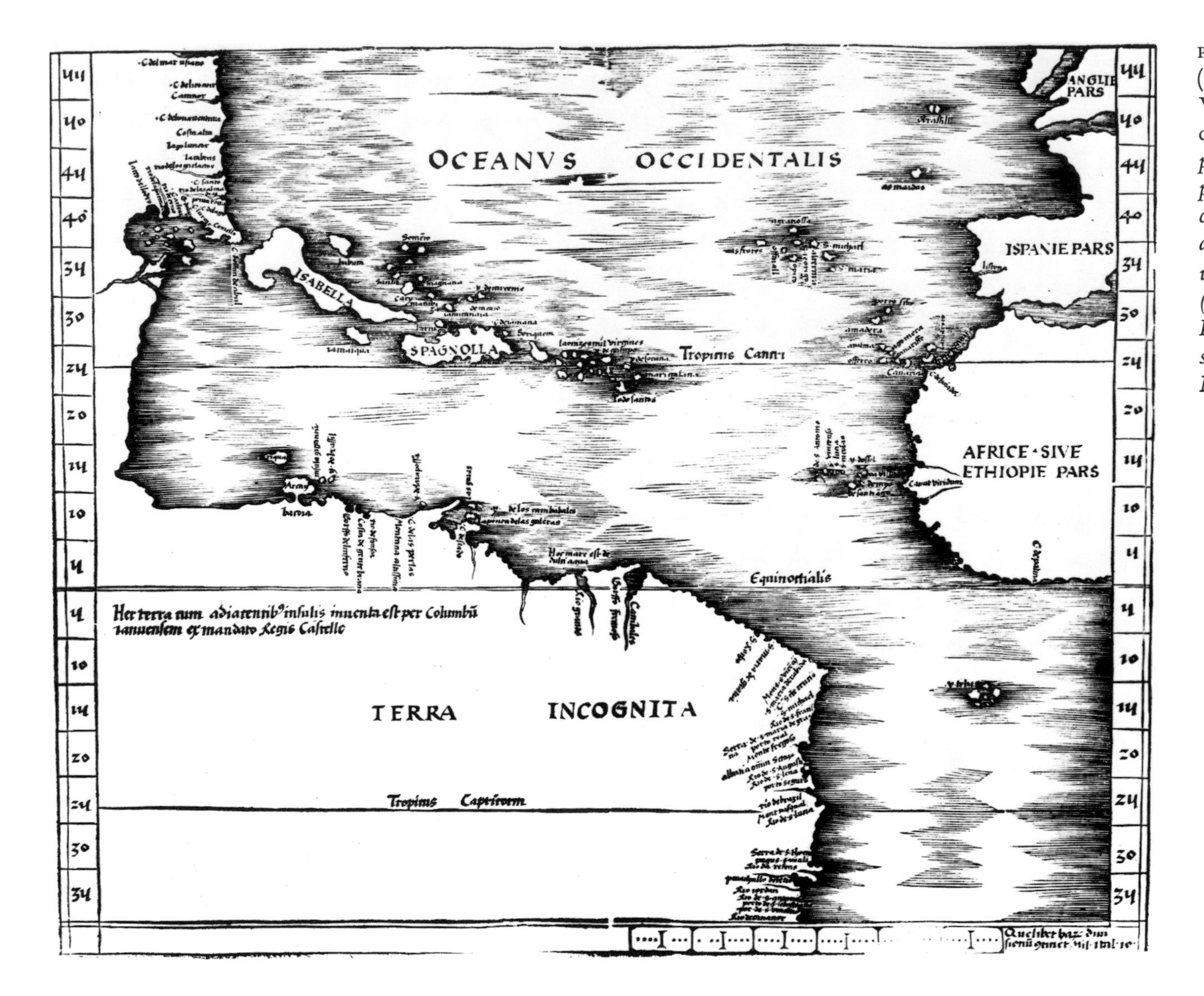

PLATE 8: Martin Waldseemüller (attr.). "Tabula Terre Nove." 1513. Woodcut, 37 × 44 cm. Private collection. *Map shows Florida peninsula, Gulf coast, and southeastern portion of the North American continent. It emphasizes the islands discovered during the Columbus voyages. From Ptolemy's* Geographia *(Strasbourg, 1513), the first edition of Ptolemy to include a map devoted solely to the islands and coasts of the New World.*

de Garay, governor of Jamaica. During a nine-month exploration that ended with Pineda's death, it was demonstrated that Florida was part of the mainland that extended from Mexico and that no passage existed from the Gulf of Mexico to the Pacific. The northern shores of the Gulf were charted during this period.

In 1521 the pilot Francisco Gordillo and Pedro de Quexos—the master of a slave-hunting caravel—sailing for Lucas Vásquez de Ayllón, a wealthy lawyer and judge of Hispaniola, landed at Winyah Bay in South Carolina. Four years later Ayllón sent Quexos on another voyage, which extended north as far as the Outer Banks of North Carolina. In 1526 Ayllón himself landed in the vicinity of the Cape Fear River and moved south to the Río Gualdape (Guadalupe) near present Wilmington, North Carolina. He established a settlement there, which included women and black slaves. It was abandoned in less than two years, Ayllón having meanwhile died; from this early settlement only the name Chicora persisted. It derived from that of a local Indian, Francisco de Chicora, whom Quexos had enslaved along with

PLATE 9: Cartographer unknown. "Paris Globe" (detail). 1515. Wood, hand painted; diameter 24 cm. Bibliothèque Nationale, Paris. *Also known as the "Green Globe," the outlines and colorings are artistically presented, continent and islands having the appearance of being raised above the seas. Area of water painted dark green, giving globe one of its common names. The name America appears in four places, and it is placed for first time on the North American continent.*

An early portrait of the American bison, from López de Gómara's La Historia General de las Indias, *1554*

other Indians. He learned Spanish and was baptized and had accompanied Ayllón to Spain in 1523 when Ayllón pleaded for a patent of possession for his discoveries. For many years Chicora was the name applied to the coastal region between Charleston Harbor and the Cape Fear River.

Several maps reflected the historical contributions of Ponce de León, Pineda, Gordillo, Quexos, and Ayllón. An interesting document, a set of eight small globe gores on which North America is depicted as two islands (Bacalar and Terra Florida), was found among the Leonardo da Vinci papers in the royal collections at Windsor Castle. It was assigned the date 1519 by one scholar but is not readily attributable to Leonardo because its inclusion of specific Spanish nomenclature indicates that it must have been drawn after 1519, the year of Leonardo's death.

The 1519 manuscript known as the "Pineda Chart" (*Plate 10*), an outcome of Pineda's expedition of that year, was the first map to show the Gulf of Mexico correctly, demonstrating unequivocally that the Gulf Stream did not flow to the Pacific Ocean. It is the first authentically dated map on which Florida is named and the first map to show Florida as part of the mainland and not as an island. It was attached to a 1521 authorization granting Francisco de Garay the right to colonize the area between "Florida formerly Bimini and Mexico." Florida is first named on a printed map on Hernán Cortés's "Map of Mexico City and the Gulf Coast" (*Plate 11*), which was published in 1524 in Nuremberg in the Latin edition of Cortes's second letter, *Praeclara Ferdinandi Cortesii de Nova Maris Oceani Hispania Narratio*. This woodcut map proffers a delineation of the Gulf coast that is amazingly accurate. It also includes a plan of Mexico City (known to the Aztecs as Tenochtitlán) as it was prior to its conquest by the Spaniards, and thus is the first published plan of a city in the New World.

The delay in the spread of geographic knowledge, or the refusal to accept new concepts, is mirrored in a manuscript world map in the Herzog-August-Bibliothek in Wolfenbüttel, Germany; it still offers Ponce de León's concept of Florida as an island. Drawn in about 1525, it is a hydrographic chart of an interrupted coastline from Florida to Brazil. The author is not certainly known, although it has been attributed to Girolamo da Verrazano, a navigator and cartographer and the brother of the explorer. The 1525 "Salviati World Map," in the Biblioteca Mediceo-Laurenziana in Florence, depicts Baya de Santa Maria, Ayllón's name for Chesapeake Bay, as an island-studded body of water. The map, whose cartographer is also unknown, is so named because it was dedicated to a member of the Florentine Salviati family, whose crest is emblazoned on the chart.

While the southeastern area of the North American continent was being explored by men established on islands in the Caribbean Sea, there were simultaneous monumental discoveries along the northeastern coast. In 1520 a Portuguese shipowner, João Alvares Fagundes, sailed along the south coast of Newfoundland and probably entered the Gulf of St. Lawrence. On a second voyage from Portugal, perhaps in 1525, he attempted to erect a Portuguese settlement on Cape Breton Island. Lasting only a year or so, it was destroyed by independent efforts of hostile local Indians and jealous Breton fishermen. In his search for a more congenial spot to settle, Fagundes discovered and mapped the Bay of Fundy. A document of this voyage describes Baya d'Agunda [watering bay]; here the crew took on fresh water. This may be a reference to a bay or tributary of the St. Lawrence River. Islands discovered during this exploration may have been the Anticosti, Prince Edward, and Magdalen islands, although Jacques Cartier is reputed to have discovered all of these in 1534. The first maps attesting to

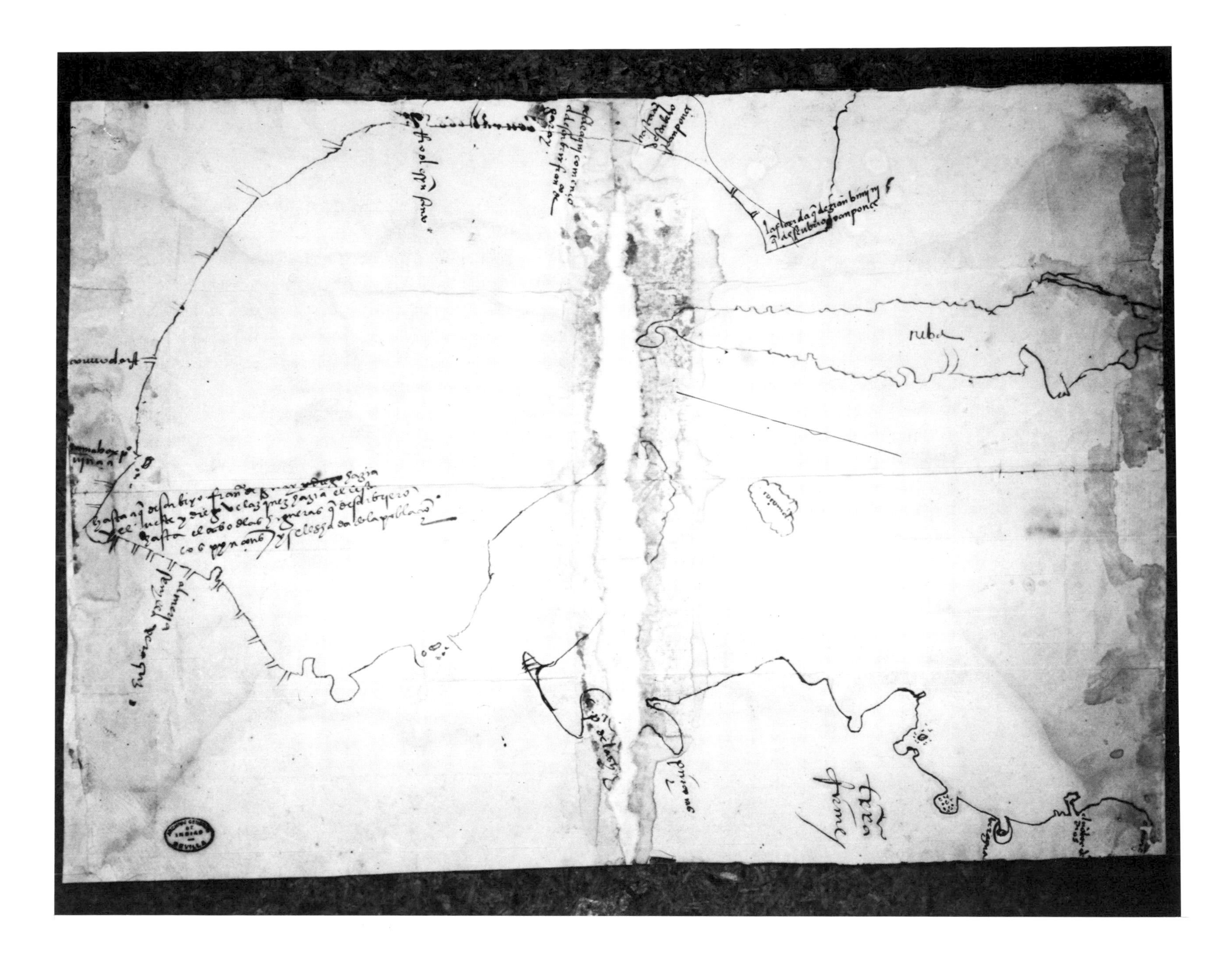

PLATE 10: Cartographer unknown. "Pineda Chart." c. 1519. Manuscript, 31 × 44 cm. Archivo General de Indias, Seville. *Map of Pineda's voyage drawn either by a member of the expedition or perhaps by Pineda himself. Earliest map to outline correctly the Gulf of Mexico, demonstrating absence of a passage from the Gulf to the Pacific. First dated map naming Florida.*

Fagundes's discoveries are the so-called Reinel-Miller manuscript map of circa 1520 (drawn by Pedro or Jorge Reinel and referred to by Harrisse in his *Discovery of North America* as "Miller Number 1") and the destroyed Maggiolo manuscript map of 1527, discussed below.

In 1524 Estevão Gomes, a Portuguese who had deserted Ma-

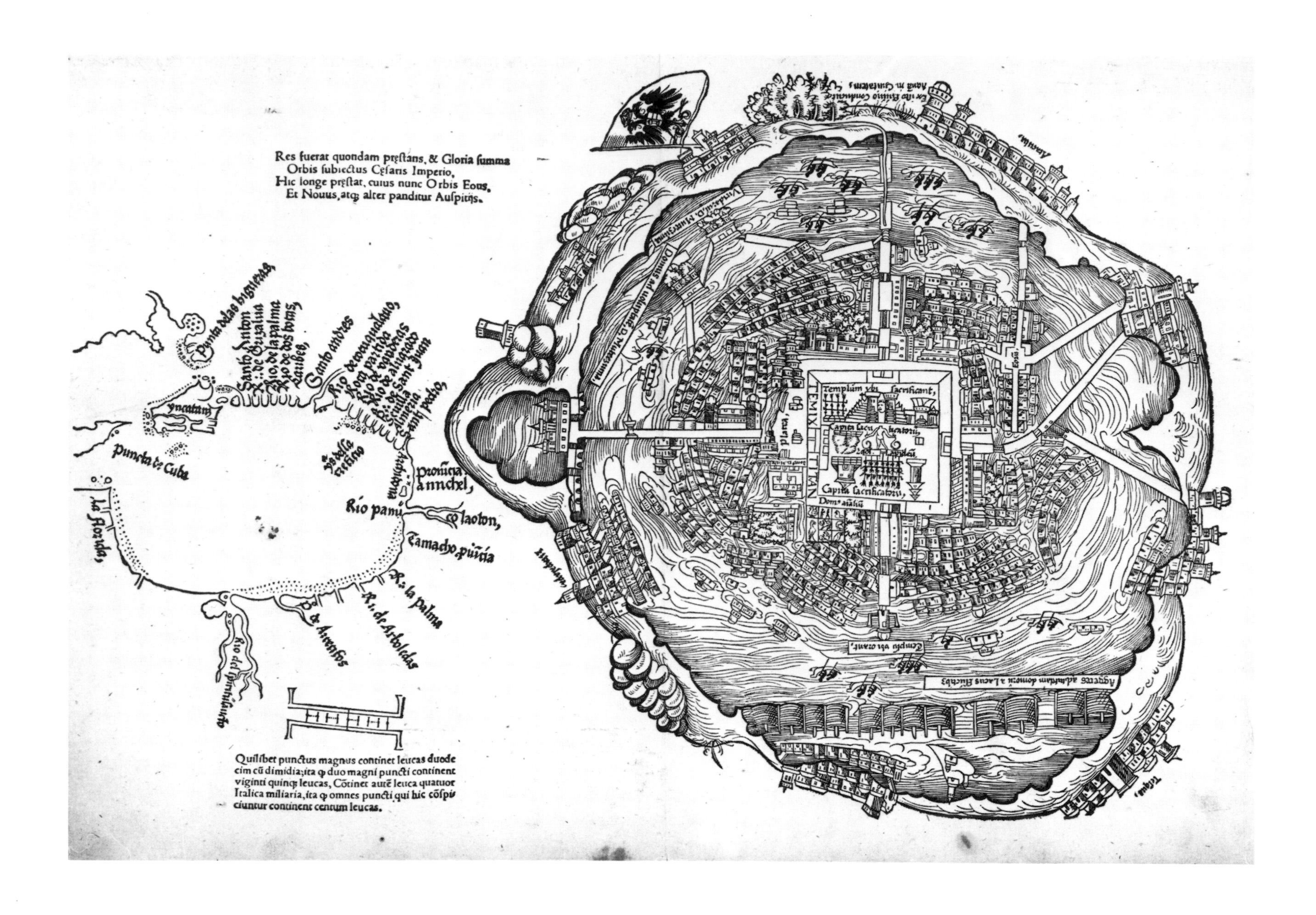

gellan during the antarctic expedition of 1521, sailed from Spain to Cuba. Bypassing the part of the coast between New York Bay and Cape Cod, later referred to as the Lost Coast, he voyaged from New England to Nova Scotia in search of a northern passage to the Orient. There is no written report of Gomes's voyage, which was first depicted on a 1525 manuscript map known as the "Castiglione World Map" (*Plate 12*). The coast actually bears little resemblance to the real geography and the Bay of Fundy is not shown. Ayllón's discoveries are also reflected. The map—so named because a tradition in the Italian Castiglioni family has it that the planisphere was a gift from Charles V to Count Baldassare Castiglione, papal nuncio of Clement VIII—does not include a cartographer's name, but certain historians have attributed it to the work of Diogo Ribeiro (Diego Ribero), a Portuguese chart maker in the service of Spain. The 1527 "Weimar Spanish Map" joined the area of Ayllón's explorations to Gomes's, *(opposite)* PLATE 11: Hernán Cortés. "Map of Mexico City and the Gulf Coast." 1524. Woodcut, 48 × 55 cm. Private collection. *The first printed map to name Florida (La Florida) and the first printed map of the Gulf coast; the earliest plan of a pre-Columbian city. Representation of the coast is surprisingly accurate in its scale and shape. Published in Cortés's* Praeclara Ferdinandi Cortesii de Nova Maris Oceani Hispania Narratio *(Nuremberg, 1524).*

PLATE 12: Cartographer unknown. "Castiglione World Map" (detail). 1525. Manuscript, entire dimensions 81 × 213 cm. Archivio Marchesi Castiglioni, Mantua. *Anonymous planisphere shows discoveries of Lucas Vásquez de Ayllón and Estevão Gomes. Drawn in the style used for Padrón General (official map of new discoveries) in Seville; earliest map to delineate the eastern coast of North America. No indication of Bay of Fundy or the peninsula of Nova Scotia. Coast from Cape Cod to Florida is poorly defined. Certain historians have attributed map to Diogo Ribeiro.*

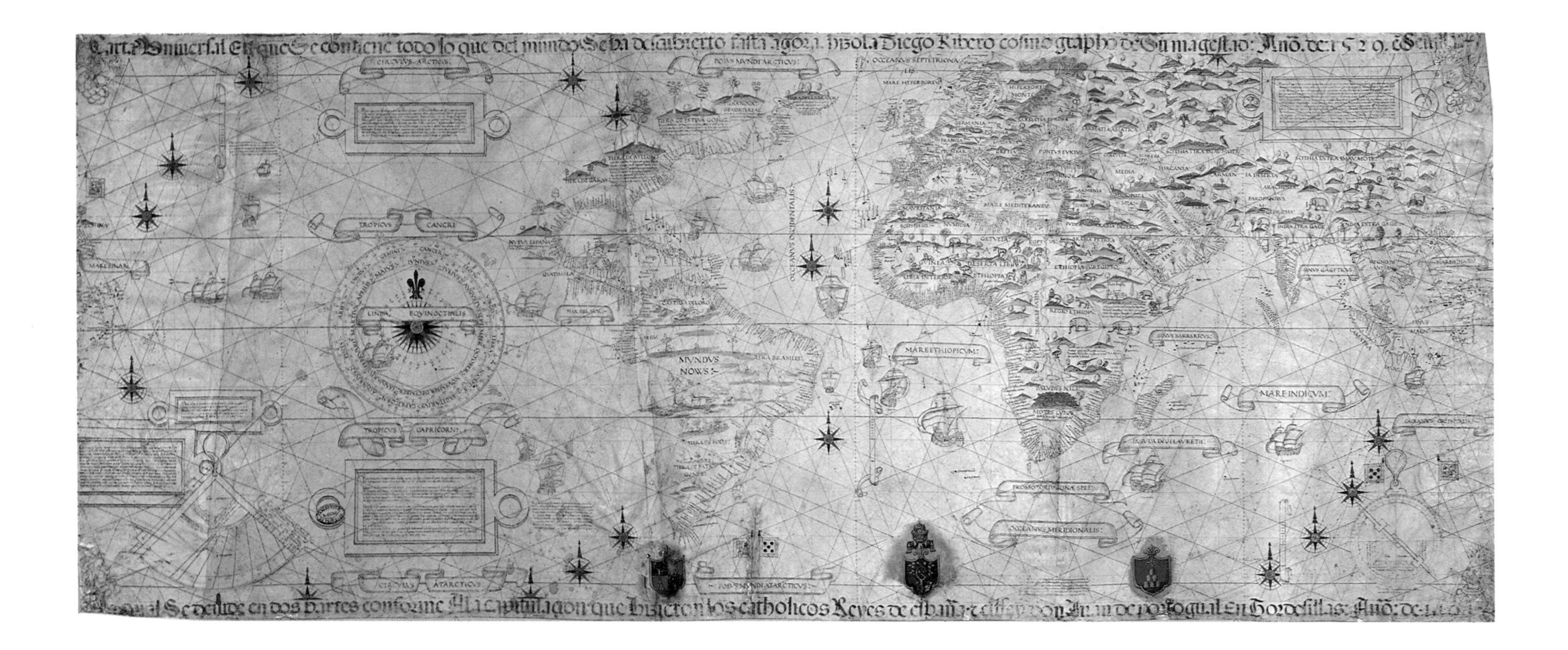

and most of Ribeiro's maps combine the discoveries of Ayllón with those of Gomes. A primary example is his 1529 manuscript mappemonde (*Plate 13*), often cited as one of the most beautiful maps of the sixteenth century. One of the most expert cosmographers of his time, Ribeiro was appointed in 1523 cosmographer major in charge of instruments at the Casa de Contratación in Seville—that great cosmographical and administrative center of Spain's overseas activities—and helped maintain the Padrón Real. Ribeiro's presentation of the North American coast was the standard for maps until the end of the sixteenth century.

Other features of the Spanish explorations on early maps are the dangerous shoals off the coast of Florida and Ayllón's Georgia and the Carolinas. The present Penobscot River in Maine, explored by Gomes, appears on "La Carte Universale," published in *Somario de la Generale Historia de l'Indie Occidentali* (Venice, 1534), edited by Giovanni Battista Ramusio. This is the earliest printed delineation of Gomes's exploration. *Islario General de Todas las Islas del Mundo* (Madrid, 1541), by Alonso de Santa Cruz, cosmographer major to the court of Charles V in Seville, included maps showing the American coast from Cape Cod to Newfoundland, including the Rio de los Gamos [river of deer], Gomes's name for the Penobscot River.

Maps engraved by Giacomo Gastaldi, particularly his 1546 "Vniversale" (*see Plate 26*), were of such stature as to perpetuate the Ribeirian-Gomes concept until the early seventeenth century. Interestingly Gastaldi's 1548 "Tierra Nueva" asserted Verrazanian geography of a continuous coastline between Florida and Newfoundland as well as a nonexistent large body of water extending eastwardly from the Pacific Ocean into the North American continent (this false Sea of Verrazano is discussed below), and thus Gastaldi perpetuated two diametrically opposed views. Other famous maps that perpetuated the Ribeirian concept of a continuous coastline (joining Gomes's discoveries in the north with Ayllón's explorations in the south) include the Gerard Mercator double cordiform map of 1538 (*see Plate 16B*), Sebastian Cabot's map of 1544, and the 1555 Gerard de Jode world map.

Spain, England, and Portugal had extended their voyages of discovery toward the New World through the inspired activities *(opposite)* PLATE 13: Diogo Ribeiro. "Mappemonde." 1529. Manuscript on parchment, pen and ink and watercolor; 89 × 217 cm. Biblioteca Apostolica Vaticana, Vatican City. *This map is considered one of the most beautiful of the sixteenth century. Inscriptions on the New World emphasize important explorations of John Cabot, Estevão Gomes, Gaspar Corte Real, and Lucas Vásquez de Ayllón.*

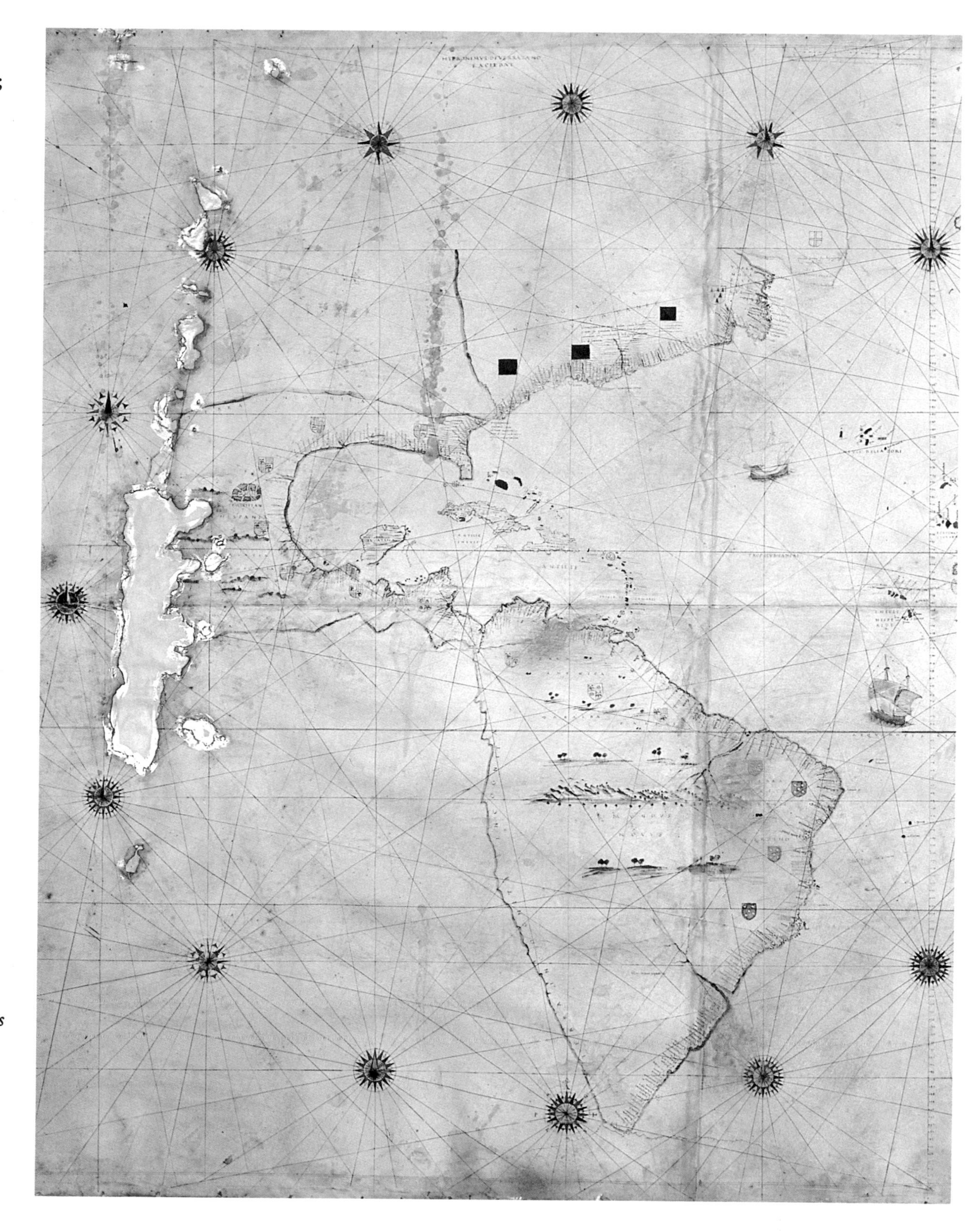

PLATE 14: Girolamo da Verrazano. "Mappemonde" (detail). 1529. Manuscript on parchment, entire dimensions 130 × 260 cm. Biblioteca Apostolica Vaticana, Vatican City. *Shows false Sea of Verrazano north of Florida. Most locations and islands in the Northern Hemisphere are placed latitudinally too high. Accepted date of 1529 is determined by an inscription over three French flags on Atlantic coast of North America, dating the voyage of Giovanni da Verrazano five years prior to map's execution.*

Giovanni da Verrazano, a 1767 engraving

of the great sixteenth-century navigators. Another powerful state entered the competition when the Florentine Giovanni da Verrazano (Verrazzano) was commissioned by Francis I, the king of France, to undertake a voyage in 1524. The primary aim was the same that pervaded the early period of discovery, a search for a sea passage to Asia, but the underlying motive was the need for wealth. France's pecuniary appetite seems to have been stimulated by large amounts of gold captured from Spanish galleons. A parallel incentive was the spice trade, and in this regard the French were doubtless spurred by the report that Magellan's one surviving ship returned to Spain in 1522 with its holds full of precious condiments. The bountiful fishing ground off Newfoundland also offered a potential source of wealth.

Verrazano's first expedition set out from Madeira Island on January 17, 1524, and lasted over seven months. It was of major importance for the mapping of North America because it definitively confirmed the concept of a continuous eastern coast. As a contribution of the first order, its only taint was the introduction of a geographic misconception that would persist for over a hundred years; namely, the Sea of Verrazano (Mare Verrazano), the erroneous notion of a large body of water leading to Cathay, separated from the Atlantic Ocean by a narrow isthmus.

Verrazano's voyage of 1524 is narrated in detail in the Cèllere Codex, named for its owner, Count Giulio Macchi di Cèllere. Authorship of the codex cannot be authenticated indisputably, but the nature of the annotations is a compelling reason to accept the explorer himself as its originator. It came to the attention of scholars in 1909, and in 1911 it was purchased by J. Pierpont Morgan. As recorded in the codex, Verrazano sailed with a single caravel, *La Dauphine*. Making landfall in the Cape Fear region off the Carolinas, he was convinced he had reached a new land rather than Asia. He sailed about 50 leagues south, and his description of this leg of the journey includes an ethnologic discussion on the Indians living in Florida north of the Gulf coast. He then headed north on a coastal voyage that extended from the Carolinas to Cape Breton and Newfoundland. From an early anchorage referred to as Annunciata, the present Cape Lookout area, he sighted a sand barrier—described in the Cèllere Codex as "one mile wide by about two hundred long"—that separates North Carolina's Pamlico and Albemarle sounds from the Atlantic Ocean. He misinterpreted it as an isthmus separating the Atlantic Ocean from a large body of water, which he called the Western Sea, extending eastwardly from the Pacific Ocean into the North American continent. Verrazano attested to his belief in the importance of this strip of land by dubbing it with his own name. For more than a century this sand barrier was erroneously considered an isthmus separating the Atlantic and Pacific oceans.

Sailing farther north, Verrazano spent three days at anchor along the Maryland and Virginia coast. He named this area Arcadia, presumably because of its similarity to the arboreal beauty of the newly discovered land described in the 1504 Italian pastoral *Arcadia* by Jacopo Sannazaro. Passing along the shores of Delaware and New Jersey, missing the entrance to Chesapeake Bay, his ship entered a bay which he named Santa Margarita, enclosed by land he called Angoulême. This first reference to the New York Harbor region was in deference to Francis I, who was also count of Angoulême. Historical consensus is that Verrazano entered the Lower Bay, the Narrows, and the Upper Bay in the New York region. He then followed the coast eastward past an island he described as resembling Rhodes, naming it Aloysia for the king's mother, although it appears as Luisa on the maps that chronicled the voyage.

The ship anchored for fifteen days in present Newport Harbor, and the name Refugio was bestowed on Narragansett Bay. The voyage continued east of Nantucket and Cape Cod and along the shores of Massachusetts and Maine. Three islands, referred to as the Three Daughters of Navarra, are perhaps Isle au Haut and Mount Desert and Monhegan islands. Maps mirroring this voyage applied the name Oranbega to the northeastern portion of the coastal region; it is a corruption of the Abnaki Indian word *norumbega*, meaning quiet waters between two rapids. The voyage's northern terminus was the Cape Breton area of Newfoundland; from here Verrazano's ship returned to France, reaching Dieppe on July 8, 1524.

The earliest extant map to show Verrazano's discoveries is a 1526 manuscript mappemonde drawn by Vespucci's nephew, Juan Vespucci. It shows an area extending from the tip of Florida to Newfoundland, with the New England coast simply a blank curve. The name R. da Sa Terazanas, placed at the same latitude as Verrazano's landfall, is likely a copyist's mistake for Verazanas. This map also includes Ayllón as the first European name for the Carolina area.

Detail from the 1540 Sebastian Münster map (see Plate 18)

The second important map influenced by Verrazano's first voyage is the 1527 manuscript world map of Vesconte de Maggiolo, unfortunately destroyed by the bombing of the Biblioteca Ambrosiana in Milan during World War II. Little significance was ascribed to this map until a close examination of the date convinced historians that an apparent 8 was really a 2, and therefore the actual dating of the map should be 1527, not 1587. Drawn only three years after Verrazano's voyage, it pictured a narrow strip of land on the Carolina coast, bordered on the west by the Mare Indicum, one of the names for the false Sea of Verrazano. To the north is Francesca and a succession of French names as well as a French flag. The map is a repudiation of a theory that North America was part of Asia, and it shows an appreciation of the actual size of the Pacific Ocean.

The third primary map depicting the Verrazano voyage was the mappemonde (*Plate 14*) drawn on parchment in 1529 by the explorer's brother, Girolamo, himself a navigator as well as a cartographer. The map, which is now in the Vatican Library, incorporates information from his brother's voyages. The Sea of Verrazano is represented but not named, and an inscription states that the isthmus between the Atlantic Ocean and the Pacific measures six miles wide. Cuba, Haiti, and Jamaica are placed incorrectly north of the Tropic of Cancer; indeed most geographic locations are latitudinally too high, while those on the Maggiolo map are too low.

Several important maps and globes are derivatives of the primary maps produced between 1525 and 1529. Some of them delineate the coast along which Verrazano sailed but do not show the false sea. The "Gilt Globe," in the Bibliothèque Nationale in Paris, is such an example; it is undated but has been ascribed to 1528. Although North America is presented as a part of Asia, the Atlantic coastline is continuous between Florida and Newfoundland and includes the Lost Coast between New York Bay and Cape Cod (the Lost Coast is so called because Gomes bypassed it and many mapmakers ignored it on their maps). The globe bears the inscription "Land of Francis lately explored." The

PLATE 15: Robert de Bailly. "Copper Globe." 1530. Gilded bronze or copper; diameter 14 cm. Pierpont Morgan Library, New York. *Shows the false Sea of Verrazano. Follows nomenclature and form of Girolamo da Verrazano's map drawn a year earlier (see Plate 14). North America called Verrazana.*

"Ambassador's Globe" of about 1530 is similar to the "Gilt Globe" but differs by depicting North America as a continent separated from Asia by a strait. This evolved into the Strait of Anian and finally the present Bering Strait, joining the Arctic and Pacific oceans.

"De Orbis Situ," a woodcut of two spheres by Franciscus Monachus, a Franciscan friar, may have been published in 1526. It would then be the first printed map to show an unbroken coastline from Labrador to Florida in addition to a representation of the North American continent as a prolongation of Asia. Several globes and maps that incorporate the findings of Verrazano's voyage reflect both his interpretation of the eastern coastline of North America and his concept of the false sea. The 1530 terrestrial copper globe of Robert de Bailly (*Plate 15*) is based in part on the Girolamo da Verrazano map; it is a good example of contemporary French expression of the new concepts about North American geography. Bailly even applied the name Verrazana to part of North America. The shape and general location of the Sea of Verrazano is similar to that shown on the 1529 Verrazano map. The beautiful double cordiform "Nova, et Integra Vniversi Orbis Descriptio" (*Plate 16A*), by the mathematician Oronce Finé and published in 1531, is the earliest engraved and precisely dated map to show the Verrazanian coastal configurations. Finé's map was frequently copied, and the double cordiform projection was borrowed by Gerard Mercator in his 1538 "A Map of the World in Two Hemispheres" (*Plate 16B*). By showing a broad strait separating the continents of Asia and North America, Mercator does not entertain the suggestion that North America is connected with Asia. His initiative in applying the name America to North America as well as to South America is one of its salient features, which therefore means that Mercator's name is to be associated with Waldseemüller's in the naming of the Western Hemisphere.

The 1543–44 manuscript oval world map of the prolific Venetian cartographer and draftsman Battista Agnese (*Plate 17*) and its derivative Atlantic hemisphere maps are the first to combine the Verrazanian and the Gomes characteristics. They display the Verrazanian false sea and a continuous coast from Florida to Bacallaos. The coast from New York Bay to Cape Cod, which Gomes bypassed, appears on the Agnese map, and the incurving Gulf of Maine, explored by Gomes in 1525, is delineated.

The concept of the Sea of Verrazano continued on the maps of Sebastian Münster published between 1540 and 1578. Münster was a German cartographer and scholar who studied at Heidelberg and for a time was a monk at the convent of Tübingen. "Novae Insvlae, XVII Nova Tabvla" (*Plate 18*), which appeared in Münster's 1540 edition of Ptolemy's *Geographia*, is the first map of the two American continents showing continuity between North and South America and no connection with any other landmass. Subsequent editions of the map were included in Münster's *Cosmographia* (Basel, 1544), which was republished well into the seventeenth century.

The 1552 world map of Giorgio Calapoda, a Greek cartographer from Crete, appeared first in manuscript and then as a copperplate engraving (*Plate 19*). Known as the "Florentine Goldsmith's Map," it gives a presentation of the false sea but gains its main distinction from the fact that it is the first dated map to show the peninsula of Lower California. The false sea concept was continued by the English geographer Richard Hakluyt, who included in his *Divers Voyages* (London, 1582) Michael Lok's "North America" (*Plate 20*), which combines an accentuated

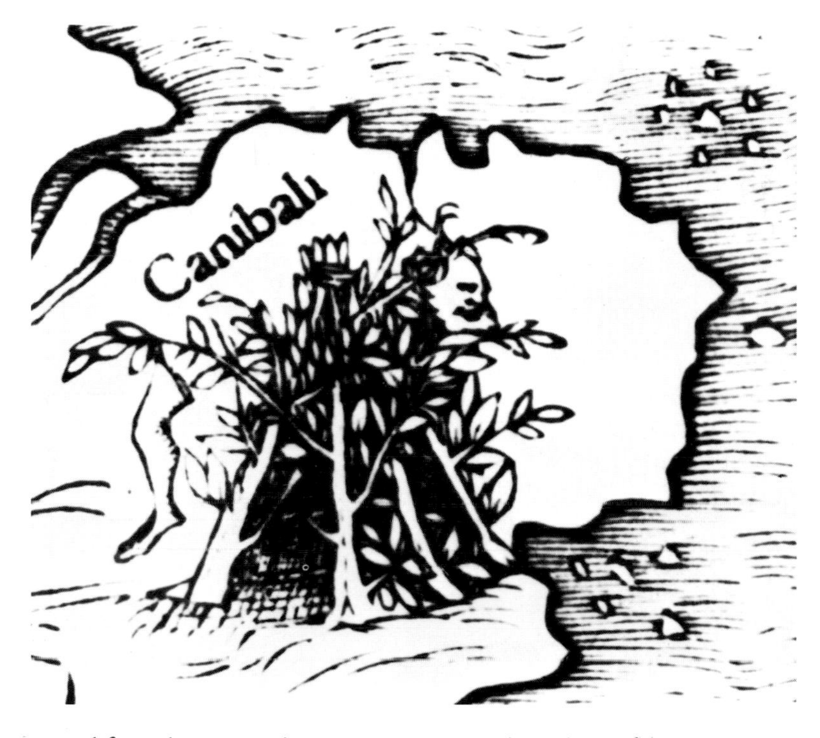

Detail from the 1540 Sebastian Münster map (see Plate 18)

PLATE 16A: Oronce Finé. "Nova, et Integra Vniversi Orbis Descriptio." 1531. Woodcut, 29 × 42 cm. Private collection. *A world map on double cordiform projection. Best contemporary representation of the concept of a North American connection to Asia. Florida is named, and Gulf of Mexico and West Indies are delineated. Map copied by many; in 1538 Mercator used this form in his famous world map (see Plate 16B). Published in* Novus Orbis *(Paris, 1532) by Simon Grynaeus and John Huttich.*

(opposite) PLATE 16B: Gerard Mercator. "A Map of the World in Two Hemispheres." 1538. Engraving, 33 × 55 cm. Rare Book Division, New York Public Library; Astor, Lenox and Tilden Foundations. *The first world map compiled by Mercator and the first map to distinguish between, and to name, both North America (Americae pars Septentrionalis) and South America (Americae pars Meridionalis). Mercator's concept that the earth was divided into three parts, the Old World (Asia, Europe, and Africa), America, and Continens Australis was heretical, and his 1595 atlas, posthumously published, was placed on the* Index Librorum Prohibitorum. *Only two copies of the map survive, one in the New York Public Library and the other, from a 1578 edition of Ptolemy, in the library of the American Geographical Society, now at the University of Wisconsin at Milwaukee.*

false sea with a delineation of Gomes's description of Cape Cod. It was not until 1587 that Hakluyt published in his Paris edition of Peter Martyr's *De Orbe Novo* a map eliminating the false sea.

Several important maps feature the Lost Coast. One of these is the "Harleian Mappemonde," drawn about 1544, attributed to Pierre Desceliers (*see Plate 23*). It also shows a strait cutting across the isthmus to the broad waters of the Verrazanian false sea, supposedly permitting a direct route to the Spice Islands and Asia. The "Paris Globe" and the maps of Finé and Agnese record the region, while Gastaldi's 1548 "Tierra Nueva" was the first printed map to show only the northeast portion of North America. Gastaldi's map includes the name Larcadia (Arcadia), designating one of the specific regions named on Verrazano's voyage of 1524.

The next major voyage of exploration that greatly affected mapmaking was also carried out for the French king. Paving the way for this voyage was the 1533 declaration of Pope Clement VII, which stated that the papal bull of Alexander VI that led to the 1494 Treaty of Tordesillas, dividing the New World between Portugal and Spain, pertained only to land already discovered.

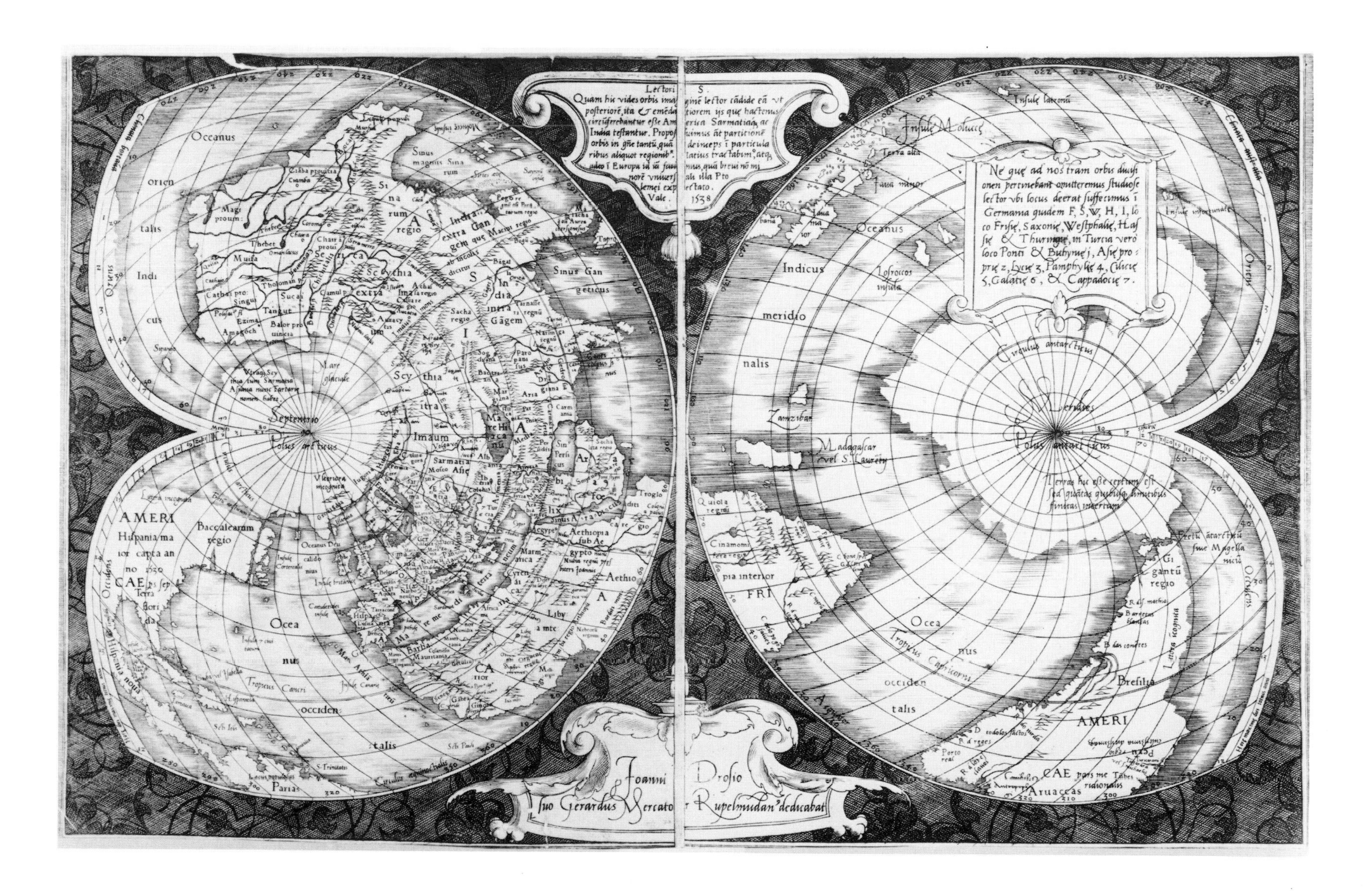

PLATE 17: Battista Agnese. "World Map." 1543–44. Manuscript on vellum, pen and ink and watercolor; 22 × 28 cm. John Carter Brown Library, Brown University, Providence. *Shows Sea of Verrazano and coast of Cape Cod and Gulf of Maine, combining the discoveries of Giovanni da Verrazano and Estevão Gomes. Found in a potpourri of manuscript maps owned by Charles V, known as the Charles V Atlas.*

With the acquisition of new lands thus allowed, Jacques Cartier sailed with two ships from St.-Malo in April 1534 on the first of his three voyages. After making landfall at Cape Bonavista in Newfoundland, the ships harbored nearby at Ste. Katherine, now Catalina. They then sailed north to Isle des Ouaisseaulx, so named for the large number of birds nesting there, including the flightless and now extinct great auk; for obvious olfactory reasons the island was named Puanto [stinking] on Guillaume Le Testu's 1555 "Terre de la Floride" (*see Plate 25*) and the same stimulus may account for its present name of Funk Island. Making way to the northern entrance of the Gulf of St. Lawrence, Cartier stopped at Les Dégrat (L'Anse Dégrat). Samuel Eliot Morison, in *The European Discovery of America: The Northern Voyages* (1971), romantically reflected that at least two explorers, Cartier and Cabot, and perhaps a third, Leif Ericson, were drawn to this very spot.

Sailing north across the Strait of Belle Isle, the ships entered Chateau Bay on the south shore of Labrador—the bay was familiar to contemporary French fishermen—and continued on to Blanc Sablon, named for its white sand. At this point Cartier sighted two nearby offshore islands, now known as Isle au Bois and Greenly Island. Cartier's ships proceeded up the St. Augustine River, which he had named St.-Jacques River, and then along the western coast of Newfoundland, where an impressive fishing ground was encountered. Making a clockwise circle in the Gulf of St. Lawrence, he named many capes, rivers, and bays. In *La Première Relation de Jacques Cartier* (his account of his first voyage, which was unpublished until recently), he noted that his observations suggested a passage between Newfoundland and the "land of the Bretons" (Cape Breton Island) and that it would greatly reduce the sailing distance from France; he actually missed such a passage (Cabot Strait) on his first voyage. After leaving Chaleur Bay, so named by Cartier, the ships continued to present New Brunswick and then sailed along the Gaspé Peninsula, where

Indians gathering seabirds, from Historiae Canadensis, *1664*

contact was made with the Huron Indians—their chief, Donnacona, allowed his two sons to join Cartier on his return to England. After leaving Gaspé Bay and the Détroit [Strait] de St.-Pierre (now Cartier Passage), the voyage of reconnaissance ended and Cartier returned home anticipating a second trip in search of a route to Cathay.

Only one extant contemporary map shows the findings of Cartier's first voyage without incorporating information gained from his second voyage. It is the manuscript "Map of North America and West Indies" (*Plate 21*), made in 1542 by the French cartographer Jean Rotz; Rotz worked in the service of England and dedicated the map to Henry VIII. It depicts the Gulf of St. Lawrence, but it records no regional placenames. The gulf's north coast represents Cartier's voyage, but the islands generally referred to as Toutes Isles are greatly multiplied. The outline of Newfoundland does not reflect the Cartier voyage but follows a Gastaldi prototype. Another distinction is that it is the first map to display an Indian wigwam.

A 1544 world map, drawn either by a Spanish compiler or by Sebastian Cabot, John Cabot's son, was an attempt to bolster England's claim to the region (*Plate 22*). The only extant copy of this engraving is owned by the Bibliothèque Nationale in Paris. It places the site of John Cabot's discovery in the Gulf of St. Lawrence, and Henry Harrisse felt that the map represented a conscious attempt of the English to counter prevalent French claims that were based on Cartier's landings along the gulf. A peninsula in the region of Lower California is depicted as well as early presentations of the discoveries of Francisco Vásquez de Coronado and other Spanish explorers. Newfoundland, New England, and the remainder of the Atlantic coastline have a reasonably appropriate shape.

Cartier's second voyage, including 112 men in three ships, was initiated on May 19, 1535. After a landfall on Funk Island, his ships proceeded to the north coast of the Gulf of St. Lawrence. On August 9 foul weather forced them into a harbor opposite the island of Ste. Genevieve, which Cartier named La Baye Sainct Laurins for the saint whose festival fell on the next day, the first appearance of the name that now is appropriated for the entire gulf and the great river. Traversing the Détroit de St.-Pierre, which Cartier and his men believed was the specific access to the Far East, they sighted the mouth of the St. Lawrence River. In this region they captured two Indians, who informed them that

PLATE 18: Sebastian Münster. "Novae Insvlae, XVII Nova Tabvla." 1540. Woodcut, 24 × 34 cm. Private collection. *First map clearly depicting the New World as a distinct insular landmass; also stresses the continuity of North and South American continents. A prime example of the false Sea of Verrazano. Strait of Magellan is shown, and Magellan's ship,* Victoria, *is pictured in the Pacific. First appeared in Münster's edition of Ptolemy's* Geographia *(Basel, 1540).*

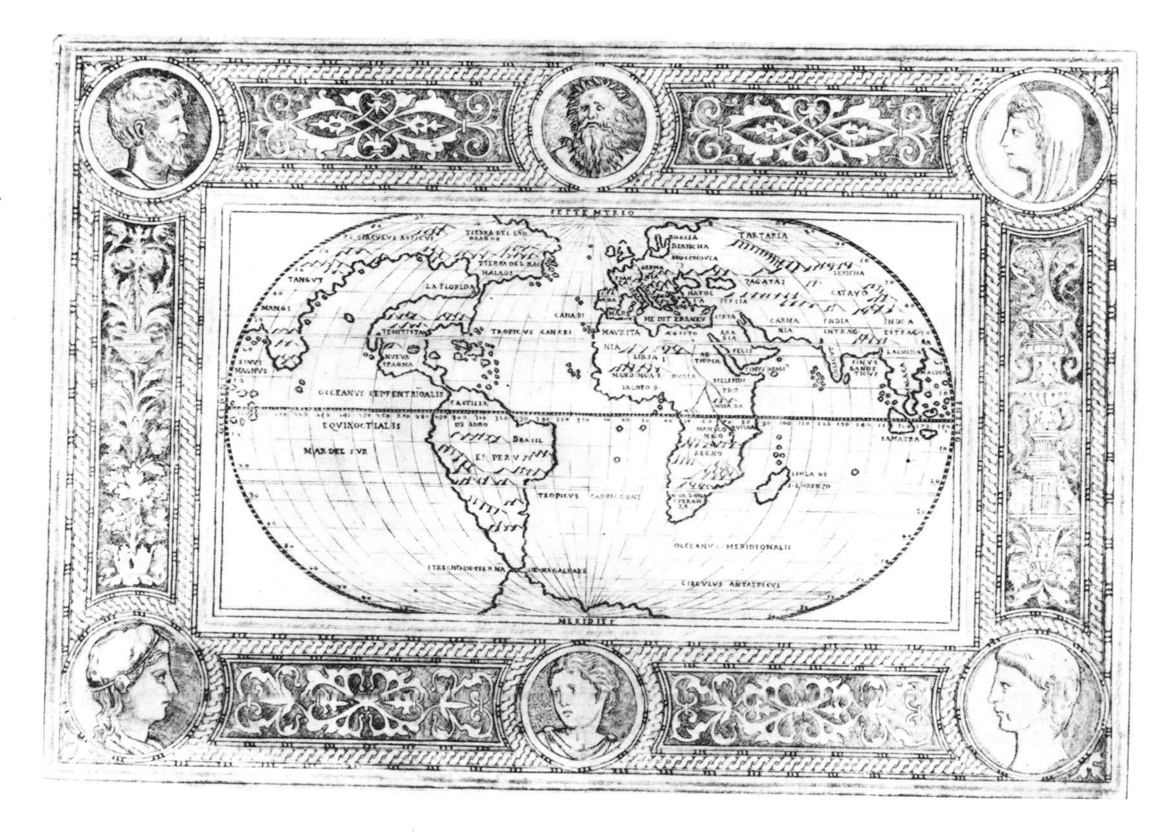

PLATE 19: Georgio Calapoda. "Florentine Goldsmith's Map." 1552. Engraving, hand colored; plate mark 29 × 29 cm. John Carter Brown Library, Brown University, Providence. *Shows the Sea of Verrazano and also demonstrates an overemphasized eastward-running North American coastline. First printed map to show peninsula of Lower California. No evidence of knowledge of Cartier's achievements. The original manuscript on vellum is in a portolan atlas of Calapoda's.*

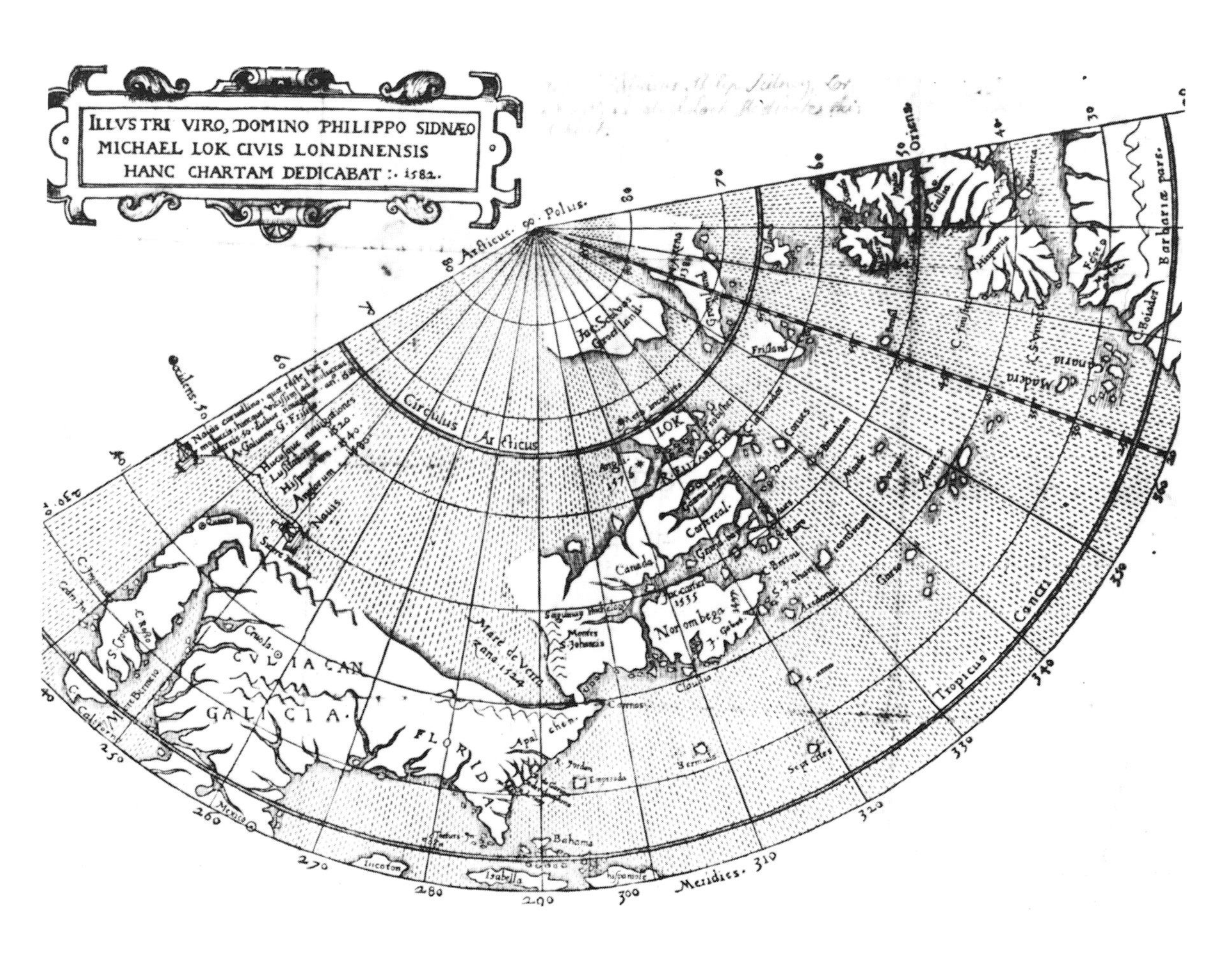

PLATE 20: Michael Lok. "North America." 1582. Woodcut, 28 × 38 cm. John Carter Brown Library, Brown University, Providence. *One of the last representations of the false Sea of Verrazano; also an early one of Martin Frobisher's explorations. Note land areas named for Queen Elizabeth I (R. [Regina] Elizabeth on the map) and Gaspar and Miguel Corte Real. Published in Richard Hakluyt's* Divers Voyages Touching the Discouerie of America and the Islands Adjacent *(London, 1582).*

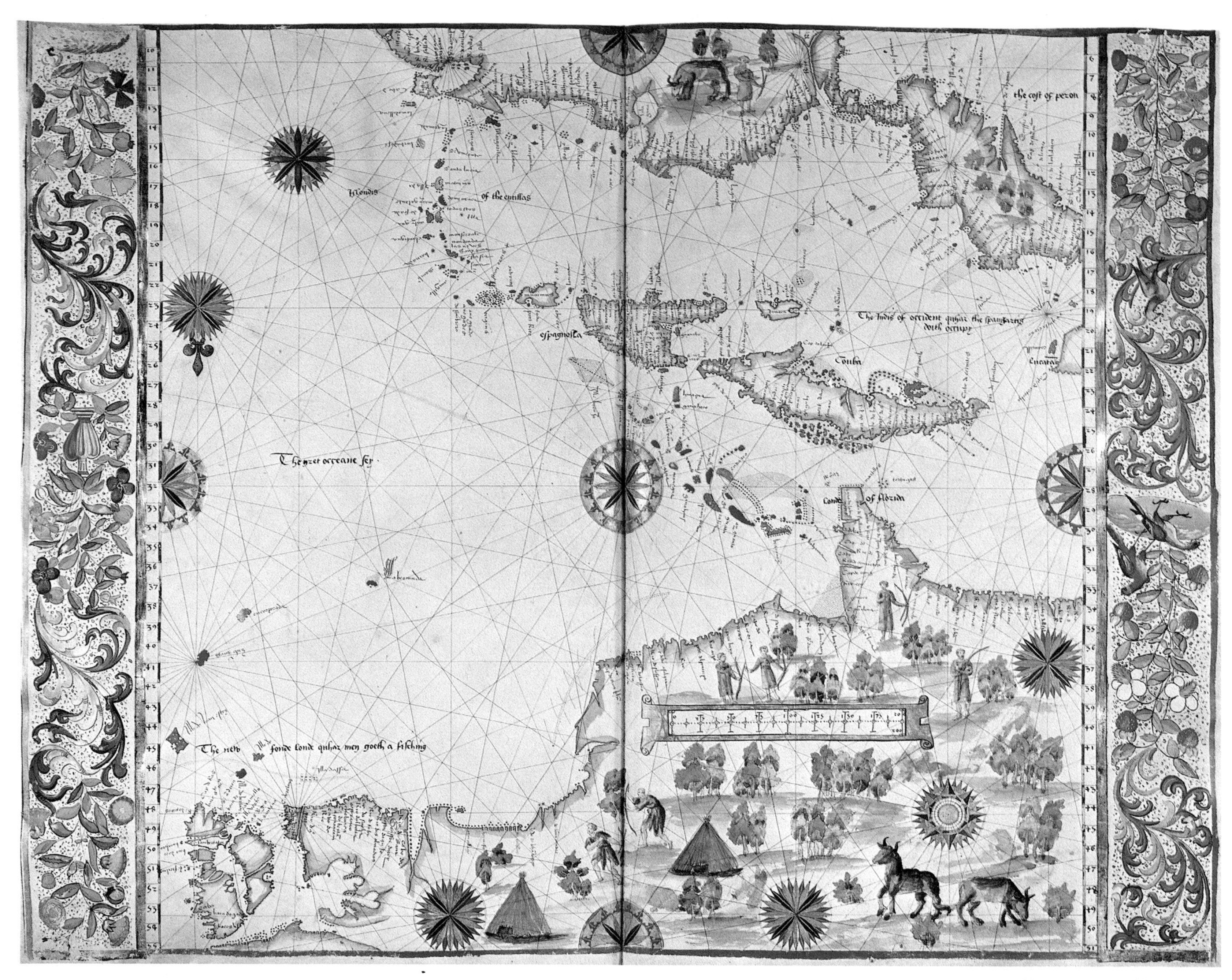

PLATE 21: Jean Rotz. "Map of North America and West Indies." 1542. Manuscript, pen and ink and watercolor with gilt; 29 × 84 cm. Department of Manuscripts, British Library, London. *Only extant map showing findings of Jacques Cartier's first voyage in Gulf of St. Lawrence. (St. Lawrence River, discovered on the second voyage, is not shown.) First appearance of wigwams on a map. Newfoundland appears as a series of islands, and a legend refers to the area as a fishing region. Map appeared in a manuscript atlas of Rotz's maps put together for Henry VIII.*

(opposite) PLATE 22: Sebastian Cabot (attr.). "World Map." 1544. Engraving, hand colored; 120 × 215 cm (including text). Bibliothèque Nationale, Paris. *Only extant copy of this elliptical map, discovered in Bavaria in 1843. Voyages of Sebastian Cabot's father, John Cabot, are depicted, but landing is erroneously placed in area of Gulf of St. Lawrence rather than on Newfoundland or Cape Breton Island. The Gulf, named Baye Sainct Laurens (derived from Cartier's original name for it), and the river are relatively accurate.*

they were on the outskirts of an inhabited region known to the Indians as Saguenay. According to Cartier's own description of this voyage, *Brief Récit et Succincte Narration* (Paris, 1545)—his only account published in France during his lifetime—they were also told that the river was the "chemyn de Canada" [road of Canada] and the route to Hochelaga—a village comprised of more than 1,000 Indians and the site of the modern city of Montreal. Canada, an Indian word that means a collection of houses, first appeared on maps as a reference to the village Stadaconé at the site of present Quebec. Cartier also applied the name to the region between the Saguenay River and Quebec.

Cartier then crossed the Saguenay River, which he originally thought was the route across all of Canada, and sailed up the St. Lawrence. Off the north shore he named a large island Ile de Bacchus for its wild grapes, later changing it to Ile d'Orléans in deference to Francis I. At this point Chief Donnacona again met Cartier, on board his ship *La Grande Hermine*. Cartier then continued up the river to Hochelaga. He traveled there much against the wishes of Donnacona, who was reluctant to have him meet the rival Huron chief, fearing that Cartier would ally himself with that chief. Passing through the Hochelay Rapids (now Richelieu Rapids) and across Lake St. Pierre, Cartier's ships arrived at Hochelaga, and the following day he named the overlooking adjacent hill Mont Réal [royal mountain]. Farther west the advance was blocked by a series of rapids that could not be bypassed; a century later these were sarcastically named Lachine Rapids by La Salle, since they had been considered by early explorers the water route to China. On his second trip Cartier

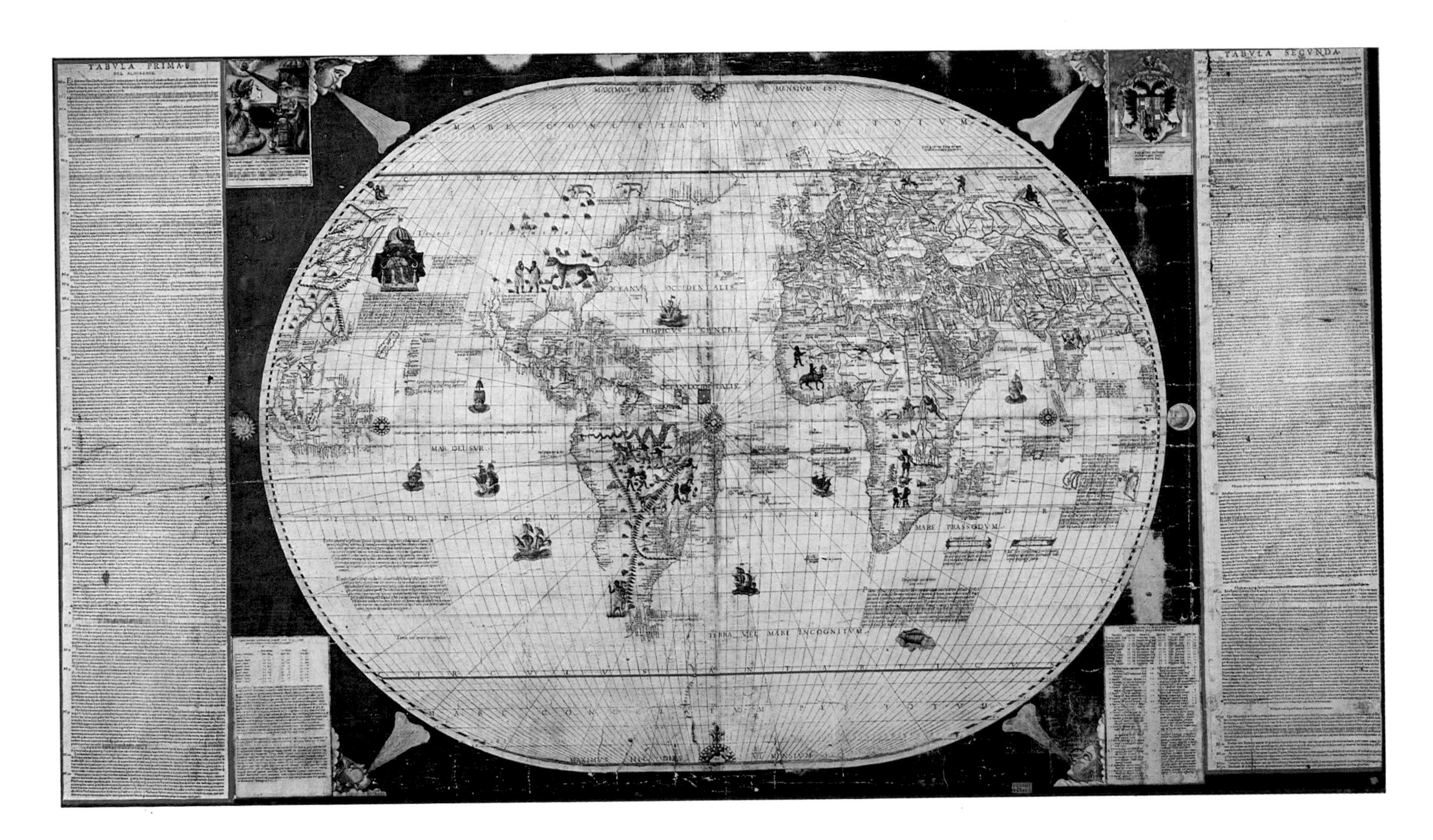

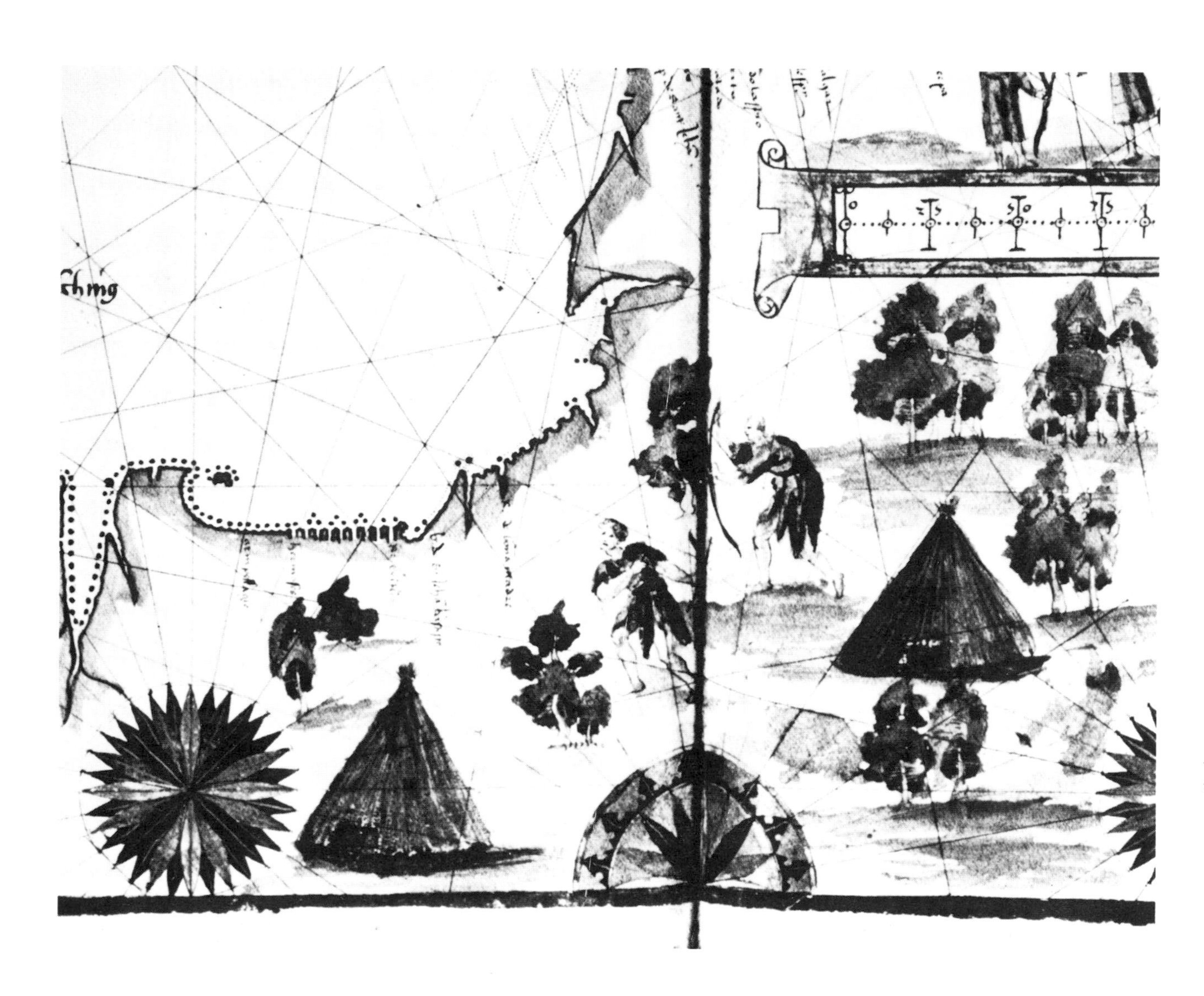

First appearance of Indian wigwams on a map, detail from 1542 Rotz map (see Plate 21)

and his men had advanced almost 1,000 miles from the open ocean. Wintering at Quebec, they returned via the strait (present Cabot Strait) between Cape Breton and Newfoundland, which João Fagundes had discovered in 1521.

The results of Cartier's first and second voyages are shown on the "Harleian Mappemonde" (*Plate 23*), now owned by the British Library. This manuscript, named for its former owner, Edward Harley, was drawn about 1544 and is attributed to the French cartographer Pierre Desceliers. It is an elaborate work of art, including a scene with the central figure believed to be Cartier and the name Canada in triplicate. The coast around the Gulf of St. Lawrence is decorated with people and animals and place-names as are the Magdalen Islands, which are fused to the mainland to the south. There is a disparity between the actual size of both the Gulf of St. Lawrence and the St. Lawrence River and their depiction on this map; the river is shown larger than it should be. The region between the Saguenay River and Quebec is reasonably detailed, while that beyond Quebec is crudely represented.

In 1540 Cartier was commissioned to undertake a third voyage to explore and penetrate Canada. In 1541, however, Francis I appointed Jean-François de La Roque, sieur de Roberval, leader of the mission with the title governor of Hochelaga and Canada, and a permanent French settlement was proposed for the area.

Hochelaga generally designated the region around Mont Réal; so Hochelaga and Canada were doubtless used by the king to be all-inclusive for the region around Quebec. Since Roberval's preparations were delayed, Cartier was the first to sail, setting out with five ships from St.-Malo on May 23, 1541. The flagship *La Grande Hermine* sailed a month earlier, making landfall at Quirpon harbor, familiar to Cartier from the previous voyages. He arrived at Stadaconé (Quebec) in late August 1541 and traveled several miles upstream to present Cap Rouge, where he established the first fort and settlement in Canada. The settlement was named Charlesbourg-Royal for the king's son, Charles, duc d'Orléans. There are few details known about this third voyage. Roberval embarked from France about a year later with approximately 200 persons, including women, and crossed paths with Cartier at St. John's, Newfoundland. Roberval erected his fort near Charlesbourg-Royal and renamed the area France-Roy, applying France-Prime to the St. Lawrence River. Roberval's settlement was not permanent, and his voyage had no cartographic effect.

Cartier's voyages were widely influential in contemporary mapping. Pierre Desceliers's 1546 mappemonde, although similar to the "Harleian Mappemonde," differs in detail. The north coast of the Gulf of St. Lawrence shows a refined topography and additional names. Because Cartier never offered a name for this body of water, the gulf is called simply La Baye, later changed to Grande Baye. Anticosti (Assumption) Island is correctly represented as an island. The major advance on this map is its more complete presentation of the St. Lawrence River system. Many animals and people are pictured, including an armored figure, possibly Roberval, addressing a group of soldiers.

A series of Portuguese maps is also based on Cartier's expeditions but shows no topography or nomenclature beyond the second journey. The 1541 French manuscript world map of Nicolas Desliens, designed as a sailing chart, uses Portuguese names. The 1547 world map of Nicholas Vallard, owned by the Huntington Library in Pasadena, California, offers an odd combination of Portuguese, French, and Spanish names and is more copiously annotated than any other map based on these voyages. The map includes a figure, believed to represent Cartier, and Indians are portrayed accurately. Belle Isle is named for the first time and the coast between Cape Breton and Florida mirrors Ribeirian concepts.

Another world map by Pierre Descèliers (*Plate 24*), a planisphere dating from 1550, has the distinctive Portuguese–Cartier features of geography and nomenclature. The name Canada appears three times, and there is an inscription stating that Cartier discovered the country and that its "austerité, intempérance et petit profit" caused it to be abandoned. The 1555 manuscript map "Terre de la Floride," by the French pilot and hydrographer Guillaume Le Testu (*Plate 25*), had an influence in later French Huguenot exploration. It is from Le Testu's manuscript atlas of fifty-six maps, *Cosmographie Universelle* (1555), and is a prime example of the Dieppe school of cartographers, which flourished in the middle of the sixteenth century. The atlas was made for Admiral Gaspard de Coligny, who later became a leader of the French Huguenots and supporter of the colonization of Florida. Also in the series of Portuguese maps are three by the Homems, who were outstanding Portuguese cartographers; one of these is the Lopo Homem map of 1554, the other two are by Diogo Homem, dated 1558 and 1568, respectively. The 1558 map shows the St. Lawrence opening to a northern ocean named the Parmamantium Sea. Inlets are drawn at points at which Cartier had probed for a westward passage. These three maps also emphasize Fagundes's exploration of the Cape Breton region of the Atlantic coast to the Bay of Fundy, which was not previously mapped.

Completing the consideration of early cartographic representations of Cartier's discoveries, a few Italian maps may be noted. A river is shown in the region of the St. Lawrence on the engraved "Vniversale" (*Plate 26*) by Giacomo Gastaldi, a Piedmontese who was cosmographer to the Republic of Venice. It bears none of Cartier's placenames and is probably intended as simply a decorative item rather than evidence of a geographic find. In 1565 Fernando Bertelli copied this river on a map, but in this instance it did represent Cartier's discovery since the name Ochelay and Canada appear. A year later the important map "Il Desegno del discoperto della noua Franza" by Bolognino Zaltieri added a dozen Cartier names, including that of R. S. Laurenzo, which was the form used in Giovanni Battista Ramusio's narratives (*see Plate 30*).

Spanish exploration during the first half of the sixteenth century also had a profound effect on the evolution of North American maps. In April 1528 Pánfilo de Narváez, having received a royal grant from Charles V to colonize the area between Rio de las Palmas in Mexico and southern Florida, arrived by ship on the

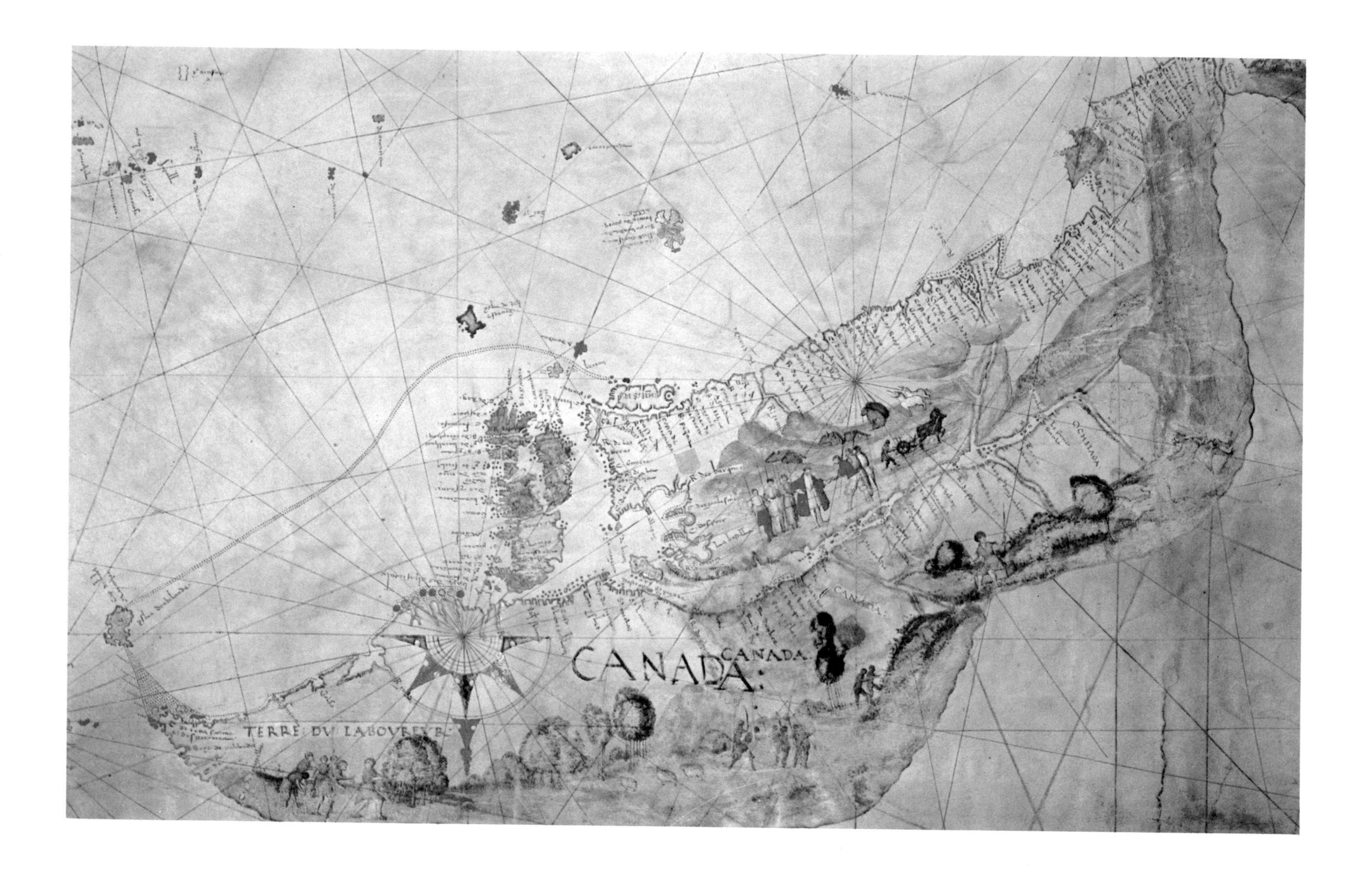

west coast of Florida near Tampa with a contingent of several hundred men. Narváez sent his ships to Mexico and with 300 of his men followed the coast north on foot in a futile search for gold. They reached Apalachen, the name for the vast region north of the Florida lake country. They built vessels and attempted to traverse the Gulf of Mexico to reconvene with the other men, but they were lost at sea. Álvar Núñez de Vaca was one of the survivors of the barges that were shipwrecked on an island off the coast of Texas. The remnants of the band of men were made slaves by the Indians who inhabited the island, but Núñez and three companions were able to escape and began a long trek overland, spending much time among nomadic Indians. When they encountered Spanish raiders in northern Mexico in 1536, Núñez related the stories of fabulous riches of a new El Dorado and the Seven Golden Cities of Cibola, lying just beyond the regions they had passed through. Núñez wrote to the viceroy of New Spain describing this unexplored part of the continent, and his letter stimulated subsequent exploration. The travels of Núñez and his companions are among the most remarkable in the annals of exploration. It is almost certain that they were the first Europeans to see the American bison, and their stories about the Pueblo Indians gave rise to the tales of the legendary Cibola [buffalo], which Fray *(opposite)* PLATE 23: Pierre Desceliers (attr.) "Harleian Mappemonde" (detail). c. 1544. Manuscript, pen and ink and watercolor; entire dimensions 117 × 249 cm. Department of Manuscripts, British Library, London. *The discoveries of Jacques Cartier during his second voyage shown along St. Lawrence River, and the name Canada appears prominently. A strait cuts across an isthmus behind the coastline to connect the Atlantic with Verrazanian false sea and provide direct access to the Orient.*

PLATE 24: Pierre Desceliers. "World Map" (detail). 1550. Manuscript, pen and ink and watercolor with gilt; entire dimensions 178 × 218 cm. Department of Manuscripts, British Library, London. *Jacques Cartier's voyages and sieur de Roberval's colony (France-Roy) described in the two legends. Representation of the St. Lawrence suggests the author had indirect access to Cartier's charts. Name of Canada appears in several places in lettering of different sizes.*

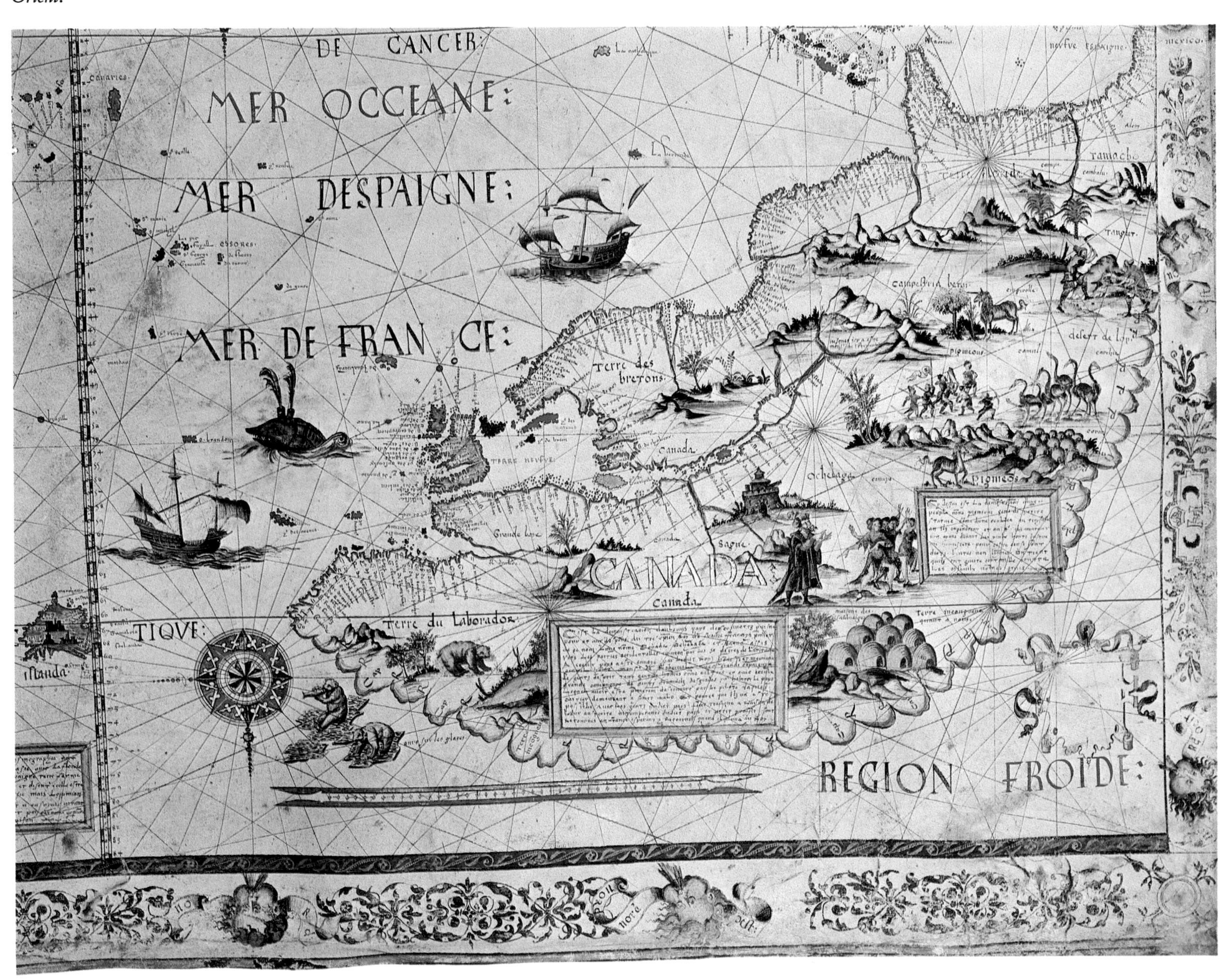

Marcos de Niza later magnified. Núñez's own account, *Los Naufragios* [the shipwrecked men] (1542), is the signal document of the startling adventures of his small party.

Three years before Cartier's final voyage, Hernando de Soto embarked on his large-scale expedition to explore North America. He already had experience as a conquistador in the New World, serving under Pedrarias (Pedro Arias de Ávila) in Central America and under Francisco Pizarro in Peru. The emperor Charles V gave the young adventurer the title of governor of Cuba with the right to conquer Florida (which meant the North American mainland). He led an expedition that set out from Spain in 1538, and his fleet of ships landed in the Tampa Bay area in 1539. Spurred by a quest for gold, silver, and jewels, De Soto started out with his men on foot and horseback on a gambit that took him and his band halfway across the continent.

On their way to Apalachen they picked up a survivor of the 1528 Narváez venture. They continued north and east to the shores of the Savannah River, where traces of Ayllón's 1526 expedition were found. When they reached northern Alabama, they fought Indians at Mavilla in present Clarke County, and many of De Soto's men perished in battle. Marching farther north and west, De Soto and his men came upon his major discovery, the Mississippi River, the "Father of the Waters." Crossing it, they traveled through Arkansas and penetrated into the plains of Oklahoma, fighting many bloody battles against the Indians. They turned south, still confident they would encounter fabulously rich cities, and wintered on the western shores of the Mississippi. On May 21, 1542, after three years of travel, the heroic explorer died near present Ferriday in Louisiana. Instead of burial, his comrades cast his weighted body into the river he had discovered, so that the Indians, whom he had intimidated and mistreated, would not learn of his death. His men subsequently reconnoitered the Arkansas River for another year and in September 1543 returned via the Gulf coast to northern Mexico. Thus came to an end an arduous 3,000-mile journey under a redoubtable and cruel commander of ruthless courage.

The first map to chronicle De Soto's monumental voyage is the manuscript "Mapa del Golfo y costa de la Nueva España" (*Plate 27*), drawn about 1544 and often attributed to Alonso de Santa Cruz; it is now in the Archivo General de Indias in Seville. The entire scope of De Soto's journey is presented, and for the first time the interior of the southeastern portion of North America is mapped. The Appalachian Mountains appear and the region's rivers are flowing appropriately in a southeasterly direction.

Other Spanish efforts at exploration began in Mexico and concentrated on the western portion of the continent. In 1535 Hernán Cortés set out from Mexico in search of pearls and sailed directly to the southeastern point of the California peninsula. Four years later, however, a more important expedition was undertaken. Having heard of De Soto's landing in Florida, Antonio de Mendoza, the first viceroy of New Spain, dispatched Francisco Vásquez de Coronado north from Mexico in search of the mythical Seven Cities of Cibola. As part of this expedition, Hernando de Alarcón sailed up the Gulf of California and proved definitively that Lower California was a peninsula. Discovering the Colorado River, he entered the river in August 1540. He is credited with being the first European to set foot in the area of present California. Coronado, with a large force, marched across Arizona to the fabled Cibola, which turned out to be seven Zuñi pueblos of no great wealth. During their trek, they passed pueblos of Tiguex along the Rio Grande and the large pueblo of Acoma, at an altitude of about 7,000 feet, on a rock in present New Mexico; founded circa 1100–1250, Acoma is the oldest continuously inhabited community in the United States. They then proceeded to Quivira (in present Kansas), an inland region of fabled treasure. Coronado's explorations spanned two years, from 1540 to 1542, and his chronicler, Pedro de Castañeda de Najera, recorded that the group believed that the Mississippi and Missouri rivers rose from the northern plains, a concept not documented cartographically until the eighteenth century. During this journey Hernando de Alvarado discovered the Rio Grande, which he named Señora because the river was first sighted on the traditional birthday of the Virgin Mary, September 18, and the scouting expedition, under the command of García López de Cárdenas, was the first group of Europeans to view the Grand Canyon.

After Coronado's failure in his quest for a city of gold, Mendoza in 1542 sent a fleet under the leadership of Juan Rodríquez Cabrillo to explore the Gulf of California, hoping he would discover a river leading to Quivira. Mendoza also directed Cabrillo to search for a strait from the Eastern Ocean or even from Cathay. Such a strait, which came to be known as the Strait of Anian (*see Plate 30*), had been mentioned by Marco Polo in his famous narrative of his travels. During this excursion Cabrillo anchored at San Diego Bay, naming it San Miguel. He also visited Santa Monica Bay near Los Angeles and then sailed as far north as present Drakes Bay. All placenames established during this voyage were superseded by the voyage of Sebastián Vizcaíno in 1602.

Expressions of these western explorations found their way onto a few maps before mid-century. The earliest extant map to show any part of the western coast of America north of Mexico based on actual discoveries is a sketch drawn between 1536 and 1541. It shows the lower tip of the California peninsula and part of the opposite mainland of Mexico at a time when Cortés ruled the region. The drawing, which is in the Archivo General de Indias in Seville, includes four placenames on the lower peninsula: S. Filite, S. Ciago, Perlas, and S. Cruz; Santa Cruz was Cortés's name for the entire region as well as for the port.

Battista Agnese's manuscript oval world map of 1541, in the Pierpont Morgan Library in New York, includes places named by Fray Marcos de Niza as he traveled through Arizona. The manuscript map of Domingo del Castillo, a pilot on the expedition of Hernando de Alarcón, drawn in Mexico in 1541, may be the earliest map that focuses specifically on California. Along the southern tip of the peninsula the name California appears for the first time. The peninsula of California (crossed by a strait) is also shown on a manuscript mappemonde, "Nova Verior et Integra Totius Orbis Descriptio," drawn in 1542 by Alonso de Santa Cruz; it is now owned by the Royal Academy in Stockholm. On Giacomo Gastaldi's famous 1546 "Vniversale" (*see Plate 26*) La Sete Cita [the seven cities] and Cipola (Cibola) appear, but none of the names designated by Coronado are noted on this or any map during the first half of the sixteenth century.

Hernando de Soto's mistreatment of the Florida Indians as portrayed in Théodore de Bry's Great Voyages, *1595 (Part 5)*

PLATE 25: Guillaume Le Testu. "Terre de la Floride." 1555. Manuscript, pen and ink and watercolor; 35 × 48 cm. Musée de la Marine, Paris. *This beautifully decorative map features a series of pictures of towns or villages, including Estadin (Estacone), Ochelassa (Hochelaga), Canada, and Saguenay. Referred to in later colonization by French Huguenots, who sailed from France in 1564. Of names along the coast only Cape Canaveral persists. From Le Testu's manuscript atlas* Cosmographie Universelle.

PLATE 26: Giacomo Gastaldi. "Vniversale." 1546. Engraving, 37 × 53 cm. Houghton Library, Harvard University, Cambridge, Mass. *Gastaldi's earliest world map. A land bridge joins North America with Asia; sixteen years later Gastaldi introduced concept of a strait separating the two. California is shown as a peninsula. One of the most important maps of the sixteenth century, it exemplifies the art of Italian engraving.*

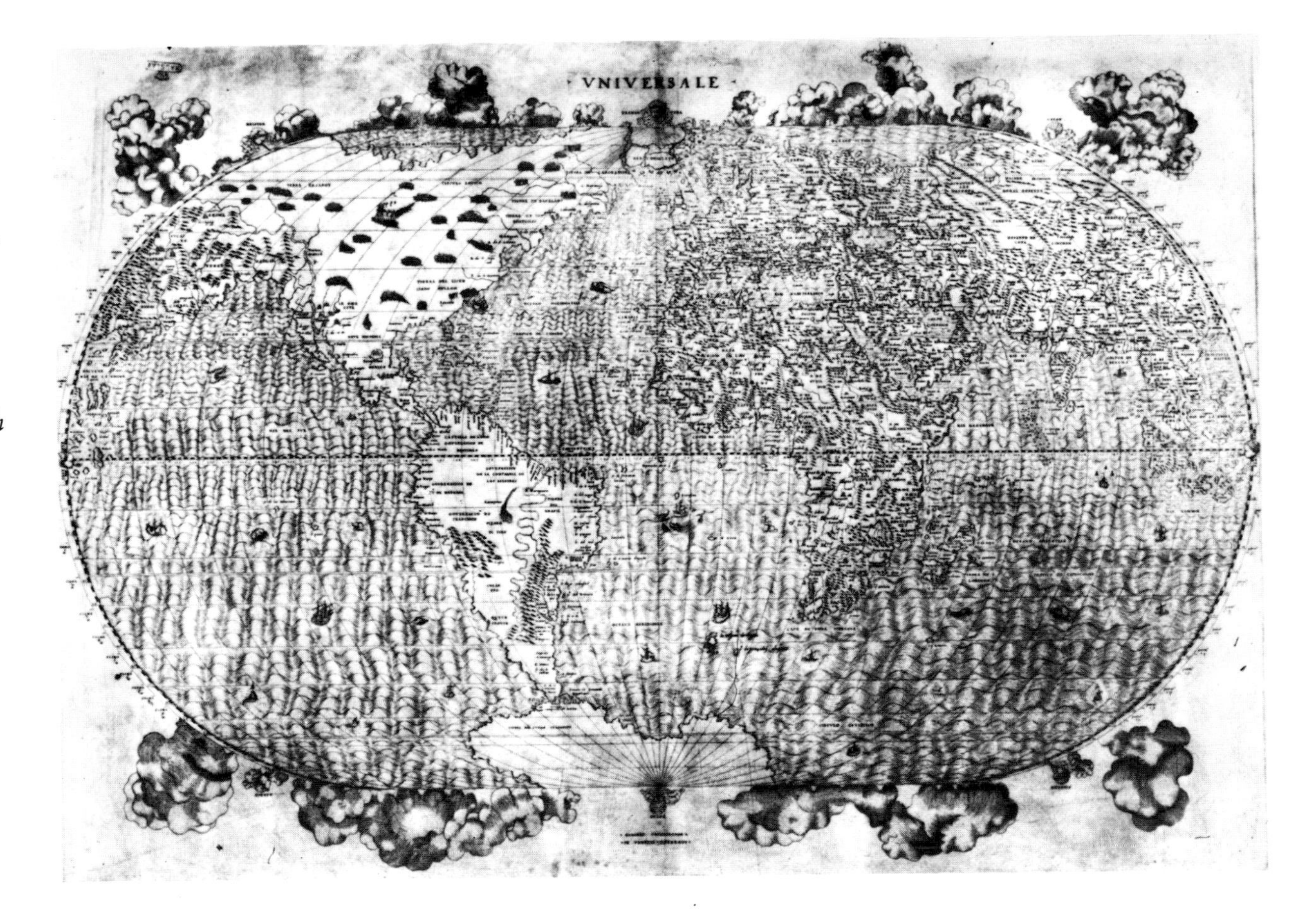

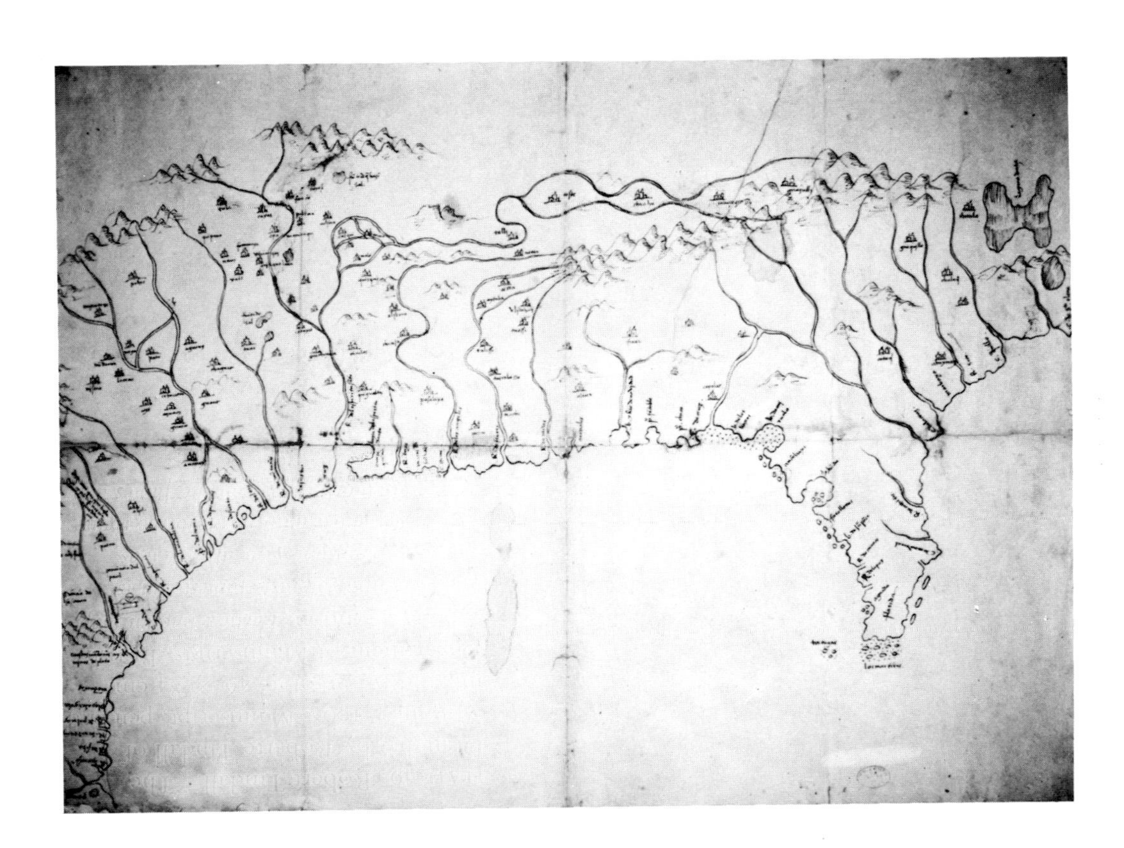

PLATE 27: Alonso de Santa Cruz (attr.). "Mapa del Golfo y costa de la Nueva España." c. 1544. Manuscript, 43 × 70 cm. Archivo General de Indias, Seville. *Only known extant contemporary map depicting Hernando de Soto's expedition of 1539–43. Mountain range in northeastern section of map incorrectly oriented east–west, but rivers shown more accurately. A large lagoon at upper right may represent Okefenokee Swamp.*

3. *Early Attempts at Colonization*

Look here, my boys; see what a world of ground
Lie westward from the midst of Cancer's line
Unto the rising of this earthly globe,
Whereas the sun, declining from our sight,
Begins the day with our Antipodes.
And shall I die, and this unconquered?

CHRISTOPHER MARLOWE
Tamburlaine the Great (c. 1587)

1550-1600

DURING THE second half of the sixteenth century there was a slow but gradual appreciation of the geography of the newly discovered continent, particularly the coastlines. Since the voyages themselves during this period added little to the exactness in the mapping of coastal areas and did not penetrate appreciably into the interior, the maps of the period show only minor alterations of the coast, including the continuation of erroneous concepts, and little definition of the vast interior. Historically it was a period of frustration for European political schemes in North America. All attempts at colonization had ended in dismal failure except for the Spanish colony at St. Augustine, Florida. Similarly the goal of discovering a Northwest Passage to Asia was not achieved.

The map "Brevis Exactaque Totius Novi Orbis," by the Flemish publisher and editor Jean Bellère and included in an edition of *Historia de México* by Francisco López de Gómara (Antwerp, 1554), showed all of South America and the eastern coast of North America. The coastal names are derived from the Ayllón, Gomes, and Fagundes expeditions and are in their proper locations. In 1554 a large manuscript world map by Lopo Homem showed for the first time on the same map both Cartier's St. Lawrence exploration and the Bay of Fundy. By contrast, "La Nuova Francia" by Giacomo Gastaldi was based solely on Verrazano's voyage and encompasses none of the features uncovered during Cartier's explorations. It was included in *Delle Navigationi e Viaggi* (Venice, 1556) by the Italian geographer Giovanni Battista Ramusio, and in the same publication there is a woodcut plan of the Indian village of Hochelaga, attributed to Gastaldi (*Plate 28*). This map picks up on Cartier by its mention of Monte Real (Cartier's Mont Réal) and is considered the very first plan of a village in the United States or Canada.

In 1558 an anonymously printed map presented the results of the apocryphal voyages of Nicolò and Antonio Zeno, which purportedly occurred in the fourteenth century (from 1380 to 1387), and led to a description of the mythical island of Friesland south of Greenland. This map, "Carta da Navegar de Nicolo et Antonio Zeni, Furono in Tramontana Lano MCCCLXXX," was printed in *De I Commentarii del Viaggio in Persia di M. Calterino Zeno* (Venice, 1558), edited by Nicolò Zeno, a decendant of the supposed explorers. It contained many geographical errors, which Gerard Mercator copied onto his landmark 1569 map (*see Plate 31*), and consequently had a significant influence on the voyages of Martin Frobisher, who innocently accepted the Mercator map as accurate and factual.

In 1562 the largest and most detailed map of the New World at that time, "Americae sive Qvartae Orbis Partis Nova et Exactissima Descriptio" (*Plate 29*) was published. It was the work of Diego Gutiérrez, Spanish chart and instrument maker and pilot major in the Casa de Contratación in Seville. Its text specifically states that America was discovered by Amerigo Vespucci in 1497; it is the earliest printed map with the name California—appearing as C. California on the tip of the peninsula. Despite its date, the map does not indicate De Soto's exploration and neglects several other early Spanish and French discoveries.

A map that includes the North Atlantic with the upper coast of North America, which appeared in the 1563 manuscript collection known as the Lázaro Atlas, presents the discoveries and nomenclature of Fagundes and Cartier. This remarkable and well-known atlas, owned by the Academia das Ciências in Lisbon, was signed and dated by Lázaro Luís, yet very little is known of his biography except that he was a Portuguese sailor who apparently visited the coasts and islands he described. The map has two main legends, which translate into English as "Terra Nova, where they fish the cod" and "Land of the Lavrador, discovered by João Álvares [i.e., Fagundes]."

Abraham Ortelius's 1564 "Nova Totius Terrarum Orbis Iuxta

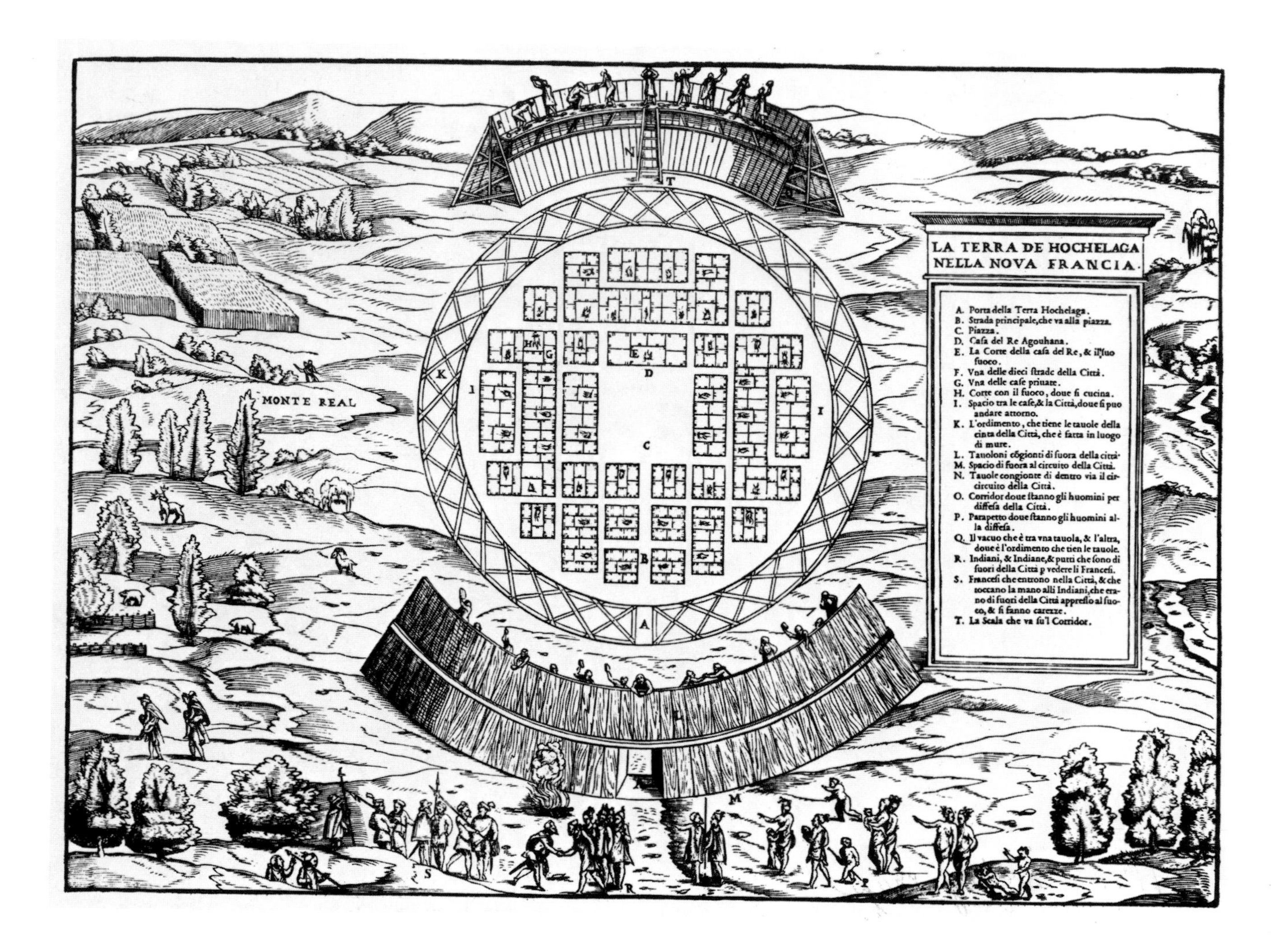

PLATE 28: Giacomo Gastaldi (attr.). "La Terra de Hochelaga nella Nova Francia." 1556. Woodcut, 26 × 36 cm. Private collection. *First published plan of a European settlement in North America. Based on Jacques Cartier's description of Hochelaga, made during his visit in 1535–36. Note adjacent Monte Real. From Volume 3 of Giovanni Battista Ramusio's* Delle Navigationi e Viaggi nel quale si Contengono le Navigatione al Mondo Nuovo *(Venice, 1556).*

Neotericorum Traditiones Descriptio," published in Antwerp, is an engraved world map on the popular cordiform projection. It is a somewhat unsuccessful attempt to reconcile information taken from earlier sources. There are several names derived from Cartier's explorations, and the Gulf of St. Lawrence erroneously leads to an open western sea. In the west is an extremely large representation of the Strait of Anian and in the southeastern region of the continent a small lake in the interior of Florida in the vicinity of the Okefenokee Swamp. A series of interesting names abound: Golfo de las Gamas (the name given by Gomes to the combined Penobscot Bay and Penobscot River, which he regarded as the seaway to a Northwest Passage), Norumbega, Canada, Quivira, Cevola, Apalchen, Florida, and C. de Cagnaueral (Canaveral).

Following Cartier's third voyage, in 1541–42, French advances into the northern part of North America came to a virtual standstill for over a decade; French interest in colonization was instead directed to Florida. Because of Catholic persecution of the Huguenots, their leader, Admiral Gaspard de Coligny, in 1562 dispatched Jean Ribaut, one of France's ablest seamen, with 150 men to set up a colony in the New World. After landing in the vicinity of St. Augustine, a group of the men sailed into the mouth of the present St. Johns River, which they named Rivière de May because they entered it on the first day of that month.

They established friendly relations with the local Indians and set up a stone column to signify French sovereignty. Ribaut's men continued north, entering the present St. Marys River and then the Satilla River, giving it the title Aine. Other waters named on that journey were Bellevue (present St. Elena Sound), Loire (Brunswick River), Charente (Altamaha River), Garonne (Sepelo River), Gironde (Midway River), Belle (Ogeechee River), and Grande (Savannah River). The northernmost anchorage during Ribaut's expedition was in a large bay that he called Port Royal, a name which still persists. Charlesfort, a small wooden structure, was erected on the banks of the bay, and thirty men were left to begin colonization, while Ribaut returned to France for supplies and reinforcements.

Ribaut expressed keen enthusiasm over his first glimpse of the Florida coast in his vivid account *The Whole & True Discouerye of Terra Florida*, printed in London in 1563: "It is a thinge inspeakable, the comodities that be sene there and shalbe founde more and more in this incomperable lande, never as yet broken with plowe irons, bringing fourthe thinges according to his first nature, whereof the eternall God endued yt." Despite the innocent awe embodied in these words, the expedition was an unsuccessful effort marred by dissension and cannibalism. Ribaut did not return in the promised six months and the remnant of the colony built a small pinnace and set sail for France; being also plagued by misfortune at sea, the survivors ultimately were picked up by a British ship in July 1563.

The earliest map reflecting French exploration of the Florida coast, "La Terre Francoise Novvellement Decovverte," was drawn in 1562 by Nicolas Barré, a pilot accompanying Ribaut. It shows the landfall in the vicinity of St. Augustine and the area north to Port Royal, South Carolina. The original manuscript was lost, but a sixteenth-century manuscript copy by an anonymous Spanish cartographer is located in the Museo Naval in Madrid.

In 1564 Coligny sent René de Laudonnière to colonize the same area as a buffer against spreading Spanish influence. The French arrived on the Florida coast near the inlet (since named Matanzas, for the subsequent massacre) which they called Rivière des Dauphins, and then sailed north to the mouth of the St. Johns River. The Indians welcomed them, revealing the stone column engraved with the royal arms and fleur-de-lys which Ribaut had placed there two years previously. Meanwhile the Indians had come to worship the stone as an idol. Laudonnière decided to establish his colony on the St. Johns and began erecting a fort on

The French sail to River of May, from Great Voyages, *1591 (Part 2)*

The French build a fort on River of May, from Great Voyages, *1591*

PLATE 29: Diego Gutiérrez. "Americae sive Qvartae Orbis Partis Nova et Exactissima Descriptio." 1562. Engraving, 107 × 104 cm. Geography and Map Division, Library of Congress, Washington, D.C.. *Largest known map to date of the New World. Includes eastern coast of North America. Credits Amerigo Vespucci with discovery of America in 1497. First printed map to name California. The map may have been engraved after Gutiérrez's death by Hieronymus Cock. Only two copies exist, one in the Library of Congress and the other in the British Library.*

(opposite) PLATE 30: Bolognino Zaltieri. "Il Disegno del discoperto della noua Franza." 1566. Engraving, 27 × 40 cm. William L. Clements Library, University of Michigan, Ann Arbor. *First map to show Strait of Anian, depicted as flowing between Mare Setentrionale in Cognito (north of North American continent) and Golfo Chinan (west of continent). Concept of strait separating America from Asia was first proposed by Giacomo Gastaldi in his pamphlet* La Vniversale Descrittione del Mondo *(Venice, 1562). Map included in the Lafreri Atlas (Rome, 1566).*

the south bank, Fort Caroline, named in honor of Charles IX. This colony also failed. Ribaut returned to the French colony in August 1565 to replace Laudonnière, and in September a fleet of Spanish ships arrived and claimed the land for Pedro Menéndez de Avilés, Spain's newly appointed governor of Florida. The French were defeated by the Spanish, and among the few who escaped massacre at Matanzas Inlet were Laudonnière and Jacques Le Moyne de Morgues, the painter who later drew the first views of Florida (*see Plate 38*), now classics in their field.

In preparing for battle with the French at Matanzas Inlet, Menéndez had established a base for troops and supplies at an inlet a short distance north, which he named St. Augustine. After he was victorious, Menéndez returned to the St. Augustine area and in 1565 initiated what was to become the oldest persisting

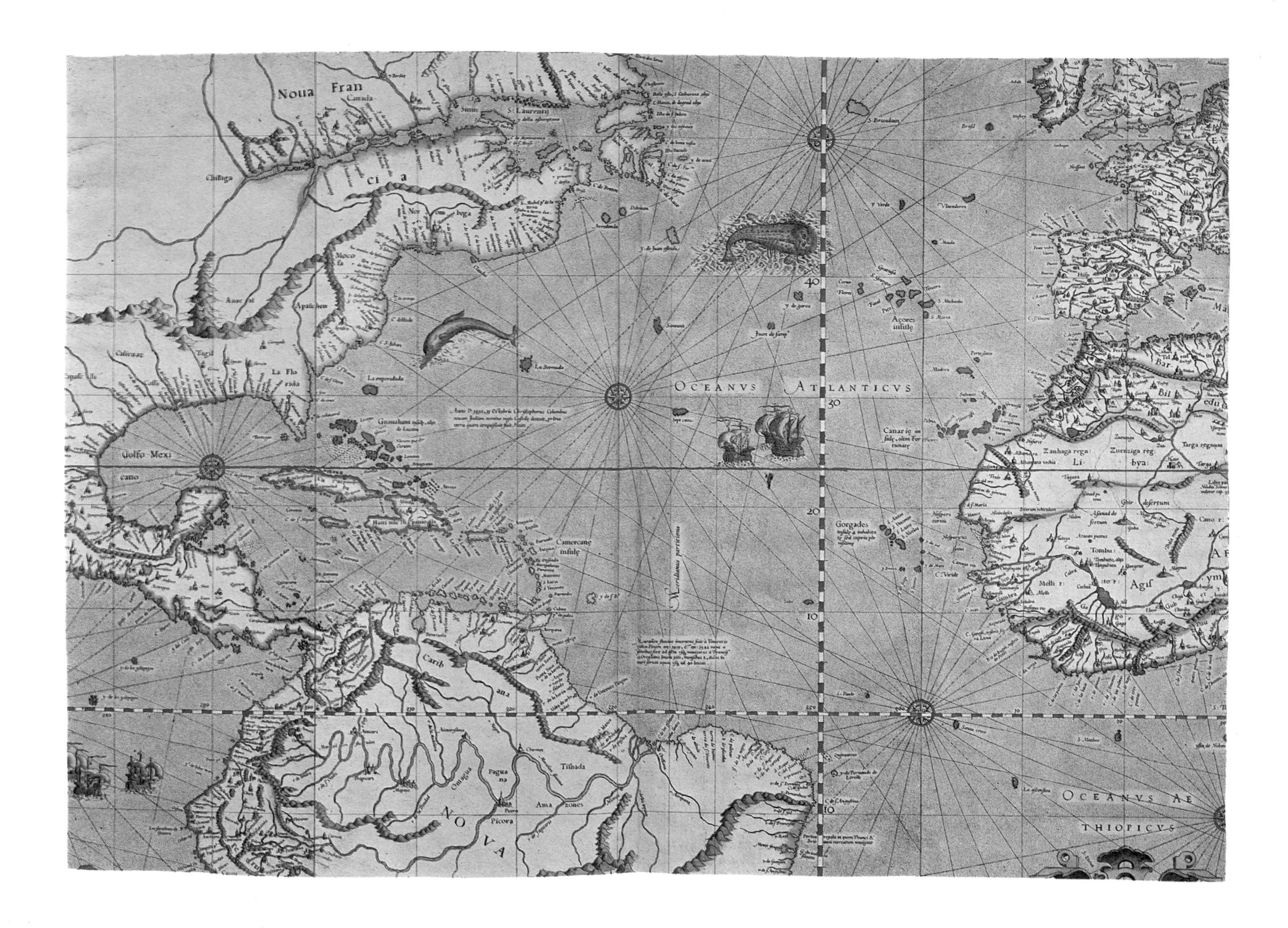

European settlement in North America. The Spaniards settled other areas along the east and west coasts of Florida, and they also sailed up the St. Johns River in search of a passage across the Florida peninsula. These other settlements were all short-lived; and attempts by the Jesuit missionary Father Juan Bautista Segura to establish Spanish missions at Chesapeake Bay in 1572 also failed. Within ten years of the founding of St. Augustine, the entire Spanish influence in the region of Florida was weakened as a result of English settlement.

At that time the cartographic concept of the continent was variable. In 1566 an attractive manuscript world map by Guillaume Le Testu was drawn with the western coast of North America missing. Also in 1566 the engraving "Il Disegno del discoperto della noua Franza" (*Plate 30*) by the Italian engraver *(opposite)* PLATE 31: Gerard Mercator. "Nova et avcta orbis terrae descriptio ad vsvm nauigantium emendate accommodata" (detail). 1569. Engraving, hand colored; entire dimensions 135 × 198 cm. Maritiem Museum Prins Hendrik, Rotterdam. *One of the most influential maps ever compiled. Isogonic cylindrical projection is presented for the first time; known as the Mercator projection, this revolutionized science of navigation. First suggestion of Great Lakes appears. References to legendary islands of Atlantic Ocean and to Strait of Anian. Expresses the sum total, both fact and fiction, of contemporary geographic knowledge; liberated cartography from its dependence on Ptolemy.*

PLATE 32: Abraham Ortelius. "Americae sive Novi Orbis, Nova Descriptio." 1570. Engraving, 37 × 51 cm. Private collection. *First map of the Americas to appear in a modern atlas, Ortelius's* Theatrum Orbis Terrarum *(Antwerp, 1570). California is shown as a peninsula. The names Sierra Nevada, Cannaveral, and Apalchen are included. Cape Cod appears as C. de Arenas. Map distinguished from Ortelius's 1587 revision, which corrected the bulge on western coast of South America.*

Laudonnière and natives of Florida, by Jacques Le Moyne, c. 1587, the first surviving original painting of America

and printer Bolognino Zaltieri presented the Strait of Anian, separating North America from Asia, for the first time on a printed map; yet just one year earlier Paolo Forlani and Fernando Bertelli—a Veronese engraver and a Venetian publisher and mapmaker, respectively—still pictured a land bridge between the two continents on their world map "Universale Descrittione di Tutta la Terra Conosciuta." The Zaltieri engraving appeared in the rare atlas *Geografia Tavole Moderne di Geografia de la Maggior Parte del Mondo* (Rome, 1566), which is known as the Lafreri Atlas. The French engraver Antonio Lafreri (Antoine Lafréry), who settled in Rome, is credited with the original idea of the atlas format, in which he bound together a number of up-to-date maps into a single volume. The Zaltieri map, one of the earliest printed maps devoted solely to North America, includes the French names Lacardia, Canada, R. S. Lorenzo (St. Lawrence River), and Nova Franza; these are complemented by Spanish names like Florida as well as Cabrillo's placenames on the western coast—Tigna (Colorado River), Tontonteac (Gila River), Quivira, and Civola. Sierra Nevada [snowy mountains] appears for the first time on a printed map. In about 1567 Alonso de Santa Cruz drew a chart of the Caribbean and the southern portion of the eastern coast of the continent, with St. Augustine (in the form r: de s: agostino) as the first map appearance of the name.

In 1569–70 the Dutch school of cartography produced two momentous works which had major cartographic influence; these were Mercator's famous 1569 world map and Ortelius's atlas *Theatrum Orbis Terrarum*. The first of these, "Nova et avcta orbis terrae descriptio ad vsvm nauigantium emendate accommodata" (*Plate 31*), by the Flemish geographer, mathematician, and cartographer Gerard (Gerhard) Mercator, introduced his revolutionary projection (known as the Mercator projection), translating distance on a sphere onto a flat surface. It later became an invaluable aid to navigators. The map provides a relatively accurate delineation of the St. Lawrence River; the freshwater lake in midcontinent flowing to it may be the first map representation of one of the Great Lakes. The Hudson River seems to be depicted, and the Appalachians are shown as a continuous mountain range for the first time on a printed map. Yet this impressive work has a number of cartographic errors. The coast from New England to Nova Scotia is placed too far easterly. Other errors are Mercator's inclusion of the false Sea of Verrazano, the mythical islands of the Zeno brothers, and a distinct Northwest Passage to Asia. Mercator, who was the greatest geographer of the sixteenth century, composed his map for the use of seamen ("ad usum navigantium"), but he gave no explanation of its principles or, a greater shortcoming, no explanation of its potential use in navigation; this was provided thirty years later by Edward Wright in his important book *The Correction of Certaine Errors in Navigation* (*see Plate 42*). Mercator's great summary map of the Renaissance is extremely rare; there were only four known specimens, and of these the one in Breslau was lost in 1945.

The second great work at this time was produced by Mercator's friend, the Flemish antiquarian and geographer Abraham Ortelius. Next to Mercator, Ortelius is the greatest of the sixteenth-century Flemish school of cartography, and he was inspired by Mercator to put together his chief work, *Theatrum Orbis Terrarum* (Antwerp, 1570), the first modern atlas of the world. This epoch-making work is the first atlas to include a world map along with appropriate component maps of the same area. It consisted of text and maps forming a unitary whole; whereas other atlases of the period—such as Ptolemy's *Geographia,* with the added tabulae novae, and the previously mentioned Lafreri Atlas—printed a group of randomly selected maps that had no relation to one another. The world map "Typus Orbis Terrarum" and the map of the New World "Americae sive Novi Orbis, Nova

Descriptio" (*Plate 32*), both included in Ortelius's atlas, are called mother maps because of their continued effects on cartography. The latter shows the Western Hemisphere with a reasonably accurate outline of North America.

In the second half of the sixteenth century maps began to crop up in unusual places. In 1571 an interesting and beautiful world map, "Sacrae Geographiae Tabvlam ex Antiquissimorvm Cvltor" (*Plate 33*), by Benito Arias Montano, a Spanish theologian, philosopher, and scientist of the Benedictine order, was included in the eight-volume monumental polyglot Bible published in Antwerp in 1571, one of the first multilingual Bibles. Keyed with a legend in Hebrew and Latin, it has only one notation in North America, namely, Ophir [land of gold], uncannily located in the approximate area of the California gold rush of the mid-nineteenth century.

In California and the western regions Spanish interest continued unchallenged. Sir Francis Drake, on his voyage of 1577–80 around the world, anchored in the bay that now bears his name. It is still debated whether Drake actually sailed his ship, *Golden Hind*, through the Golden Gate—given its name by John Charles Frémont in the 1840s—into present San Francisco Bay. During his voyage Drake did make a significant landfall in the region and took

Indians hunting deer, from Great Voyages, *1591 (Part 2)*

possession of a broad expanse of land he named New Albion. A 1589 map by Nicola van Sijpe, "La Herdike Enterprinse Faict par le Signeur Draeck d'Avoir Cirquit Toute la Terre," gave Drake's name for the Pacific Northwest as Nova Albio [New England], and the following year, in an attempt to define the bay Drake had anchored in, the Flemish cartographer and engraver Jodocus Hondius included on a map inset the name Portus Nova Albionis.

Drake's voyage to the Northwest had been preceded by Spanish ships sailing from the Philippines. Trade was established between Mexico and those islands in 1542, and when it became apparent that the winds and currents created significant difficulty in the eastern leg of the voyage, a new route was established, the vessels sailing north and easterly to the area of Cape Mendocino in northern California and then south along the coast. A Spanish sea captain, Sebastián Cermeño, while plying this route in 1595, traded in present Drakes Bay but he called it San Francisco Bay. Thus the appellation of one of the nation's most famous bodies of water was first applied to a less significant inlet.

Continued Spanish exploration and expansion in the western portion of North America was by land. In 1581 missionaries advanced to Puaray, the central pueblo of Tiguex, and also visited the plains of Zuñi and Acoma. In their various chronicles of their journeys the missionaries mentioned a large lake and the fact that the shores were populated with Indians wearing large amounts of gold jewelry, which may explain the appellation Lago del Oro [lake of gold] on many contemporary maps. From the same area in Mexico several Spanish explorers attempted colonization in the region of the Río Bravo del Norte (Rio Grande). In 1593 a group of explorers led by Antonio de Humana reached the Arkansas River in Kansas and north as far as the Platte River in present Nebraska. In 1598 Don Juan de Oñate led an expedition along the Rio Grande, exploring the Quivira region and traveling down the Colorado River to the Gulf of Mexico. Oñate, whose wife was a granddaughter of Cortés and great-granddaughter of Montezuma, was a wealthy citizen of Zacatecas, Mexico, and later became the governor of the Rio Grande region. During this journey, a regional capital was established at San Juan de los Caballeros, north of present Bernalillo, New Mexico. The offshoot of this small settlement was Santa Fe, which in 1610 was established as the capital of the Spanish colony.

These Spanish expeditions had little influence on sixteenth-

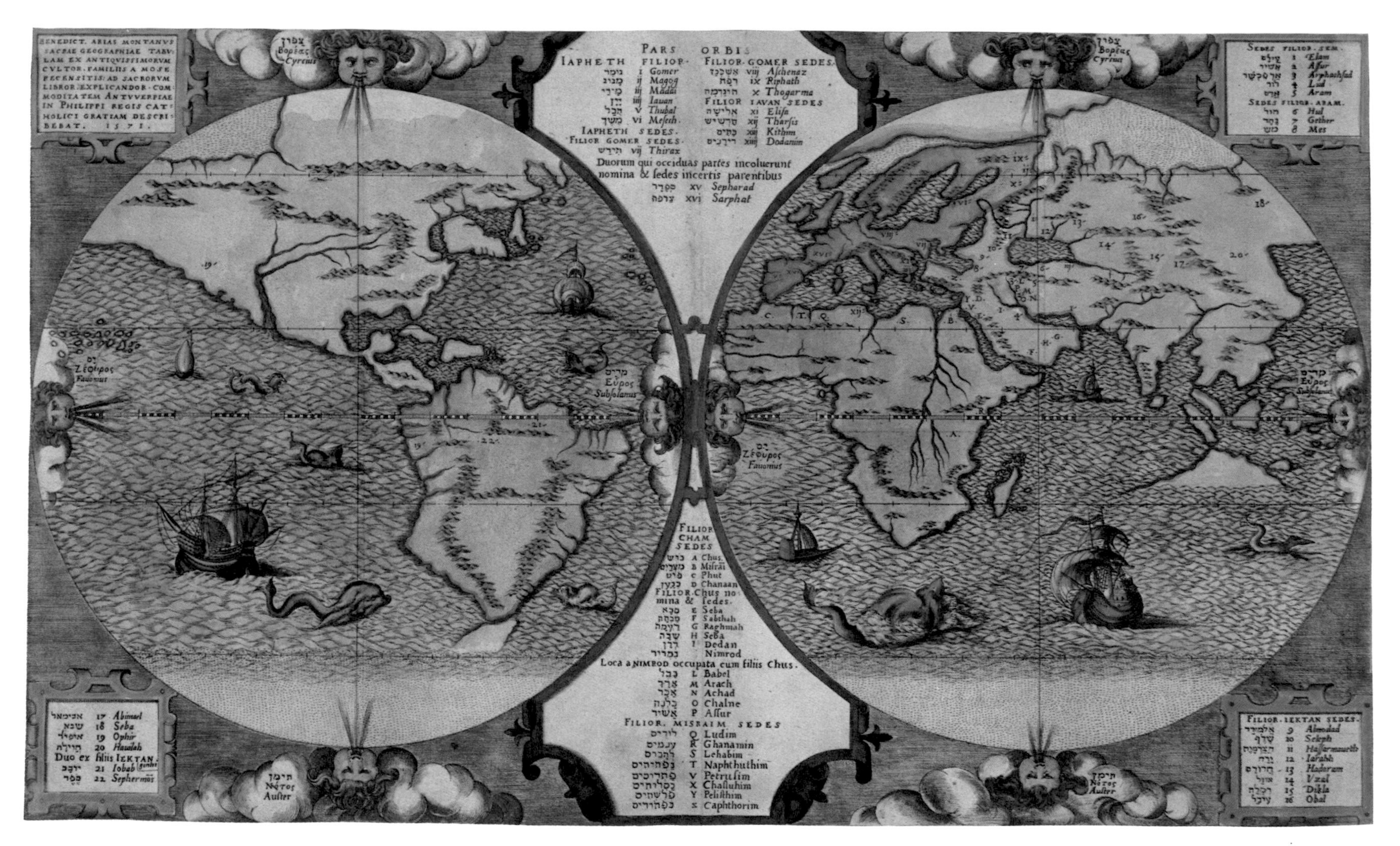

PLATE 33: Benito Arias Montano. "Sacrae Geographiae Tabvlam ex Antiquissimorvm Cvltor." 1571. Engraving, hand colored; 32 × 53 cm. Private collection. *A double hemispheric map engraved for the eight-volume polyglot Bible compiled by Montano and published in 1571 by the Plantin Press in Antwerp. In North America only Ophir [land of gold] is named, and placed in California. Map based on Giacomo Gastaldi's geographic concepts; North America is continuous with Asia.*

century maps. Most of the region already had been placed speculatively on maps, and names such as Tiguex, Acoma, Cibola, Axa, and Río Bravo del Norte had already been assigned. Christian Sgrooten's 1592 manuscript world map showed a separate kingdom of Anian north of Quivira, and it relocated Tiguex from the interior to the coast and the mythical city of Cibola onto the Colorado River. Sgrooten, a Flemish cartographer, included the map in a manuscript atlas he prepared for Philip II of Spain; the atlas is presently in the Biblioteca Nacional in Madrid.

England's explorations in the New World had essentially ceased after John Cabot's voyage and were not rekindled until

PLATE 34: Sir Humphrey Gilbert. "A General Map, Made onelye for the Particuler Declaration of This Discovery." 1576. Woodcut, 23 × 33 cm. John Carter Brown Library, Brown University, Providence. *Concept of Northwest Passage illustrated. The earliest surviving world map printed in England. Published in Gilbert's* A Discourse of a Discoverie for a New Passage to Cataia *(London, 1576).*

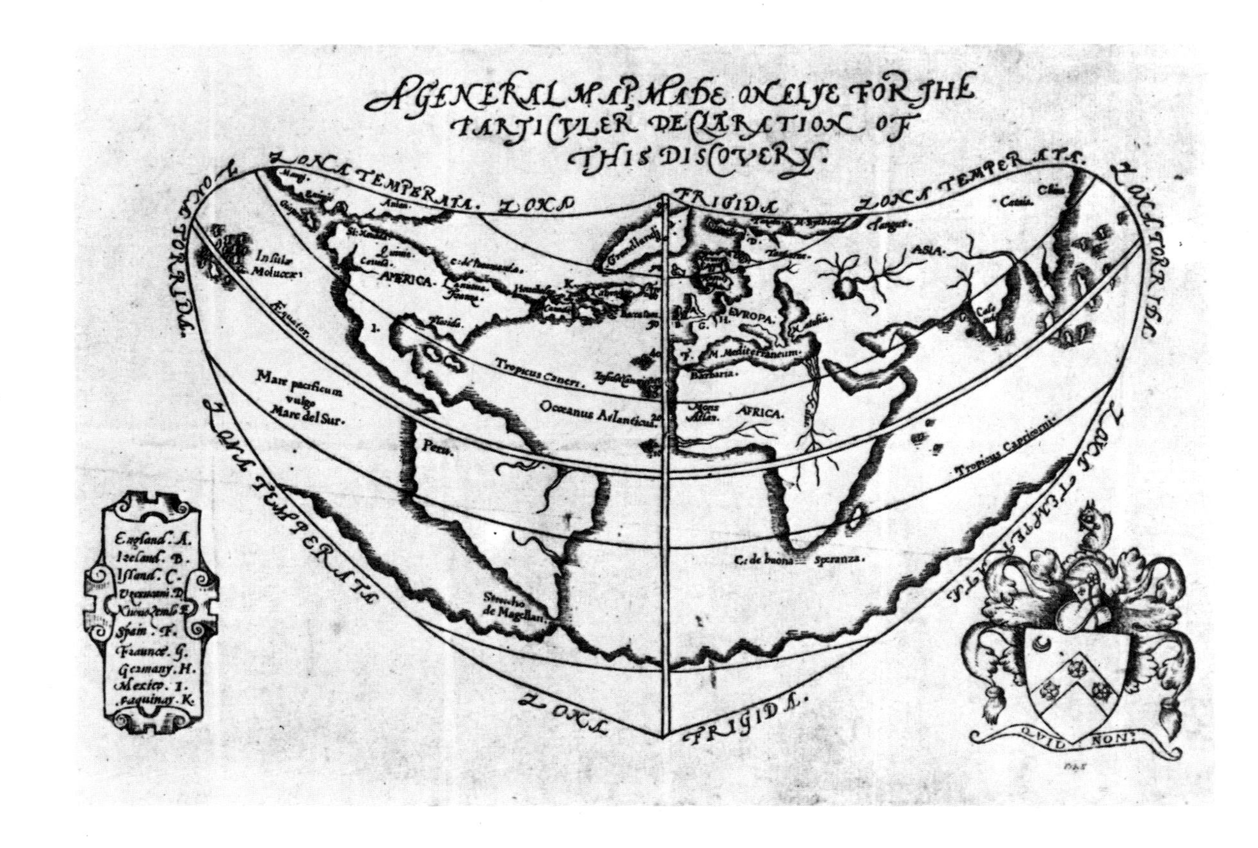

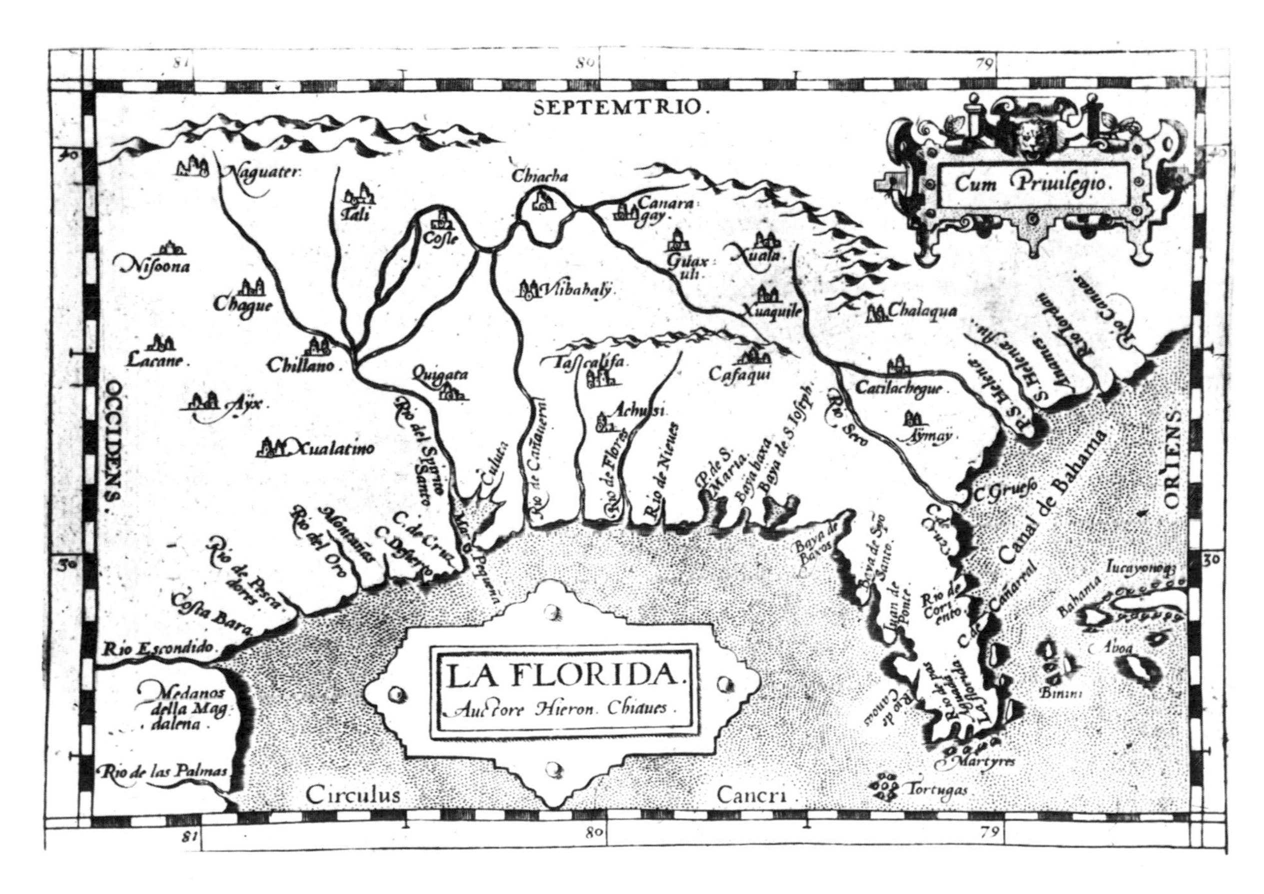

PLATE 35: Gerónimo de Chaves. "La Florida." 1584. Engraving, 15 × 23 cm. John Carter Brown Library, Brown University, Providence. *First regional map of Florida, shown in coastline from Carolina to Mexico. Coastal names similar to those on Spanish maps of the period. Interior placenames comparable to those on earlier manuscript map depicting Hernando de Soto's expedition (see Plate 27), but details of Chaves's sufficiently different from those of De Soto's that it is unlikely manuscript served as reference. Published in the* Additamentum III *(1584) to Abraham Ortelius's* Theatrum Orbis Terrarum.

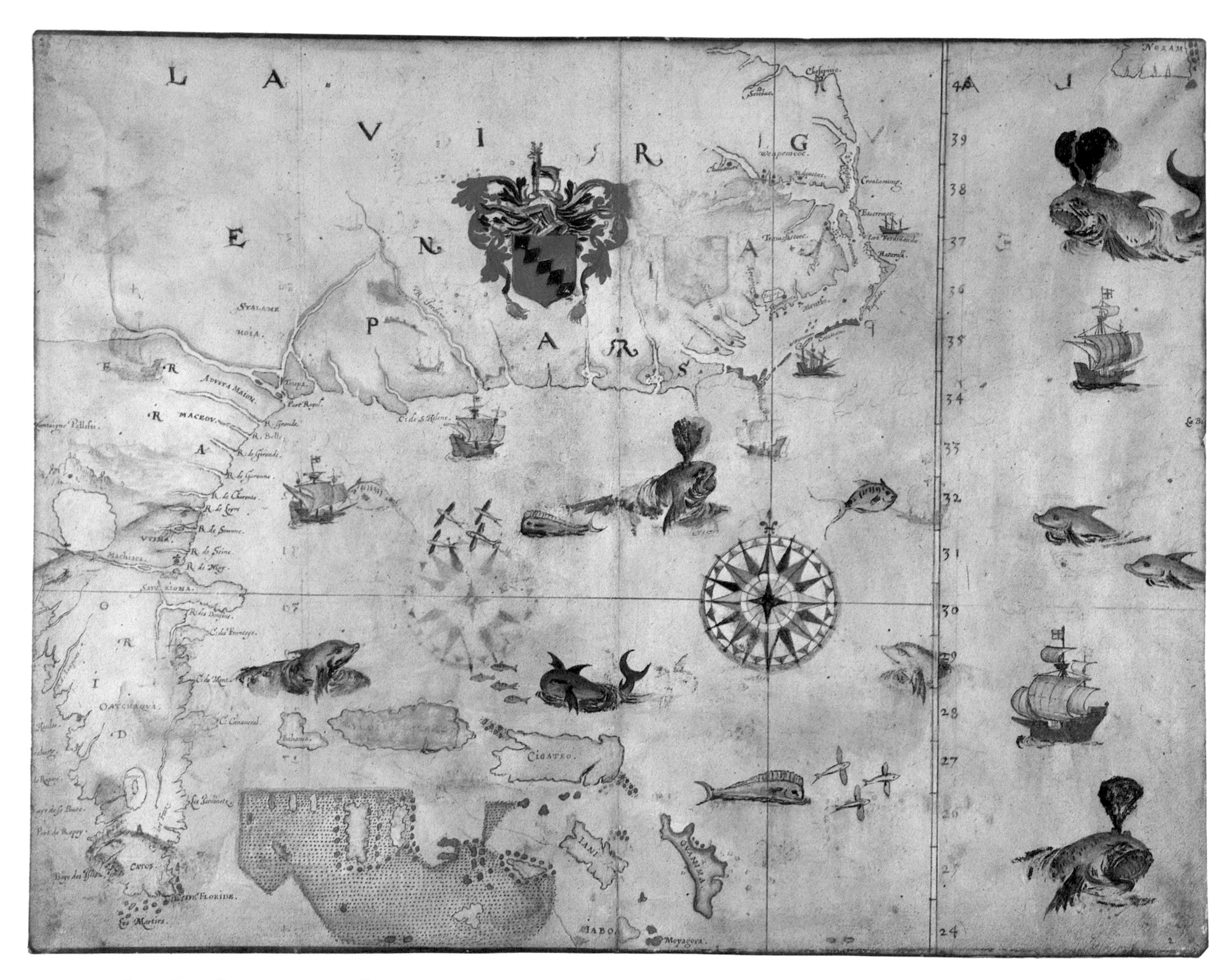

PLATE 36: John White. "La Virgenia Pars." 1585. Manuscript, pen and ink and watercolor; 37 × 47 cm. Department of Manuscripts, British Library, London. *This beautiful map shows southeastern coast from Chesapeake Bay to tip of Florida. The arms of Sir Walter Raleigh illustrated as well as English ships along the coast. A channel runs from Port Royal westward to a large body of water (Sea of Verrazano), suggesting a passage to the Pacific.*

Elizabeth's reign. Between 1553 and 1580 the East India Company and the Muscovy Trading Company, both based in London, made several attempts to discover a route to the north of Asia. The first of three formal English expeditions was led in 1576 by Sir Martin Frobisher with three ships in search of a northwest sea passage to the Pacific Ocean. On this voyage he carried the 1569 Mercator map (*see Plate 31*). Because it was erroneous in many details—especially its inclusion of the geography of the apocryphal voyage of the Zeno brothers—Frobisher ascribed his landfall on Baffin Island to Greenland, and he interpreted the

Engraved portrait of Sir Francis Drake

Greenland coast as the imaginary Friesland Islands. Frobisher sailed into the bay in Canada known later as Frobisher Bay, which he initially considered a strait to Asia. He eventually reached the northwest coast of Baffin Island, or Meta Incognita [unknown goal], a name bestowed by Queen Elizabeth when Frobisher returned. The following year Frobisher reentered the bay and mined 200 tons of iron ore, which he hoped contained gold, and transported this back to England. On his third voyage, in 1578, he sailed along the north coast of Hudson Strait and proceeded no farther in a westerly direction, since the expedition's goal was the mining of this ore, which the English eventually deemed worthless.

The next important English navigator in the area was John Davis, who conducted three voyages—in 1585, 1586, and 1587—in quest of a passage to Asia. On the first voyage Davis entered Cumberland Sound, but no additional geographic knowledge was yielded, and the second voyage also added little significant new information. The third voyage was a specific test of the thesis that the Davis Strait was a potential passage to the west. Although this was later disproved, Davis remained convinced that America was an island that could be circumnavigated.

Presentation of the Northwest Passage dominated maps of the 1570s. This is evidenced by a cordiform 1576 map, published in London, entitled "A General Map, Made onelye for the Particuler Declaration of This Discovery" and credited to Sir Humphrey Gilbert (*Plate 34*). An oval world map, which may have been drawn by James Beare, was published in *A True Discourse of the Late Voyages of Discoverie; For Finding a Passage to Cathaya* (London, 1578) by the English navigator George Best, who was a lieutenant of Martin Frobisher; it depicts a body of water (named Frobisshers Streights) as a Northwest Passage opening to the Strait of Anian, thus suggesting a continuous passage from the Atlantic to the Pacific.

The remaining English efforts at exploration had more romantic overtones. In 1578 Sir Humphrey Gilbert received from Queen Elizabeth letters patent to search for lan din North America. Initially he sent the Portuguese pilot Simão Fernandes on an exploratory trip about which little is known. In 1583 Gilbert himself set out to establish a settlement, but his ship sank in a storm. A 1583 manuscript map by the polymath John Dee, "Sir Humfray Gylbert knight his charte," may have been drawn as propaganda for Gilbert's voyage of that year; focusing on the

Northwest Passage, it pictured a long arm of the Pacific Ocean extending almost to the northern part of the Atlantic.

Gilbert's grant was transferred to his half brother, Walter Raleigh, who in 1584 sent Captain Philip Amadas and the gentleman Arthur Barlowe to search out sites for a colony. Upon reaching North America, they entered an inlet at the northern end of Hatarask Island (the Indian name for the long barrier island that extends south toward Cape Hatteras) and eventually came upon another island, known to the Indians as Roanoke. After six weeks of exploration they returned to England, and to encourage colonization, members of the expedition gave out enticing reports on the abundance offered by the new land. Arthur Barlowe issued a charming and favorable account in which he extolled the fruitfulness of the soil—providing three crops of maize each year—and the plentifulness of game. The English leaders were soon to realize that because the North American climate was similar to England's, their surplus population could practically be resettled in the New World. The colonies would supply England with a wealth of raw materials and in return they would provide a market for Britain's manufactured goods.

Sir Walter Raleigh, who was keen on establishing a permanent settlement for further exploration as well as a base for privateering against the Spanish, immediately began preparations for a second expedition. Recently knighted, he had received regal allowance from Queen Elizabeth to name the colony Virginia in her honor. Sir Richard Grenville sailed from Plymouth in April 1585 with seven ships, and after exploring the Carolina sounds, he left Ralph Lane at Roanoke to serve as governor over 108 colonists. This first English colony in North America failed as a result of both internal and external causes. The colony was beset by antagonism among its leaders as well as by hostility from the local Indians. Despite the earlier glowing reports about the abundance of food, there was in reality an inadequate supply, and provisions promised from England were not replenished. In the summer of 1586 the colonists went back to England with Sir Francis Drake on his return from plundering the West Indies. Later that year Grenville returned to the area, and, finding the colonists departed, left behind him a holding force of fifteen men, all of whom were eventually killed by Indians. It is this group that came to be known as the Lost Colony.

That the first group of colonists at Roanoke, left under the leadership of Ralph Lane in 1585, included so many specialists proves the seriousness of the venture. There was a physician, a clergyman, a metallurgist, and apothecaries, as well as Thomas Hariot, the brilliant mathematician and naturalist, and John White, the watercolorist who later drew the first maps of the area (*see Plates 36, 37*).

Roanoke Indians, watercolor by John White, c. 1585

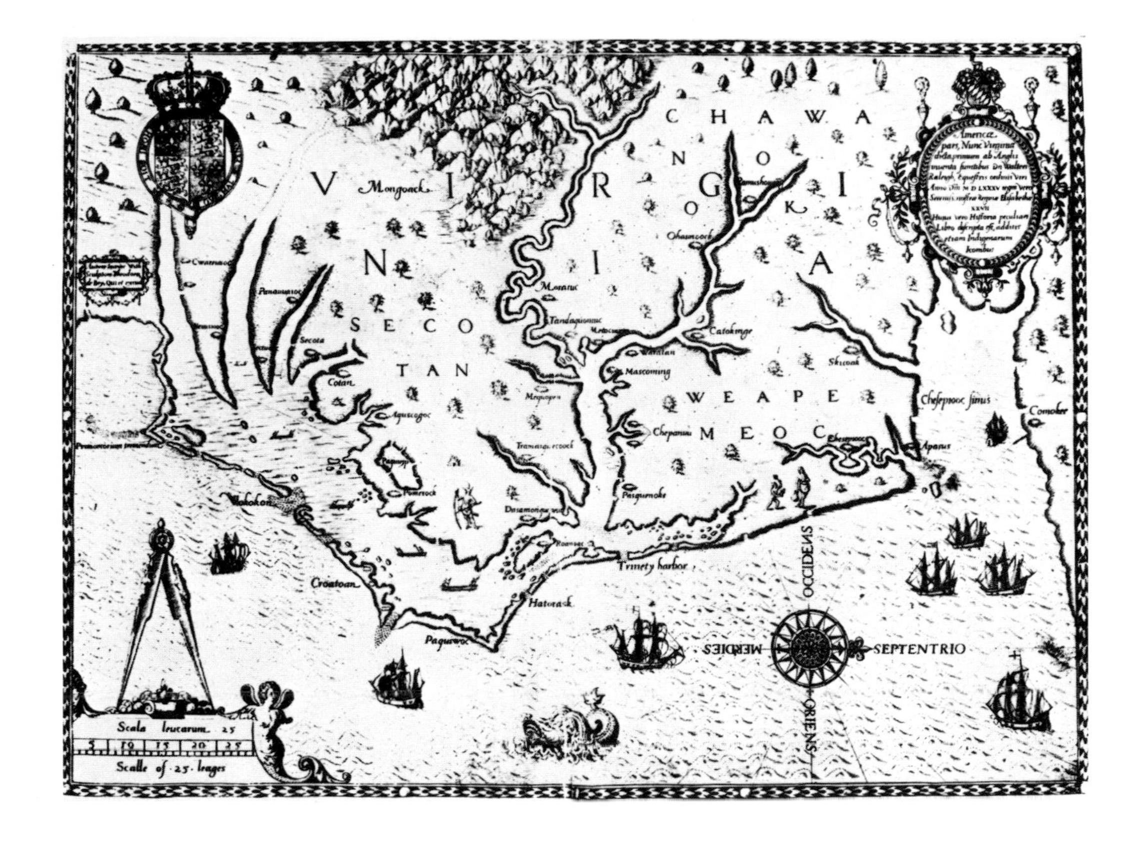

PLATE 37: John White. "Americae pars, Nunc Virginia dicta." 1590. Engraving, 30 × 42 cm. Private collection. *First map focusing only on Virginia. Map extends from the Chesapeake Bay to Cape Lookout. First appearance of name Roanoke (as Roanoac). Inlets along Albemarle and Pamlico sounds and topography of area are shown. Defines placement of Indian villages. Published in Thomas Hariot's* A Briefe and True Report of the New Found Land of Virginia, of the Commodities, and of the Nature and Manners of the Naturall Inhabitants *(Frankfurt am Main, 1590), which comprised Part 1 of Théodore de Bry's* Great Voyages.

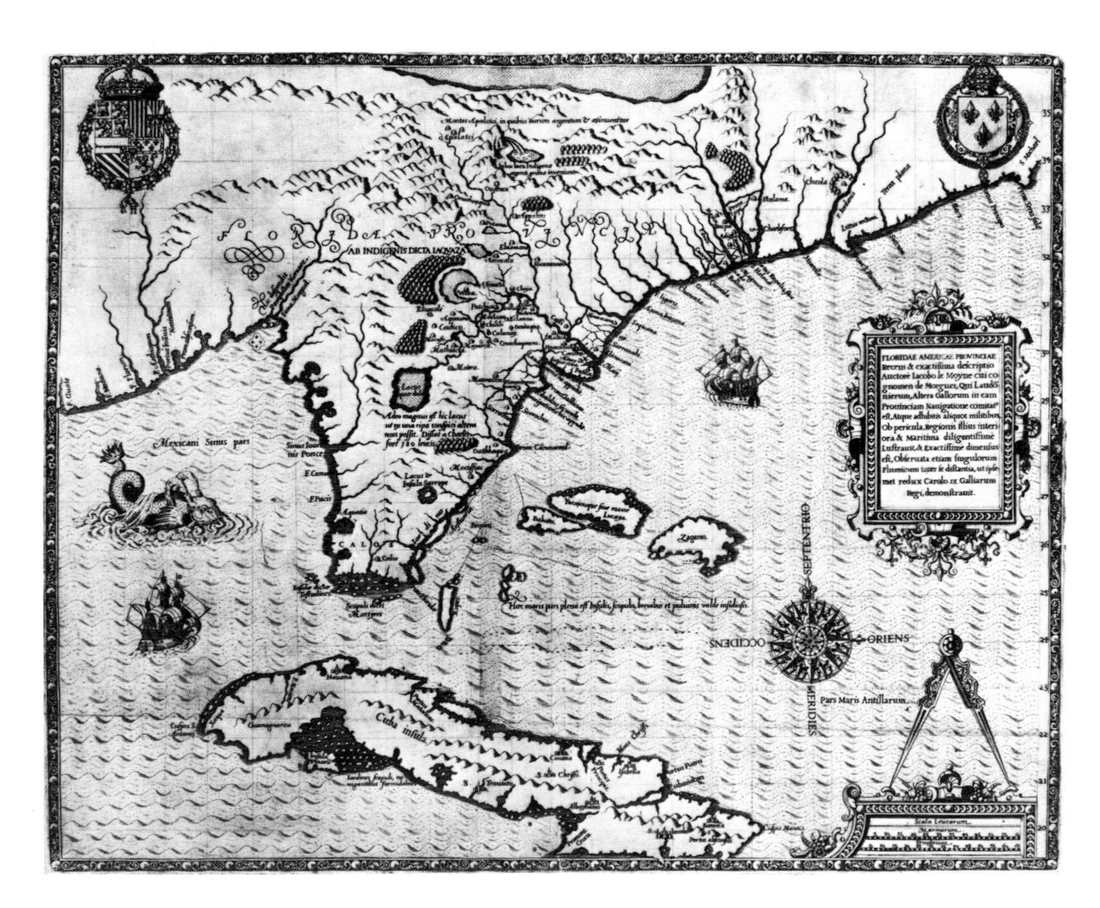

PLATE 38: Jacques Le Moyne de Morgues. "Floridae Americae Provinciae Recens & exactissima descriptio." 1591. Engraving, 37 × 45 cm. Private collection. *Not an accurate map of the Florida region; northeastern coastline too far east. Port Royal (as Portus Regalis) appears for first time on a printed map, and Fort Caroline shown as Carolina. Names and positions of many rivers and cities and other geographical entities derived from regional Indians or other unreliable sources. Published in Le Moyne's* Brevis Narratio Eorum quae in Florida Americae Provincia Gallis Acciderunt *(Frankfurt am Main, 1591), Part 2 of Théodore de Bry's* Great Voyages.

PLATE 39: Cornelis de Jode. "Americae. Pars Borealis, Florida, Baccalaos, Canada, Cortercalis." 1593. Engraving, 38 × 53 cm. Private collection. *Geography is a consolidation of concepts shown on maps of John White (see Plate 37) and Jacques Le Moyne (see Plate 38). There are many errors: Chesapeake Bay is at latitude of Boston, Virginia is north of Cape Cod (C. de las Arenas on map). A Northwest Passage is prominent. One of earliest relatively accurate representations of North America. Appeared in Cornelis de Jode's revised edition of the atlas* Speculum Orbis Terrarum *first published by his father, Gerard de Jode (Antwerp, 1593).*

White had been commissioned to go on this expedition to record the natural and aboriginal curiosities of Virginia, and his paintings are among the earliest and most valuable representations of natural history of the North American continent. They are considered the finest depictions of the native scene before the rich output of the nineteenth-century artist-naturalists; according to the historian Samuel Eliot Morison, White's series of paintings include the best portraits of the American Indian before George Catlin, of flora before William Bartram—the son of naturalist John Bartram—and of birds before John James Audubon. Twenty-three of White's Virginia scenes were later engraved by the Flemish engraver and publisher Théodore de Bry and included in the first volume of his *Great Voyages*, as illustrations to Thomas Hariot's description of Roanoke Island and its commodities and inhabitants.

In 1587 Raleigh dispatched a group of 110 persons under the leadership of John White as governor to establish, according to Raleigh's charter, the "Cittie of Raleigh in Virginea," with specific instructions to locate on Chesapeake Bay. The sailing master, however, put the colonists ashore at Roanoke in order to expedite his goal of privateering. These settlers included women and children, and in August 1587 White's married daughter gave birth to Virginia Dare, the first child born of English parents in North America. White once again sailed back to England to establish a better supply line. Setting sail for his return to the colony in 1588 with supplies and additional colonists, his ships were looted en route by the French, and he was forced back to England empty handed. When he finally reached the colony in the summer of 1590, he found nothing left of his second Lost Colony. St. Augustine persisted as the only European settlement along the eastern coast of North America.

In the 1580s the French cosmographer André Thevet and the Flemish engraver Franz Hogenberg published world maps distinguished by their rarity rather than by their cartographic importance. Thevet's "Le Nouveau Monde Descouverte et Illustre de Nostre Temps" was published in Paris in 1581, only two copies of which are extant. He had sailed along the southern and northern coast of America in 1555, and therefore his map incorporated information gained from personal experience. Hogenberg's map "Americae et proximarum regionum orae descriptio" was published in Cologne in 1589. Working in Cologne, he engraved many maps for Abraham Ortelius, the important map publisher Christoffel Plantin, and others. With his collaborator, the German geographer Georg Braun, Hogenberg produced the six-volume *Civitates Orbis Terrarum* (Cologne, 1572–1617), which included topical drawings of the principal cities of the world. The most significant map of this period covers the southeastern portion of North America; entitled "La Florida" (*Plate 35*), by the Spanish cosmographer royal Gerónimo de Chaves, it appeared in the 1584 *Additamentum* to Ortelius's atlas *Theatrum Orbis Terrarum*. Gerónimo's father, Alonso de Chaves, was examiner of pilots and tester of instruments at the Casa de Contratación, and in 1552 Gerónimo was appointed to that bureau's newly established chair of nautical science. His map was the first regional map representation of Florida. It mirrors the Spanish definition of the coast and the interior as described by

Indians fishing, watercolor by John White, c. 1585

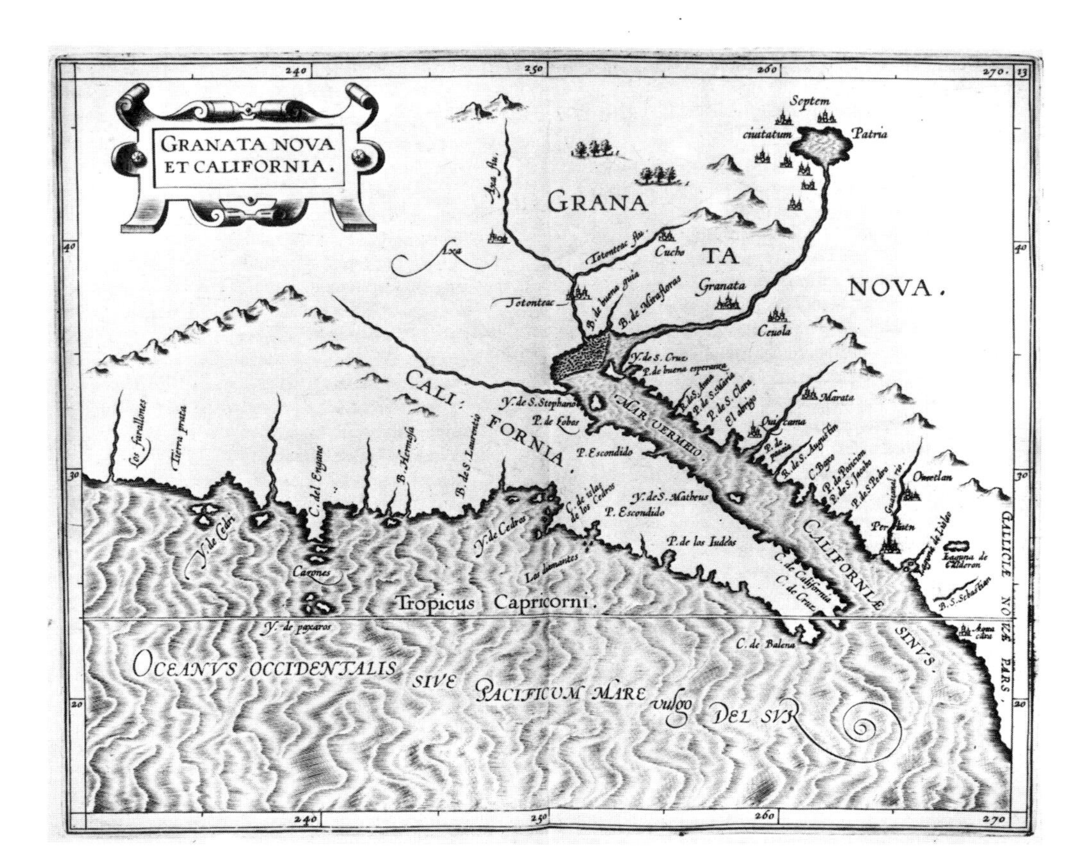

PLATE 40: Cornelis van Wytfliet. "Norvmbega et Virginia." 1597. Engraving, 23 × 29 cm. John Carter Brown Library, Brown University, Providence. *Included in first atlas devoted solely to America, Wytfliet's* Descriptionis Ptolemaicae Augmentum *(Louvain, 1597). East-west extent of New England is too great. Names Chesipooc (Chesapeake Bay), Hatarask (Hatteras), and Roanoac. Utilizes topography and nomenclature of John White (see Plate 37).*

PLATE 41: Cornelis van Wytfliet. "Granata Nova et California." 1597. Engraving, 23 × 28 cm. John Carter Brown Library, Brown University, Providence. *Only sixteenth-century printed map specifically devoted to southern California. Based on work of Abraham Ortelius and other contemporary authorities. Includes all of Gulf of California and lower Colorado River. Legendary Seven Cities (Septem ciuitatum Patria) are shown around a large lake. Ceuola (Cibola) also appears. Printed in Wytfliet's atlas* Descriptionis Ptolemaicae Augmentum *(Louvain, 1597).*

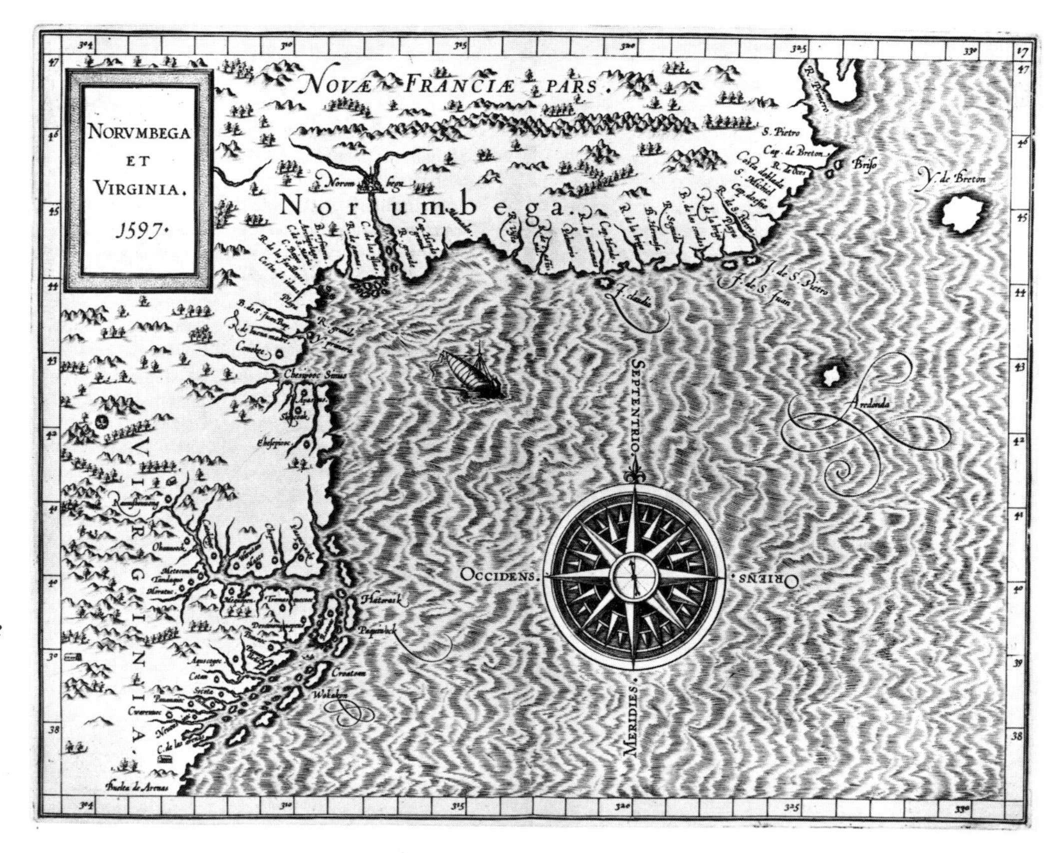

The village of Secoton, Virginia; engraving by Théodore de Bry, after drawing by John White, c. 1585

Hernando de Soto, including a large lake in the region of the Okefenokee Swamp.

Francis Gaulle's map "Novus Orbis," often known as the "Hakluyt-Martyr Map," was published in *Decades* (Paris, 1587). On this map, to the north of the Raleigh settlement, is the phrase "Virginea 1584," the first cartographic reference to Virginia. Priority for a regional map of Virginia and the Carolinas, however, is assigned to the beautiful 1585 manuscript map "La Virgenia Pars," drawn from personal observation by John White (*Plate 36*). Chesepiooc Sinus (Chesapeake Bay), Hatrask (Hatteras), Croatoan, and Roanoc all appeared for the first time, and Indian settlements are depicted around Pamlico and Albemarle sounds. Two major geographic misrepresentations occur: a strait running from Port Royal to a large body of water (the infamous false Sea of Verrazano), and the St. Johns River originating in the region of the present Okefenokee Swamp. This manuscript was the model for the printed mother map of the region, White's "Americae pars, Nunc Virginia dicta" (*Plate 37*), which appeared along with his engraved views of Virginia in Thomas Hariot's narrative of the first English plantation of Virginia, *A Briefe and True Report of the New Found Land of Virginia* (Frankfurt am Main, 1590), Part 1 of Théodore de Bry's series *Great Voyages.* This first separate printed map of the region from the Chesapeake Bay to Cape Lookout emphasizes shoals and wrecks. It was the archetypal map of the area until James Moxon's "A New Discription of Carolina By Order of the Lords Proprictors" was published about eighty years later—in John Ogilby's *America* (London, 1671).

In 1591 the classic map "Floridae Americae Provinciae Recens & exactissima descriptio" (*Plate 38*) by Jacques Le Moyne de Morgues, a native of Dieppe, was included in his *Brevis Narratio Eorum quae in Florida Americae* (Frankfurt am Main, 1591), comprising Part 2 of De Bry's *Great Voyages*; it is thought of as a companion to White's map of Virginia published in Part 1 of De Bry's work. Le Moyne was the earliest known artist to visit what is now the continental United States. Accompanying René de Laudonnière's expedition to Florida, Georgia, and the Carolinas in 1564, he was hired to map the seacoast and harbors, indicate the position of towns, plot the depth and course of the rivers, and portray the dwellings of the natives and anything else worthy of observation. His vivid views of Florida, along with White's paintings, are the best visual records of North America during the period of discovery. Le Moyne's watercolors of American scenes and natural curiosities were later engraved and published by De Bry, along with Le Moyne's narrative of the experiences of Ribaut and Laudonnière, as Part 2 of the *Great Voyages.*

Although De Bry himself did not visit the American shores, he has become a leading character in the drama of documenting

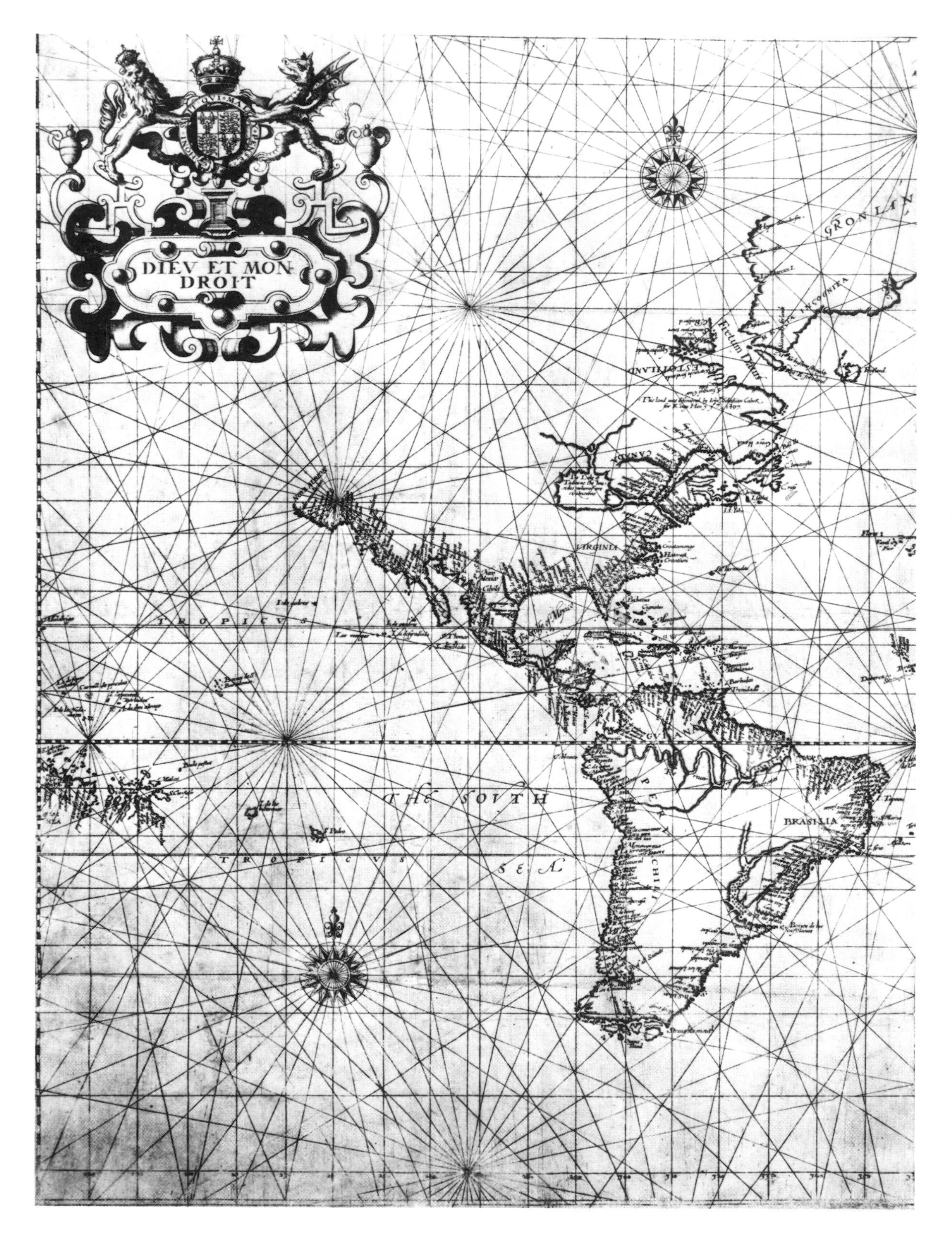

PLATE 42: Edward Wright. "A Chart of the World on Mercator's Projection" (detail). c. 1599. Engraving, entire dimensions 42 × 64 cm. John Work Garrett Library, Johns Hopkins University, Baltimore. *Commonly known as "Wright-Molyneux Map," first engraving in England based on Mercator projection as improved by Wright. Detail is left half—Western Hemisphere portion—of map on which a suggestion of a Great Lake (Lake of Tadouac), Virginia, and Davis Strait (Fretum Dauis) appear. This is first state, which does not include second-state cartouche statement, southwest of South America, concerning Sir Francis Drake's voyage through Strait of Magellan in 1577. Perhaps most advanced cartographic production of the sixteenth century. Published in* The Principall Navigations, Voiages, Traffiques, and Discoueries of the English Nation *(3 vols., London, 1598–1600) compiled by Richard Hakluyt.*

the early American struggle of recording the native life and mapping the area. De Bry was a Flemish engraver and publisher and book seller who worked most of his life in Germany. His profusely illustrated works included finely executed copperplates —based on original work of other artists like White and Le Moyne—of maps and pictures of the natives and the flora and fauna of America in two monumental series, popularly known as *Great Voyages* and *Little Voyages* (1590–1618).

Le Moyne's 1591 map was the definitive map of the region for over a hundred years. Although correct about places the French had visited, its accuracy extends only to a limited region. The coast is shown at a reasonably correct latitude, yet it extends too far east, resulting in an erroneous enlargement of Virginia. There is a probable representation of Lake George in Florida, the Okefenokee Swamp, and the Appalachian Mountains bordering the Sea of Verrazano. The 1593 engraving "Americae. Pars Borealis, Florida, Baccalaos, Canada, Corterealis" by the Dutch map publisher Cornelis de Jode (*Plate 39*) shows obvious influences of the White and Le Moyne maps and is one of the earliest separate presentations of the North American continent that corresponds to geographic realities. Yet there are glaring errors: Chesapeake Bay is positioned at the latitude of Boston, Virginia placenames appear north of Cape Cod (C. de las Arenas), the New England coastline runs in an incorrect direction, and a Northwest Passage is depicted.

In 1597 the Flemish geographer Cornelis van Wytfliet published in Louvain the first atlas entirely devoted to the Americas; entitled *Descriptionis Ptolemaicae Augmentum*, it was published as a supplement to Ptolemy's *Geographia*. Among its nineteen maps are regional representations of New France and Canada, New England (Norumbega) and Virginia, Florida and Apalche, New Granada and California, and Quivira and Anian. "Norvmbega et Virginia" (*Plate 40*) is the most accurate antecedent to Joannes de Laet's 1630 "Nova Anglia, Novvm Belgivm et Virginia" (*see Plate 57*). "Granata Nova et California" (*Plate 41*) is the only printed sixteenth-century map specifically focusing on southern California and New Mexico.

The cartographic potential of the sixteenth century is best exemplified by "A Chart of the World on Mercator's Projection" (*Plate 42*) by the brilliant English mathematician Edward Wright, professor of mathematics at Cambridge. It is commonly known as the "Wright-Molyneux Map" because the geography is based primarily on an important globe engraved by the English globe maker Emery Molyneux in 1592; it was once believed that this map was prepared for the engraver by Molyneux, yet it has now been established that he was no longer in England when it was being produced. A legend on the map states that the sea between Asia and the West coast of America is 1,200 leagues at latitude 38° and the distance between Cape California and Cape Mendocino is 600 leagues rather than the 1,300 leagues that had been previously determined. Frobusshers Straightes (Frobisher Bay) is erroneously placed at Greenland and appears that way on maps for the following 200 years. It includes Davis Strait (Fretum Dauis on the map), correctly located, Albemarle Sound and Chesapeake Bay inappropriately enlarged, coupled with a reduced Pamlico Sound and an early suggestion of one of the Great Lakes.

Mercator, the inventor of the projection that bears his name (*see Plate 31*), did not elucidate the mathematical principles on which it is based nor the tables necessary for its construction. These were not available until thirty years later, with the publication of Edward Wright's important book *The Correction of Certaine Errors in Navigation* (London, 1599). His map, later included in Richard Hakluyt's massive work *The Principall Navigations, Voiages, Traffiques, and Discoueries of the English Nation* (3 vols., London, 1598–1600), is a pioneering example of the projection. Wright's *Certaine Errors* provided new mathematical tables that would rectify errors in using compass, chart, and cross-staff. It also showed pilots how to plot straight-line courses using Wright's interpretation of Mercator's projection. Wright's map appeared at a time when England was on the brink of a long career as a colonizing power, and it manifests in fullest form the state of geographical science at the close of the century. Considered the finest map of the sixteenth century, its reputation is enhanced by romantic associations with William Shakespeare. Scholarly consensus has concluded that it is specifically referred to in *Twelfth Night*, where Maria speaks teasingly of Malvolio in Act 3, Scene 2: "He does smile his face into more lynes, then is in the new Mappe, with the augmentation of the Indies."

4. *Permanent Colonization Reflected on Maps*

As Geography without History seemeth as carkasse without motion, so History without Geography wandereth as vagrant without a certaine habitation.

JOHN SMITH
The Generall Historie of Virginia, New-England, and the Summer Isles (1624)

1600-1650

THE MAPPING of North America intensified notably in the early seventeenth century when colonization became successful. The four great powers at the time—England, France, Spain, and the Netherlands—all contributed to the effort. As exploration and settlement of the transoceanic continent began, first peripherally and then gradually toward the interior, there were improved geographic definitions on maps, with the addition of placenames. At the very beginning of the seventeenth century the engraved 1600 "Nova et Rece Terrarum et Regnorum Californiae Novae Hispaniae Mexicanae et Peruviae" by the English hydrographer Gabriel Tatton shows the southern part of the continent, incorporating many new names. However, the Virginia and Roanoke region is omitted. Another Tatton map, "Maris Pacifici" (*Plate 43*), published in the same year, elegantly displays the entire western coast.

At the beginning of the century only Spain had established successful colonies on the continent; one was firmly instituted in the area of Mexico and Central America and the other was tenuously begun in Florida. Spanish interests are reflected in the 1601 "Descripcion de las Occidentales" by Antonio de Herrera y Tordesillas, Cortes's chronicler who had been appointed official historiographer of Castile and of the Indies under Philip II. It was usually found at the end of the second volume of his *Historia General de las Hechos de los Castellanos en las Isles y Tierra Firma de Mar Oceano* (4 vols., Madrid, 1601).

Sebastián Vizcaíno voyaged along the California coast and discovered Monterey Bay at the close of 1602. By 1603 the entire Pacific coast had been surveyed as far north as Cape Blanco (latitude 43° north), but the 5,000 miles between that point and the area opposite Kamchatka Peninsula in northern Asia remained uncharted for many years. Simultaneous with these coastal explorations were the interior treks of the Spanish missionaries based in Mexico, who by 1603 had arrived north as far as California's Sonora Valley. In 1609 missionaries founded Santa Fe on ancient Indian ruins; it is the third oldest permanent existing European settlement in the United States, after St. Augustine and Jamestown. In the Southeast, other Spanish missionaries set out from St. Augustine and by mid-century had established at least two dozen missions in Spanish Florida. Neither regional accomplishment found expression on maps during the first half of the seventeenth century.

Several English voyages were undertaken along the New England coast during the first decade of the century. In 1602 Captains Bartholomew Gosnold and Bartholowmew Gilbert sailed directly from England and anchored perhaps in Casco Bay, Maine. Their ships remained for a short time at Cuttyhunk, which was named Elizabeth's Isle, and landings were made at Nantucket, Martha's Vineyard, and Cape Cod, the last named for the plentiful fish in the surrounding waters. In 1603 Martin Pring set anchor in present Plymouth Harbor and in 1605–06 George Weymouth journeyed to Nantucket and the Maine coast in an abortive attempt to establish a colony for oppressed British Catholics.

The first seventeenth-century exploration that had a major cartographic effect was led by Samuel de Champlain, the noted French explorer whose claims in the New World helped establish French possession of New France. In 1603 Champlain sailed to Tadoussac—already a functioning trading post on the St. Lawrence River—and explored the Lachine Falls. On a second voyage, begun in 1604, Champlain and Pierre du Gua, sieur de Monts, who had a monopoly of trade in the region, explored the Atlantic coast south of the Gulf of the St. Lawrence River. During this voyage they entered Nauset Harbor on Cape Cod and Plymouth Harbor, naming the latter Port St. Louis. Champlain's chronicles of this journey, *Les Voyages du Sieur de Champlain* (Paris, 1613),

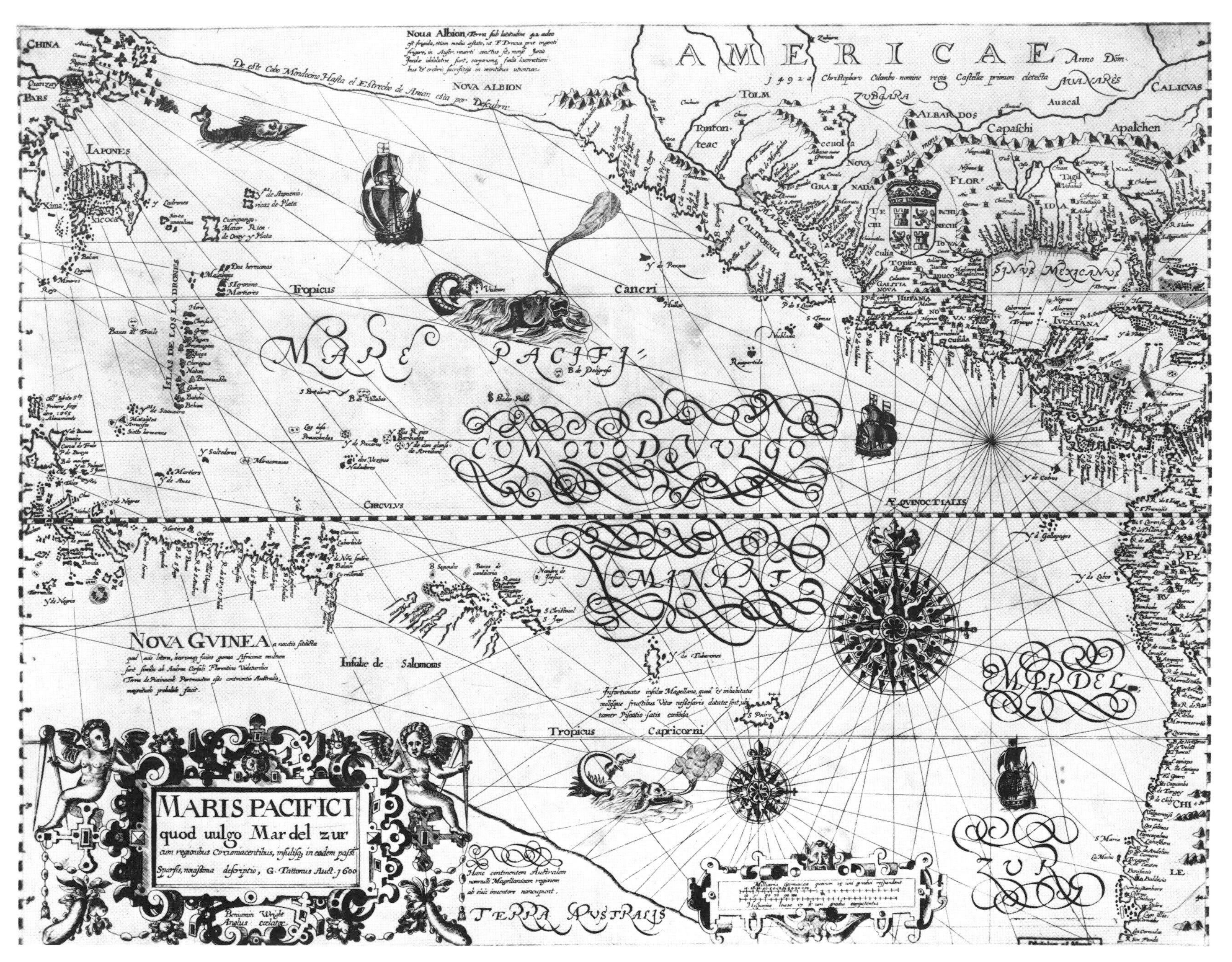

PLATE 43: Gabriel Tatton. "Maris Pacifici." 1600. Engraving, hand colored; 48 × 58 cm. Geography and Map Division, Library of Congress, Washington, D.C. *Detailed map of the known part of the Pacific Ocean, emphasizing its size. Spanish possessions in the Western Hemisphere are specifically detailed. Tatton drew the map, but it was engraved by Benjamin Wright, one of earliest engravers native to England, and republished with corrections in 1616.*

(opposite) PLATE 44: Samuel de Champlain. "Descripsion des costs, pts, rades, Illes de la nouuele france faict selon son vray méridien." 1607. Manuscript on vellum, pen and ink and watercolor; 36 × 54 cm. Geography and Map Division, Library of Congress, Washington, D.C. *Map, personally executed by Champlain, ranks as one of the great cartographic treasures of the United States. First delineation of coast from Cape Sable to south of Cape Cod. Port Royal on Bay of Fundy (La Baye Francoise on map), St. Croix (Sentecroys), Mount Desert Island (Isle Mont Deserts), and Isle Haute appear for first time. Plymouth shown as Cap St. Louis. La Douteuse Isle applied to Martha's Vineyard. Prime source of Champlain's 1613 "Carte Geographiqve de la Novvelle Franse" (see Plate 46).*

which cover the years 1604 to 1612, include a reasonably precise description of Boston Harbor and the Charles River.

Champlain was his own cartographer, and in 1607 he drew a manuscript map, "Descripsion des costs, pts, rades, Illes de la nouuele france faict selon son vray méridien" (*Plate 44*), now one of the cartographic treasures of the Library of Congress thanks to a bequest by the historian Henry Harrisse. It documents the two-year reconnaissance Champlain made with Monts in 1604–05 and covers an area from Sable Island off Cape Breton to the latitude of Martha's Vineyard. This is the first accurate mapping of that coastline. Port Royal appears on the Bay of Fundy (titled La Baye Francoise), and the names of Sentecroys (St. Croix), derived from the junction of three rivers, Isle Mont Deserts, and Isle Haute also are shown. Penobscot is cited as Pentegoet, Cape Ann as Cap aux Isles, and Plymouth as Cap St. Louis. Elizabeth Island is outlined but not named, while Gosnold's Cape Cod is designated as Cap Blanc. The island of Martha's Vineyard is called La Douteuse Isle [doubtful island] because of the explorers' uncertainty that it was really an island. In 1608, beneath the area known as the Rock of Quebec on account of its location at the top

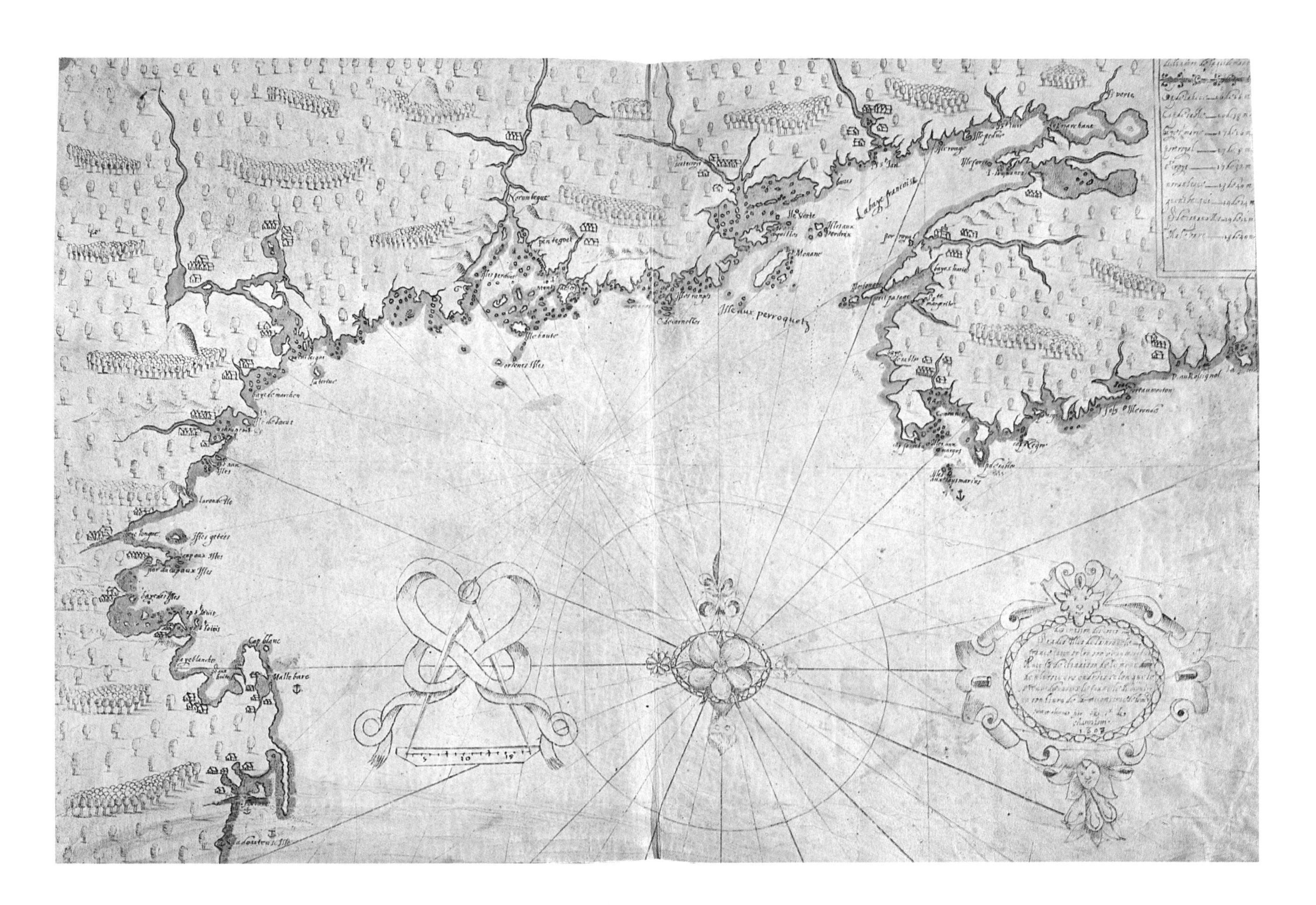

Samuel de Champlain, fighting at Lake Champlain in 1609, from his Voyages de la Nouvelle France Occidentale, *1632*

of a rocky part of the St. Lawrence shore, Champlain founded the first French trading post that evolved into a great city. The next year he journeyed to the lake that now bears his name, where he assisted the Montagnais Indians in defeating the Mohawks.

The first contemporary map of New France, "Figvre de la Terre Nevve, Grande Riviere de Canada, et Côtes de l'Ocean en la Novvelle France" (*Plate 45*), was not made by Champlain; engraved by Jan Swelinck, it was drawn by Marc Lescarbot and appeared in his descriptive *Histoire de la Novvelle France* (Paris, 1609). Lescarbot, a lawyer-poet, had been with the sieur de Monts at Port Royal, Nova Scotia, in 1606. The map offered one of the most accurate contemporary representations of the region as far west as the village of Hochelaga (now Montreal). By 1613 missionaries and fur traders had abandoned the post at Port Royal and relocated on Mount Desert Island, and that same year the East Virginia Company at Jamestown dispatched Captain Sir Samuel Argall to break up the marquis de Guercheville's Jesuit colony on the island. He demolished the settlements and returned to Jamestown with some of his prisoners.

Champlain's map "Carte Geographiqve de la Novvelle Franse" (*Plate 46*) is included in his previously mentioned *Les Voyages du Sieur de Champlain*, and illustrates three excursions he made into the interior. The coastal nomenclature of his 1607 manuscript map is repeated, and in addition four important lakes, with their quaintly descriptive names, are noted: Lac Contenant 15 Journees des Canaux des Sauuages (Lake Ontario), Lac des Irocois (a misplaced Lake Oneida), Grand Lac Contenant 300 Lieux de Long, and Lac de Champlain. Champlain probably bestowed his own name on this last lake by reason both of his battle with the Iroquois near present Crown Point and of the strategic importance he attached to its location. The distances named are approximations of Indian descriptions; at the time Champlain had not progressed that far west along the St. Lawrence River. French flags of settlement are drawn on the map at Quebec, Po. [Port] Royal, and Ille de Sable, but not at Montreal. Also to be found in the same book are charts of Mallebarre (Nauset Harbor on the south shore of Cape Cod), Port St. Louis (Plymouth Bay), Port Royal (Annapolis Royal, Nova Scotia), Port Fortune (Stage Harbor, Cape Cod, Massachusetts), and Quebec, showing some of the original structures.

In 1615 Champlain embarked on a journey that took him to the Georgian Bay region of Lake Huron; on his return he encountered Lake Ontario for the first time. Another volume describing his voyages, covering the years 1615 to 1618, *Voyages et Descouvertures Faites en la Nouvelle France* (Paris, 1619), contains no map, but a once-lost Champlain map of 1616, now in the John Carter Brown Library at Brown University, may have been intended for that work. Identification of this map exemplifies detective-like inquiry into the history of cartography. In 1953 the John Carter Brown Library acquired an engraved map of New France inscribed "faict par le Sr. de Champlain 1616." If the inscription is valid, this then would be the first printed map by a European explorer of those regions on which Lake Huron

(Mer Douce on the map) and Lake Ontario (Lac St. Louis) are shown. This is the only known copy of the map, but research has demonstrated that the rare 1653 map "Le Canada" by the French cartographer Pierre Duval (*Plate 47*), with the inscription "faict par le Sr. de Champlain," unquestionably used the same engraved copperplate as the 1616 Champlain map and modernized its legend. The map apparently was to be included as part of Champlain's 1619 edition of his chronicles, but finally it was not added. It is an interesting discovery to find "concealed" in a 1653 map a lost map by the great French explorer and colonial official of New France.

The last and most detailed of Champlain's great maps of New France, "Carte de la Nouuelle France" (*Plate 48*), was published in his book *Les Voyages de la Nouvelle France Occidentale* (Paris, 1632). It was an amplification of his previous maps, with Mer Douce [freshwater sea] representing Lake Huron and Lac St. Louis representing Lake Ontario, both discovered and named by Champlain. Lake Superior is called Grand Lac, a name based on information given the explorer by the local Indians. According to Emerson D. Fite and Archibald Freeman in their compilation *A Book of Old Maps Delineating American History* (1926), the river running south of Grand Lac with the inscription "Grande riviere qui vient du midy" is an analogue of Lake Michigan. Lake Erie, which is untitled, is pictured simply as a strait extending from Lake Huron to the Niagara Falls and Lake Ontario region.

Champlain's astrolabe, marked 1603

While the French were achieving success at their Canadian colonization, the English established their first firm foothold on the continent in Virginia. This was effected by a 1606 treaty between James I and the king of Spain, the two parties having made peace in 1604. This subsequently allowed England to devote substantial economic interest and energy toward American colonization, the chief stimuli for which were manifold: the pressures of an increasing population in England, the need for new markets for woolen goods, the concern about new sources of precious metals, the possibility of cultivating olives and grapes for oil and wine to be exported to England. The enduring quest for a shorter route to the Indies as well as complex religious issues, among them the desirability of limiting the spread of Catholicism, were other primary incentives.

Two companies were chartered by James I in 1606 to found colonies in America: the Virginia Company of London (London Company), which was granted permission to plant a colony 100 miles square between latitude 34° north and latitude 41° north, and the Virginia Company of Plymouth (Plymouth Company), which was allowed to found a colony between latitude 38° north and latitude 45° north. The overlapping area was open to settlement by either company, although in order to provide a buffer zone, neither could settle within 100 miles of each other. Despite the declared peace with Spain, the Plymouth Company's first expedition, which left England in August 1606, was intercepted and captured by the Spaniards in the West Indies. A second expedition, outfitted by Sir Ferdinando Gorges and led by George Popham and Raleigh Gilbert, set out from Plymouth, England, in May and June of the following year. It explored the Maine

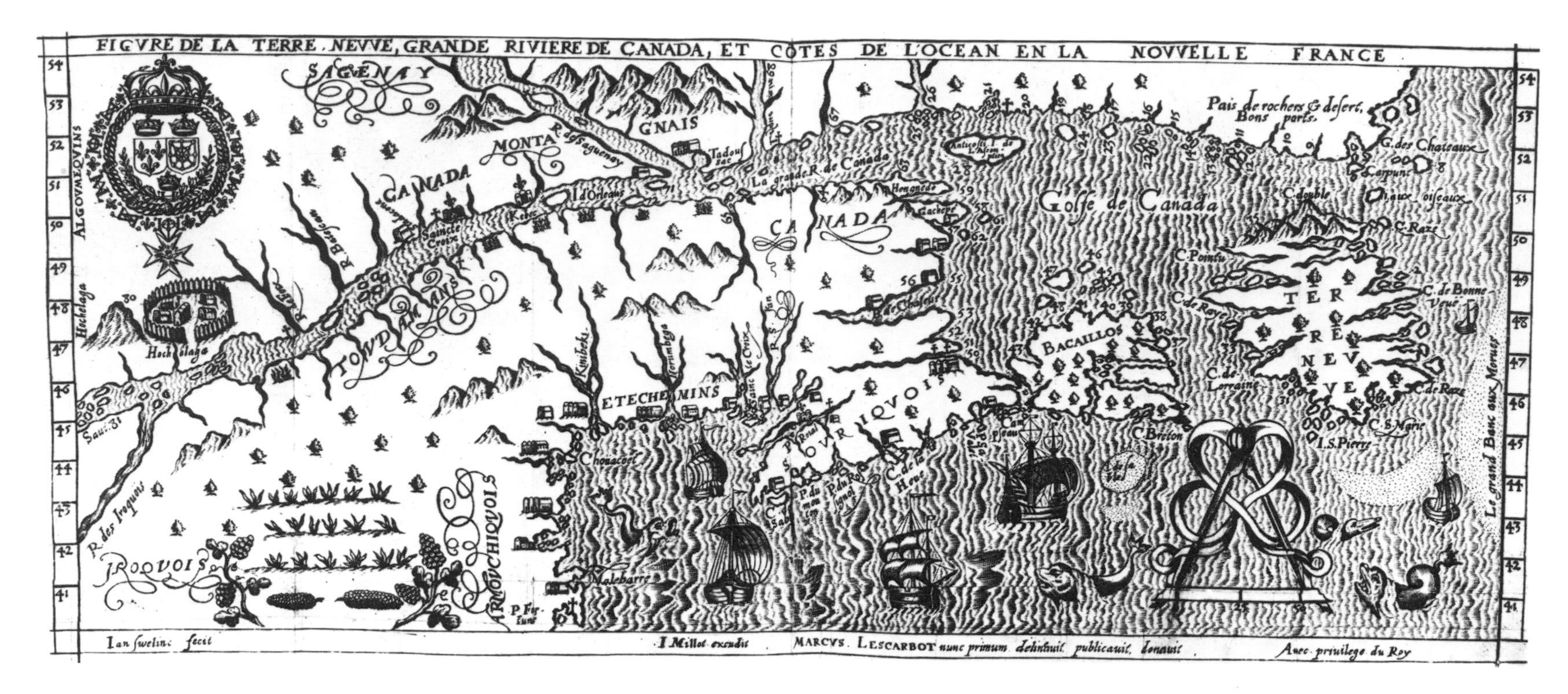

PLATE 45: Marc Lescarbot. "Figvre de la Terre Nevve, Grande Riviere de Canada, et Côtes de l'Ocean en la Novvelle France." 1609. Engraving, 17 × 43 cm. Newberry Library, Chicago. *The most exact contemporary published map of New France, preceding Champlain's first printed map by three years. Shows Montreal (Hochelaga), as well as the Saguenay, St. Croix (Saincte Croix), and Kennebec (Kinibeki) rivers. Map engraved by Jan Swelinck after a drawing by Lescarbot; from the latter's* Histoire de la Novvelle France *(Paris, 1609).*

coast and settled at the mouth of the Sagadahoc River (present Kennebec River). A fort was erected for a trading post, but the colony was abandoned the following summer. This expedition produced a relatively accurate delineation of the Maine coast in manuscript sketches and journal narratives.

The London Company underwrote a venture that began on December 20, 1606, when the three ships *Constant*, *Godspeed*, and *Discovery*, under the command of Captain Christopher Newport, left London. On April 26, 1607, the group reached Chesapeake Bay, and on May 14, after preliminary exploration of the bay, they selected a low swampy peninsula as the first site for settlement, naming it Jamestown, after the king. Captain John Smith, who earlier had been a soldier of fortune, was chosen president of Captain Newport's council. Within six months 51 of the 144 original settlers had died. The salvage of the settlement was in large part due to the amicable relations between Captain Smith and the powerful Chief Wahunsonacock (known to the English as Powhatan), who controlled a large confederacy of Algonquian-speaking Indians and who recognized the benefits of peaceful trade with the newcomers. The marriage in 1614 between his daughter Pocahontas and the prominent colonist John Rolfe helped maintain peace between the Europeans and the Indians for a time, but war broke out following Wahunsonacock's death in 1618. In 1608 Robert Tindall's manuscript "The Draughte by Robarte Tindall of Virginia" (*Plate 49*) was prepared; it is the earliest extant map of the area by a Jamestown colonist. It accurately locates the James and York rivers, which were explored by Captain Newport in the summer of 1607 and

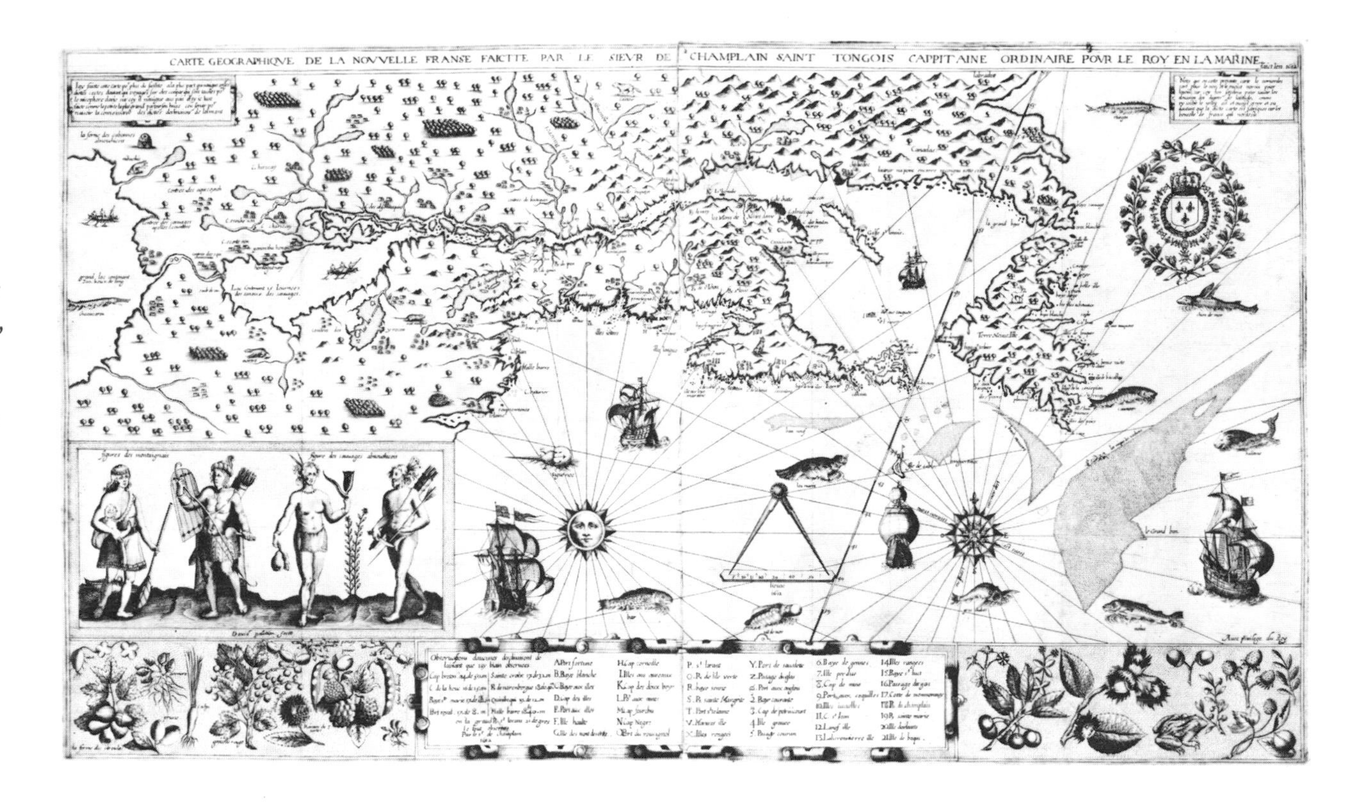

PLATE 46: Samuel de Champlain. "Carte Geographiqve de la Novvelle Franse." 1613. Engraving, 43 × 76 cm. Rare Book and Special Collections Division, Library of Congress, Washington, D.C. *First attempt to show the latitude of New England. Quebec, Port Royal, and Ille de Sable are marked by tiny flags. Lac Contenant 15 Journees de Canaux des Sauuages (Lake Ontario), Lac des Irocois (Oneida), Grand Lac Contenant 300 Lieux de Long, and Lac de Champlain appear. Published in Champlain's* Les Voyages du Sieur de Champlain *(Paris, 1613).*

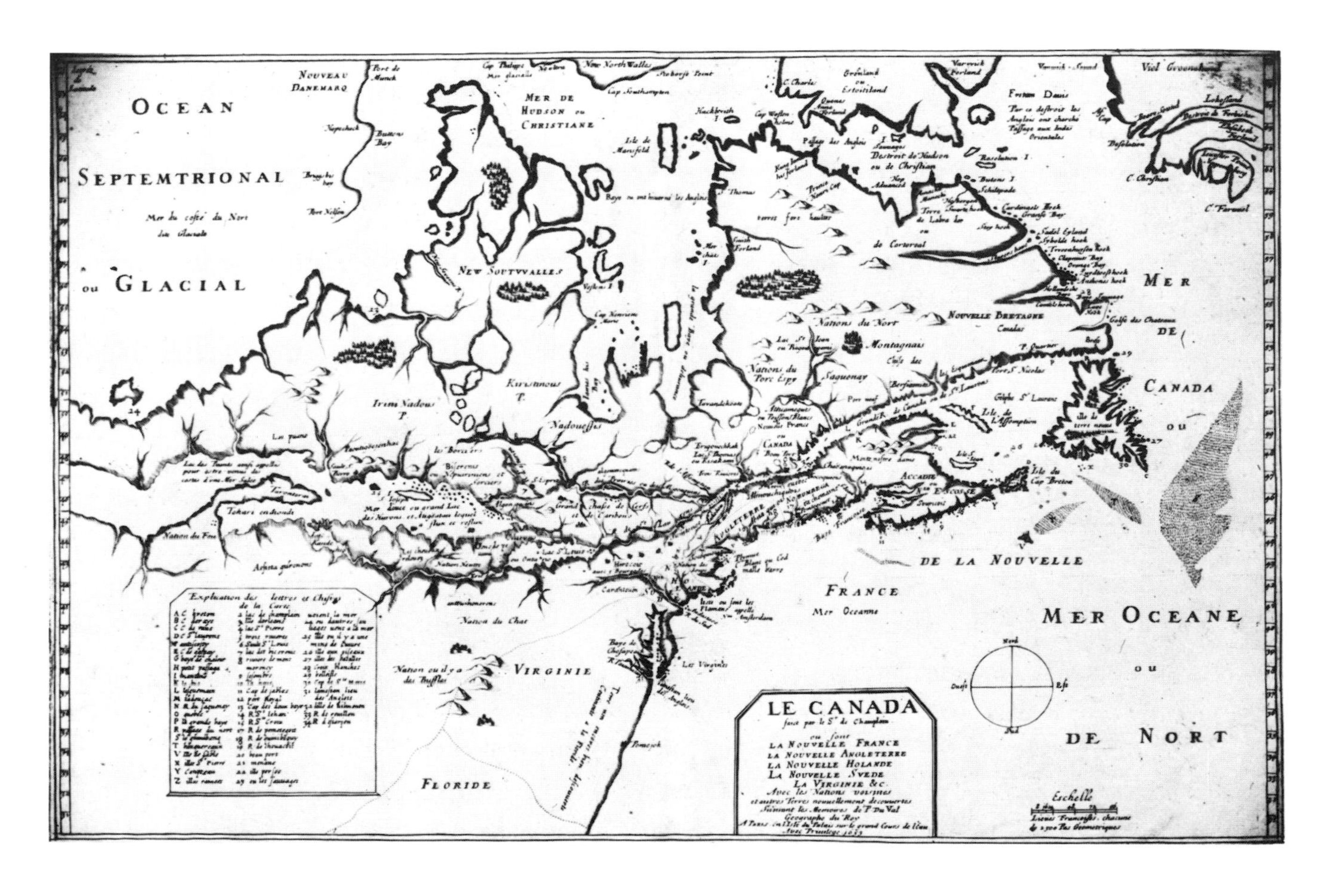

PLATE 47: Pierre Duval. "Le Canada." 1653. Engraving, 36 × 54 cm. Private collection. *Supplies the link in Champlain's cartography between his 1613 and 1632 maps (see Plates 46 and 48) since it uses plate of an unpublished 1616 map by Champlain. Thus it is the first printed map by a European who had explored those regions to show Lake Huron (Mer Douce) and Lake Ontario (Lac St. Louis).*

Champlain, aided by Indian allies, defeats Iroquois in a battle on Lake Champlain

(opposite) PLATE 48: Samuel de Champlain. "Carte de la Nouuelle France." 1632. Engraving, 52 × 86 cm. Private collection. *Most detailed and final published map of Champlain. Grand Lac (Lake Superior) appears, but its representation is based on Indian descriptions. Lake Michigan (Grand Riviere) and Lake Erie, unnamed, are represented as rivers. Published in Champlain's* Voyages de la Nouvelle France Occidentale *(Paris, 1632).*

the spring of 1608, shortly after the Jamestown colony was established. A royal charter was issued in 1609 and Thomas West, baron de la Warr, was appointed governor. As an inducement to colonize the area, the Virginia Company established the headright system, which promised that any Englishman who arranged for 250 of his countrymen to be transported to the new colony, at the expense of the proprietor, would be granted a 1,250-acre tract. These tracts were known as hundreds, or particular plantations, and they were ruled autonomously. In 1609 a new charter extended the colonies' boundaries 200 miles north and south from Old Point Comfort and from sea to sea east and west. This charter was revoked in 1624 and Virginia became a royal colony.

The mother map of the region, John Smith's "Virginia" (*Plate 50*), was issued as a separate publication in 1612. Although Smith left Virginia in 1609 and never returned to the area, the map chronicles early journeys from the Jamestown settlement. The historian Coolie Verner (in his article "The First Maps of Virginia, 1590–1673," *Virginia Magazine of History and Biography*,

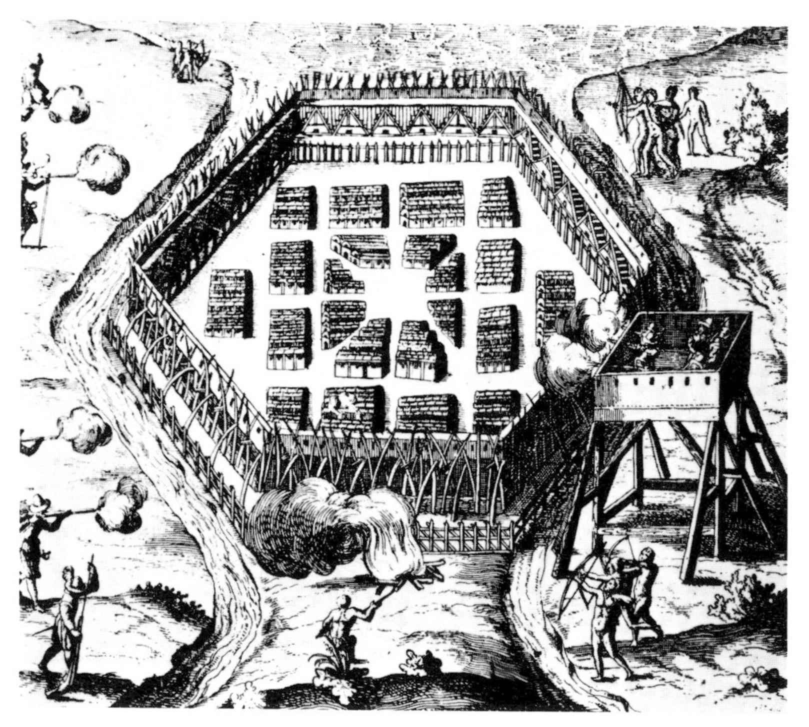

Iroquois village under siege, from Champlain's Voyages, *1632*

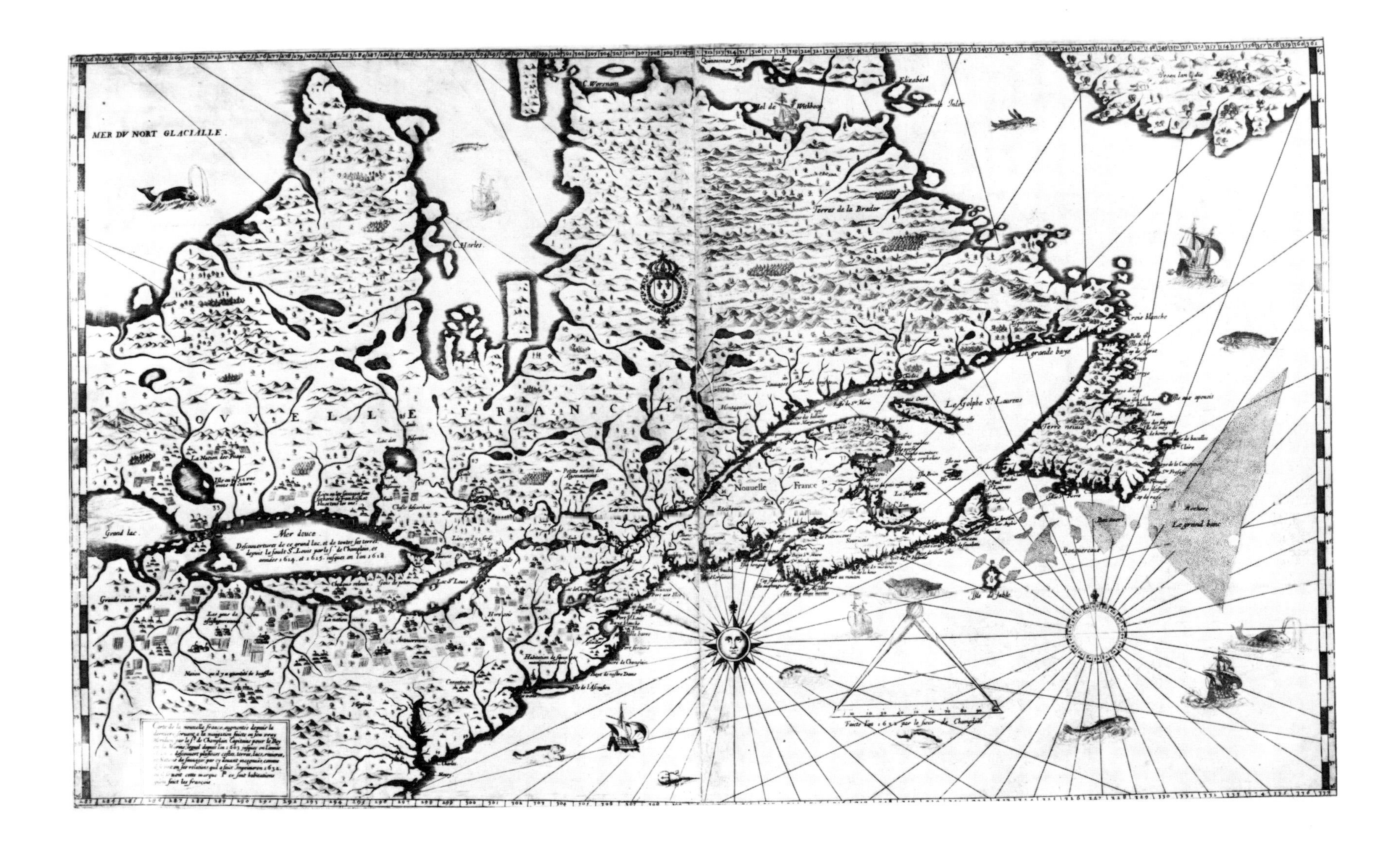

vol. 58, 1950) acknowledges it as the "most important map to appear in print during the period of early settlement and the one map of Virginia that has had the greatest influence upon map making for a longer period of time." It first appeared in Smith's *A Map of Virginia* (Oxford, 1612) and was found in numerous editions of his *Generall Historie of Virginia, New-England, and the Summer Isles*, published in London from 1624 to 1632, as well as in other histories of the seventeenth century. Ten different issues or states of this map evolved. Certain historians have argued that it is not the work of Smith, since he had no skill as a draftsman, but that he may have personally directed the actual draftsman.

The map is oriented with north to the right, a common practice at the time, and mentions approximately 200 names, including those of the following rivers: Powhatan (James), Toppahanock (Rappahannock), Chickahomania, Patawomech (Potomac), Patuxent, and Sasquesanaough (Susquehanna). Also designated are Smyths Iles, Russel Isles (named for the colony's doctor), Stinga Isle (Stingray Isle), Cape Henry, Poynt Comfort, Appamatuck, and Jamestowne. A drawing of a Sasquesahanough Indian and a picture of the inside of Wahunsonacock's lodge (Powhatan on the map) with the chief holding court adorn the sheet.

The Dutch entered the arena of North American exploration in 1609 with Henry Hudson, an Englishman in their employ.

PLATE 49: Robert Tindall. "The Draughte by Robarte Tindall of Virginia." 1608. Manuscript, pen and ink and watercolor; 46 × 84 cm. Department of Manuscripts, British Library, London. *Earliest known map by a Virginia colonist. Jamestown is named on map one year after it was settled. Oriented with north to the right. Locates Indian villages on the James and York rivers.*

Sailing in the *Halve Maen* [*Half Moon*] for the Dutch East India Company, he proceeded up the river that bears his name as far north as the Albany Rapids in search of a Northwest Passage. An anonymous English manuscript map of North America (*Plate 51*), ascribed with a date of 1610, documents Hudson's navigation of this river. His name appears on the river, and the names Manahata and Manahatin are placed respectively on its west and east banks (these names may have been derived from the French *manants*, meaning an ignorant, uninformed people). Also included are Whitsons Bay, Marthays Viniard, Elizabethes Ile, Cladia (Block Island), R Pomerogoit (Penobscot River), and R. Sagadohock (Kennebec River). The term C. Cod is applied to the Malabar region, while Whitsuns Hed refers to present Cape Cod proper. In the Chesapeake region (Chesepiock on the map) are forty-eight new geographical names, including Appamatuck, Powhatan, Jeamestown, Patawomech (Potomac), C. Henree, and C. Charls; the presence of these argues against the assertion that John Smith was first responsible for them.

In 1611 Hudson, this time sailing in the *Discovery* for the English, reconnoitered the northern strait and bay that are also named for him. Hessel Gerritsz, a cartographer for the Dutch East India Company, charted these discoveries on a 1612 map, "Tabula Nautica," the first to show a part of the untitled Hudson Bay. It was published in Gerritsz's book *Descriptio ac Delineatio Geographica Detectionis* (Amsterdam, 1612). The bay was not charted in its entirety until Jens Munk's woodcut map appeared in Munk's book *Navigatio Septentrionalis* (Copenhagen, 1624).

Between 1610 and 1612 a series of trading and fishing missions under the auspices of various nations led to improved coastal surveys and the establishment of temporary posts at Monhegan Island, Damariscotta, and Pemaquid Point. Explorations of Hudson Strait were also sponsored by the North West Company, a fur-trading organization, and William Baffin, an English navigator, was the pilot on several of these expeditions seeking out a Northwest Passage. His name became a permanent geographic reference in respect to the bay he discovered during these travels.

In 1613 Adriaen Block, a fur trader sailing for the Dutch, discovered the Housatonic and Connecticut rivers, Rhode Island, and the island that bears his name; he also sailed around Manhattan Island. Block in 1614 drew up a manuscript map of the East coast, from Chesapeake Bay to Penobscot Bay, which is

PLATE 50: John Smith. "Virginia." 1612. Engraving (6th state, 1625), 32 × 41 cm. Private collection. *The most influential map of Virginia. First detailed delineation of Chesapeake Bay area and prototype for most later maps of region until Augustine Herrman's great 1673 map "Virginia and Maryland" (see Plate 67). Persisting names include Capes Henry and Charles, Poynt Comfort, Smyths Iles, Appamatuck, and Jamestowne. Oriented with north to the right. Note vignette of the council of Chief Wahunsonacock (commonly known to the English as Powhatan). Published in London, first separately, and then in Smith's* A Map of Virginia *(Oxford, 1612). In this state the engraved map appeared in Samuel Purchas's* Purchas his Pilgrimes *(4 vols., London, 1625).*

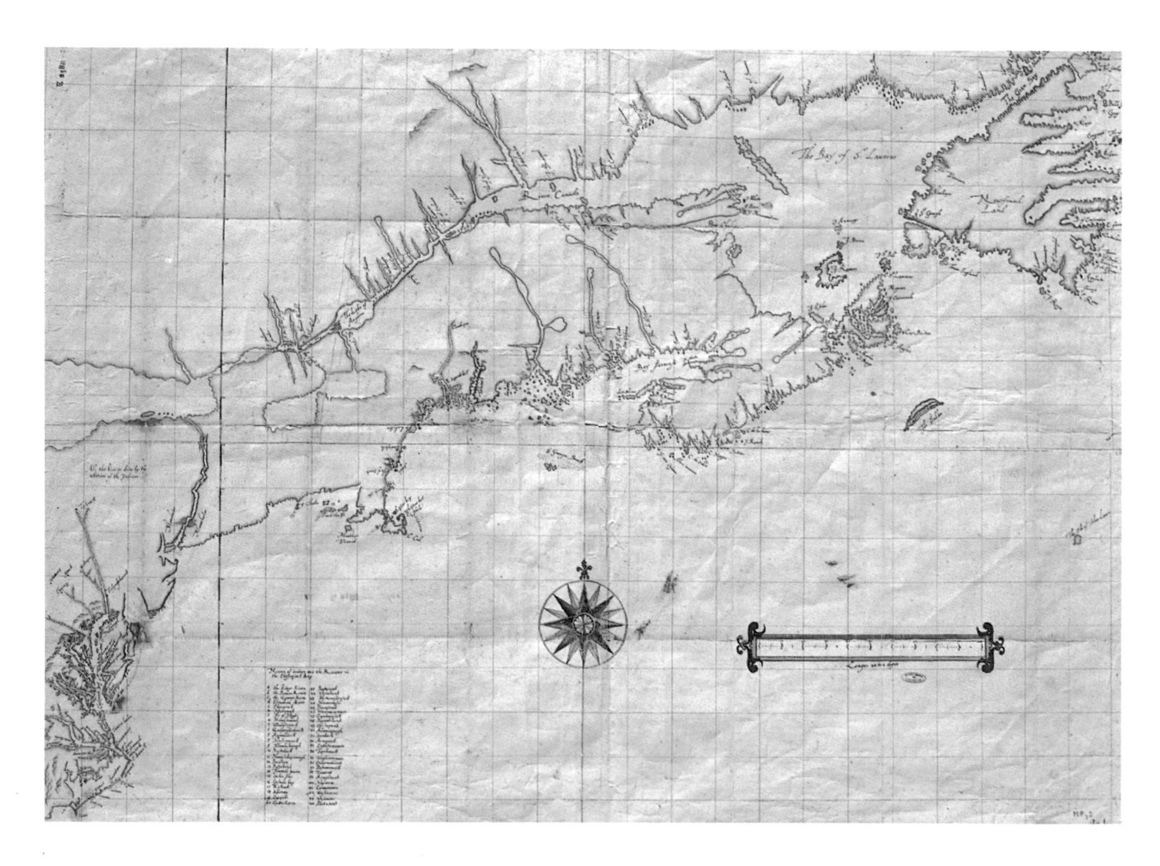

PLATE 51: Cartographer unknown. "Map of North America." c. 1610. Manuscript, pen and ink and watercolor; 78 × 109 cm. Archivo General, Simancas, Spain. *Documents Henry Hudson's navigation of the river named for him. Absence of Long Island suggests the draftsman used Hudson's notes. Map names Manahata on the west bank and Manahatin on the east bank of the Hudson. If dating of map is correct, Virginia and Chesapeake Bay are shown prior to John Smith's 1612 map of Virginia (see Plate 50), and New England coast before publication of Smith's 1614 map of New England (see Plate 53).*

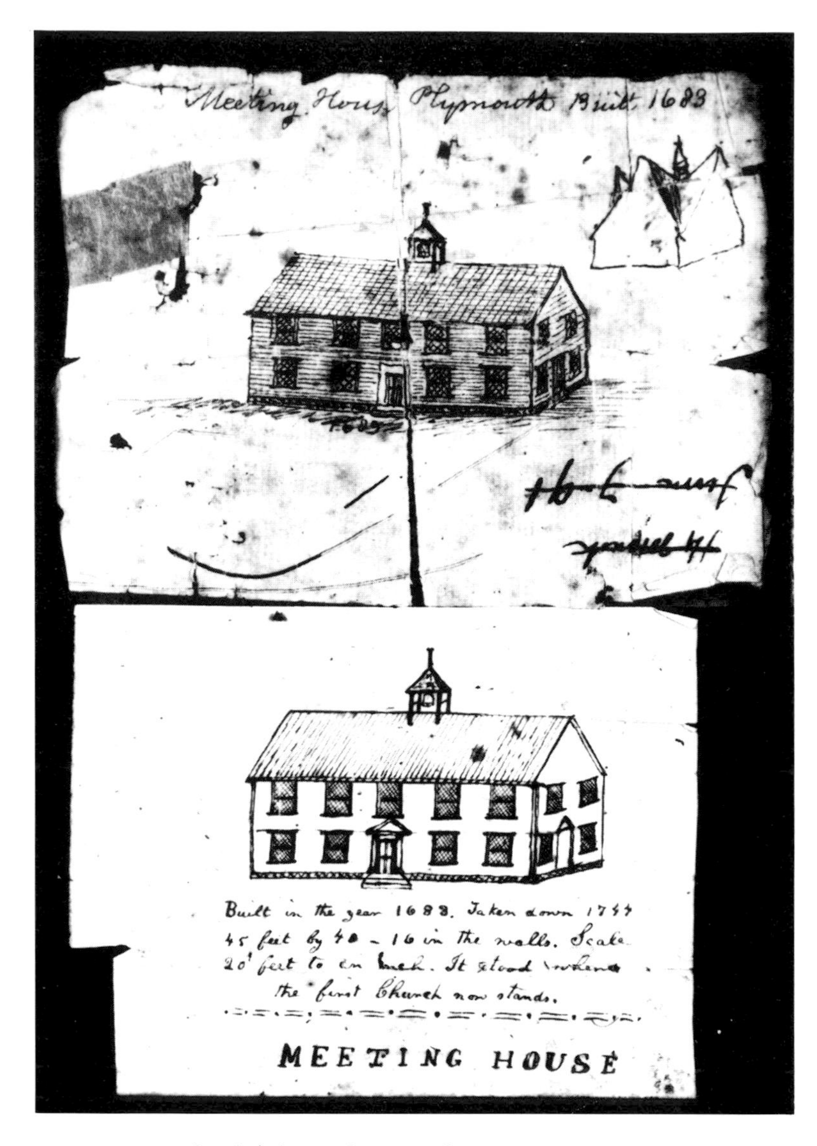

Two versions of early Plymouth meetinghouse, built in 1683 and taken down in 1744

preserved in The Hague (*Plate 52*). This is the first document showing Manhattan as an island separate from the mainland, and here it is called Manhates. Block first applied the name Hellegat (Hell Gate) to the narrow section of the river at the island's northern end (though the name does not appear on the map). Lake Champlain, as Meer Vand Irocoisen, is situated incorrectly east of the Connecticut River.

In 1614 the Council for New England, which succeeded the Plymouth Company, sent John Smith to America again to lay the groundwork for a new plantation in New England. His voyage along the New England coast was the basis for his second major cartographic achievement. His map of New England (*Plate 53*) was prepared in 1614 and later published in his book *A Description of New England* (London, 1616). Featuring Smith's portrait, the map was modified and republished at least nine times. An area from Aborden at Penobscot Bay to Cape James (Cape Cod) is delineated. New England, Smith's Iles (Isle of Shoals), and Poynt Suttliff (Brant Rock) are the only names on the map proposed by Smith himself; Plimouth, Cape Anna, and the River Charles are names that correspond to their present locations. This important map offers an example of the capriciousness of placenaming: the Scottish name Aborden, in place of the Indian name Penobscot, and Leth, in place of Sagadahock, are but two of the many placenames demanded by the fifteen-year-old Prince Charles of Scotland.

In 1616, the year that Smith's New England map was published, the Dutch built Fort Nassau at Castle Island in upstate New York. During the same year the French adventurer and trader Étienne Brûlé explored the Susquehanna Valley. In 1617 the fort was moved to the present site of Albany, renamed Fort Orange, and was used as a springboard for traders expanding their territories along the Mohawk River to Lake Otsego and then down the Susquehanna River.

Both John Smith's map of New England and his book describing that area played a role in the most significant colonization of the early seventeenth century; these two sources revived the interest of the Plymouth Colony in colonizing the area and also appealed to the Puritans in their pursuit of a refuge from the mockery and criticism of the Church of England. As testimony to this influence, the Pilgrims retained the map's name for their landing site at Plymouth. Having received a patent from the Plymouth, or North Virginia, Company, the Pilgrims set out on September 16, 1620, in the *Mayflower* from Plymouth, England. Thirty-five of the 104 passengers constituted a group of English Puritans who had settled in Leiden, the Netherlands, under the leadership of William Brewster. Among the remainder many were wholly distinct from Church of England "separatists," including indentured servants and hired artisans. Captain Miles Standish was the military leader.

On November 19 the Pilgrims reached Cape Cod and anchored off the coast of present Provincetown. The leaders did

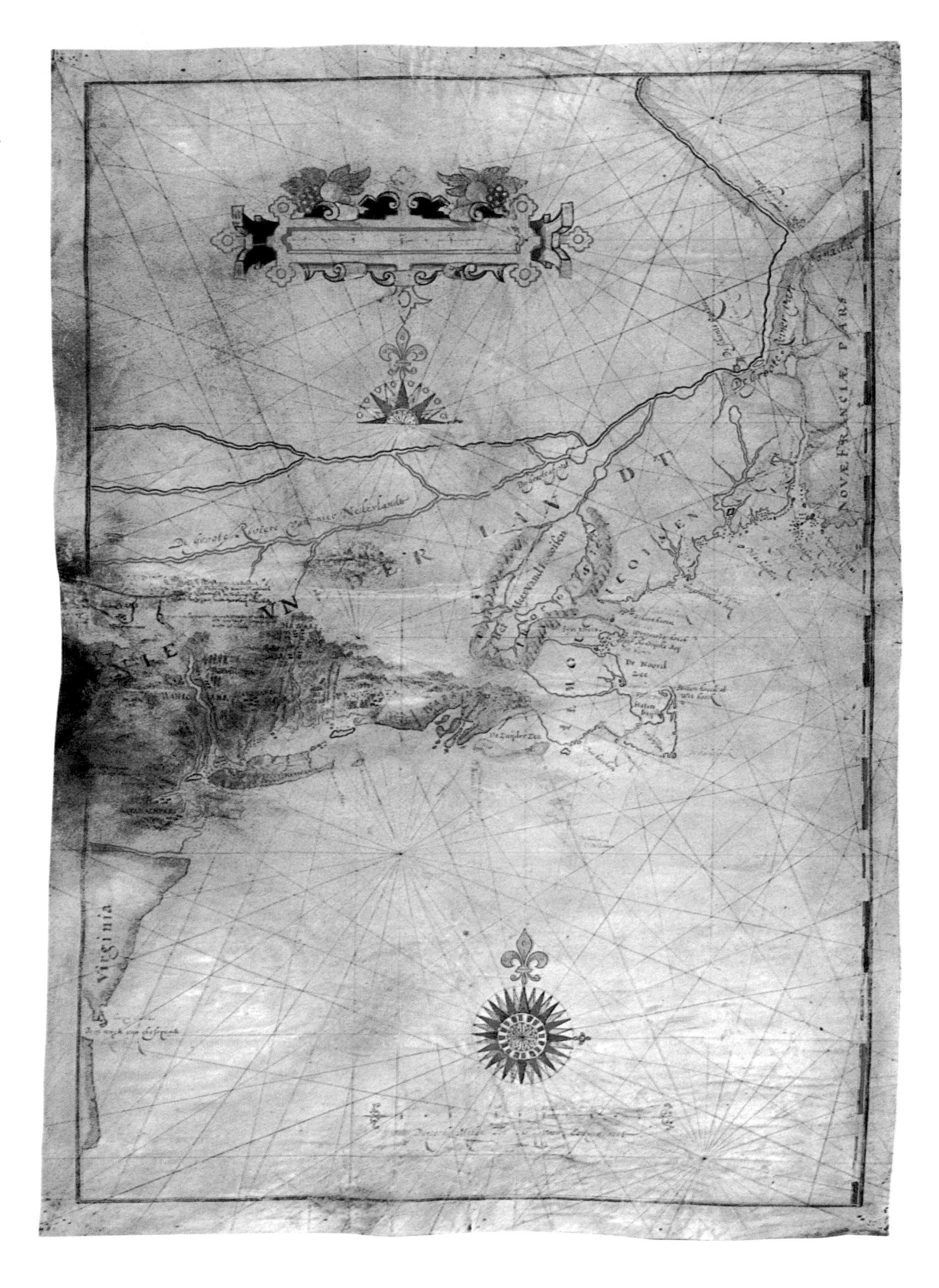

PLATE 52: Adriaen Block. "Map of the East Coast from Chesapeack Bay to Penobscot Bay." 1614. Manuscript, pen and ink and watercolor; 66 × 47 cm. Map Room, Algemeen Rijksarchief, The Hague. *First map to show Manhattan as a separate island. Lake Champlain (Meer Vand Irocoisen on map) is erroneously placed east of Connecticut River. Long Island and Long Island Sound are shown, as well as territories of the Mohegan, Pequot, and other Indian tribes.*

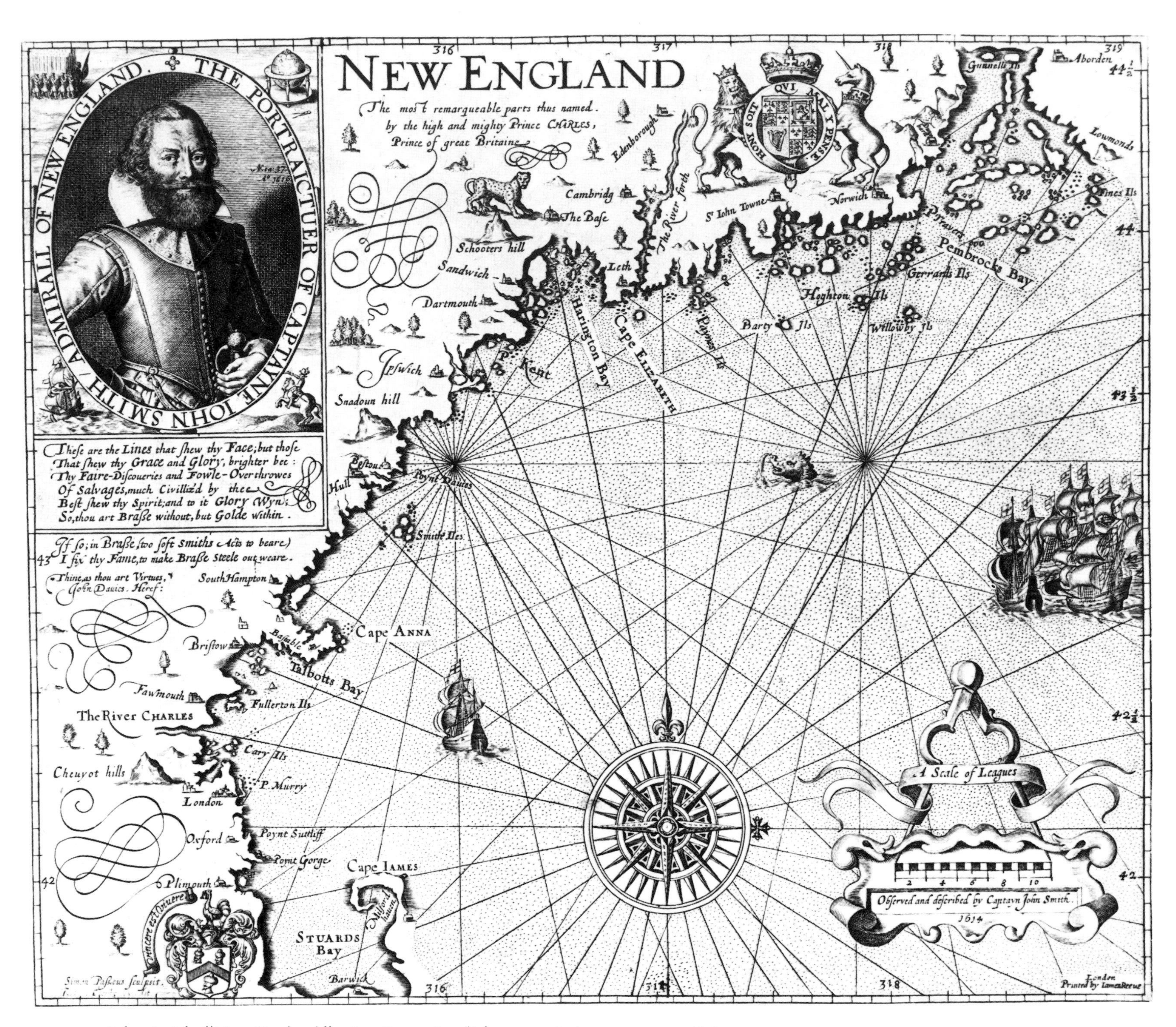

PLATE 53: John Smith. "New England." 1614. Engraving (6th state, 1625), 30 × 35 cm. Private collection. *Plimouth, Cape Anna, and the River Charles are three names that correspond to their present locations. Boston is located at present York, Maine. Pilgrims were cognizant of Smith's map, and they retained settlement name upon landing at Plymouth in 1620. Prepared in 1614, it was first published in Smith's* A Description of New England *(London, 1616) and later in* Purchas his Pilgrimes.

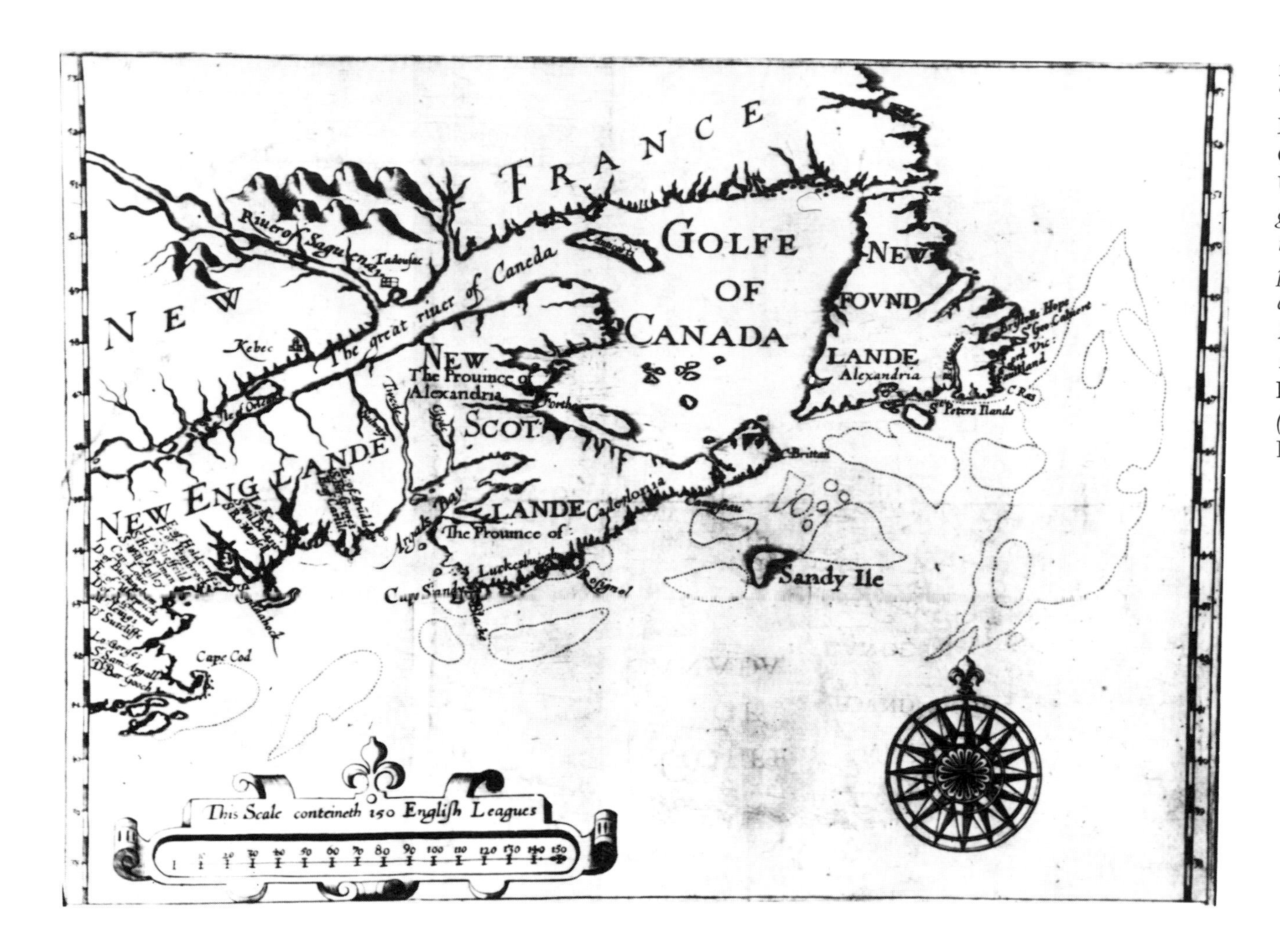

PLATE 54: Sir William Alexander. "A Mapp of New Englande." 1624. Engraving, 25 × 34 cm. John Carter Brown Library, Brown University, Providence. *Alexander gave Nova Scotia (New Scotlande on this map) its name. Map locates twenty patentees, among whom New England coast was divided by Council for New England in 1623. First appeared in 1624 in Alexander's* The Mapp and Description of New England *(London) and the following year in* Purchas his Pilgrimes.

not think this area would adequately provide livelihood over a long period of time, so the *Mayflower's* shallop, a thirty-three-foot boat equipped with oars and sails, was reassembled to explore the coast. On December 14 a safe landing was made at Plymouth. During the third decade of the seventeenth century satellite settlements were rapidly developed by the Plymouth colony. In 1623 a colony evolved at Wessagusset but was short-lived. The following year the Dorchester Company, an English corporation also sponsoring New England colonization, established a settlement on Cape Ann in the region of what is now Gloucester. After several months it was relocated to a site the Indians called Naumkeag (present-day Salem) and was formalized in 1628 by grant of the Council for New England.

The colony of Maine originated in August 1622 as the personal estates of John Mason and Sir Ferdinando Gorges, who jointly were granted all lands lying between the Merrimack and Kennebec rivers. In 1629 the two men divided their holding, Gorges retaining the land north of the Piscataqua River and Mason the land south. Mason's 1624 map of Newfoundland, published in William Vaughan's *Cambrensium Caroleia* (London, 1625), is the first map of that region drawn by an Englishman.

Many of these settled areas in New England were presented in 1624 on "A Mapp of New Englande" by Sir William Alexander, earl of Stirling (*Plate 54*). This document, first included in Alexander's *The Mapp and Description of New England* (London, 1624), locates twenty patentees among whom the region extending from Cape Cod to Maine was divided by the Council for New England in 1623. Alexander was the first viscount of Canada, having re-

The South part of New-England, as it is Planted this yeare, 1634.

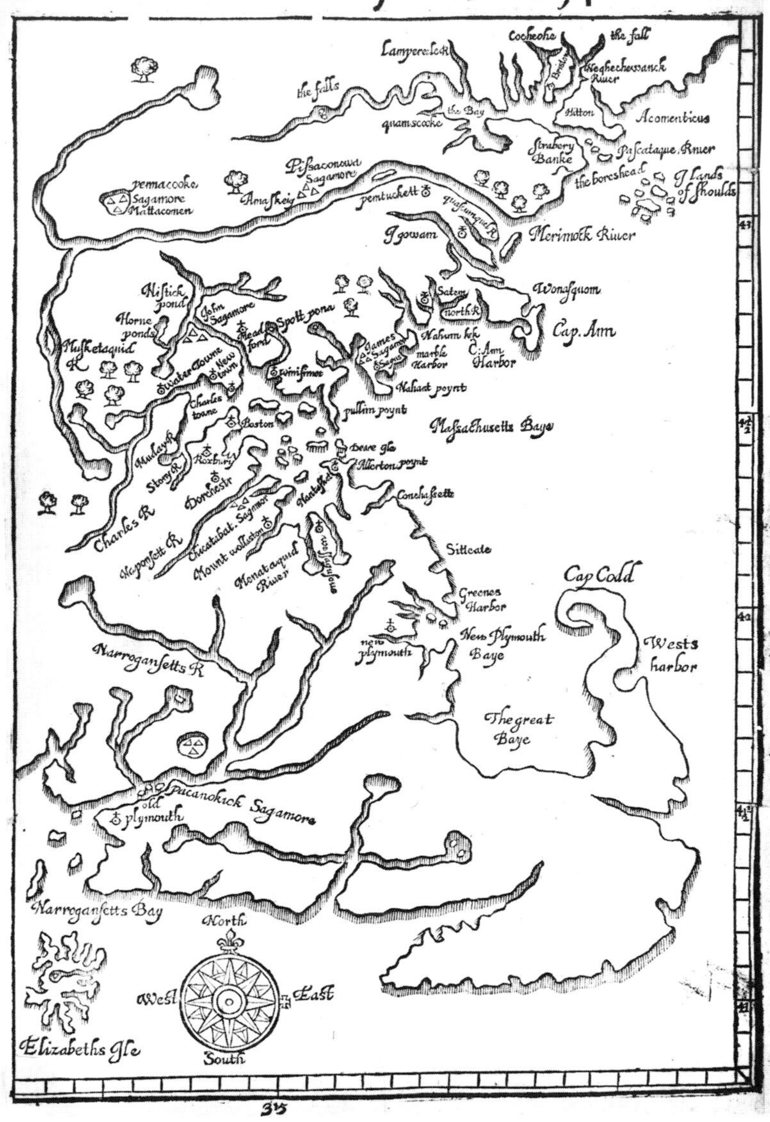

PLATE 55: William Wood. "The South part of New-England, as it is Planted this yeare, 1634." 1634. Woodcut, 30 × 18 cm. John Carter Brown Library, Brown University, Providence. *Map has errors, one of which places Old Plymouth near the mouth of the Narragansett River, but Boston area is correct. First map of the region by a resident. Published in Wood's* New Englands Prospect *(London, 1634).*

ceived grants from James I and Charles I for most of eastern Canada and New England. His attempt to colonize Nova Scotia was ultimately futile.

British influence in New England was augmented in 1630 when John Winthrop led a group of Puritans from Salem to the peninsula of Shawmut. Their settlement became the nucleus of Boston, which may have been named through the efforts of Thomas Leverett, who had been an alderman of Boston, England. Leverett was one of the 1,000 immigrants who sailed from England in 1630 shortly after the newly formed Massachusetts Bay Company received a royal charter. During the 1630s, settlements germinated at Passonagessit (Quincy) and Penobscot, and Springfield was established on the Connecticut River by William Pynchon, who had been squire of Springfield, England.

More intensive English immigration is reflected on William Wood's woodcut "The South part of New-England, as it is Planted this yeare, 1634" (*Plate 55*), which appeared in Wood's *New Englands Prospect*, published in London in 1634. This map, the first map of the area drawn by a resident, extends from the New Hampshire coast northeast of the Pescataqua River (present Piscataqua) south to Narragansett Bay. New Plymouth is properly located where the Pilgrims first settled, but the name Old Plymouth on the mouth of the Narragansett River is difficult to explain since there was no settlement in that area until 1680. Other towns on this map include Mount Wollaston (Braintree), Roxbury, Boston, Watertowne, Newtown (Cambridge), Charlestowne, Meadford, Winnisimet (Chelsea), Sagus (Lynn), and Dorchester, referred to in the text of Wood's book as the "greatest town in New England."

The third English colonization foray in the New World, following Jamestown and Plymouth, was not on the mainland of the continent, but on the Caribbean island of St. Kitts in 1625 after Charles I gave Thomas Warner patent to colonize St. Kitts, Nevis, Barbados, and Montserrat, and named him governor of the Leeward Islands. The French gained patents in the same year for the middle of St. Kitts, and the right to colonize Guadeloupe and Martinique. Two years later the earl of Carlisle acquired rights to Barbados, which became the wealthiest and most profitable British colony in the first half of the seventeenth century. In the northernmost part of North America the British energetically continued their quest for a Northwest Passage. As a result of definitive observations made by Captain Luke Fox and

PLATE 56: Henry Briggs. "The North part of America." 1625. Engraving, 29 × 36 cm. Private collection. *First large map to show California as large elongated island. The earliest map on which Hudson Bay is named, here applied to James Bay. Plymouth is located in New England; Boston does not appear. Hudson's River and James Citti are located. No definition of Great Lakes or of any part of Mississippi River system. Published in Samuel Purchas's* Purchas his Pilgrimes *to accompany Briggs's text "A Treatise of the North-West Passage to the South Sea, Through the Continent of Virginia, and By Fretum Hudson."*

Mother Maria de Jésus de Agréda preaching to Indians in Spanish Southwest, 1631

Thomas James on voyages in 1631, a conjectural western outlet from Hudson Bay was permanently deleted from maps. No European ship was to sail that bay for the next four years. The engraved "Polar Map or Card" by Fox, which appeared in his *North-West Fox, or Fox from the North-West Passage* (London, 1635), names several geographic points on the south shore of Hudson Bay.

Attempting to keep pace with the English, the Dutch accelerated their drive for colonization. The Dutch West India Company was founded in 1621 with the privilege of colonizing the New World and the western coast of Africa below the Tropic of Cancer. It was the means for the Dutch to carry on economic warfare with Spain and Portugal by striking at their colonies in the West Indies. In 1624 the first Dutch settlement was established on Nut Island (now Governor's Island) off the tip of the Battery at the lower end of Manhattan, and the trading posts at Fort Orange (Albany) and at Fort Nassau (Gloucester, New Jersey) were expanded. By 1626 there were three trading posts at the newly founded New Amsterdam, which was named after Peter Minuit made his famous purchase of the island of Manhattan from the Indians for trinkets valued at sixty guilders (twenty-four dollars). In 1629 Kiliaen van Rensselaer had the Dutch West India Company issue charters of privileges to patroons, who received a feudal domain with fifteen miles of riverfront along the Hudson River in return for bringing fifty Dutch people to the area. This led to the settlement of Rensselaerwyck; by 1630 the villages of Breuckelen (Brooklyn) and Haarlem were founded, and New Amsterdam boasted a population of 300 inhabitants.

French and Spanish efforts of colonization during the first third of the seventeenth century were limited. While French fur traders continued their western incursions in Canada, it was not until 1628 that significant farming was begun. During the second decade a brief French–English skirmish had the Acadian peninsula as its focal point. After Captain Samuel Argall destroyed the French settlements along the coast of the Bay of Fundy in 1613, the English crown granted the peninsula to the Scot Sir William Alexander in 1621. He renamed the region Nova Scotia [New Scotland]. Following the cessation of the unnamed 1627–29 war between England and France, the Treaty of St. Germain in 1632 restored Acadia, Quebec, and the St. Lawrence River to France, and in effect this permitted earnest French settlement of Acadia. Under the auspices of the Company of New France (Company of One Hundred Associates) they began to exploit the fur trade, yet immigration was sparse. Fewer than 300 settlers had arrived between 1608 and 1640, a significant contrast to the English colonies along the Atlantic seaboard to the south. By 1634 there was a small French settlement at Trois Rivières (Three Rivers). In the west the Spanish missionaries, led by Father Benevides, continued their travels up the Rio Grande to Santa Fe, Acoma, and the Nueces River.

The world maps of the first third of the seventeenth century

PLATE 57: Joannes de Laet. "Nova Anglia, Novvm Belgivm et Virginia." 1630. Engraving, hand colored; 28 × 36 cm. Private collection. *Dutch map showing eastern coast from Nova Scotia to North Carolina. First printed map of New Netherlands as well as first printed map that names New Amsterdam and Manhattan (here Manbattes). Published in Laet's* Beschrijvinghe van West-Indien *(Leiden, 1630).*

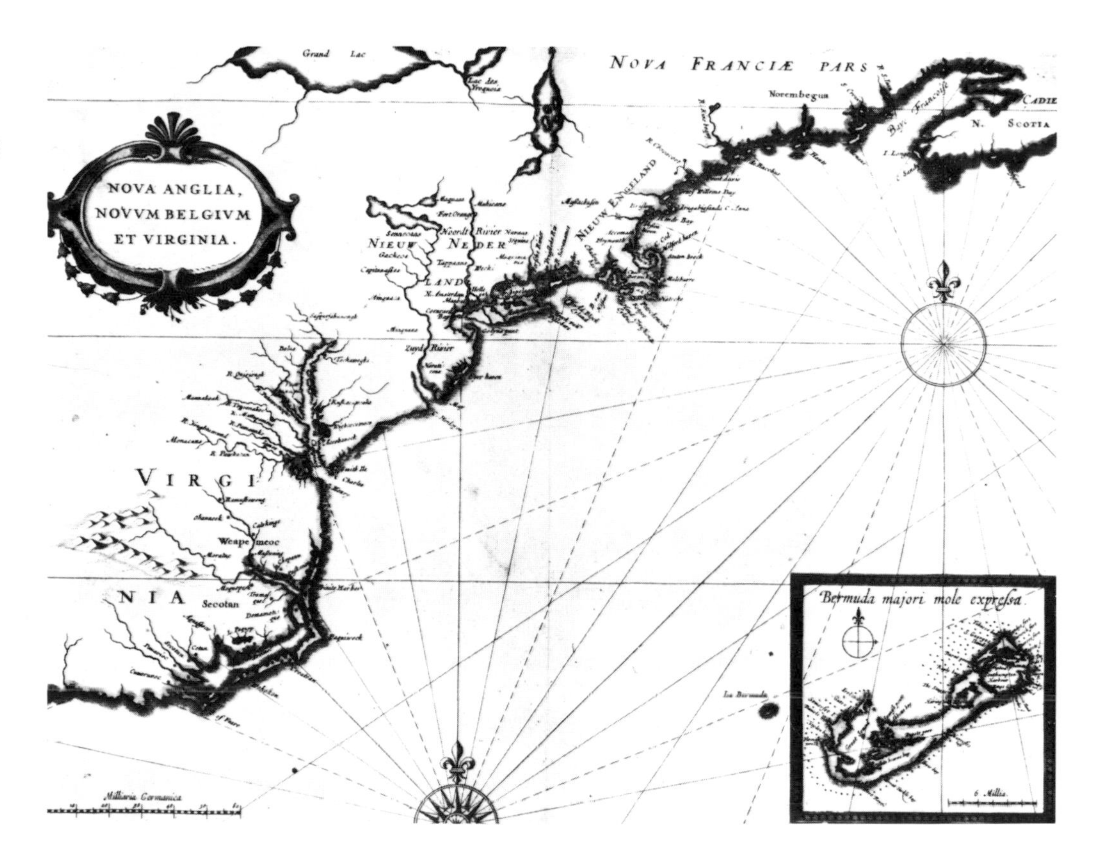

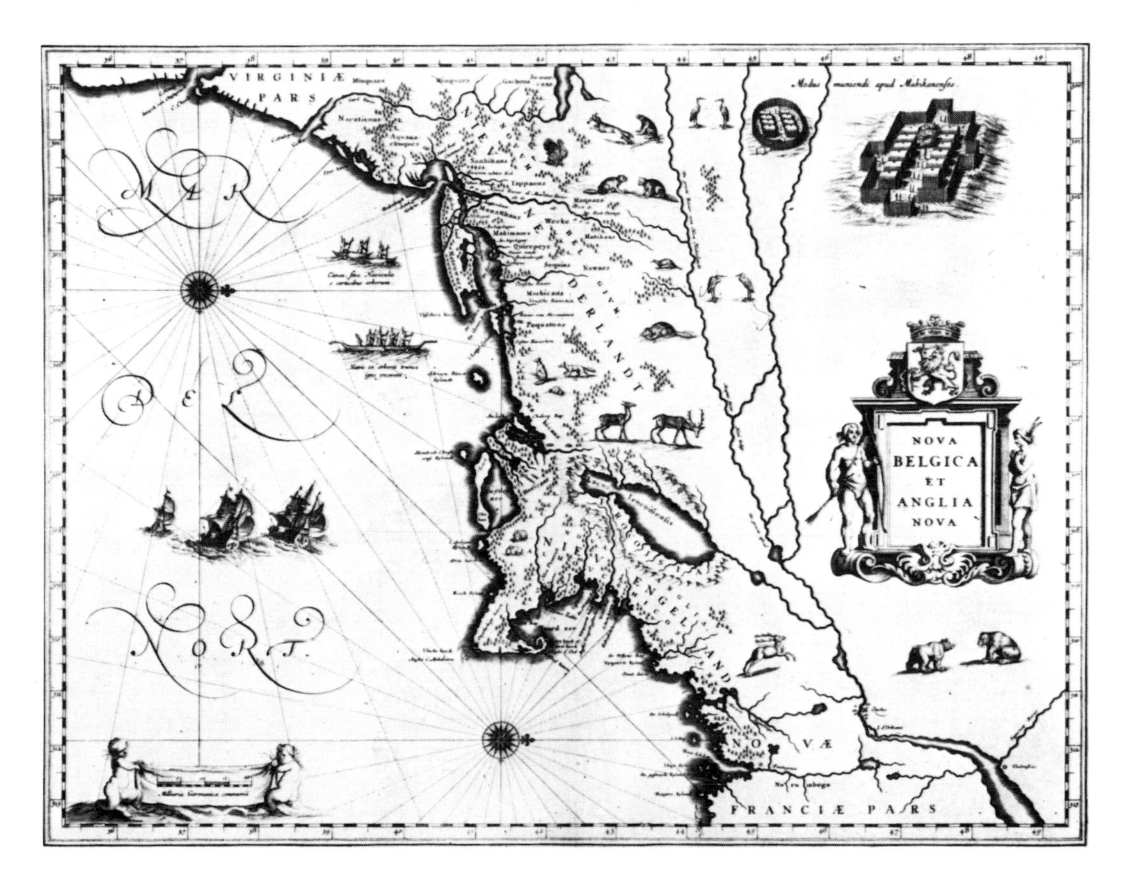

PLATE 58: Willem Janszoon Blaeu. "Nova Belgica et Anglia Nova." 1635. Engraving (a later state, 1662), 38 × 50 cm. Private collection. *One of earliest large-scale maps to include the part of North America settled by Dutch. First printed map that depicted canoes and North American fauna. Lake Champlain (Lacus Irocoisiensis) shown incorrectly, as in other maps of the period (see Plate 52). Printed separately as a double-page spread—originally intended for Blaeu's* Novus Atlas *but not included in that work until 1640. Was also included in Blaeu's* Theatrum Orbis Terrarum sive Atlas Novus *(Amsterdam, 1635). Map shown is a later state, from the great* Atlas Major *(Amsterdam, 1662) by Blaeu's son, Joan Blaeu.*

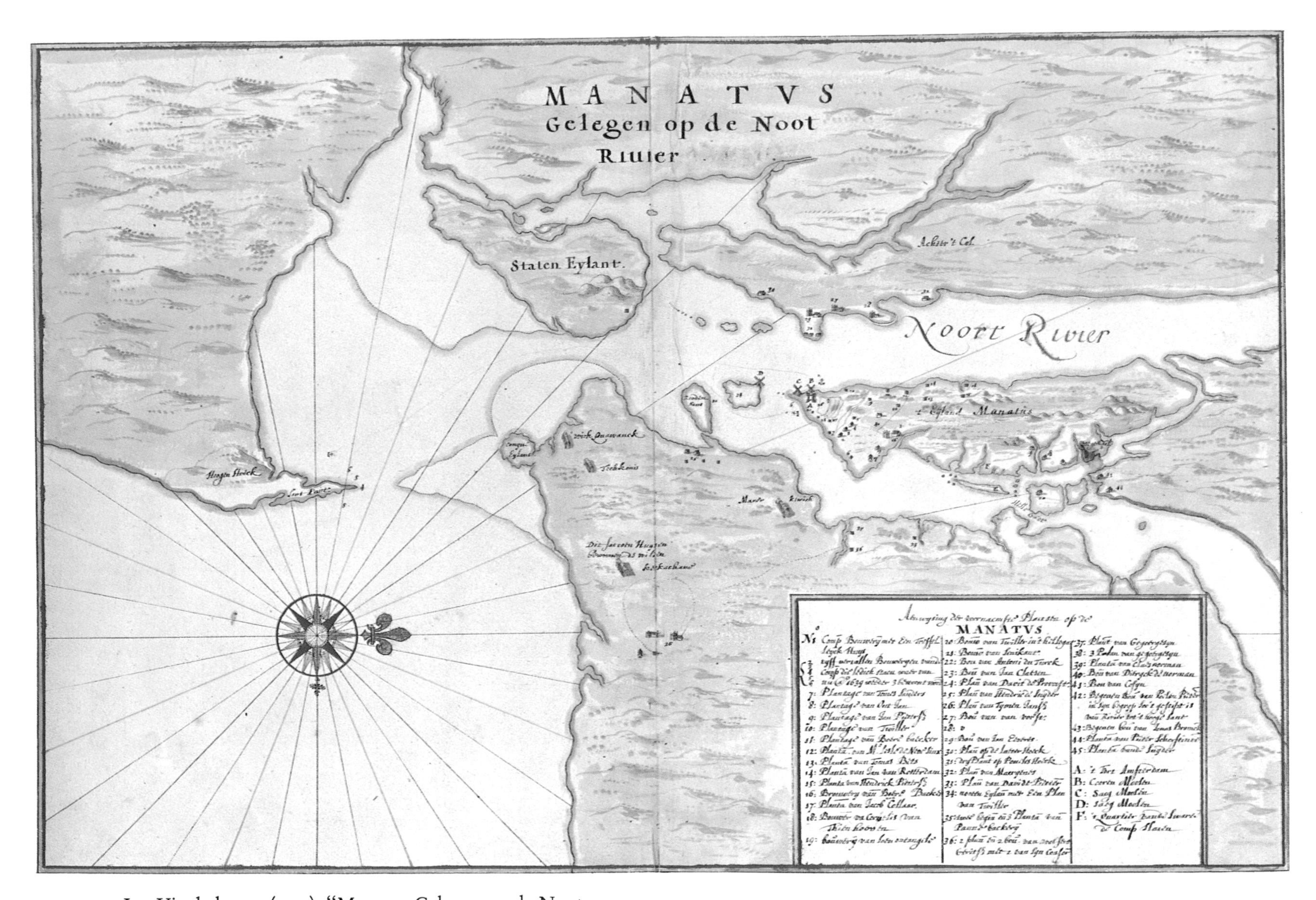

PLATE 59: Jan Vinckeboons (attr.). "Manatvs Gelegen op de Noot [sic] Riuier." 1639. Manuscript, pen and ink and watercolor (manuscript copy, c. 1665–70); 46 × 68 cm. Geography and Map Division, Library of Congress, Washington, D.C. *Drawn for Dutch West India Company. The original of this earliest known survey of Manhattan Island is lost, but two known contemporary manuscript copies, drawn approximately thirty years later, exist: the one in the Library of Congress and the other in Villa Castello near Florence. Traditionally assigned to Vinckeboons (attribution determined by Henry Harrisse), although I. N. Phelps Stokes refutes this in detail in second volume of his* Iconography of Manhattan Island *(1916). Colonial Dutch boweries, or farms, are located and keyed to names of their owners in the legend, thus establishing many present-day land titles.*

showed little change over those of the late sixteenth century. "A New and accurate Mappe of the World," by Sir Francis Drake, published in *The World Encompassed* (London, 1628) by Nicholas Bourne, depicts Drake's circumnavigation of the world in 1577–80 and shows California as an island. This island concept was first represented on an inset on the title page of the 1622 Latin edition of Antonio de Herrera y Tordesillas's *Historia General*. However, it was the 1625 map "The North part of America" by Henry Briggs (*Plate 56*) that had a major influence in establishing the notion of insularity. This was not disproved until 1701 and was finally dispelled in a 1747 royal decree of Ferdinand VII. Briggs, a leading English mathematician, was a contemporary of Edward Wright and a patron of Luke Fox and other explorers of the time. The island of Santa Catalina is named on the Briggs map, and the phrase "Po. Sr. Francisco Draco" in the vicinity of present San Francisco honors the noted explorer. James Citti is shown in Virginia; Plymouth and Cape Cod (C. Codd), but not Boston, are among the Massachusetts names.

The 1630 "Nova Anglia, Novvm Belgivm et Virginia" by Joannes de Laet (*Plate 57*) shows the northeast section of the continent from Nova Scotia to North Carolina and is considered the first printed map to mention the name Manhattan, which appeared as Manbattes. It is also presumed to be the first printed map to specify the name New Amsterdam and to sketch the region known as New Netherlands. The appearance of Novum Belgium on this and other maps of the period refers to the fact that the Dutch West India Company was underwritten in part by Protestant Belgians.

By the middle of the seventeenth century the events that would shape furture American mapping were centered in New England and in the middle Atlantic coastal area. Owing to Bishop William Laud's increased pressure on the Puritans in England, by 1634 over 10,000 men and women had emigrated to America and contributed to the rapid development of new townships. When members of any established community felt crowded, they merely petitioned for the organization of a new township, usually six miles square. In this manner Concord, Cambridge, Lynn, and Saugus sprang up between 1635 and 1638.

The area of Connecticut was settled in 1632, and the initial result was two Connecticut colonies. A Dutch fort, erected on the Connecticut River in 1633, was short-lived. It was called Fort Good Hope and was at the site of present Hartford. The English Connecticut colony ensued from what may be regarded as the

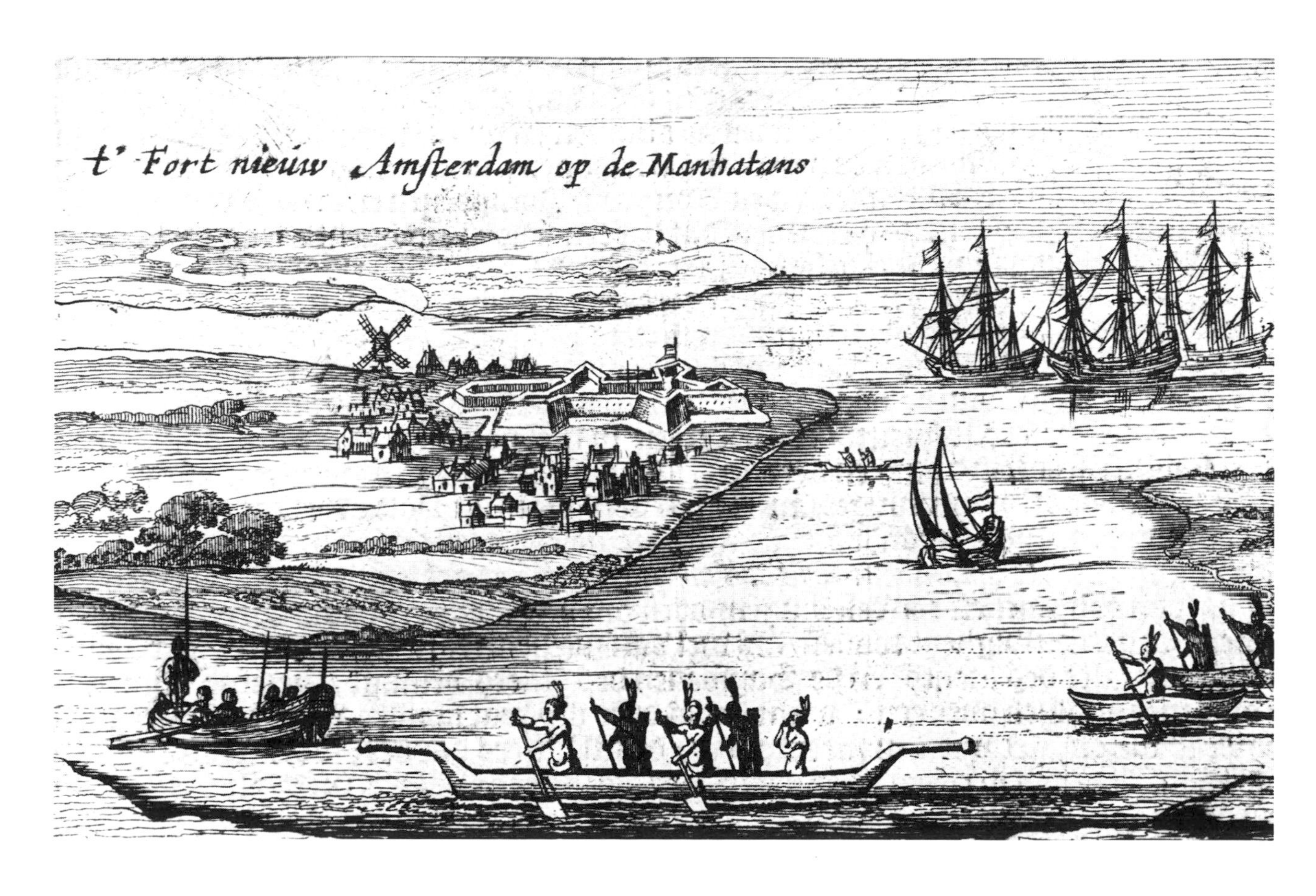

Fort New Amsterdam in 1626–28, earliest known view of New York; Amsterdam, 1651

Detail from 1635 Willem Janszoon Blaeu map (see Plate 58)

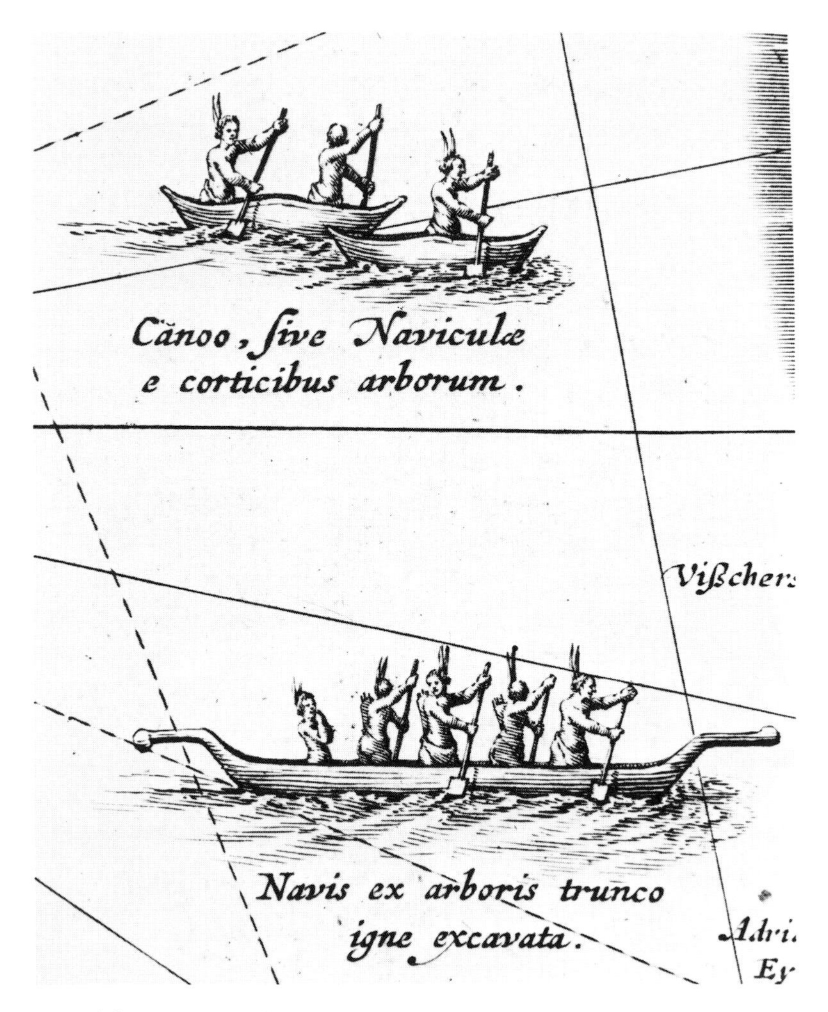

Detail from 1635 Willem Janszoon Blaeu map (see Plate 58)

first western migration in North America when John Oldham, banished from Plymouth because of his opposition to a stringent government, led a group overland from the Massachusetts Bay colony in 1634. Hartford, Windsor, and Wethersfield were established by 1639, and they conjointly adopted a frame of government. In 1638 a New Haven colony was created by Puritans from London as a coastal trading town they hoped would rival Boston and New Amsterdam. Long Island was temporarily incorporated under the jurisdiction of this New Haven colony. The two Connecticut colonies were not united for almost thirty years.

Rhode Island evolved during the same period, after Roger Williams, banished for radical religious beliefs and political theories, purchased land from the Narragansett Indians in 1636 at the site of Providence. Two other religious exiles from the Massachusetts Bay colony, Anne Hutchinson and William Coddington, founded Pocasset (Portsmouth) in 1638, and Coddington moved on to found Newport in 1639. These three towns, along with Warwick, were joined in the royal charter granted to Williams in 1644. Land in New Hampshire was appropriated by colonists after John Mason's death, and the first town, Exeter, was established in 1638 by John Wheelwright, who also had been exiled from Massachusetts.

In the 1640s English settlements proliferated in Westchester, New York, and on Long Island. A group in Branford, Connecticut, left that colony to start another that led to the foundation of Newark in East Jersey, thereby opening the way for further English colonization in that region. During this period boundary disputes among the various British colonies lent an impetus to mapping in order to substantiate or strengthen individual claims.

The first half of the seventeenth century produced no maps that served as authoritative documentaries of the sprouting English colonies. The period was dominated by the great Dutch cartographic publishing houses managed by the families of Hondius, Jansson, and Blaeu. Jodocus Hondius (Joost de Hondt) was the Flemish cartographer and engraver from Ghent who in 1583 settled in London, where he engraved the globe gores of Emery Molyneux. Around 1593 he established himself in Amsterdam, building up a map-publishing business that produced world maps and globes. In 1604 he acquired the copperplates of Mercator's Atlas and in 1606 published the first edition of the Mercator-Hondius Atlas with thirty-seven new maps and text by the geographer Pieter van den Berg (Petrus Montanus), his brother-

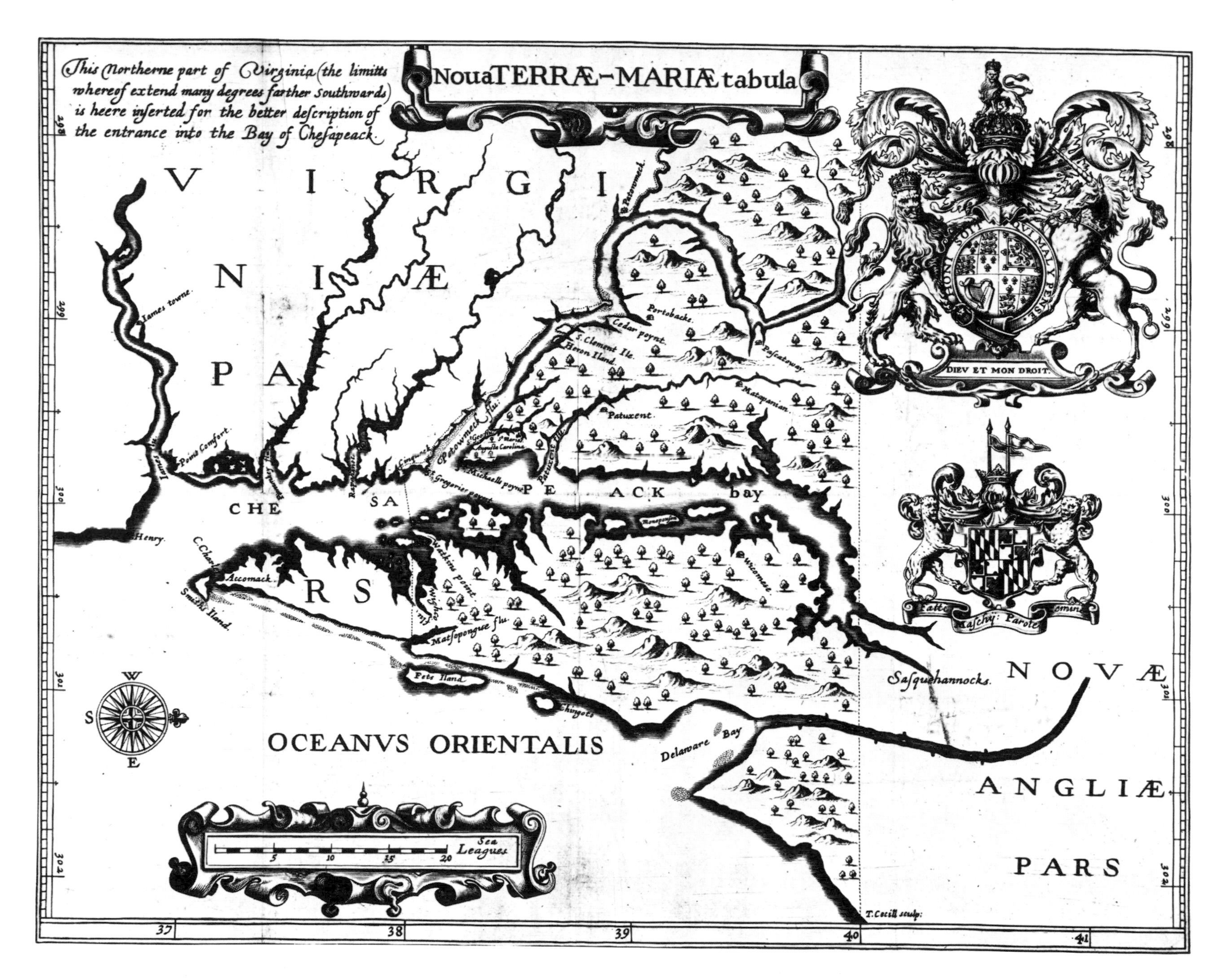

PLATE 60: Cartographer unknown. "Noua Terrae-Mariae tabula." 1635. Engraving, 30 × 39 cm. Newberry Library, Chicago. *Known as "Lord Baltimore's Map," it is first separate map of Maryland and presents boundary lines of Maryland, between Pennsylvania and Virginia. Also published in* A Relation of Maryland *(London, 1635), by Cecilius Calvert, 2nd Baron Baltimore, to encourage settlement. Specifically delineates northern line of Maryland at 40th parallel and shows a dotted line running along south bank of Potomac River as southern boundary claimed by the proprietor.*

in-law. The business was carried on by his sons Jodocus and Henricus, and the latter, with his brother-in-law, Jan Jansson, continued to publish innumerable editions of the Mercator-Hondius-Jansson Atlas in direct competition with the Blaeu firm.

Willem Janszoon Blaeu founded in the early seventeenth century a cartographic firm that took a leading place in Holland for almost a century. His early atlas, *Appendix Theatri Ortelii et Atlantis Mercatoris*, was published in Amsterdam in 1631. Blaeu leaned on the names of Ortelius and Mercator, just as early map producers had on that of Ptolemy, not only because it lent an air of authenticity but also because he had borrowed freely from their maps. His important atlas. *Theatrum Orbis Terrarum sive Novus Atlas*, was published in Amsterdam originally in 1635 and in subsequent editions and languages for many years. Blaeu's map "Americae nova Tabula" from the 1635 *Novus Atlas* clearly shows an absence of appreciation of the interior of the North American continent.

Two 1636 maps by Jan Jansson, "America septentrionalis" and "Nova Anglia, Novum Belgium et Virginia," proffer dissimilar representations of the Great Lakes, both generally following the lead of Joannes de Laet's 1630 map "Nova Anglia, Novvm Belgivm et Virginia" (*see Plate 57*) and ignoring the more exact Champlain maps. Jansson's 1636 map of the Arctic, "Poli Arctici et Circumiacentium Terrarum Descriptio Novissima," which was published by Henricus Hondius, reflects the Luke Fox and Thomas James expeditions for a Northwest Passage and suggests the possibility of a channel through Jones Sound and Lancaster Sound, which proved to be accurate two and a half centuries later.

Proposed coat of arms of the Dutch West India Company, 1621–23

The 1640 edition of the *Novus Atlas*, by Willem Janszoon Blaeu and his son, Joan Blaeu, includes two American maps, "Virginia et Floridae" and "Nova Belgica et Anglia Nova." The former, based on the Mercator-Hondius map "Virginiae Item et Floridae Americae Provinciarum nova Descriptio" from the 1606 Mercator-Hondius Atlas, adds little new information for the southeastern region; it shows two large bays spanning the South Carolina coast and also includes previously misrepresented large inland lakes. The second, "Nova Belgica et Anglia Nova" (*Plate 58*), had been issued separately in 1635; it is the first printed map that was decorated with canoes, bears, beavers, turkeys, and other animals. Like other maps of the era, it is oriented with east at the bottom, and also perpetuates Champlain's misrepresentation of Lacus Irocoisiensis (Lake Champlain).

Perhaps the most dramatic of the Dutch maps of the period is the manuscript "Manatvs Gelegen op de Noot [sic] Riuier" (*Plate 59*) attributed to Jan Vinckeboons (Joan Vingboons), a cartographer for the Dutch West India Company, another gift from Henry Harrisse to the Library of Congress. This map, generally dated 1639, is considered the earliest survey of Manhattan Island (Eyland Manatus on the map). It delineates the boundaries of the original Dutch farms (boweries) and also shows Staten Eylant and Conyne Eylant, after a corruption of the Dutch word *konije* meaning rabbit.

Peter Minuit, the area's foremost real estate agent, accepted employ by Sweden after Dutch and Swedish investors formed the New Sweden Company in 1633. It was granted a charter by Sweden for settlement along the Delaware River, and in 1638 Minuit was the overseer of the first Swedish community in North America, at Fort Christina (Wilmington, Delaware). The Swedes then bought out the Dutch interest and established on their own several settlements in the Delaware and Pennsylvania regions. But Swedish rule in North America ended with the Dutch conquests of 1655, although literary and cartographic ref-

Swedes peacefully bargaining with Indians in Pennsylvania, from Campenius's Kortbeskrifning om Provincien Nya Swerige, *1702*

erences to New Sweden continued to appear after that date.

The Dutch increased and expanded their permanent settlements during the 1640s. In 1641 Tappan Zee, Hackensack, and Staten Island were settled. The following year Jonas Bronck built a home on the present Bronx River; the modern name of both the river and the borough is obviously derived from the possessive form of his name, that is, Bronck's. The Dutch purchased the western portion of Long Island and formally settled Breuckelen in 1644, at a period when the English were developing Flushing and Hempstead.

Another major English colonization venture was underway before mid-century and once more the basis was religious. In 1632 Charles I granted a slice of northern Virginia to George Calvert, Lord Baltimore, a Catholic convert who remained in royal favor. The southern boundary of this land was defined as the further bank of the Potomac River to Chesapeake Bay. This refuge for English Catholics was established in 1634, with St. Marys, its first township, named for the Virgin Mary. The engraved map "Noua Terrae-Mariae tabula" (*Plate 60*), known as "Lord Baltimore's Map," appeared in 1635. This first separately published map of Maryland was publicized to recruit new settlers and includes important information on boundary lines between Maryland and Virginia as well as between Maryland and its future neighbor colony, Pennsylvania.

Rounding out the historic events of the first half of the seventeenth century were the French exploratory efforts inland in the region around Lakes Michigan and Huron. In 1634–35 Jean Nicolett journeyed to Green Bay and became the first European to view Lake Michigan. He then traversed the Fox River valley in Wisconsin and on his return related stories of the great river of the interior, the first mention of the northern reaches of the Mississippi. In 1641 Jesuit missionaries advanced west as far as Sault Ste. Marie, and a year later Montreal was founded at the junction of the St. Lawrence and the River of the Prairies (Ottawa River); this city offered a safer route west. A French seigneury system, similar to the English plantation and the Dutch patroon systems, was instituted along the St. Lawrence and Richelieu rivers, but at the beginning of the 1640s there were only about 300 Frenchmen in all of New France. This small group contributed significantly to the mapping of the interior, and their activity would highlight the remainder of the century.

5. Expansion of Seaboard Colonies and Exploration of Inland Waterways

Moxon who drew two Globes, or whosoere,
Must make a third, or else the old ones tear,
To find a Room for thy new Map, by which
Thy Friends and Country all thou dost enrich.

B. J.
Introduction to William Hubbard,
A Narrative of the Troubles with the Indians in New-England (1677)

1650-1700

MAPPING IN the second half of the seventeenth century provides graphic evidence of both the development of new English colonies and the westward expansion of those that were already established. The termination of Dutch and Swedish rule was also reflected by changes in placenames. A more profound cartographic effect was produced by a small cadre of French explorers in Canada as they filled out their maps of the North American continent with lakes, rivers, and valleys of the interior.

In 1650 a fifth volume was added to Jan Jansson's *Novus Atlas*. Included in it is the engraved map "Belgii Novi, Angliae Novae, et Partis Virginiae Novissima Delineatio," which is the second state of Jansson's previously mentioned 1636 "Nova Anglia, Novum Belgium et Virginia." This document provides a good example of how a plausible date for a map often is arrived at: since the important name Fort Casimir, founded by the Dutch in 1651, does not appear, a 1650 date is assigned. The map incorporates features of earlier maps by John Smith, Samuel de Champlain, and Johannes de Laet and combines Smith's placenames with Dutch names. The Connecticut River is named Versche Revier [freshwater river], Hartford appears as Herfort, the Delaware River is the Zuydt River, and Fort Orange is located at present Albany. Other Dutch names on the map include Naiack, Breukelen, Kinderhoeck, Renselaer Wyck, and Noort Rivier (Hudson River). Indian names such as Sinsing and Tappans, the names of local Indian tribes, add an exotic flavor.

The most important map of the year 1650 is "Ameriqve Septentrionale" (*Plate 61*) by Nicolas Sanson, called Sanson d'Abbeville, founder of the French school of cartography in the seventeenth century. This Paris publication is based on reports from the missionaries and is the first to present all five of the Great Lakes in a somewhat realistic relationship. The names Ontario and Superior (as Lac Superieur) appear for the first time on a printed map, as does a representation of Lake Erie. Lake Huron is reasonably well shaped, but Lac des Puans [lake of stenches], representing Green Bay, is not distinguished as a geographic entity from Lake Michigan. "Le Canada, ou Nouvelle France, &c." (*Plate 62*), published by Sanson in 1656, is the first large-scale comparatively accurate portrayal of the five Great Lakes, and it served as the paradigm for mapping the region for half a century. Lake Erie is so named, and is augmented by the phrase "ou du Chat," referring to the much-feared Erie Indians, who lived along the shore; they were often called People of the Panther, which accounts for the French word *chat*.

Since each original royal grant to a colony encompassed an area from the Atlantic to the Pacific, the colonists began probing westward from the established English settlements, exploiting the land originally specified in the grant. In 1650 Edward Bland and Captain Abraham Wood, starting at Appomattox Falls, reached the Hocomowananck River (Roanoke) and named the surrounding area New Brittaine. In the early 1650s colonists in Virginia, eager to expand their settlements, set their sights on North Carolina and the Albemarle Sound. "A mapp of Virginia discouered to ye Falls" by John Farrer, an official of the Virginia Company in London (*Plate 63*), was published in the third edition of Edward Williams's *Virgo Triumphans: or Virginia Richly and Truly Valued* (London, 1651). It shows a late perpetuation of the false Sea of Verrazano and also specifies that it is a ten-day march from sea to sea, that is, from the Atlantic to the Pacific oceans. On all five distinct states of this rare map, the Canada Flu (St. Lawrence River) and Hudson River join to enter a "mighty great Lake" which widens to become the Sea of China and the Indies. Swedish settlements along the Delaware River are located, and the name Carolana, referring to a land grant by Charles I to Sir Robert Heath in 1629, appears for the first time on a

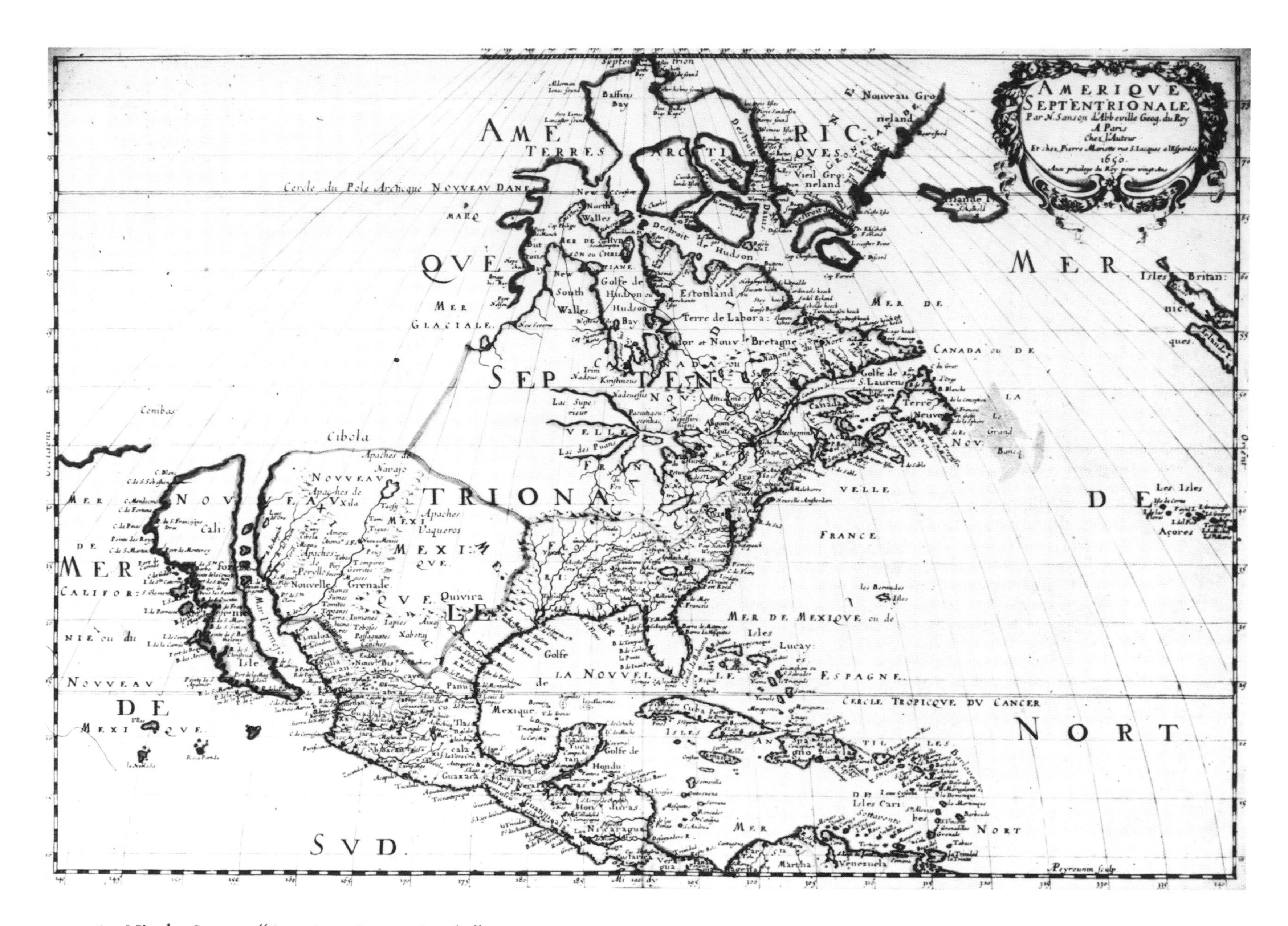

PLATE 61: Nicolas Sanson. "Ameriqve Septentrionale." 1650. Engraving, hand colored; 38 × 56 cm. Private collection. *A predominant map for remainder of seventeenth century. First printed map to show all five of Great Lakes; first to name Superior (Lac Superieur) and Ontario. Santa Fe is shown as the capital of New Mexico, but it is located on the west bank of Rio Grande. California is still a large island.*

map; it was derived from the Latin form of the king's name.

As part of the Dutch attempt to secure a portion of the New World, Peter Stuyvesant in 1650 engineered a short-lived coexistence policy with both the Indians and the New England Confederation. The confederation had been formed by the Massachusetts Bay, Plymouth, New Haven, and Connecticut colonies in acknowledgment of the colonists' poorly coordinated military activities in the Pequot War of 1635–37. In consequence of a treaty signed at Hartford, a boundary between New York and Connecticut was established. Two years later New Amsterdam became a municipality. In 1655, because of insecurity felt by the Dutch over their military position and because of their small population, which was only half that of the Connecticut colony, Stuyvesant annexed New Sweden. Prior to this, the Dutch in 1648 had built Fort Beversrede at present Philadelphia and Fort Casimir in 1651 at what is now New Castle, Delaware.

Dutch expansion continued in the 1660s with Arent Van Curler's founding of Schenectady in 1662, a town that remained the westernmost community in New York until 1712. But Dutch colonization was soon to be defeated in the New World. After Charles II was restored to the throne in England in 1660, his attention turned toward war against Holland. Charles had been denied entry into Holland during his exile, and this doubtlessly contributed to his hatred of the Dutch. In 1664 he declared war on Holland and granted to his brother, James, the duke of York (also the duke of Albany), the entire region between the Connecticut and Delaware rivers plus Long Island, Nantucket, Martha's Vineyard, and that portion of the present state of Maine which lies east of the Kennebec River. On August 18, 1664, Stuyvesant surrendered without battle to an English fleet, and New Amsterdam became New York, Fort Orange became Albany, and Fort Casimir became New Castle. "A Description of the Towne of Mannados: or New Amsterdam," an attractive and often reproduced manuscript known as "The Duke's Plan" (*Plate 64*), which was drawn in 1664, shows New Amsterdam shortly after its capture by the British.

A new colony developed in the region bestowed upon the duke of York after the duke granted part of his land to Sir George Carteret and Lord John Berkeley. In 1665 Philip Carteret, Sir George's fourth cousin, acting as their agent, took over New Caesaria (New Jersey); at this time the area was inhabited by only a few hundred Puritans and Dutchmen. The colony's first assembly met at Elizabethtown in 1668. The province was divided into East and West Jersey in 1676, and the two areas were not politically joined until 1702. The first English settlement in the western portion of the province was established at Salem in 1675. John Seller's "A Mapp of New Jarsey" (*Plate 65*) was published in 1675 but shows the area of New Jersey as it was in 1664. The first delineation of New Jersey and the surrounding area on a separate map is also the first to use the present state's proper name (as the variant New Jarsey). It is the earliest English map to include the so-called Visscher View of New York. This view of the southern end of New Amsterdam, which originally appeared on a map by Nicolas J. Visscher in 1656, depicted specific buildings and survived as a decorative inset on maps for several decades.

In the southern portion of what was to become the United States, another colonial name was being established. Carolana, which had been introduced on John Farrer's 1651 "A mapp of Vir-

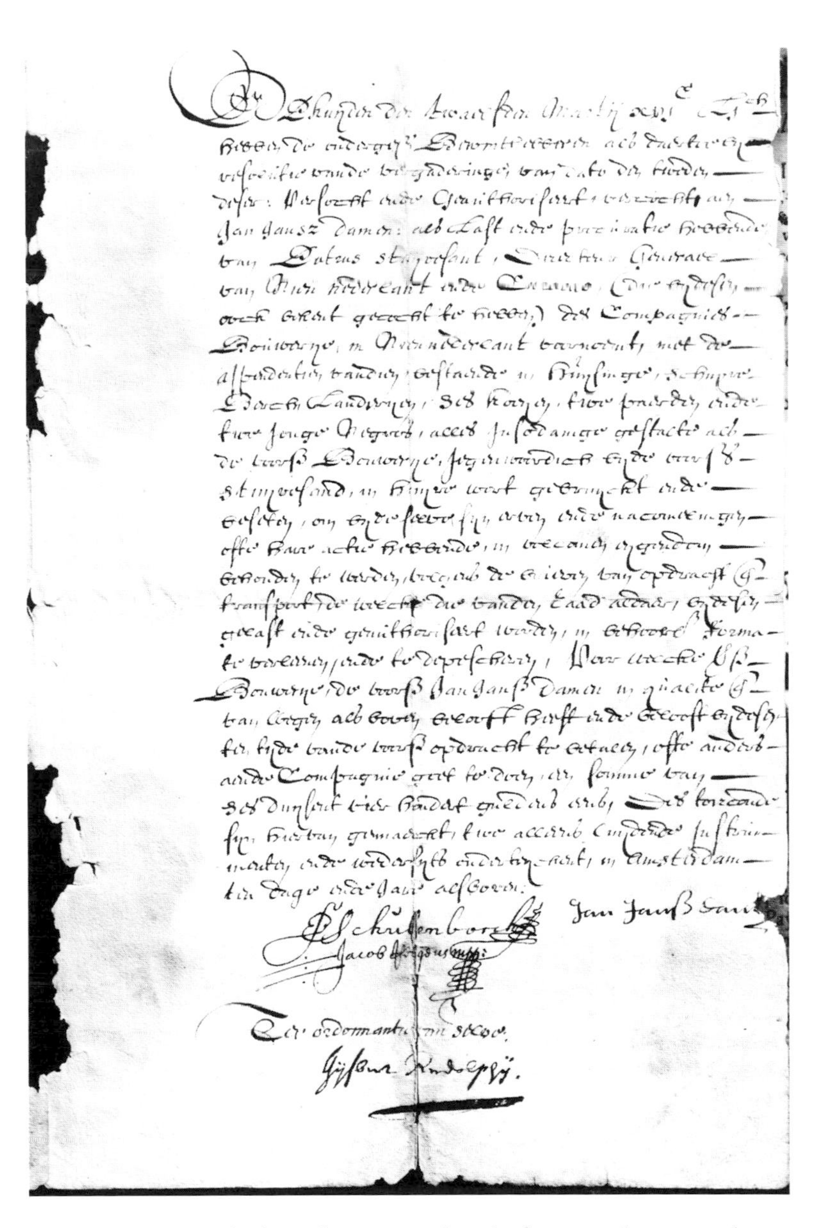

Stuyvesant's 1651 deed to The Bowery, bought from Dutch West India Co.

PLATE 62: Nicolas Sanson. "Le Canada, ou Nouvelle France, &c." 1656. Engraving, hand colored; 39 × 53 cm. Private collection. *First large-scale relatively correct delineation of the Great Lakes by same cartographer who first showed the five lakes on a single map (see Plate 61). Extends from Florida's northern border to the Arctic. Published separately, but also appeared in the 1658 and later editions of Sanson's* Cartes Generales de Toutes les Parties du Monde, *published in Paris.*

ginia" (*see Plate 63*), reappears on the 1657 manuscript map "The south part of virginia now the north part of Carolina" by Nicholas Comberford (*Plate 66*). It is accompanied by new English placenames, many still in use. A manuscript map in the British Library, "Discovery Made by Wm. Hilton on Charlestowne," drawn by Nicholas Shapley in 1662, chronicles William Hilton's exploration of the Cape Fear River. Although Carolina had been

settled mainly by colonists from the crowded neighboring settlements in the Virginia colony, exploratory excursions in this area were sponsored by two distant colonies. In 1660 the Massachusetts Bay colony sent Hilton to determine the feasibility of developing a colony at Cape Fear. A second trip by Hilton to that area, underwritten by a group of proprietors from overpopulated Barbados, led to the naming of Hilton Head Island. A settlement was established on the Cape Fear River in 1664 and named Charlestown; it did not survive, and must be distinguished from the present Charlestown, a later South Carolina settlement.

In 1663 Charles II awarded to a group of promoters and politicians the land extending from Virginia to the Florida peninsula and from the Atlantic to the Pacific. A year later "Americae Septentrionalis Pars" by the English hydrographer and globe maker Joseph Moxon became the first printed map that bore the name Carolina referring to the general area of this province. This map also has the distinction of being the first to show Manhattan Island following the British occupation, and the first on which the name New York appears. In 1666 the map "Carolina Described" was included as a frontispiece in *A Brief Description of the Province of Carolina, on the Coasts of Floreda* (London, 1666), printed for Robert Horne to attract settlers. The authorship of neither the map nor the book is known. This is the first printed map of the province per se that included the name Carolina in its title. The temporary town of Charlestown is shown on the west bank of the Cape Fear River.

The present Charleston was not settled from the existing American colonies but rather from the efforts in 1670 of a group of English settlers led by Joseph West. They initially built at Port Royal Sound but, fearing attacks by the Spanish in the adjacent region, they moved to Albemarle Point on the Ashley River. This settlement was named Charles Town. The population grew when poor immigrants moved in from Virginia, French Huguenots arrived to cultivate silkworms, and Scots immigrated to the Port Royal Sound region. In 1680 Charles Town was relocated at the junction of the Ashley and Cooper rivers, both named for Anthony Ashley Cooper, earl of Shaftesbury, a cavalier who had become chancellor of the exchequer and was appointed one of the proprietors of Carolina and who took considerable interest in plans for the colony. The original community thereafter was called Old Charles Town, while the new one was named Charleston.

Chronologically the next map of Carolina is a 1671 manuscript to which the eminent philosopher John Locke gave his approval; Locke at the time was secretary to Lord Ashley. This map records the regional names that were assigned during explorations by John Lederer, a German surgeon who immigrated to Virginia and showed interest in the region's natural resources and Indian culture. Anticipating westward expansion, Sir William Berke-

The Indian warrior, King Philip, engraved by Paul Revere, 1772

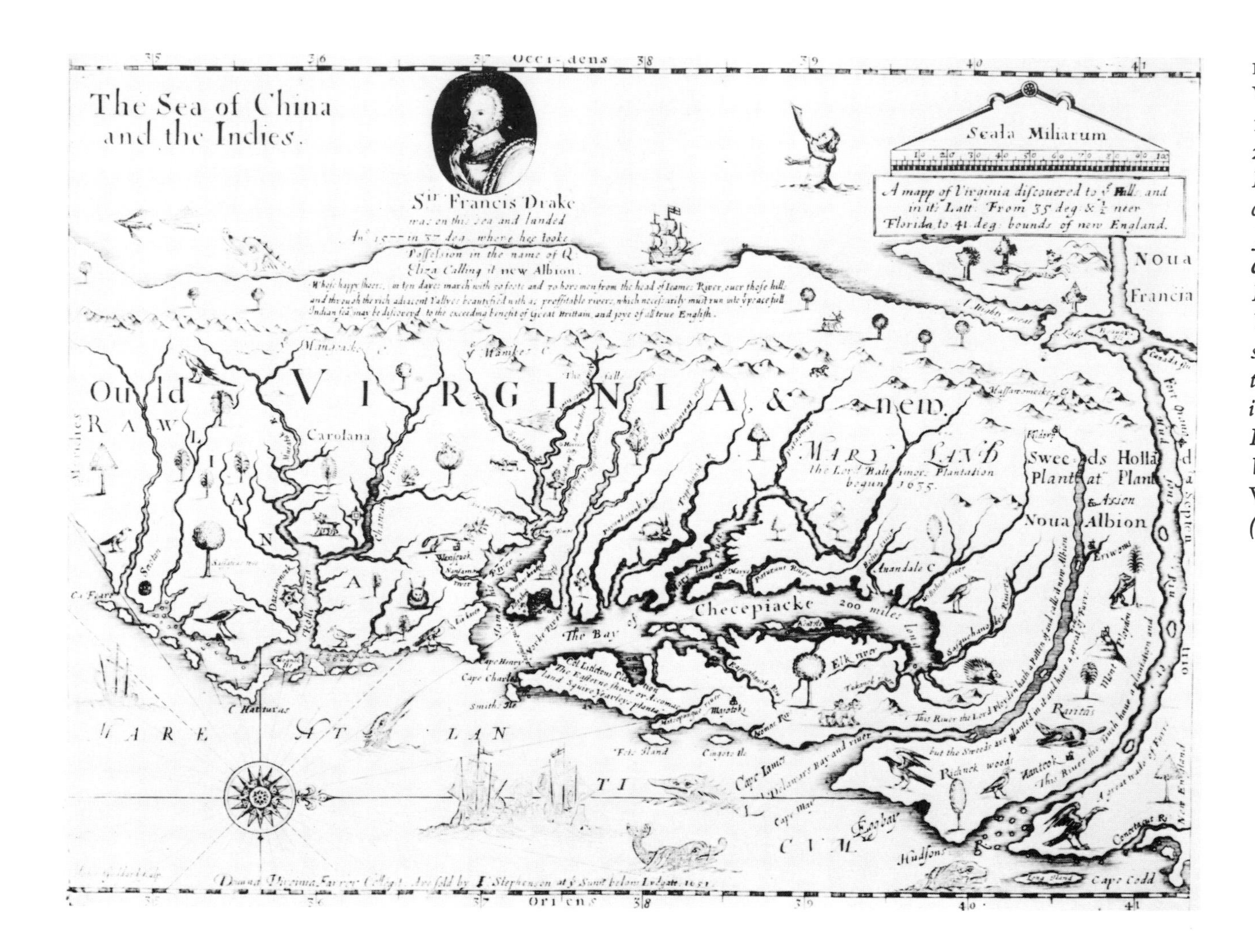

PLATE 63: John Farrer. "A mapp of Virginia discouered to ye Falls." 1651. Engraving (4th state, 1652), 27 × 35 cm. Private collection. *Indicates a narrow isthmus that can be crossed in ten days' march at the head of James and Hudson rivers to reach a lake connected with the Sea of China and the Indies. Map details county divisions in Virginia and Maryland for first time and shows Dutch and Swedish settlements to the north (right). In the 4th state, "Falls" in the title was changed to "Hills." Published in third edition of Edward Williams's* Virgo Triumphans: or Virginia Richly and Truly Valued *(London, 1651).*

ley, governor of Virginia, commissioned him in 1669 to determine what was beyond the regional mountains (the present Blue Ridge Mountain range). On his first trip, begun in March 1669, Lederer reached the Blue Ridge northwest of Charlottesville. On his second and most important journey, which was initiated in May 1670 and lasted two months, he reached a branch of the Roanoke River and skirted the southern end of the Appalachian Mountains into Georgia, trekking across the Piedmont region in North Carolina and into South Carolina. In a later account of his travels he described a large lake in the area of Rock Hill, South Carolina, thereby perpetuating the error originally made on the 1606 Mercator-Hondius map "Virginia Item et Floridae Americae Provinciarum nova Descriptio." On his way back to Virginia Lederer crossed the pine barrens of North Carolina, which he called the Arenosa Desert. His third and final journey, begun in August 1670, ended on a Blue Ridge Mountain peak, which he dubbed King Charles Peak. Lederer's three marches are first depicted on "A Map of the Whole Territory Traversed by John Lederer in His Three Marches," drawn by the explorer himself, which appears in his descriptive account of his travels, *The Discoveries of John Lederer in Three Several Marches from Virginia, to the West of Carolina, and Other Parts of the Continent* (London, 1672), which Sir William Talbot translated from the original Latin into English. This was the first scientific report on the geology, botany, fauna, and indigenous tribes of the broad territory it covered.

PLATE 64: Cartographer unknown. "A Description of the Towne of Mannados: or New Amsterdam." 1664. Manuscript, pen and ink and watercolor; 56 × 71 cm. Map Library, British Library, London. *Known as the "Duke's Plan," it shows Manhattan and the Dutch settlement after British capture. Little is known about the creation of this map.*

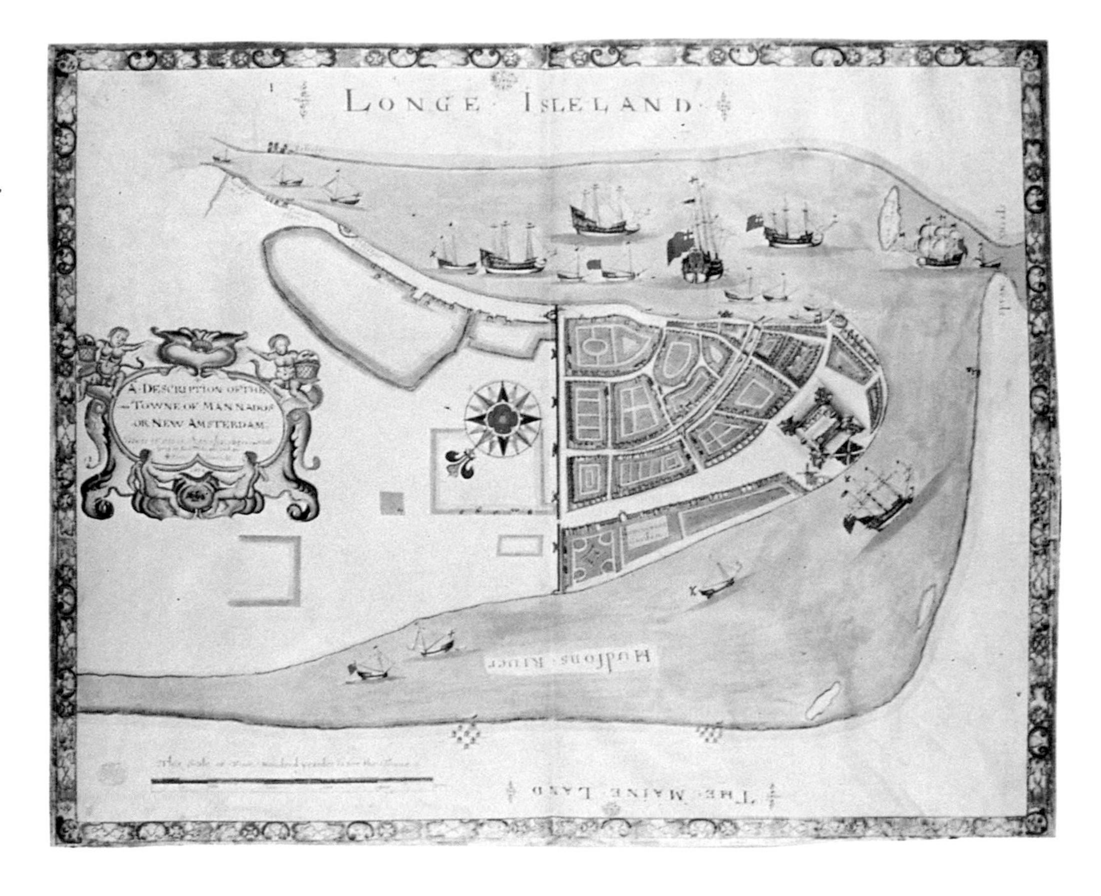

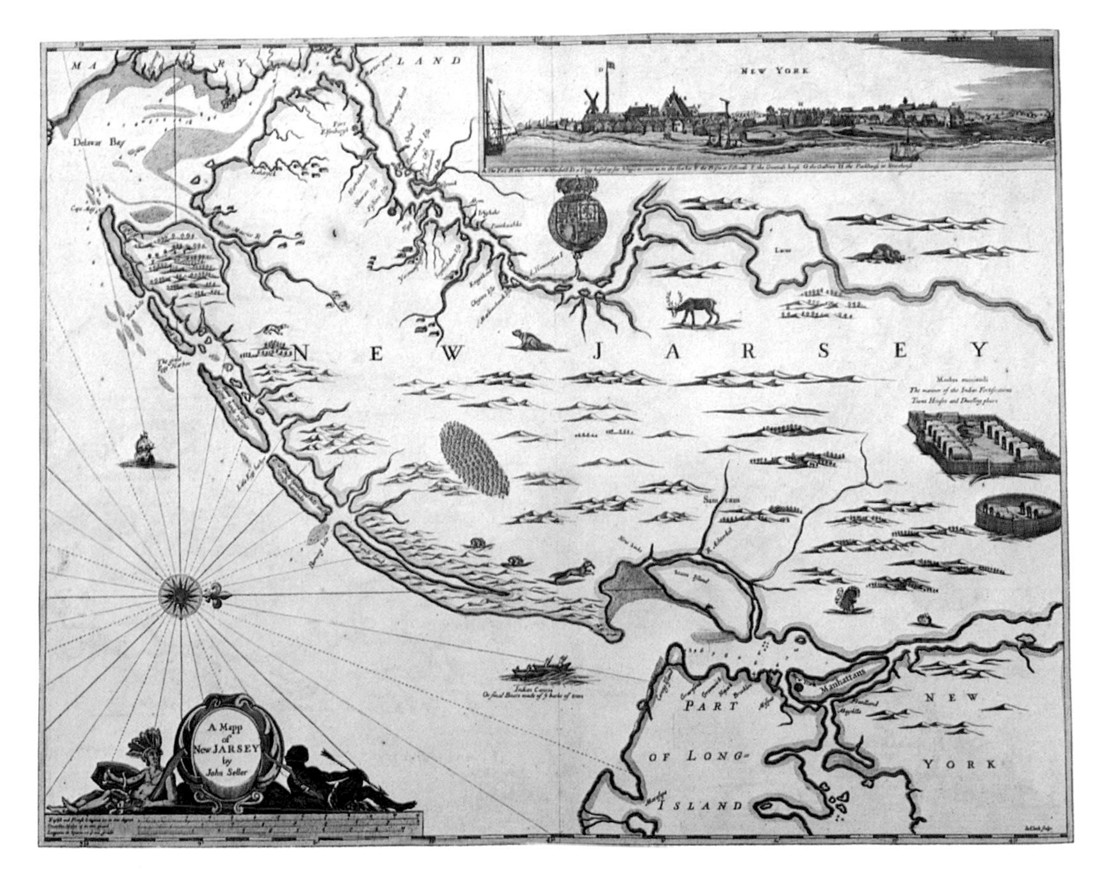

PLATE 65: John Seller. "A Mapp of New Jarsey." 1675. Engraving, hand colored; 52 × 60 cm. New Jersey Historical Society, Newark. *Shows New Jersey as it was in 1664. First map to use name New Jersey (as New Jarsey). First English map to include Visscher View of New York (top right); earliest New York view with the city's present name. Appeared in 1675 edition of Seller's* Atlas Maritimus, *published in London.*

William Penn's treaty with the Indians, 1682;
engraved after a 1771 painting by Benjamin West

In 1671 Arnoldus Montanus published in Amsterdam a compilation of material relating to America, *De Nieuwe en Onbekende Weereld,* which is considered the first encyclopedia of the Americas. John Ogilby's *America,* published the same year in London, is an English translation of Montanus's work. Included in both heavily illustrated volumes are a number of regional maps that are derivatives of previous classic works. Published only in Ogilby is James Moxon's "A New Discription of Carolina By Order of the Lords Proprietors," commonly known as the "First Lord Proprietors' Map." This cartographic competition between the Dutch and English was paralleled by military activities in the colonies. In 1673 the Dutch recaptured New York and held it for fifteen months, only to lose control again to the English. Finally their power was effectively broken in North America, and the glittering dream of extending their already vast empire into the New World spanned only half a century. One legacy of the phlegmatic merchants of Nieu Nederlandt was an infusion of bloodlines—Roosevelts, Stuyvesants, Van Rensselaers—and another was a heritage of names on the eastern seaboard. It is still Hellegat that separates Lang Eylandt from Bronck's farm, and Conyne Eylandt in Breuckelen is where New Yorkers seek amusement or respite from the heat on summer weekends.

Three other western explorations took place during this period. In 1671 Thomas Wood left Appomattox and, crossing the Blue Ridge Mountains into the Great Appalachian Valley, or Valley of Virginia, he followed the Roanoke River to the present West Virginia line. Erroneously thinking he noted an ebb and tide to the river's water, he consequently convinced himself he had reached part of the Western Sea (Pacific Ocean) and took possession of the land in the name of Charles II. In the same year Henry Woodward, the first European to penetrate the western wilderness in the region of South Carolina, opened a land route from Charleston, South Carolina, to Virginia. In 1673 James Needham and Gabriel Arthur explored western North Carolina as far as the neighborhood of Asheville. Much of the geographic information gained on these journeys is reflected in Joel Gascoyne's 1682 "A New Map of the Country of Carolina," included in *A True Description of Carolina* (London, 1682) by Joel Gascoyne and Robert Greene. It is known as the "Second Lord Proprietors' Map" and remained the most accurate map of the region until well into the eighteenth century.

Certain refinements in colonial mapping at this time—namely, the substitution of English names for Indian names and the addition of numerous plantations—occur in the 1673 map "Virginia and Maryland" by Augustine Herrman (Augustus Heermans) (*Plate 67*). Only four copies of this map have survived. It has been described by the historian Lawrence Wroth as being of "such rarity as to be almost the subject of legend" (see *Annual Report, 1929–30,* John Carter Brown Library, Brown University, Providence). It is the only known map by Herrman,

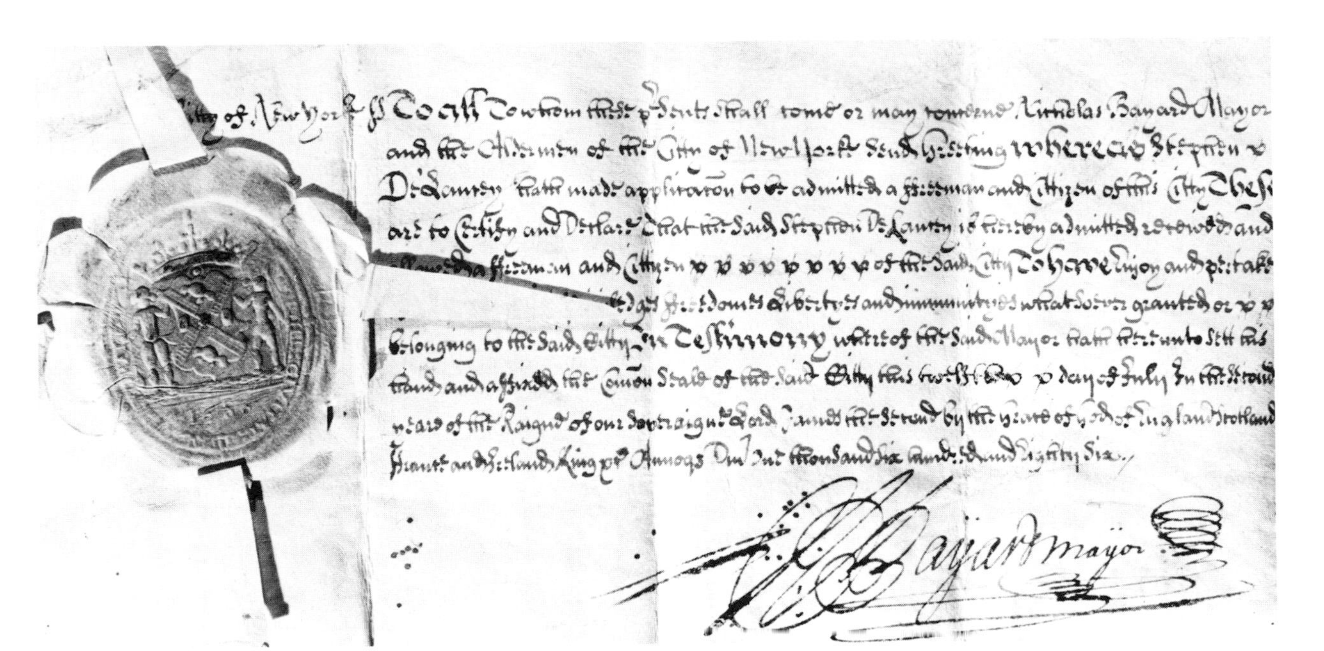

Earliest known impression, 1686, of the seal of New York City

who surveyed the area for the first proprietor of the colony of Maryland—Cecilius Calvert, second Baron Baltimore—in return for a 20,000-acre land grant, and it presents no topographic changes from the earlier 1612 John Smith map of Virginia and uses the same orientation of north to right (*see Plate 50*). But in consequence of its innovative nomenclature, it superseded the Smith map as prototype for future maps of the region and maintained this status for more than three-quarters of a century. It was used to settle many boundary disputes between Pennsylvania and Maryland, until publication of the Fry and Jefferson map in 1754 (*see Plate 92*).

A conflict between New England colonists and a confederation of Indians in 1675–76, known as King Philip's War, led to the partial or total destruction of several New England communities. A by-product of this war made cartographic history: the first map engraved and published in North America. "A Map of New-England" (*Plate 68*), a crude woodcut ascribed to John Foster, accompanied Reverend William Hubbard's *A Narrative of the Troubles with the Indians in New-England* (Boston, 1677). Conceived as a guide to the military campaign (battles and massacres are keyed by numbers), the map utilizes perpendicular lines (oriented north to right) to demarcate the northern and southern boundaries of the Massachusetts Bay colony according to the 1629 Massachusetts Bay Company charter. There are two versions of the map, one bearing the name White Hills (on the right-hand side just below the cartouche) and the other bearing the name Wine Hills (in the same location). The map historian David Woodward has concluded that the wood block from which the White Hills version was printed had been cut by John Foster in Boston and the Wine Hills block is a copy, cut later in London (see "The Foster Woodcut Map Controversy: A Further Examination of the Evidence," *Imago Mundi* 21, 1967). Hence, the White Hills version was the map first published in America.

Numerous other important changes took place in the British colonies in the last quarter of the seventeenth century. New Hampshire was separated from Massachusetts in 1680 by royal decree. (Later, in 1691, Massachusetts was designated a royal province and Maine was included within its boundaries; *see Plate 135*.) In 1681 William Penn received a charter from Charles II for an area between latitude 43° north and latitude 40° north running west from Delaware through five degrees of longitude. This ambiguous description was responsible for future boundary disputes in the lower Delaware region. In the following year Penn received another grant from the duke of York, who in

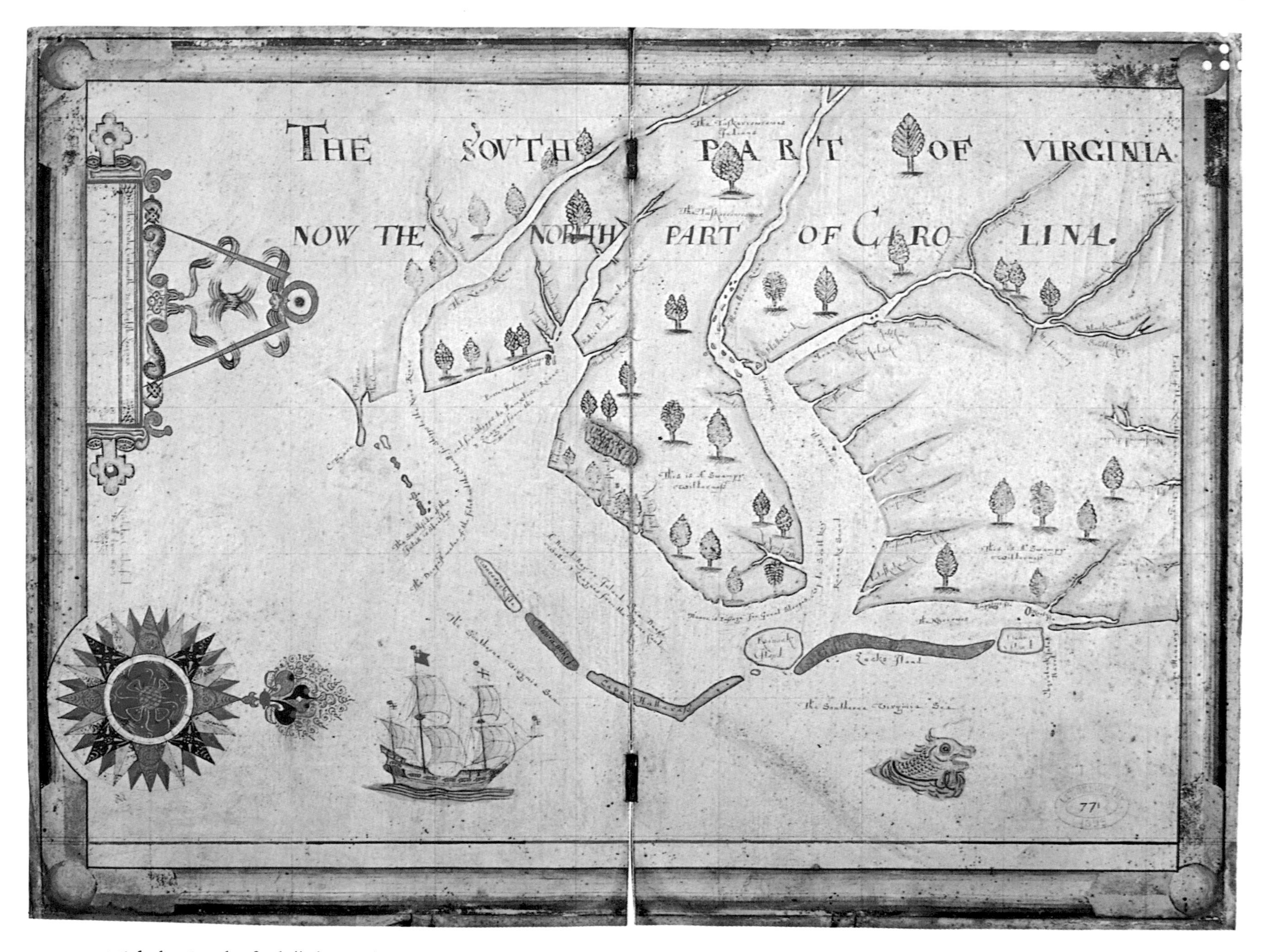

PLATE 66: Nicholas Comberford. "The south part of virginia now the north part of Carolina." 1657. Manuscript on vellum, pen and ink and watercolor with gilt; 35 × 47 cm. Manuscripts Division, New York Public Library; Astor, Lenox and Tilden Foundations. *Map of Pamlico–Albemarle Sound area, identifying what may have been first permanent settlement in North Carolina. It presents for the first time many English names that still persist: Knot Ile (Knott Island), Machepoungo R. (Pungo River), Pamxtico Riuer (Pamlico).*

actuality lacked legal title to the area. This grant included the western shore of the Delaware Bay from New Castle to Cape Henlopen. Penn accepted his grants while resident in England. English and Welsh Quakers rapidly settled the region and in 1682 Penn himself arrived in Philadelphia to serve as his own governor. That year he and Commissioner Thomas Holme planned Philadelphia, thereby making it the first American city of predetermined design. Holme's 1683 "A Portraiture of the City of Philadelphia" (*Plate 69*), credited as the first printed map of a city within the area that became the United States, plots Philadelphia as confined by two rivers, the Schuylkill and the Delaware. Eight of the nine streets running east and west were named for trees. The remaining one, near the middle, was High Street and eventually became Market Street. Twenty north–south streets were designated by consecutive numbers; the two that bordered the rivers were each named Front Street, and the central north–south street was Broad Street.

The province of Pennsylvania had a firm population base from the beginning since it already included the inhabitants of New Sweden. In 1683 German Mennonites settled Germantown, Pennsylvania, and English and Welsh Quakers rapidly joined them. Another important work by Thomas Holme, the 1687 "A Mapp of ye Improved part of Pensilvania in America, Divided into Countyes Townships and Lotts" (*Plate 70*), shows the boundaries of some 800 tracts of land in the southeastern part of the colony. In 1689 a grant of five million acres between the Rapahannack and Potomac rivers was made initially to Lord Hopton, who reassigned it to Thomas Culpeper (Baron Culpeper), the colonial governor of Virginia. On his death the proprietary rights descended to his grandson, Thomas Fairfax. The resultant placenames became apparent on the maps of the following century.

The most important transformations on maps during the second half of the seventeenth century were related to the great rivers of the interior and their surrounding valleys. In 1656, the same year that he produced his map "Le Canada, ou Nouvelle France, &c." showing the five Great Lakes (*see Plate 62*), Nicolas Sanson published "La Nouveau Mexique, et La Floridae," treating an area extending from the South Carolina coast to California and from Canada to Mexico. It reiterates the common misconception of the Mississippi River's origin from four rivers hemmed in by mountains which converge at the Gulf of Mexico.

The efforts of French Jesuits and coureurs des bois, or trappers, led to a better appreciation of the geography of the Great Lakes and accurate descriptions and cartographic representations of the great rivers of the interior. In 1654 Father Simon LeMoyne returned to France with the first account of the Indian homelands south of Lake Ontario. By the middle of the 1650s the French fur trade was concentrated beyond Lake Superior, and the fur traders related that the Hudson Bay was preferable to the St. Lawrence's shores as an ingress to the region since ships could travel directly from Europe, making the distance to the trapping region shorter. Because Louis XIV was reluctant to commit monies and troops to control the Hudson Bay region, some traders switched alle-

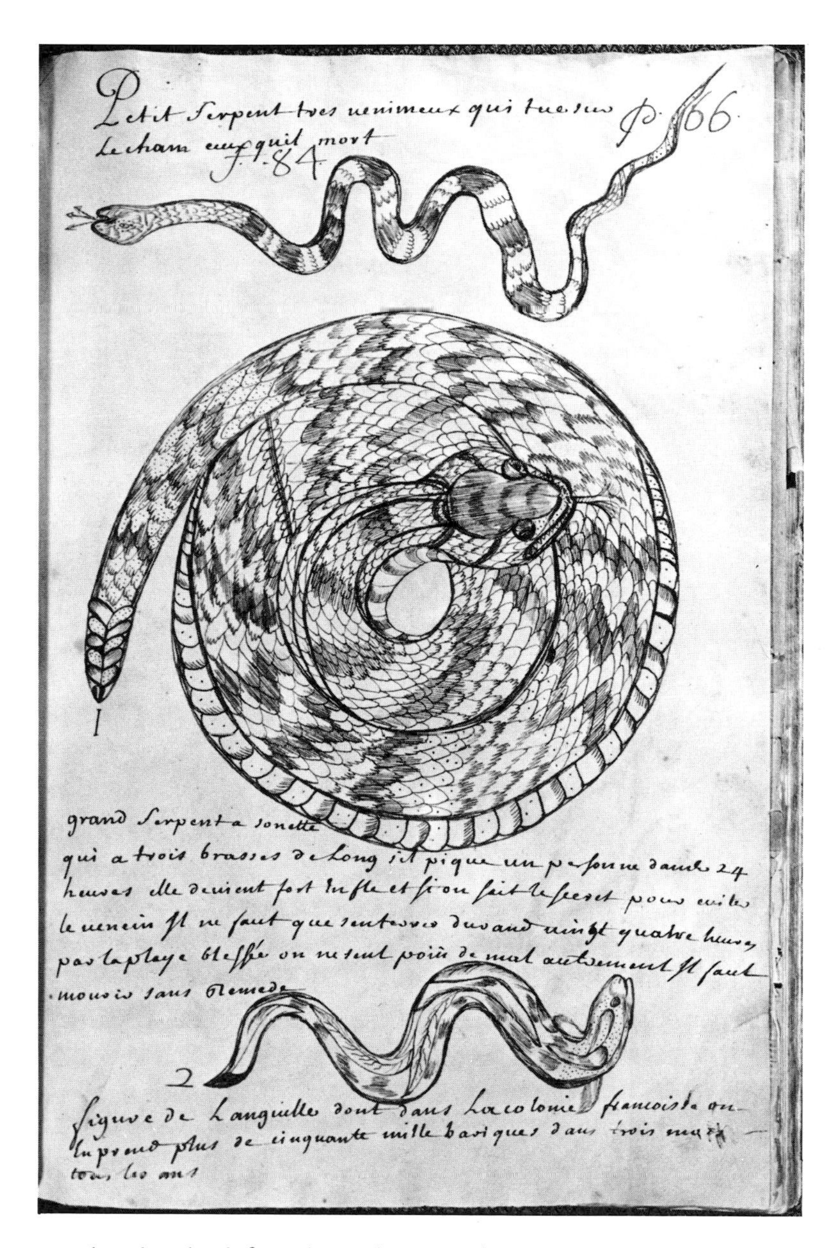

Rattlesnake, sketch from the Codex Canadensis, *c. 1700*

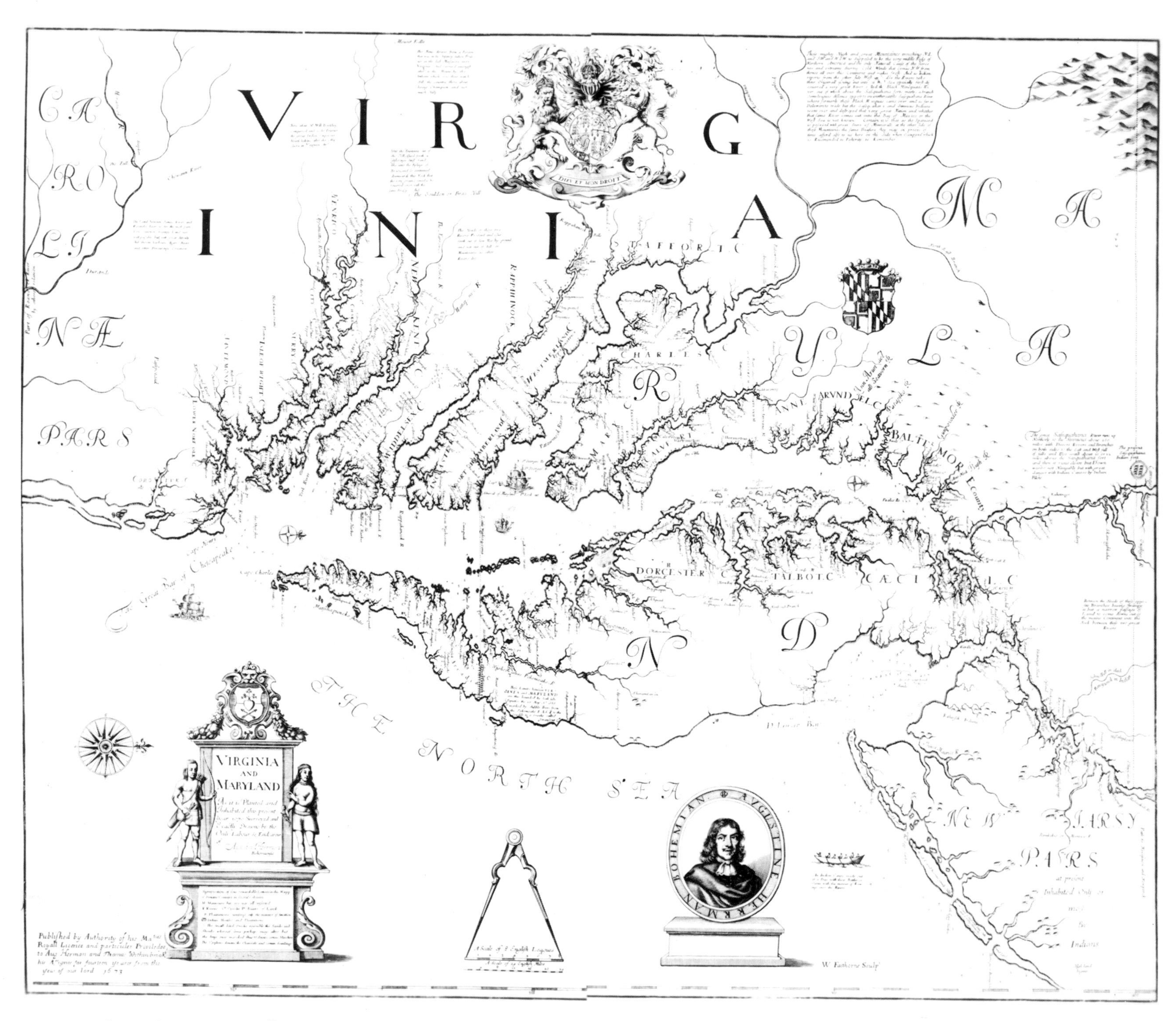

PLATE 67: Augustine Herrman. "Virginia and Maryland." 1673. Engraving, 79 × 95 cm. Geography and Map Division, Library of Congress, Washington, D.C. *A major cartographic publication of seventeenth-century America, it embodies results of some of the best surveying in the colonies. Plantation names included, and English placenames replace previous Indian names.*

PLATE 68: John Foster. "A Map of New-England." 1677. Woodcut, 30 × 38 cm. Rare Books and Special Collections, Princeton University Library, Princeton. *White Hills version reproduced. First map drawn, engraved, and printed in America. Illustrates Reverend William Hubbard's text on King Philip's War,* A Narrative of the Troubles with the Indians in New-England *(Boston, 1677); map is keyed by number for battles and massacres. River across top is Connecticut River; one that begins at bottom and turns right is the Merrimack. Shows boundaries of Massachusetts Bay colony according to 1629 charter. Direction north is oriented right.*

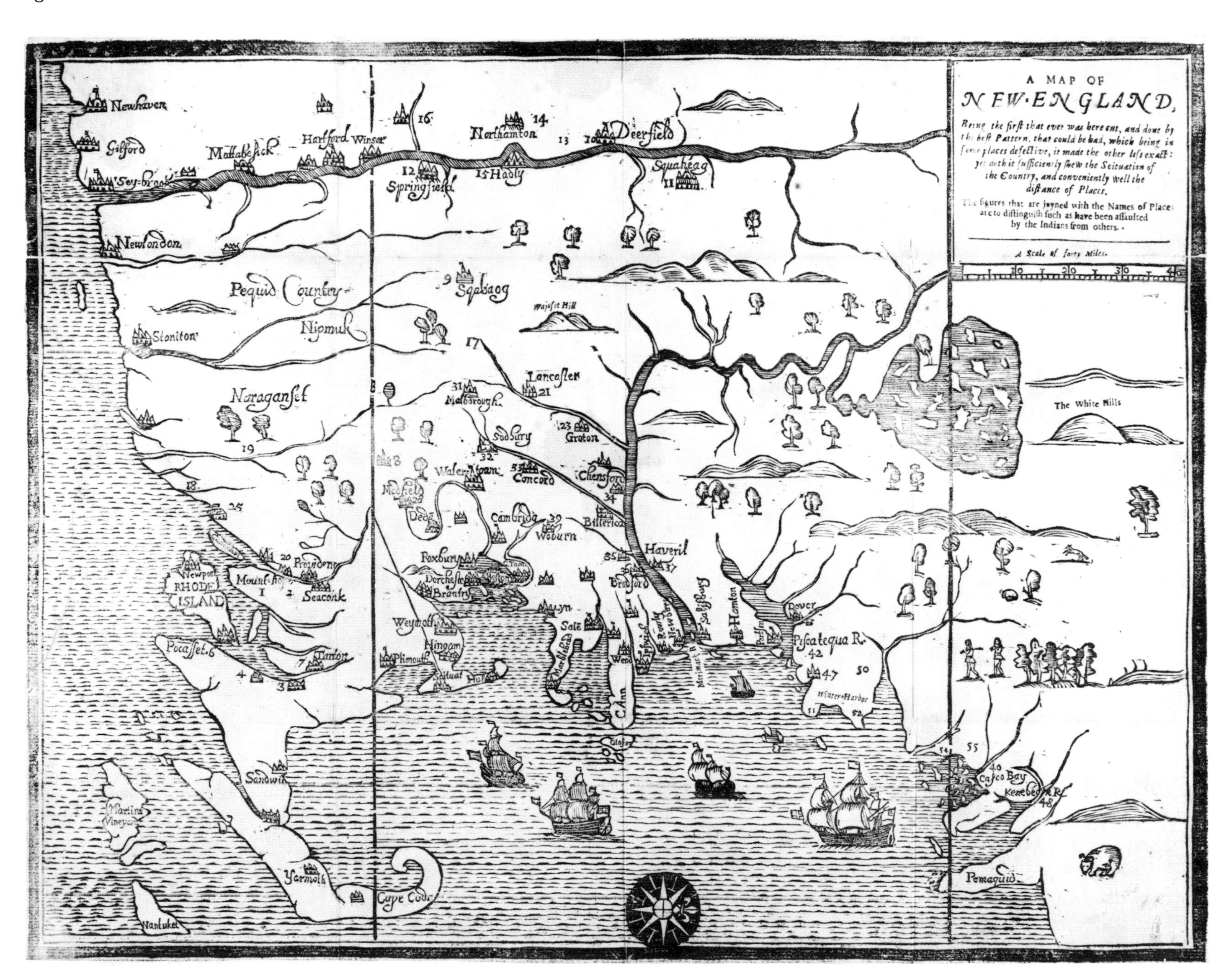

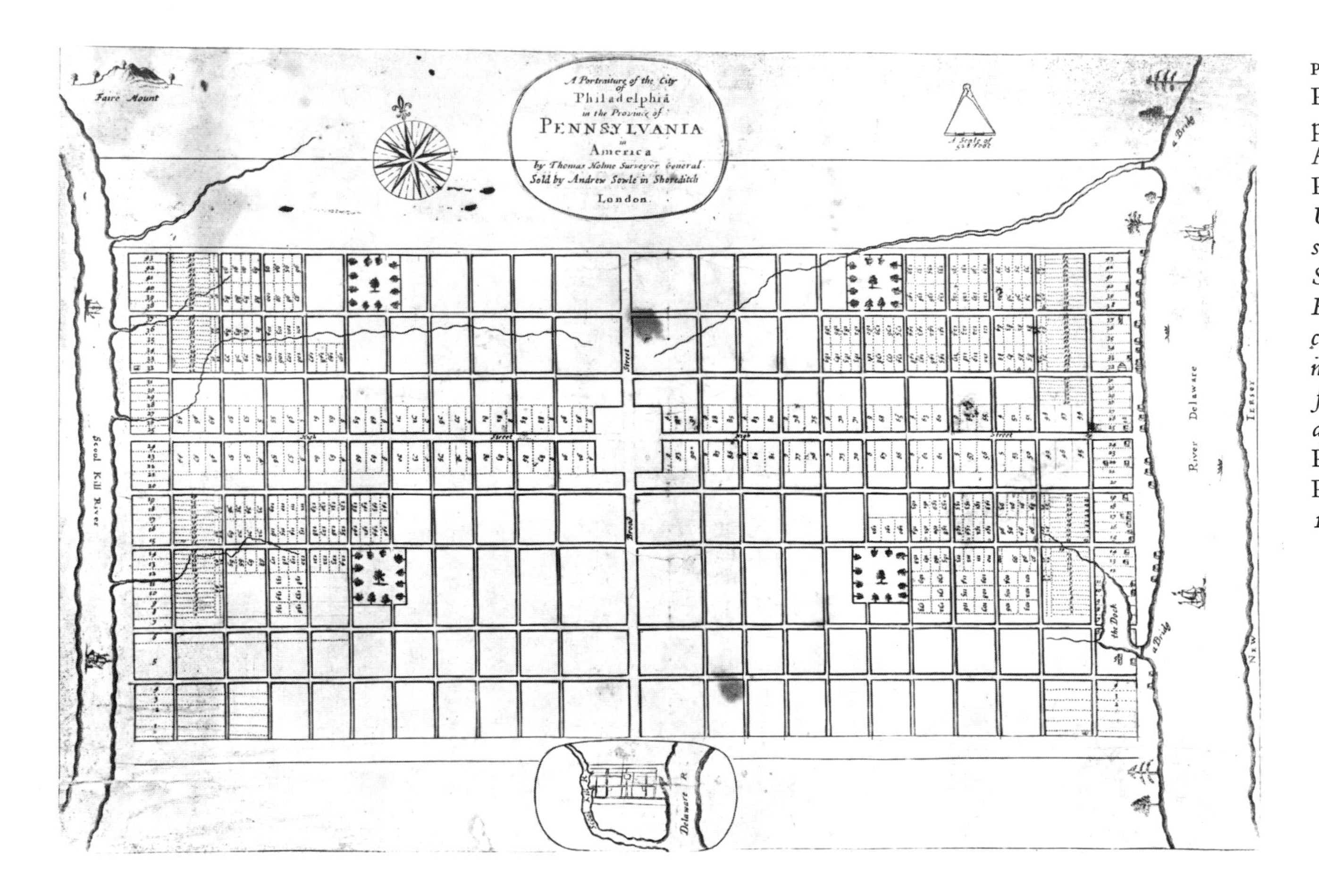

PLATE 69: Thomas Holme. "A Portraiture of the City of Philadelphia." 1683. Engraving, 29 × 44 cm. American Philosophical Society, Philadelphia. *First printed plan of a United States city. Area is laid out in squares between Delaware River and Schuylkill River (Scool Kill on map). High Street and Broad Street intersect at a central square. North and south streets are numbered, eight east-west streets named for trees. Published separately and also appeared in* A Letter from William Penn, Proprietor and Governour of Pennsylvania in America *(London, 1683).*

giance to the English, who in 1670 created the Hudson's Bay Company.

Under a policy initiated earlier in the century by Champlain, the French supported the Huron Indians in their warfare with the Iroquois. When the Iroquois finally crushed the Huron in the early 1660s, the French colony was nearly extinct. In 1663, because they were unable to deal with the Iroquois, the ruling body of the Company of New France surrendered its charter to Louis XIV and New France became a crown colony. During the 1660s the *Relations des Missions aux Outaouacs*, an annual publication in Paris describing the activities of the Jesuit religious order, issued excellent surveys of the Great Lakes and also carried the first mention of the Mississippi River (Messi-sipi, derived from two Algonquian terms, *messi* [big] and *sipi* [river]). In 1669–70 members of a missionary expedition of the newly founded Sulpician order were the first Europeans to spend a winter on the shores of Lake Erie.

In 1670 Nicolas Denys was awarded Cape Breton as a feudal estate by Louis XIV, and an overland route was cut out between the St. Lawrence River and James Bay. The following year Jesuits were well established at Sault Ste. Marie and took possession of the entire western continent in the name of their king. The *Relations des Missions* for 1670–71, published in 1672, includes a map, "Lac Svperievr," credited to the French Jesuit missionaries Claude Dablon and Claude Allouez (*Plate 71*). It is surprisingly accurate in its definition of Lake Superior and northern Lake Michigan, and is the first map to distinguish between Lake Michigan (Lac des Illinois) and Green Bay (Baye des Puans), which is actually a bay of the lake. The map may be regarded as a historical springboard for the first great river journey of the interior,

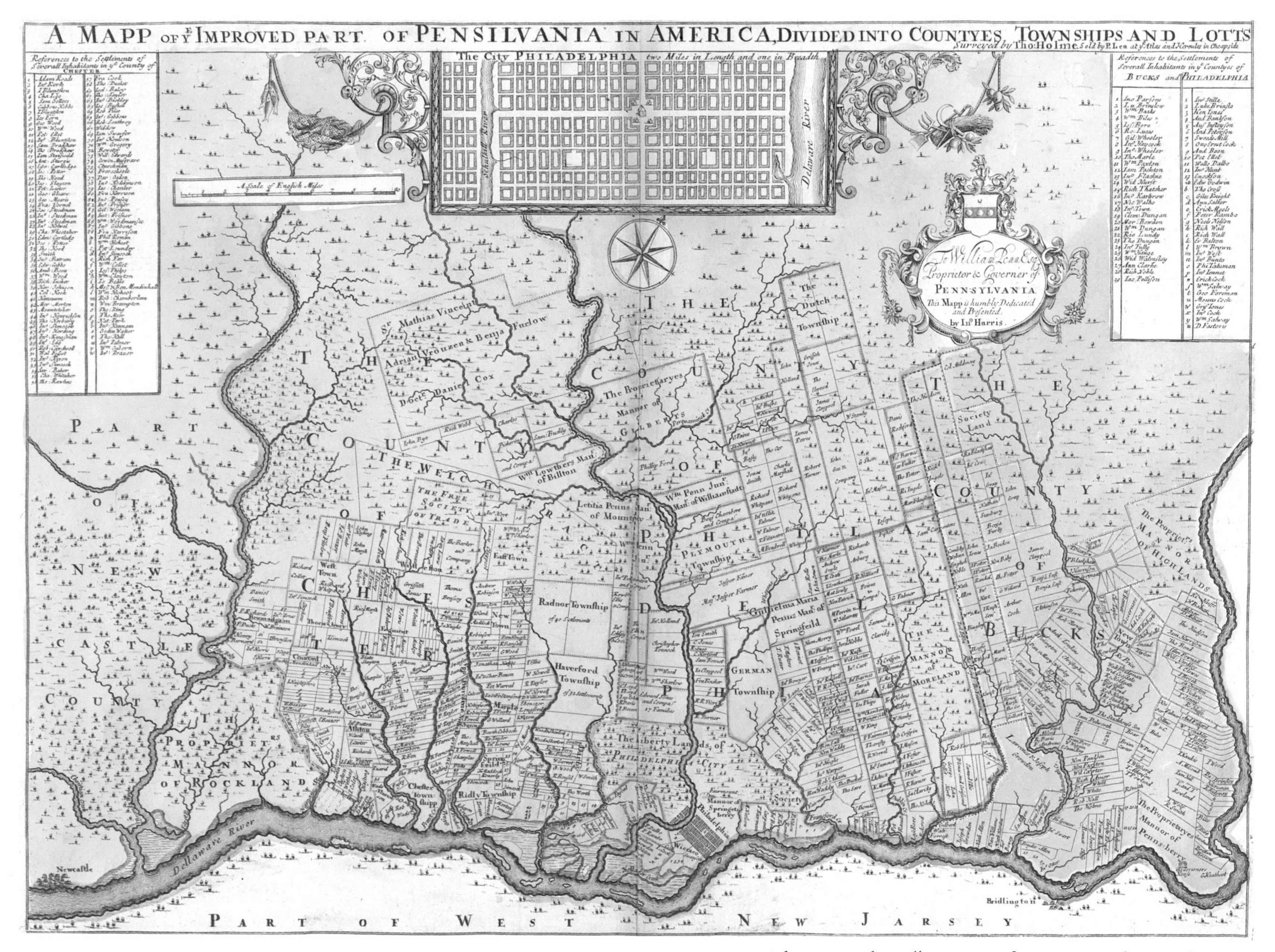

PLATE 70: Thomas Holme. "A Mapp of ye Improved part of Pensilvania in America, Divided into Countyes Townships and Lotts." 1687. Engraving, hand colored; 40 × 54 cm. Private collection, Philadelphia. *Early map of grants made to William Penn. Settlements west of Delaware River are shown, and landowners in Chester, Bucks, and Philadelphia counties are listed in the legends. Inset of Philadelphia city plan.*

since it locates the missions from which the Jesuit explorers embarked down the river, including Mission de Ste. Marie du Sault at the eastern end of Lake Superior, Mission du St. Esprit at the western end, Mission de St. Fr. Xavier at Green Bay (Baye des Puans), and Mission de St. Ignace on Mackinac Island in the Straits of Mackinac (S. Missilimakinac) connecting Lake Michigan (Lac des Ilinois) and Lake Huron (Lac des Hurons).

Arrival of La Salle at Matagorda Bay, Texas, from Hennepin's A New Discovery of a Vast Country in America, *1698*

In 1673, at a time when the French colonists were safeguarding themselves by building Fort Frontenac at present Kingston on the northeastern shore of Lake Ontario, Louis Joliet and Father Jacques Marquette left the mission of St. Ignace and launched their boats into the Straits of Mackinac. They proceeded to Green Bay, then followed the Fox River to a portage from which they entered the Mississippi River and continued south past the mouth of the Pekittanoui River (Missouri River) and on to the junction of the Arkansas and Mississippi rivers. They were the first Europeans to glimpse either the Missouri River or the Ohio River (at that time named the Ouabouskigou). On the equally important return journey they discovered a shortcut to Lake Michigan along the Illinois and Des Plaines rivers and then portaged to the area that is now Chicago.

Several manuscript maps of the Ohio Valley were the ultimate yield of this trip. But the only extant document by a member of the Mississippi expedition is a manuscript map by Father Marquette, drawn in 1673–74, now in the Archives de la Compagnie de Jésus, St. Jérôme, Quebec. Following Marquette's route, beginning at the Green Bay mission and extending south to Akansea [downstream people], it shows the mouth of the present Arkansas River entering the Mississippi River (R. de la Conception). This map displays for the first time Lake Winnebago, the Wisconsin and Illinois rivers, and the mouths of the Missouri River (Pekittanoui on the map, from an Indian term meaning muddy river) and the Ohio River (Ouabouskigou).

The 1674 "Nouuelle Decouuerte de plusieurs Nations Dans la Nouuelle France En l'année 1673 et 1674" (*Plate 72*) was considered for many years an original manuscript map drawn by Louis Joliet, but closer inspection has revealed that neither the handwriting nor the signature matches Joliet's and that it is one of several contemporary copies drawn in Quebec. Riviere de Buade (Mississippi River) is shown originating from three imaginary lakes, and in Joliet's letter—appearing at the left of the map—to the French governor of New France, Louis de Buade, comte de Palluac et de Frontenac, it is postulated that a river runs from the Mississippi to Mer Vermeille (Gulf of California). There is another large river, titled Ouabouskigou, a name that the French subsequently changed to Ouabache, which the English then rendered Wabash. This persistent geographic term actually was first assigned to the Ohio River, and it was not until the eighteenth century that the confusion about the two rivers with one name was resolved.

Another manuscript map, "Carte de l'Amerique Septentrionale Depuis l'embouchure de la Riviere St. Laurens jusques au Sien Mexique," now in the John Carter Brown Library in Providence, has been attributed to Hugues Randin, cartographer to the comte de Frontenac, and assigned a date between 1672 and 1682. Deference to the patron—a common practice at the time—is made conspicuous by the name Riviere Buade affixed to the Mississippi and that of Frontenacie to the area northwest of the Ohio River. The manuscript "Carte de l'Amerique Septentrionale," generally ascribed to the date 1682, warrants consideration since it is replete

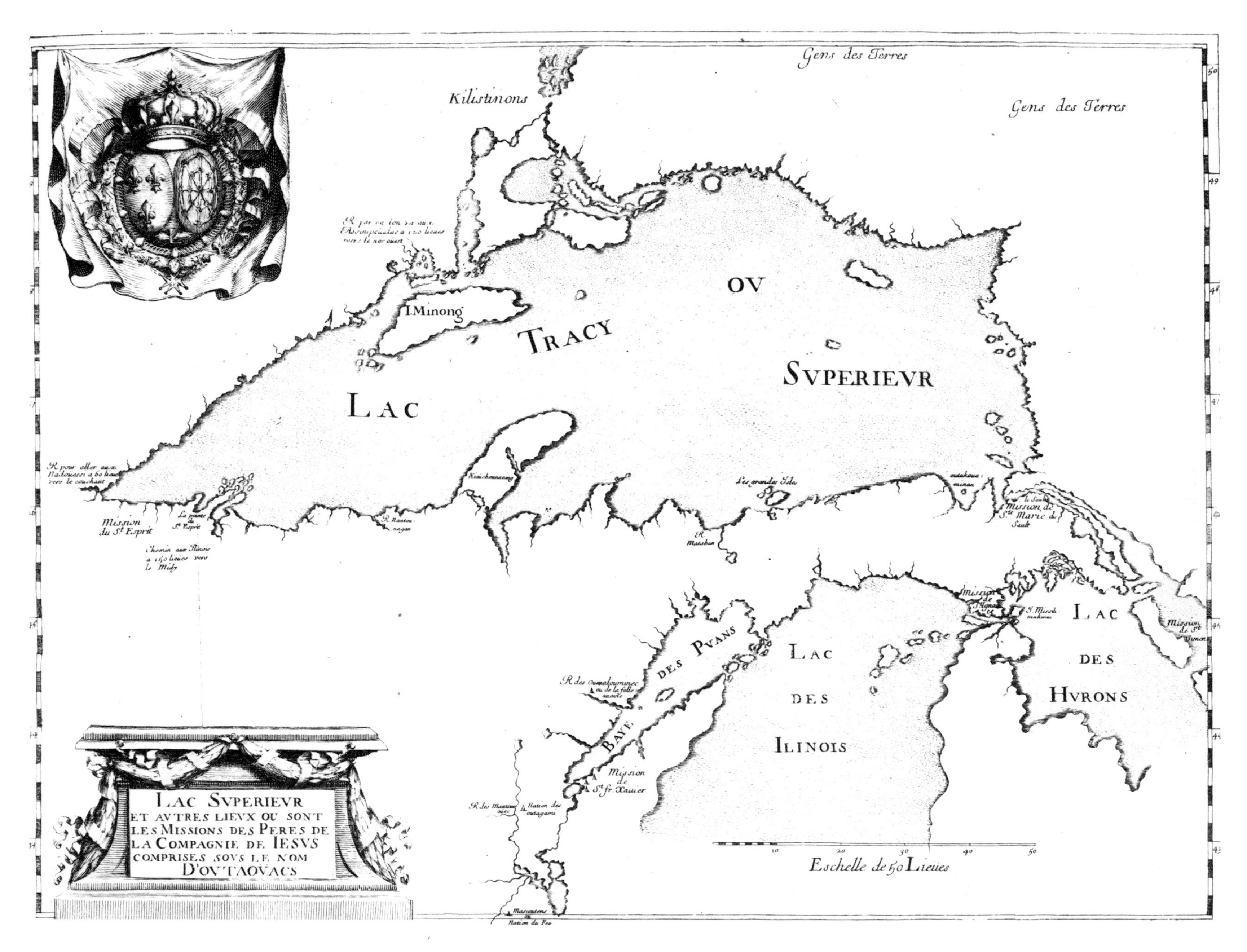

with important new placenames. It was long attributed to Jean-Baptiste-Louis Franquelin, but Father Jean Deglanglez, a Jesuit scholar specializing in the history of the Mississippi Valley region, has pinpointed its authorship to Claude Bernou with the assistance of M. Peronel (see *Indian Villages of the Illinois Country*, compiled in 1942 by Sara Jones Tucker). The many new names include La Louisiane and the Mississippi (as Riviere Missisipi ou

PLATE 71: Claude Dablon and Claude Allouez (attr.). "Lac Svperievr." 1672. Engraving, 17 × 23 cm. Newberry Library, Chicago. *Accurate presentation of Lake Superior and northern part of Lake Michigan (Lac des Ilinois). First map to distinguish Green Bay (Baye des Puans) from Lake Michigan. Locates Jesuit missions in the area. Published in* Relation des Missions aux Outaouacs des Années 1670 et 1671 *(Paris, 1672).*

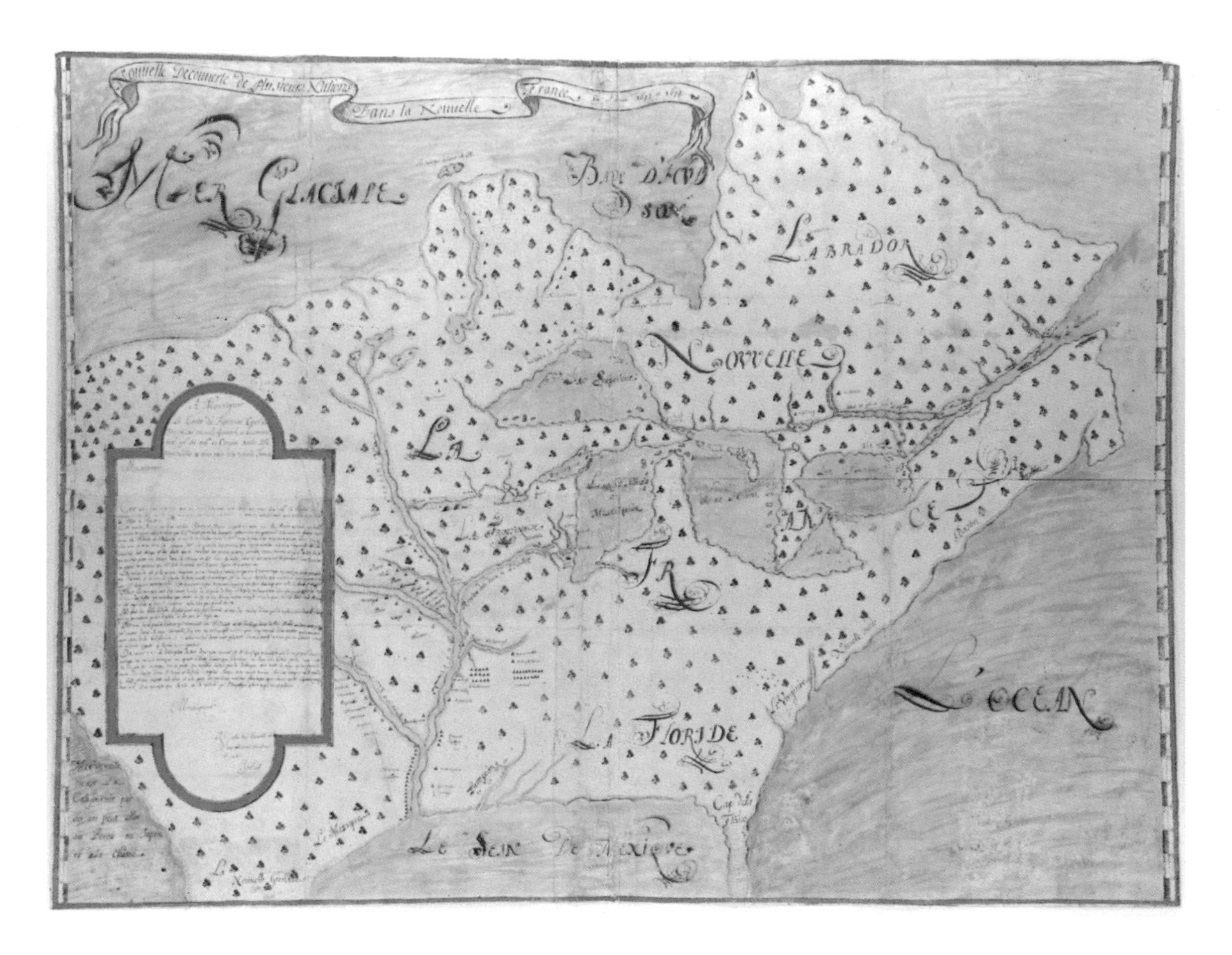

PLATE 72: Louis Joliet. "Nouuelle Decouuerte de plusieurs Nations Dans la Nouuelle France En l'année 1673 et 1674." 1674. Manuscript, pen and ink and watercolor; 66 × 86 cm. John Carter Brown Library, Brown University, Providence. *Locates Indian nations and iron deposits. Shows two rivers from the west entering the Mississippi (Riviere de Buade on map), which in turn empties into Gulf of Mexico (Le Sien De Mexique). Within bordered cartouche a letter to the comte de Palluac et de Frontenac erroneously states there is a river, by which one could reach China, connecting Mer Vermeille (Gulf of California) and the Mississippi and Gulf of Mexico.*

PLATE 73: Louis Hennepin. "Carte de la Nouuelle France et de la Louisiane Nouuellement découuerte." 1683. Engraving, 26 × 44 cm. Private collection. *First map to show Falls of St. Anthony (Sault de St. Antoine de Padoü) at site of present Minneapolis. Surmised lower course of Mississippi River, exhibited by a faint dotted line, is approximately correct. Louisiana (as La Louisiane) named on a printed map for first time. Atlantic Ocean is designated Mer de Canada. Appears in Hennepin's* Description de la Louisiane Nouvellement Decouverte au Sud'Oüest de la Nouvelle France *(*Paris, 1683*).*

PLATE 74: Jean-Baptiste-Louis Franquelin. "Carte de l'Amerique Septentrionale." 1688. Manuscript copy, pen and ink and watercolor; 146 × 152 cm. Original: Archive du Dêpot des Cartes et Plans de la Marine, Paris. Manuscript copy: Geography and Map Division, Library of Congress, Washington, D.C. *Mississippi courses too far westerly below mouth of the Ohio. Certain historians suggested the compiler lacked information of La Salle's journey; others that La Salle deliberately distorted westerly course of the river to promote settlement. The Mississippi appears as Fleuve Missisipi, and Louisiana as Contrée de la Louisiane. Ouisconsing is derived from Indian name for the Wisconsin. Sault St. Antoine, Lac du Buade, and Ohoio, ou Belle Riviere are noted.*

Colbert), which is truncated below the Ohio. Because Joliet had had a falling out with the comte de Frontenac, he picked the name Colbert, rather than Frontenacie, for the country west of the rivers, thus honoring Jean-Baptiste Colbert, the powerful French comptroller general of finances. Fort de Crevecoeur, the first settlement built by La Salle in present Illinois, is cited; the Ouisconsenk (Wisconsin River) retains a variant of its Indian name; and Lake Michigan is labeled with the phrase "Mitchiganong Ou le Grand Lac des Illinois dit Dauphin." The first published map that describes the Joliet–Marquette discoveries is the 1681 "Carte de la decouverte faite l'an 1673 dans l'Amerique Septentrionale" by Melchisédech Thévenot, which was included in *Recueil de Voyages de Mr Thevenot* (Paris, 1681). This is also the first published map to apply the name Michigan to one of the Great Lakes.

Exploration of the great Mississippi was completed by René Robert Cavelier, sieur de La Salle, who in 1682, in the name of the king of France, took possession of the river and all the rivers entering it and the region watered by them. At the end of the 1670s La Salle procured a seigneury on the shore of Lake Ontario and immediately made plans to journey to the mouth of the Mississippi in order to establish a commercial empire in the middle of the continent. In 1678 he and the Flemish Recollect friar Louis Hennepin proceeded west to prepare for their trip down the Mississippi. They traveled independently but at roughly the same time, planning to compare notes from their separate voyages and thereby gain more intelligible and precise information. Early in his journey Hennepin passed Niagara Falls and thus became the first European to describe the natural wonder; by 1679 La Salle had paddled by canoe past the site of the present Notre Dame campus at South Bend, Indiana. The two explorers built forts at St. Joseph, Michigan, and along the Illinois River. During the same year another French explorer, Daniel Greysolon Du l'Hut, pacified Indians at the place that now carries the corruption of his name, Duluth. In 1680 Hennepin was dispatched by La Salle to explore the upper Mississippi River and in so doing he discovered Sault de St. Antoine de Padoü (Falls of St. Anthony), on the site of present Minneapolis. He later maintained that during the year 1680 he followed the Mississippi south to the Gulf of Mexico, but this claim has been generally rejected by historians.

Two books by Hennepin, which were widely read in France, included two interesting maps. *Description de la Louisiane* (Paris, 1683) contains "Carte de la Nouuelle France et de la Loüisiane Nouuellement découuerte" (*Plate 73*), showing for the first time on a printed map La Louisiane, Sault de St. Antoine de Padoü, and Lac de Pleurs [lake of tears], present Lake Pepin. A faint dotted line indicating the surmised course of the lower Mississippi River is approximately located. Hennepin's second book, *A New Discovery of a Vast Country in America* (London, 1698), relates his alleged discovery of the mouth of the Mississippi and also includes the first textual description as well as the first printed picture of Niagara Falls. It further incorporates the map "Carte d'un tres grand Pais Nouvellement decouvert dans l'Amerique Septentrionale," which places the Mississippi considerably west of its authentic location. The river is named Mechasipi and is described as being full of pillicans [pelicans].

In 1681 La Salle commanded his own expedition that started at Fort St. Joseph and ended in the Gulf of Mexico the following year. The land along the Mississippi, including the surrounding area drained by the rivers, was given the name La Louisiane.

Assassination of La Salle by his men, from Hennepin, 1698

Since La Salle entertained visions of a large personal domain in the New World, he returned to France with his conviction that the French should enter the river from the Gulf of Mexico to confirm the right of possession. In 1685 he sailed from France seeking the mouth of the Mississippi. Unable to establish its identity, he landed in the region of Metagorda Bay, Texas, and began a trek on foot back to Canada. Unfortunately his grand design ended with his murder by his own rebellious men at the River Brazos. The French position in North America at this time was weak, and there were only 10,000 French settlers on the entire continent. In the north Jacques de Noyon canoed to Rainy Lake and Lake of the Woods in 1688; subsequent French efforts at western exploration ceased for many years. Henry Kelsey, an Englishman, established an inland route across the Winnipeg Basin and the Great Plains of Canada in 1692.

A 1688 manuscript map of Jean-Baptiste Louis Franquelin, "Carte de l'Amerique Septentrionale" (*Plate 74*), illustrates the Mississippi Valley in detail. As hydrographer to Louis XIV, Franquelin worked under various governors in Canada. His map reflects La Salle's belief that the Mississippi flowed into the Gulf of Mexico far to the west of its actual location, thus explaining the error of La Salle's disastrous journey of 1685. The map also locates the Missouri River too far west but correctly distinguishes between the Ohio River (shown as Ohoio, ou Belle Riviere) and the Wabash (Riviere Ouabach). Fort Checagou also appears. This early name of the present Illinois city (as Chekagou R. Portage) as well as the Chicago River (Checagou R.) is found on the 1688 globe "America Settentrionale colle Nuoue Scoperte" by Vincenzo Coronelli, cosmographer of the Republic of Venice.

In 1699 Pierre le Moyne, sieur d'Iberville, sailing from France, entered the Mississippi River delta, discovered Lake Maurepas and Lake Pontchartrain, and erected a fort in Biloxi Bay. In the same year, as part of their grand effort to establish control of the Mississippi Valley, the French founded a mission at Cahokia across the river from St. Louis. By 1698 Thomas Welch, a Carolina trader, had opened relations with the Chickasaw Indians in the northern Mississippi Valley. They became allied with the English and thus partially undermined French control. French influence was introduced into an English colony when the Huguenots settled New Rochelle, New York, in 1688. None of these activities was mirrored on maps until well into the eighteenth century.

Spanish activities in the New World during the second half of the seventeenth century were limited. In the 1660s an expedition from Florida crossed into present Georgia. In 1675 Spanish priests carried out the first missionary expedition from Mexico into Texas, and in 1686 the first Spanish chapel was built in that region. For a thirteen-year period between 1680 and 1693, the Spaniards lost control of New Mexico to the Apache and fled from Santa Fe to El Paso. In the Southeast St. Augustine was the point of origin for three dozen satellite missions, including one on Parris Island and one near present Tallahassee, Florida. In its search for La Salle's lost colony a Spanish expedition out of Texas rediscovered Pensacola Bay and erected a settlement in the vicinity.

The expeditions and maps of the Jesuit missionary Eusebio Francisco Kino are a fitting chronological transition from the seventeenth to the eighteenth century. In 1683 Kino drew two maps that have survived: one is of southern Lower California and the other a plan of Fort San Bruno in that region, both maps are in the collection of the Archivo General de Indias in Seville. In 1696 his most artistic and detailed map. "Teatro de los Trabajos Apostolicos de la Camp[añi] a de Iesus en la America Septentrional," now in the Central Jesuits Archives in Rome, was sent to Rome to illustrate a manuscript biography of Father Francisco Saverio Saeta. It shows California as an island. Between 1698 and 1701 Kino's efforts were concentrated on determining whether California was an island or a peninsula, a fact not definitively accepted until the first decade of the eighteenth century (*see Plate 75*).

6. *European Claims in America*

They [American Indians] are as ignorant of *Geography* as of other *Sciences,* and yet they draw the most exact Maps imaginable of the Countries they're acquainted with, for there's nothing wanting in them but the Longitude and Latitude of Places: ...The Ports, Harbours, Rivers, ...&c. counting the Distances by Journeys and Half-Journeys of the Warriers.... These *Chorographical Maps* are drawn upon the Rind of your *Birch* Tree; and when the old Men hold a Council about War or Hunting they never fail to make use of them.

BARON DE LAHONTAN
New Voyages to North-America (1703)

1700-1750

FEW TRULY significant maps of the North American continent were produced during the first half of the eighteenth century. At the beginning of the century the populated area was fairly continuous from York, Maine, to Albemarle Sound, North Carolina; it rarely extended inland more than fifty miles from the coast or from the shores of the large navigable rivers. The 200-mile area between Albemarle Sound and the northern fringe of South Carolina remained under the control of several Indian tribes.

The estimated population of the English colonies in 1700 was 284,000, distributed as follows: Massachusetts Bay, 80,000; Virginia, 55,000; Maryland, 32,000; New York, 30,000; Connecticut, 30,000; Pennsylvania and Delaware, 20,000; South Carolina, 12,000; New Hampshire, 10,000; Rhode Island, 10,000; and North Carolina, 5,000. Outside the mainland, Jamaica had a population of 50,000 and Barbados 71,000, both islands having an overwhelming majority of black slaves. French Canada consisted of a string of farms, or seigneuries, seldom more than one deep, extending from l'Acadie along the St. Lawrence River to Montreal and up the Richelieu River; at the beginning of the eighteenth century this entire region's estimated population was 6,200. In the Southwest the Spanish settlements were insignificant in terms of population, and activities related to expansion were dormant.

In the first year of the century the French geographer Guillaume Delisle, a pioneer in scientific cartography and perhaps the greatest mapmaker of his time, published "L'Amerique Septentrionale," which offered revised and more realistic concepts of both the Mississippi River and the western coast of America than those prevalent in the previous century.

As was noted in the previous chapter, it was not until 1701 that Eusebio Kino gave cartographic expression to a land passage from the Sonora Valley to California. His 1701 manuscript map affirming the peninsularity of California has disappeared, but copies of it made in Spain were sent to Jesuits in Paris, and his discovery was finally published in 1705 when his engraving "Passage par terre A la Californie" (*Plate 75*) appeared in print twice, first in the popular mission magazine *Lettres Edifiantes* and then in the Jesuits' scientific journal *Mémoires de Trévoux*. Although some cartographers continued to show an insular California until 1747, when King Ferdinand VII issued a royal decree that California should no longer be considered an island, most followed the lead of Guillaume Delisle, who showed California as a peninsula. In the last quarter of the century, in 1779, Didier Robert de Vaugondy published "Carte de la Californie" (*Plate 76*), a pictorial summary of the history of the mapping of California, taking it from its original peninsula presentation, through the island phase, then to Kino's rediscovery, and finally showing the permanently reestablished peninsularity.

As Kino explored the interior in the continent's southwestern portion, the interior of the Northeast was also being surveyed. In 1700 Colonel Wolfgang Römer conducted a gross survey of lands between Albany and the Genesee River in upstate New York, including the Finger Lakes region. He drew a manuscript map (*Plate 77*) chronicling his journey among the Iroquois, or Five Nations. In 1701 the Board of Trade in England recommended that the crown resume control of the private colonies; in the same year Delaware was granted authority for a separate government, and its first assembly met in New Castle in 1704.

The first general map of New England published in the eighteenth century, "An Exact Mapp of New England and New York," appeared early in the century in Cotton Mather's *Magnalia Christi Americana: or the Ecclesiastical History of New England from Its First Planting* (London, 1702). Although it added little

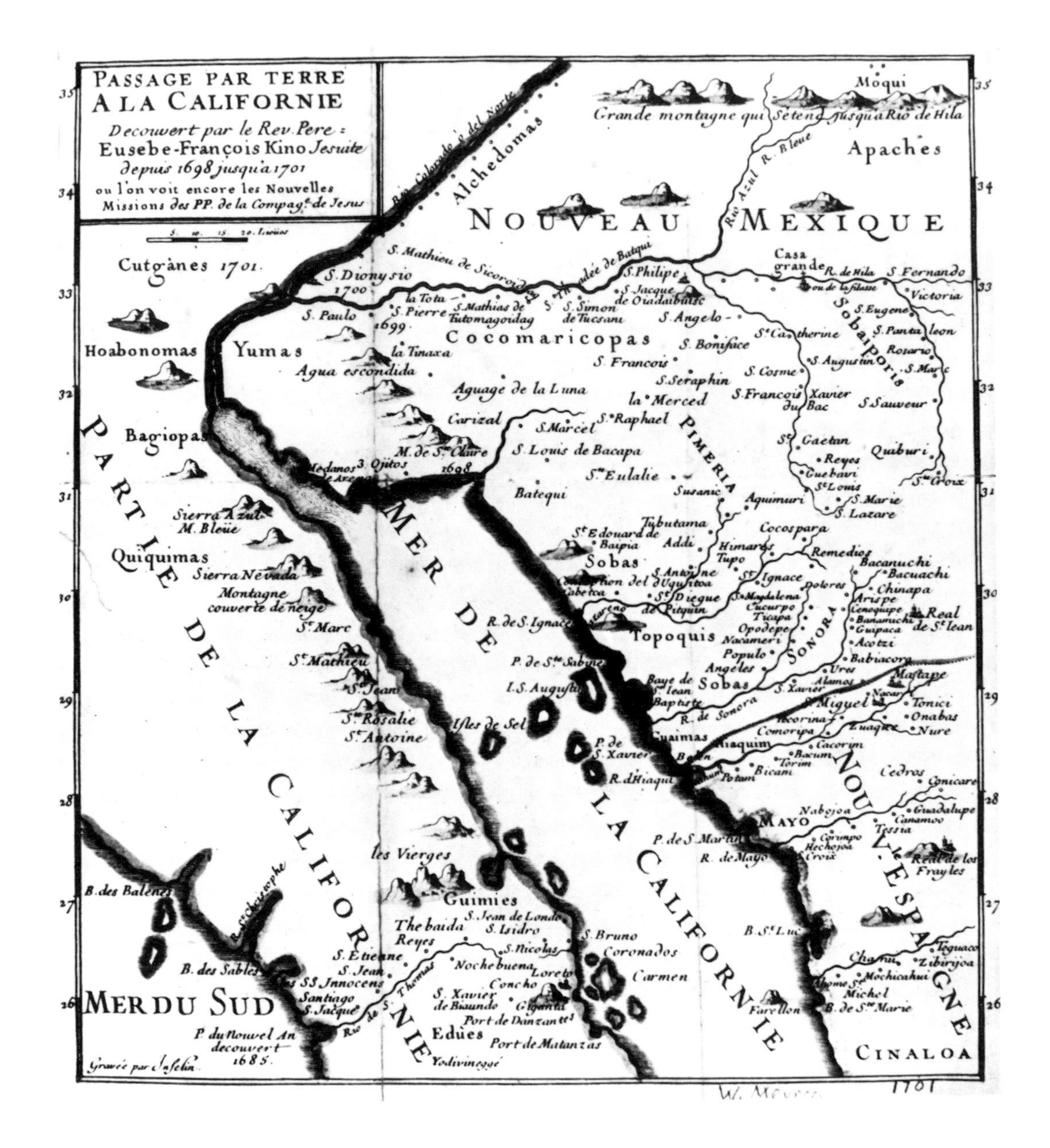

PLATE 75: Eusebio Kino. "Passage par terre A la Californie." 1705. Engraving, hand colored; 24 × 21 cm. Map Division, New York Public Library; Astor, Lenox and Tilden Foundations. *The first engraving of Kino's lost 1701 manuscript map was published in Paris in 1705, once in the popular mission magazine* Lettres Edifiantes *and once in the Jesuits' scientific journal* Mémoires de Trévoux. *First map disproving the California-as-island concept, which originated in 1622.*

new geographic information, the map focused on the region later affected by the Queen Anne's War, the first of four eighteenth-century wars involving North America. This war, known in Europe as the War of the Spanish Succession, lasted from 1702 to 1713. In its American counterpart there were Indian raids on Maine settlements and the destruction of Deerfield, Massachusetts. French and Indians demolished the settlement at Bona Vista, Newfoundland, and in 1708 captured St. John's. At the conclusion of the war the Treaty of Utrecht ceded Newfoundland, Acadia, and Hudson Bay to England; France retained Cape Breton Island and the small islands in St. Lawrence Bay. The treaty's failure to define precise boundaries in the region surrounding the bay led to later conflicts as did the vague definition of the frontier between Carolina and Florida.

The status of the English colonies and England's claims at the end of the war are shown on Herman Moll's 1715 engraving "A New and Exact Map of the Dominions of the King of Great Britain on ye Continent of North America" (*Plate 78*), which is famous for the so-called Beaver Inset, a picture of the cataract of Niagara. This map and Moll's 1720 map of North America (*Plate 79*) were published as pictorial counterclaims to offset earlier maps by Delisle (*see Plates 80, 82*), particularly Delisle's descriptions of the land west of the Appalachian Mountains. Moll's map also proffers one of the earliest references to postal routes in North America and includes, as an inset, an important map of Carolina.

In the area of Carolina, John Lawson, an Englishman appointed by the lords proprietors to make a reconnaissance survey inland in the Carolinas, left Charles Town in December 1700 on a trip down the Pamlico River and early in 1701 built a house near the future site of New Bern. In 1708 Lawson arranged for the sale of land from the lords proprietors to the organizers of a Swiss and Palatine colony, leading to the permanent settlement of New Bern. The expansionist effort of the colonists from Carolina, based at Charles Town and extending south to the Everglades and west to the Mississippi, was first depicted on Thomas Nairne's inset map, "A Map of South Carolina," which appeared on Edward Crisp's 1711 "A Compleat Description of the Province of Carolina in 3 Parts," an engraving published in London. Nairne's map showing routes used by Charles Town frontiersmen who traded with Indians west as far as the Mississippi, locates specific Indian settlements. It also reflects the English colonists' need for cartographic evidence of territorial claims. The Crisp map names the plantations along the Ashley and Cooper rivers and their tributaries. To establish these claims further the Nairne and Crisp drawings were included on Moll's 1720 engraved map of North America.

French expansion at the beginning of the eighteenth century placed major emphasis on securing the Grand Water route, which comprised the St. Lawrence River, the Great Lakes, and the Mississippi River down to its exit in the Gulf of Mexico. In 1700 the frontier fort protecting the Straits of Mackinac was reinforced and the following year Antoine de la Mothe Cadillac established a fort at Detroit, since this area was recognized as a strategic key to the upper three Great Lakes and would offer a better position against the English than would the fort at Mackinac. A fort was built in 1703 at Cahokia near present East St. Louis, where a Sulpician mission had been located in 1699, and another the same year at Kaskaskia in Illinois territory.

In 1703 Guillaume Delisle published two very important maps. The first of these, "Carte du Canada ou de la Nouvelle France"

Encouragement given for People to remove and ſettle in the Province of New-York *in* America.

THe Honourable *George Clarke*, Eſq. Lieut. Governour and Commander in chief of the Province of *New-York*, Hath upon the Petition of Mr *Lauchline Campbell* from *Iſla, North-Britain*, promiſed to grant him Thirty thouſand Acres of Land at the *Wood-Creek*, free of all Charges excepting the Survey and the King's Quit-Rent, which is about one Shilling and Nine Pence Farthing *Sterling* for each hundred Acres. *And alſo*, To grant to thirty Families already landed here Lands in proportion to each Family, from five hundred Acres unto one Hundred and Fifty only paying the Survey and the King's Quit-Rent. And all *Proteſtants* that incline to come and ſettle in this Colony may have Lands granted them from the Crown for three Pounds *Sterling* per hundred Acres and paying the yearly Quit-Rent.

Dated in New-York *this 4th Day of December,* 1738.

GEORGE CLARKE.

Printed by *William Bradford*, Printer to the King's moſt Excellent Majeſty for the Province of *New-York*, 1738.

Broadside, 1738, encouraging settlement in New York Province

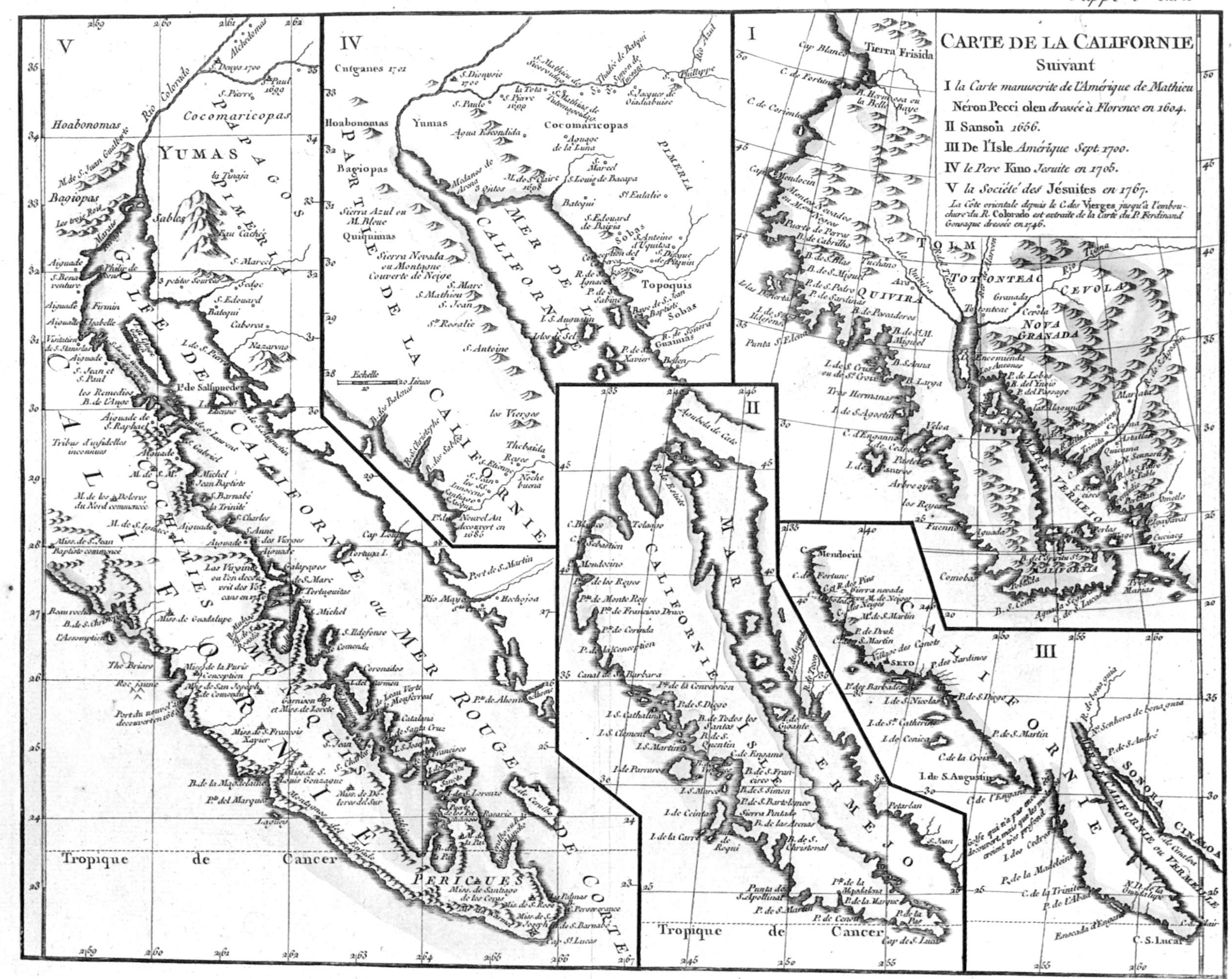

PLATE 76: Didier Robert de Vaugondy. "Carte de la Californie." 1779. Engraving, hand colored; 29 × 38 cm. Private collection. *Represents various stages in mapping of California: I. Italian map, by Mathieu Nérön Pecci in 1604, depicting Sebastián Vizcaíno's expedition (showing California as a peninsula); II. 1656 Nicolas Sanson map showing island concept; III. Guillaume Delisle's map of 1700, where island concept is not ruled out; IV. Eusebio Kino's engraved map of 1705; V. Later Jesuit map of 1767. Published in Vaugondy's* Recueil de 10 Cartes Traitant Particulièrement de l'Amérique du Nord *(Leghorn, 1779).*

(*Plate 80*), shows the French efforts at fortification and is the first printed map to locate Detroit, only two years after the founding of that village. This description of Canada and the Great Lakes region, which influenced later maps of the area, realistically situates the Ohio River but confuses its name with the Wabash River. *Nouveaux Voyages de M. le Baron de Lahontan dans l'Amérique Septentrionale* (The Hague, 1703) by Louis-Armand de Lom d'Arce, baron de Lahontan, which in the same year in London was expanded in translation under the title *New Voyages to North America*, reported what Lahontan surmised to be a waterway beginning in the distant western mountains and entering the Mississippi River from the west. His engraving "A Map of ye Long River" (*Plate 81*) depicts this waterway (Morte or River Longue) as flowing into a great salt lake. Delisle's 1703 "Carte du Canada ou de la Nouvelle France" utilizes this concept as Rivière Longue.

Delisle's second 1703 map, "Carte du Mexique et de la Floride" (*Plate 82*), is the earliest printed map to show an accurate definition of the lower Mississippi River and its delta. It includes the 1702 relocation of the French garrison Fort Maurepas (built in 1699 on Biloxi Bay) to Fort Louis on Mobile Bay. This move resulted from threats presented by the Carolinians as well as the

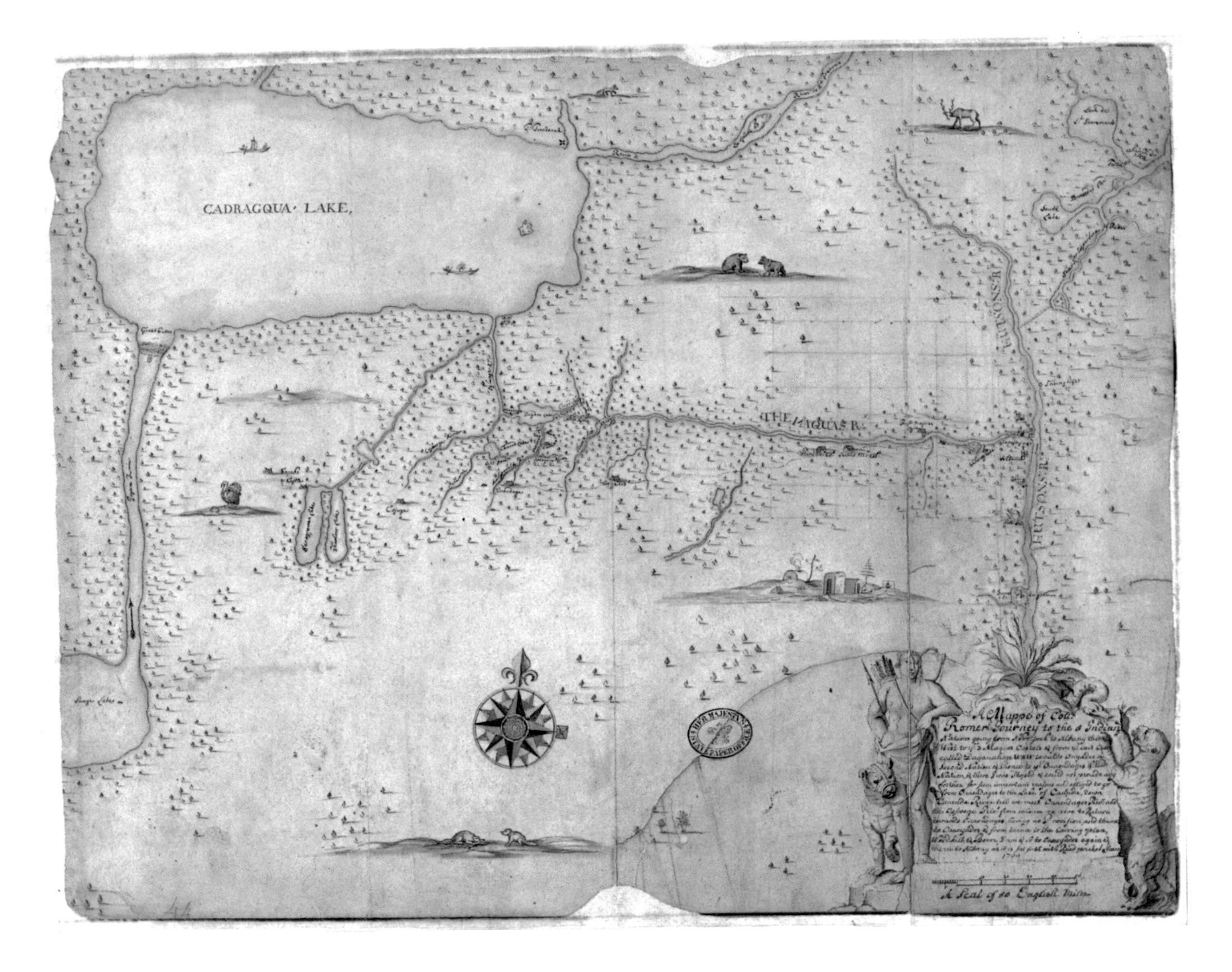

PLATE 77: Wolfgang Römer. "A Mappe of Coll. Romer his Journey to the 5 Indian Nations going from New Yorck to Albany." 1700. Manuscript, pen and ink and watercolor; 43 × 57 cm. Map Department, Public Record Office, London. *Maquas River (Mohawk River) is shown in its full length. Greatest detail is around Onydea Lake (Oneida). Two of the Finger Lakes are shown and these connect via a waterway to Cadragqua Lake (Lake Ontario). Falls are shown on Iagera Rivier (Niagara), which connects Lake Ontario and Large Lake (Lake Erie).*

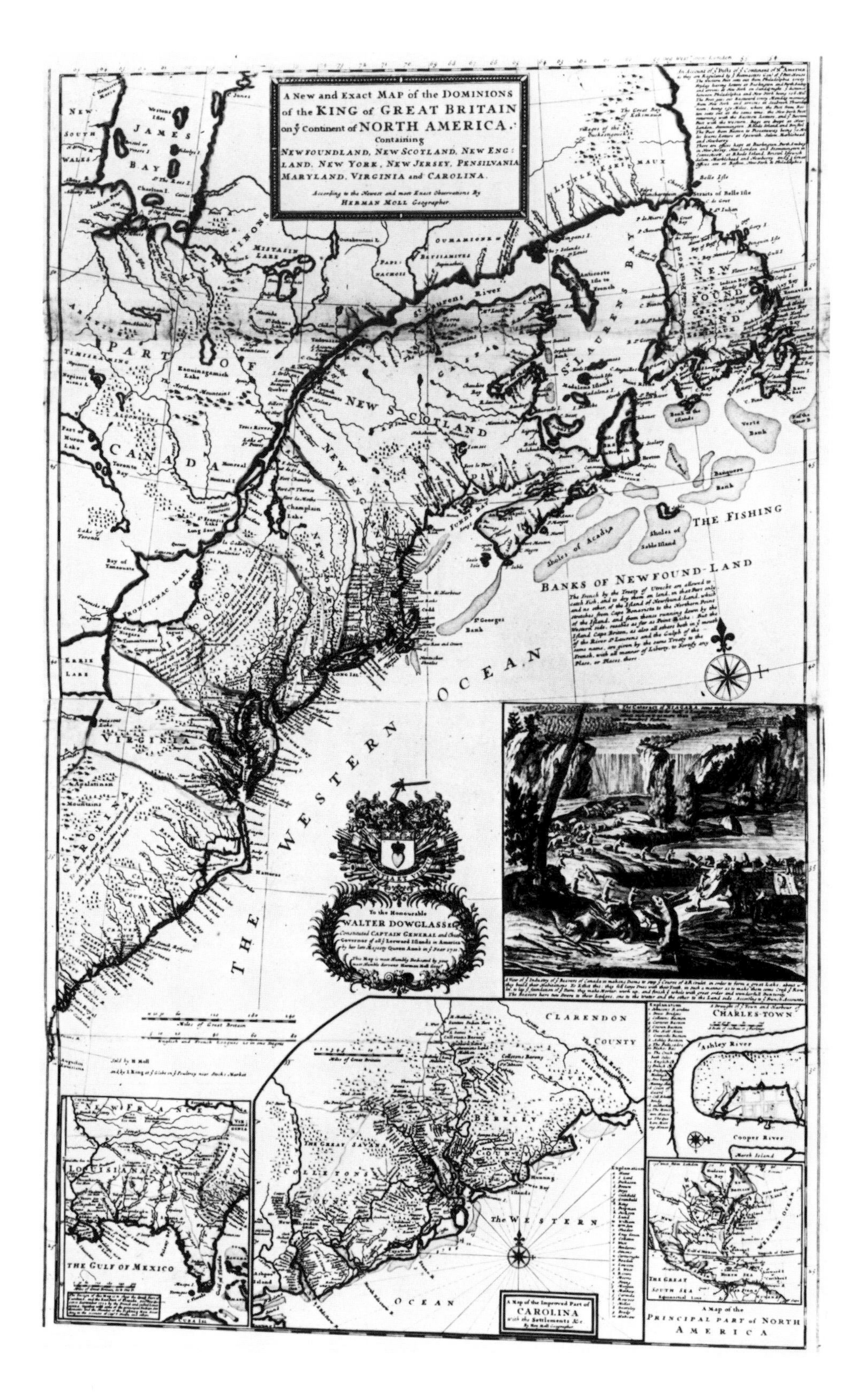

PLATE 78: Herman Moll. "A New and Exact Map of the Dominions of the King of Great Britain on ye Continent of North America." 1715. Engraving, hand colored (3rd state, c. 1726); 101 × 62 cm. Private collection. *Insets (counterclockwise from left): Thomas Nairne's map of South Carolina and English, French, and Indian settlements; part of Carolina; principal part of North America; Charles-Town harbor; view of Niagara Falls, known as the Beaver Inset. Published in Moll's* The World Described *(London, 1708–20).*

Indian warrior carrying scalps of three Natchez men, watercolor by Alexandre de Batz, c. 1732

Spaniards in Pensacola. In 1704 the French erected Fort Miami to safeguard the route to the Mississippi River by way of the Maumee and the Wabash rivers.

In 1713 European population in the continental colonies was approximately 360,000. By 1755 the number would quadruple to approximately 1.5 million, due in part to the migration of non-English people to the New World, facilitated by liberalized naturalization acts of the 1740 Parliament. A large number of townships had been founded by 1713 in New England by entrepreneurs as a speculation, hoping to attract settlers to the area. In the middle and southern colonies land was sold outright by assemblies, proprietors, or speculators rather than granted by the headright system that had been instituted in Virginia and Maryland. Owing to William Penn's connections in Germany with nontolerated Protestant sects, Philadelphia had become the principal port of entry for foreigners who settled in Lancaster County. Also by 1713 Scotch-Irish from Ulster followed and settled the frontier from Maine to the area of present Georgia. At about that time Norfolk was developed as an outlet for lumber from North Carolina. By 1715 the frontier had moved as far west as the Wabash and Miami rivers. In 1716, at the insistence of Governor Alexander Spotswood of Virginia, settlement of the southern Piedmont began. Thomas Fairfax, the sixth Baron Fairfax, proprietor of the Northern Neck of Virginia, sold land he had inherited from the second Baron Culpeper to immigrants from Pennsylvania, and these settlers populated the Shenandoah Valley and the Piedmont region of Virginia and the Carolinas.

Much of this territorial advance is shown on Cyprian Southack's 1717 "A New Chart of North America" (*Plate 83*), the first known general map published in America of the eastern part of the present United States. The only extant copy of this relatively crude document is reposited in the John Carter Brown Library at Brown University. It shows the Atlantic coast from Newfoundland to Florida and includes the interior west to the Mississippi River. The map was drawn up to voice French political designs on the transallegheny west, the area between the Allegheny Mountains and the Mississippi River.

In 1717 there were only twenty-seven French families in present Louisiana, but the following year Jean Baptiste le Moyne, sieur de Bienville, founded New Orleans in order to control traffic on the Mississippi. The French erected Fort Toulouse on the eastern shore of the river and pushed on into the Alabama area in order to counter incursions made by British traders from the southeastern colonies. Other French explorations were carried out to buffer Spanish progress. Jean Baptiste Bénard de La Harpe, a French explorer, built a fort at Natchitoches on the Red River and from there conducted several inland expeditions up that river and the Osage River and into present Oklahoma. Between 1712 and 1718 Étienne Venyard, sieur de Bourgmont, the region's foremost contemporary explorer, investigated the Missouri River north as far as the mouth of the Nebraska River and lived in this area with a Missouri Indian tribe. He eventually returned to France but was ordered back to serve as military commander of

PLATE 79: Herman Moll. "Map of North America According to ye Newest and most Exact observations." 1720. Engraving, hand colored; 57 × 97 cm. Private collection. *Attacks Guillaume Delisle's expression of French claims (see Plate 80). A late map to show California as an island. Large vignette shows codfish processing at Newfoundland. Indians and Eskimos displayed on cartouche. Insets of Boston, New York, Charlestown, Port Royal, St. Johns, and New Albion according to Sir Francis Drake.*

the area surrounding the Missouri River. In 1723 he supervised construction of the post called Fort Orléans on the Missouri just above Grand River.

In 1718 Guillaume Delisle's most influential map, "Carte de la Louisiane et du Cours du Mississipi" (*Plate 84*), brought the Mississippi Valley and delta area into focus. This chauvinistic pictorial argument supporting French authority showed the British colonies surrounding the French possessions in the West, and it claimed the Carolinas for France. Its designation as a mother map is owed mainly to its detailing of the lower Mississippi River and the region adjacent to the Gulf of Mexico. It is also the first printed map to trace Hernando de Soto's sixteenth-century travels and to include, in the phrase "Mission de los Teijas etablie en 1716," a variant of the name Texas. This map was copied by many cartographers and obviously plagiarized by John Senex as "A Map of Louisiana and of the River Mississipi" in Senex's *A New General Atlas*, published in London in 1721. Others credited Delisle, but Senex did not acknowledge his source. In 1719

PLATE 80: Guillaume Delisle. "Carte du Canada ou de la Nouvelle France." 1703. Engraving, hand colored; 50 × 65 cm. Private collection. *Locates and names Detroit for first time on printed map, two years after its founding. West of Mississippi it incorporates Baron de Lahontan's imaginary geography (see Plate 81). Lac de Assenipoils (Lake Winnipeg) connects to Hudson Bay.*

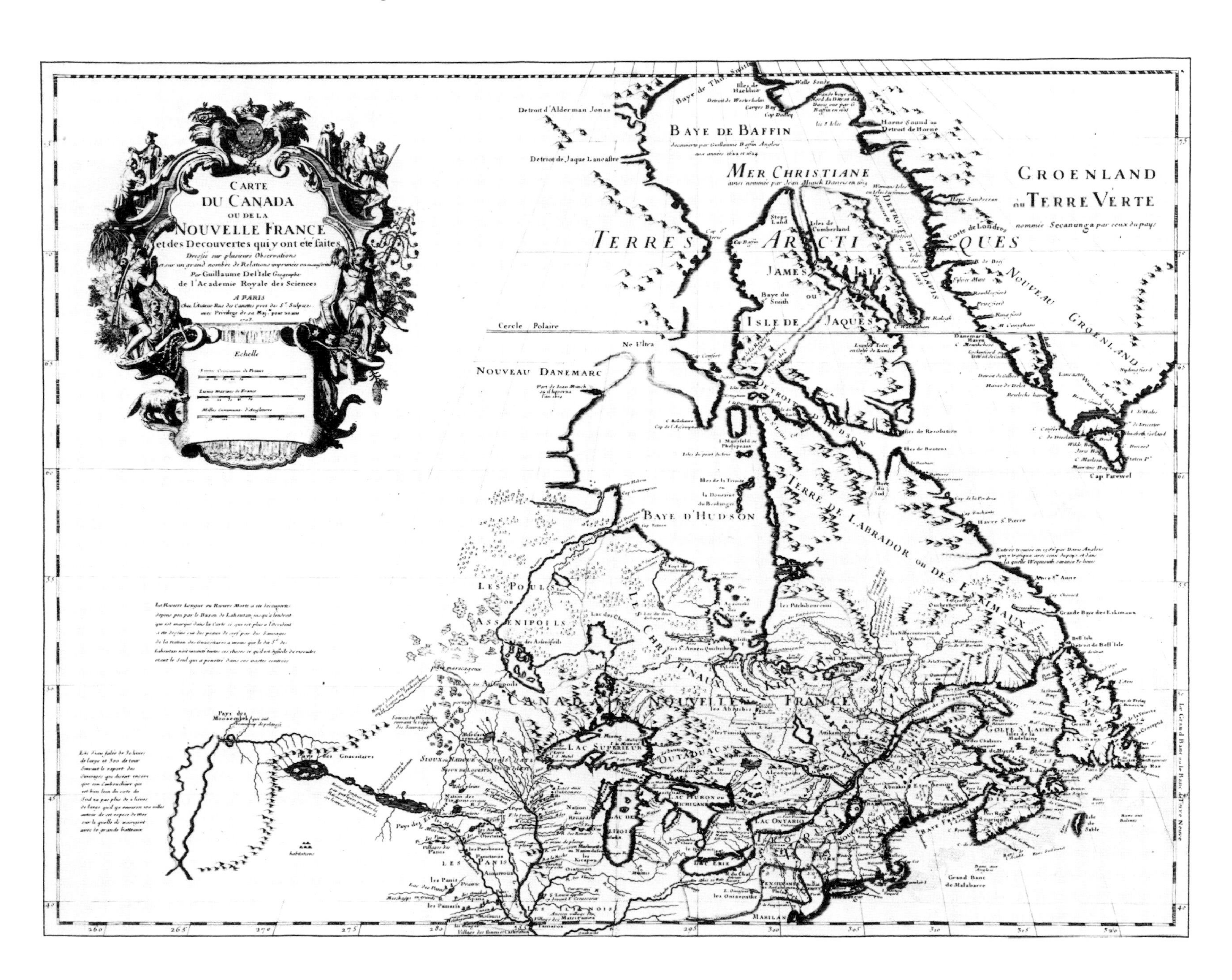

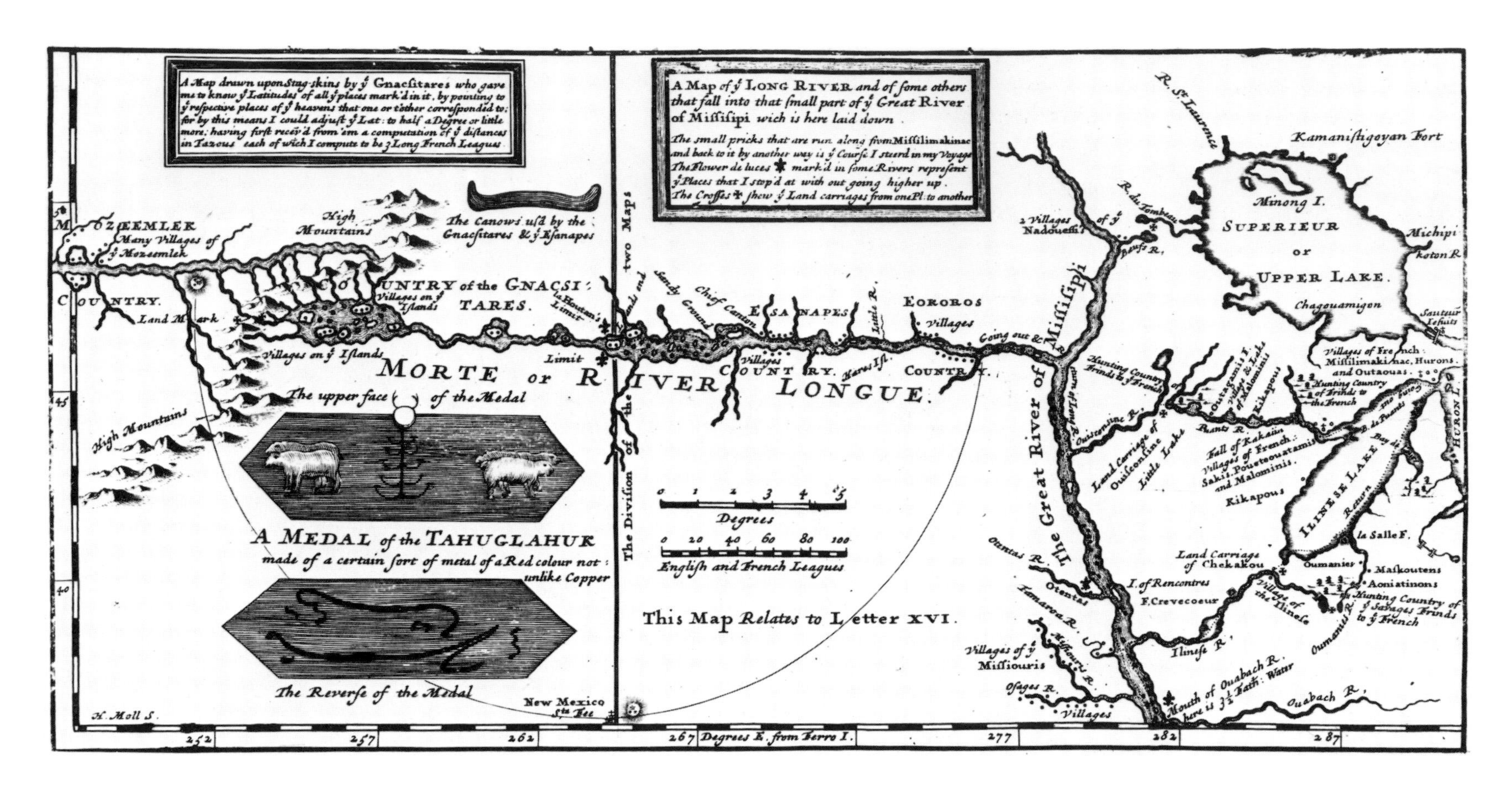

another famous French map, Henri Abraham Chatelain's "Carte Tres Curieuse de la Mer du Sud" (*Plate 85*), was published; it is one of the most elaborately engraved maps of the Western Hemisphere ever produced, yet California still appears as an island.

The British were disturbed by the French claims made explicit on Delisle's 1718 map (*see Plate 84*) and immediately proclaimed their own cartographic counterevidence, citing the 1715 Herman Moll map of North America (*see Plate 78*). In another attempt to counter French claims Tuscarora Jack Barnwell, trader, Indian fighter, and antiproprietary leader, in 1723 displayed to the overseers of the American colonies, the Lords of Trade and Plantations, his manuscript, regarded as one of the most important maps of the southeastern colonies, locating Indian settlements, trading posts, forts, and river systems.

Significant changes of governance and settlement occurred in the Southeast during the first half of the eighteenth century.

PLATE 81: Baron de Lahontan (Louis-Armand de Lom d'Arce). "A Map of ye Long River." 1703. Engraving, 14 × 34 cm. Newberry Library, Chicago. *Shows legendary River Longue flowing into Mississippi River from the west, with a western extension of River Longue flowing into a large salt lake. Published in Lahontan's* Nouveaux Voyages de M. le Baron de Lahontan dans l'Amérique Septentrionale *(The Hague, 1703).*

(opposite) PLATE 82: Guillaume Delisle. "Carte du Mexique et de la Floride." 1703. Engraving, hand colored; 48 × 65 cm. Private collection. *Mouth of Mississippi and its delta accurately shown on a printed map for the first time. Map influenced delineation of the Mississippi Valley for many years. John Lederer's names for Indian villages are noted. Missouri River is so named with added phrase "ou R. de Pekistanoui" (derived from early Jesuit maps).*

During the first decade the lord proprietors were losing control in North Carolina, causing Britain's dissatisfaction with the work of the proprietors. Attempting to settle a boundary dispute between North Carolina and Virginia, Colonel William Byrd, one of the wealthiest gentlemen in Virginia, in 1728 described the geography of the Dismal Swamp area in a manuscript diary—part of the so-called *Secret Diaries of William Byrd*—now in the possession of the American Philosophical Society in Philadelphia. In 1729 North Carolina was declared a royal colony when the earlier government under the proprietors proved unsatisfactory. More immigrants were attracted to the valleys of Virginia by offers of cheap land, and Winchester was founded in 1732 as a result. Richmond was projected as a town in 1733 by Colonel Byrd and under his patronage it was laid out in 1737. To the

Beaver Inset from 1715 Moll map (see Plate 78)

north Baltimore was established in 1729 and eventually became the principal port for export of Maryland and Pennsylvania wheat. As trade widened, hydrographic surveys became increasingly important, and the 1738 "Chart of His Majesties Province of North Carolina" by James Wimble is a prime example of such headway. It remained the best coastal chart of that area for the remainder of the eighteenth century.

By the 1730s, when the Spanish forts in western Florida and in Louisiana were well established, England acknowledged its error in having only passively supported settlers in the South Carolina region during the Queen Anne's War. England's desire to recover its superiority was dramatically heightened by the massacre in 1730 of 700 Carolinians by the regional Indians. The aftermath was the promulgation of a new colony to be situated between South Carolina and Florida. A royal charter for Georgia was issued to include land south of the Savannah River and north of the Altamaha River, an area originally part of South Carolina. Colonization here was stimulated initially by General James Edward Oglethorpe's philanthropic desire to offer the chance for a new start to debtors sentenced to life in English prisons; Parliament's interest in colonial expansion was another motivating factor. An international quality pervaded the region when Germans from Salzburg settled in 1733–34 up the Savannah River near Ebenezer and members of a Scotch Highland clan founded Fred-

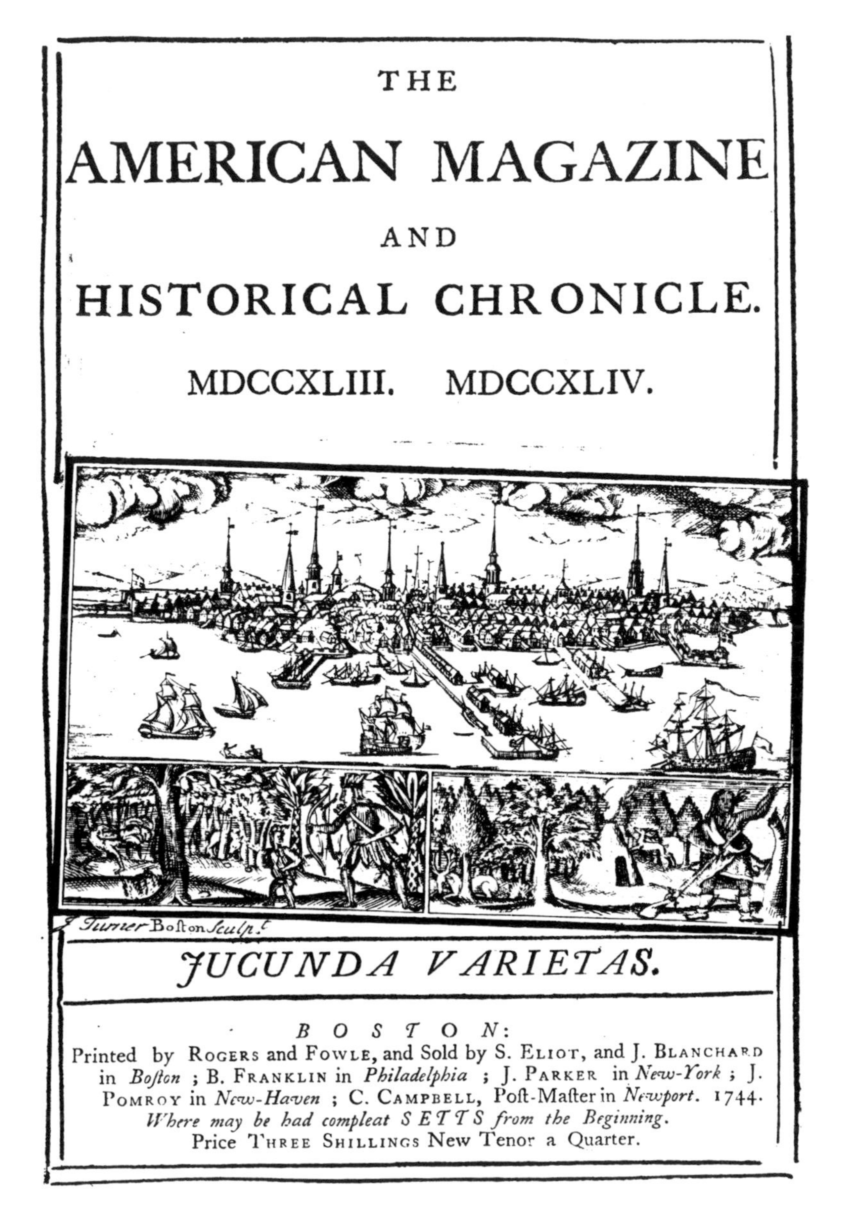

THE

AMERICAN MAGAZINE

AND

HISTORICAL CHRONICLE.

MDCCXLIII. MDCCXLIV.

Turner Boston Sculpt.

JUCUNDA VARIETAS.

BOSTON:

Printed by ROGERS and FOWLE, and Sold by S. ELIOT, and J. BLANCHARD in *Boston*; B. FRANKLIN in *Philadelphia*; J. PARKER in *New-York*; J. POMROY in *New-Haven*; C. CAMPBELL, Post-Master in *Newport*. 1744.
Where may be had compleat SETTS from the Beginning.
Price THREE SHILLINGS New Tenor a Quarter.

Boston in 1744, a hundred years after its founding

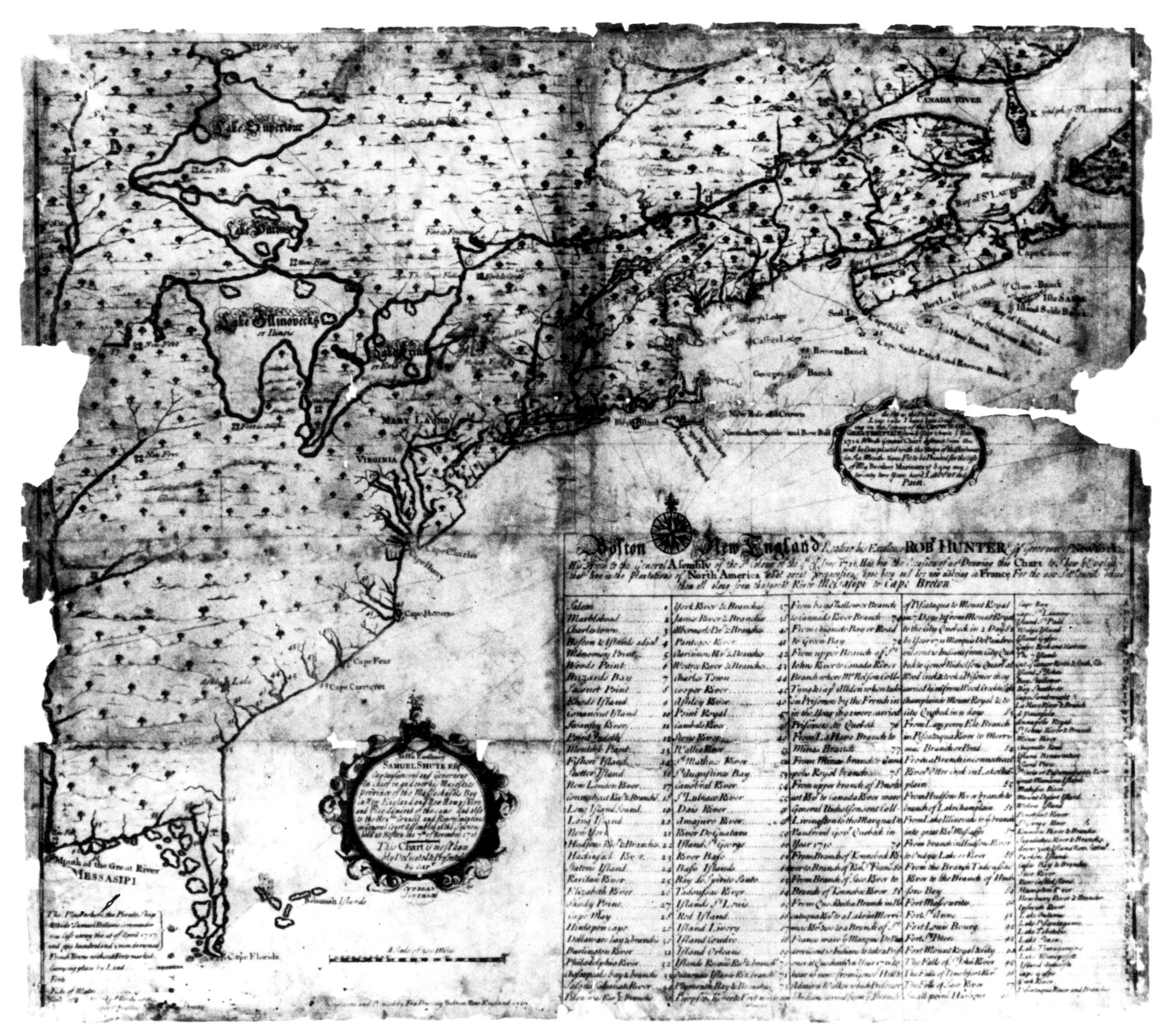

PLATE 83: Cyprian Southack. "A New Chart of North America." 1717. Engraving, 69 × 78 cm. John Carter Brown Library, Brown University, Providence. *First map published in America displaying the majority of North America. The oldest copper engraving, still extant, which was published in America. Shows full length of Atlantic seaboard. Great Lakes have a peculiar location, size, and shape. Drawn to expose French political designs on the territory in the western portion of the continent. Published in Boston.*

PLATE 84: Guillaume Delisle. "Carte de la Louisiane et du Cours du Mississipi." 1718. Engraving, hand colored; 50 × 65 cm. Private collection. *Generally regarded as main source of all later maps of the Mississippi. First large-scale map accurately showing lower Mississippi River and surrounding areas (inset on map: "Carte Particuliere des Embouchures de la Rivie S. Louis et de la Mobile"). Also first to reflect accurately the expeditions of Hernando de Soto, Henri de Tonty, and Louis de St. Denis. The first map with the name Texas (in phrase "Mission de los Teijas etablie en 1716"). New Orleans is not on map.*

(opposite) PLATE 85: Henri Abraham Chatelain. "Carte Tres Curieuse de la Mer du Sud." 1719. Engraving, 81 × 140 cm. Private collection. *One of most elaborately engraved maps ever published that includes North America. Large vignette of Niagara Falls; others show hunting and drying of cod. Many historical notes and explorer's tracks. California depicted as an island. Published in Chatelain's* Atlas Historique *(7 vols., Amsterdam, 1705–20).*

erica on the Altamaha River. Oglethorpe set up Savannah in 1733, and the town of Augusta evolved as a trading post at the head of the navigable Savannah River in 1735. All these placenames are important in dating maps of the region.

As towns and cities developed along the continent's eastern portion, the larger cities were mapped in detail. In 1722 John Bonner produced the earliest and most important engraved plan of Boston (*Plate 86*). The merit of this work is demonstrated by its republication at least nine times during the remainder of the century. The only known extant copy of its first state is in the Stokes Collection in the New York Public Library. Only two copies of James Lyne's 1731 "A Plan of the City of New York from an actual Survey" (*Plate 87*) have survived. It is believed to be the first detailed map of New York City published in the city itself. It identifies the New York wards as they were laid out by Governor John Montgomery's charter of 1730–31.

The map generally reputed as the first published in New York, Cadwallader Colden's "A Map of the Countrey of the Five Nations belonging to the province of New York" (*Plate 88*), is assigned a date of 1724. It crudely illustrates an area east of Lakes Michigan and Superior extending to Lake Champlain and the Hudson River, and concentrates on Iroquois lands in western New York. Its title credits Guillaume Delisle's 1718 map (*see Plate 84*) as its prime source, and the text specifically refers to the movement of the Tuscarora Indians from North Carolina to western Pennsylvania and New York, where they became the

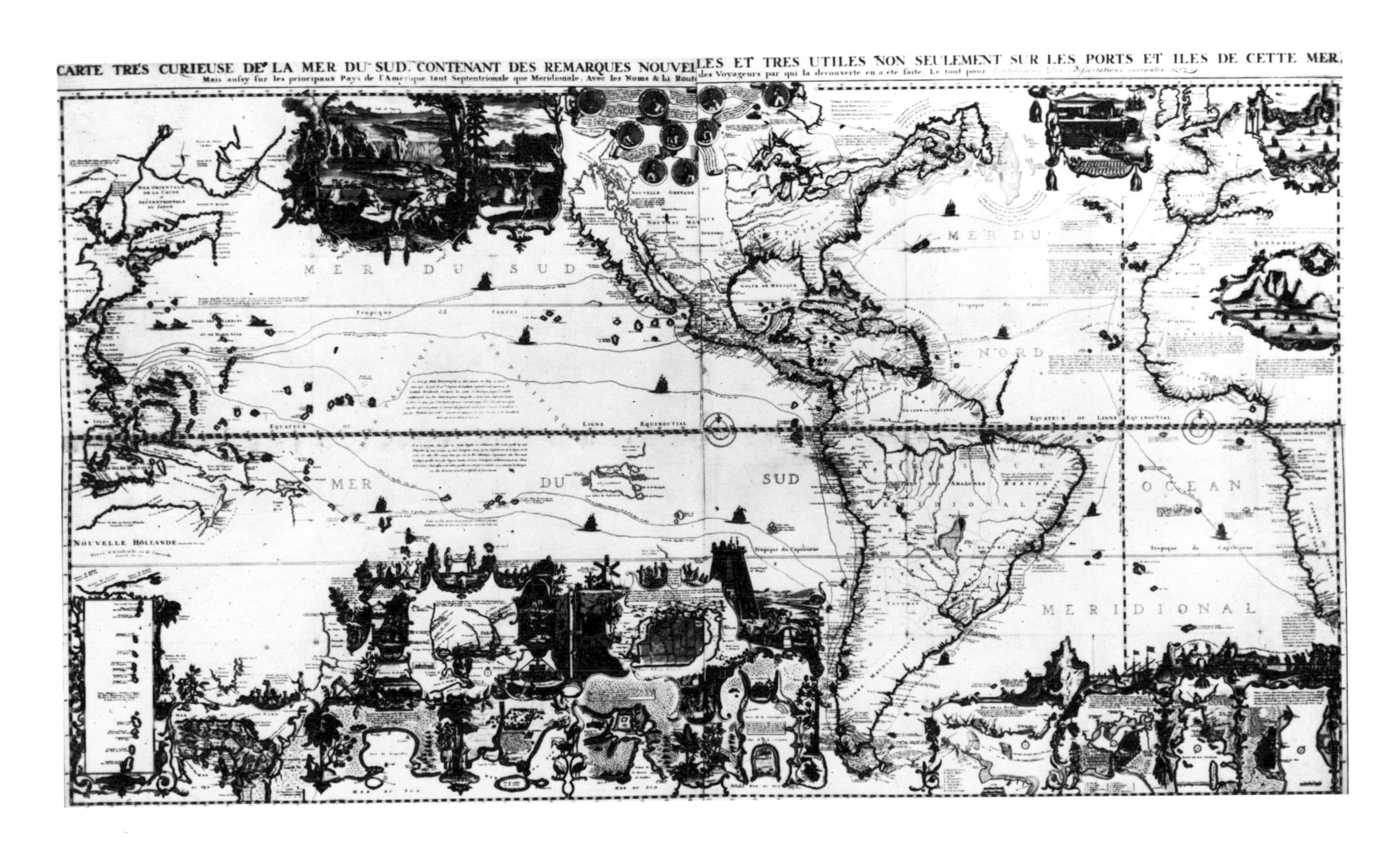

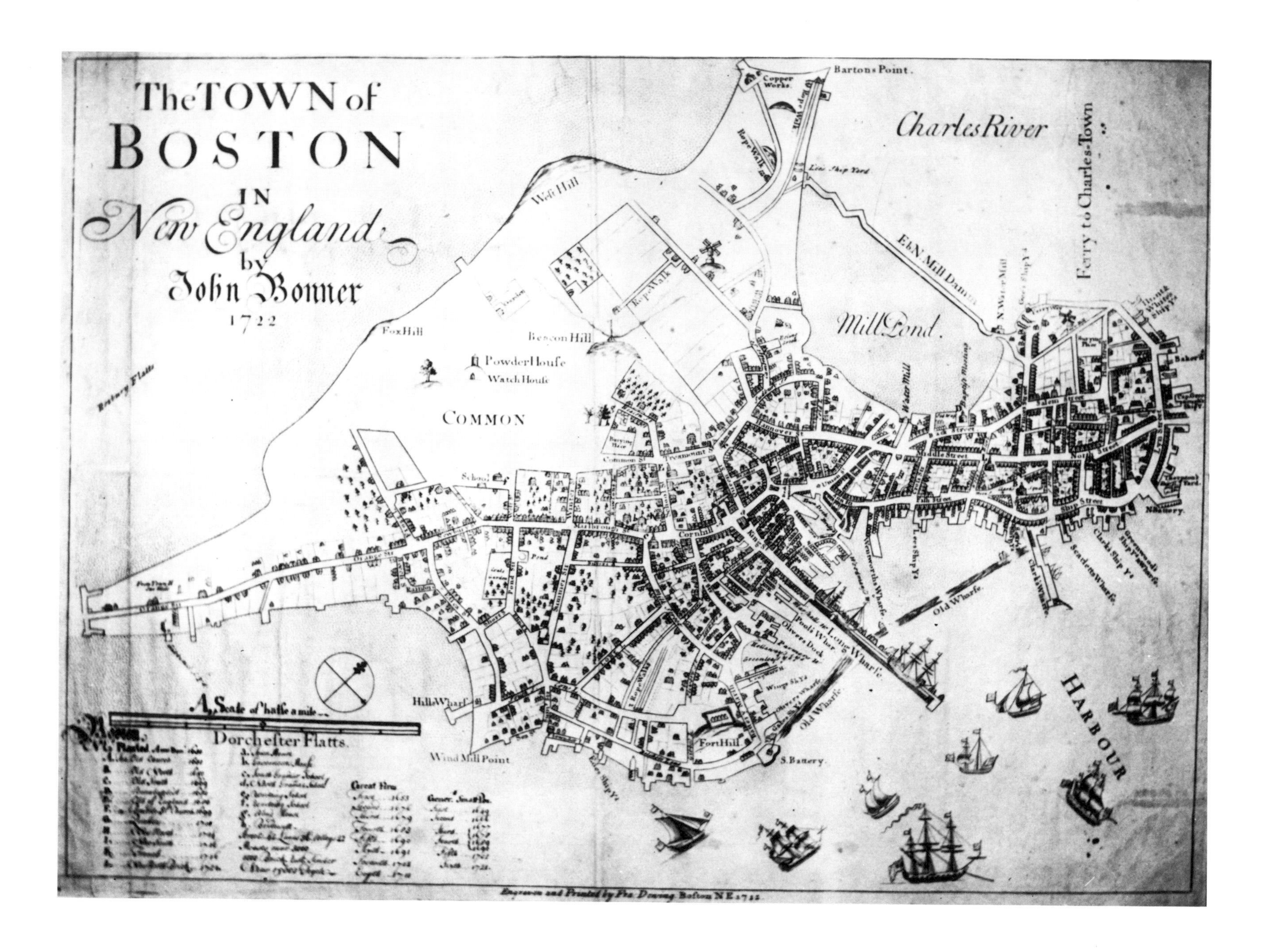

sixth nation in the Iroquois Confederacy. In its time the map was of great strategic importance in locating waterways and points of portage.

While the Colden map was important for illustrating inland streams, another map emphasized coastal sailing. "The New England Coasting Pilot from Sandy Point of New York, unto Cape Canso in Nova Scotia, And Part of Island Breton" (*Plate 89*) is a very large map, and it contains over 100 descriptive notes concerning the places named on the map. It is actually eight maps, which when joined form a single large sheet. The information was gathered by its author, Cyprian Southack, while he was in successive command of several ships from 1680 to 1723. Cartographic authorities generally believe the map was published in London between 1718 and 1734; yet Clara Egli LeGear of the (opposite) PLATE 86: John Bonner. "The Town of Boston in New England." 1722. Engraving, 43 × 59 cm. Prints Division, New York Public Library; Astor, Lenox and Tilden Foundations. I. N. Phelps Stokes Collection. *Earliest engraved plan of Boston, frequently republished in the eighteenth century. Addition of dates and new streets and buildings gives clues for determining states of various reissues.*

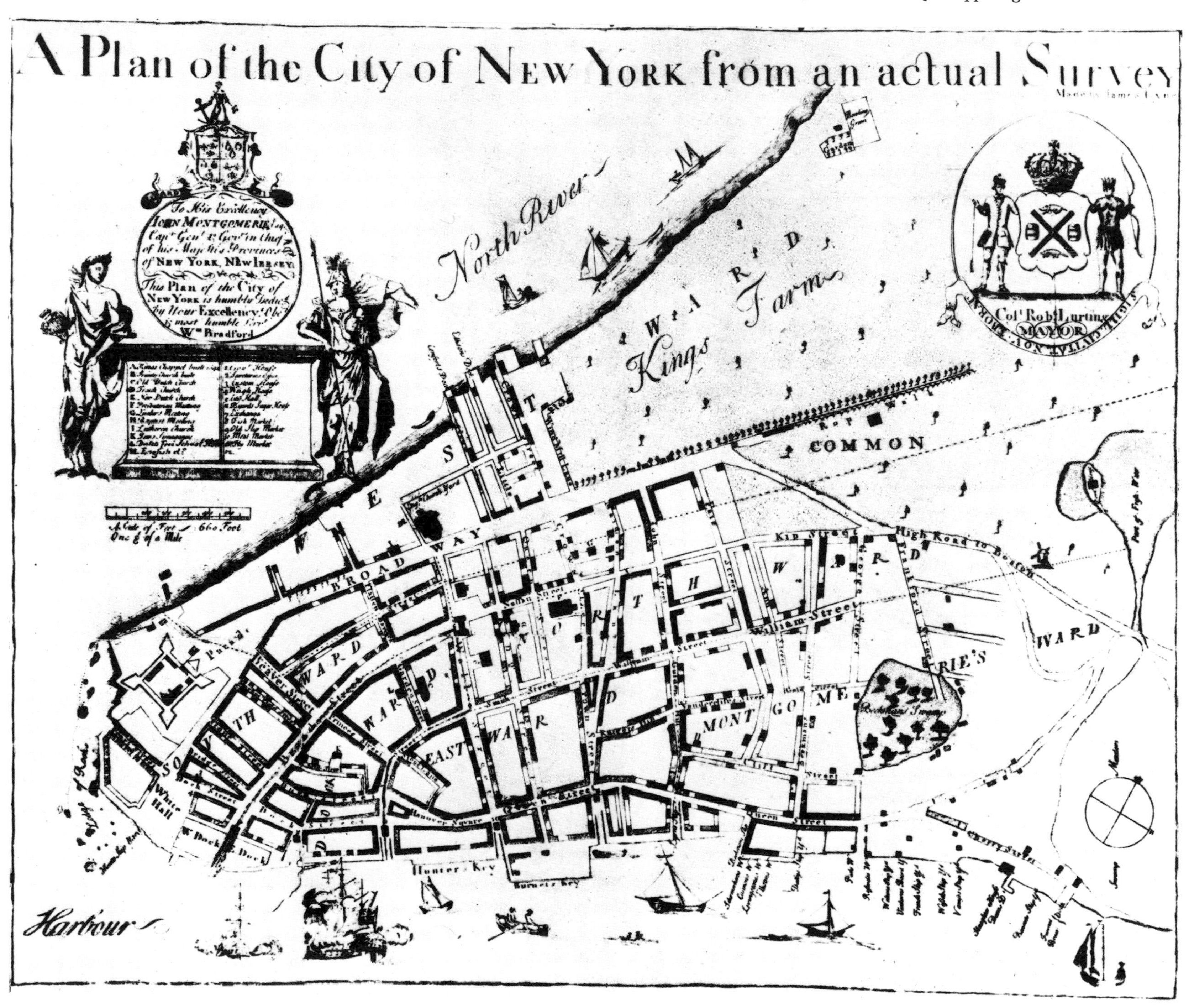

PLATE 87: James Lyne. "A Plan of the City of New York from an actual Survey." 1731. Engraving, 45 × 57 cm. Rare Book Division, New York Public Library; Astor, Lenox and Tilden Foundations. *First plan of New York published in the city. Several wards laid out by 1730–31 Montgomery charter are shown. Note Montgomerie's Ward (lower right). Numerous locations referenced between two figures in cartouche at upper left. Cartouche of the seal of New York City at upper right.*

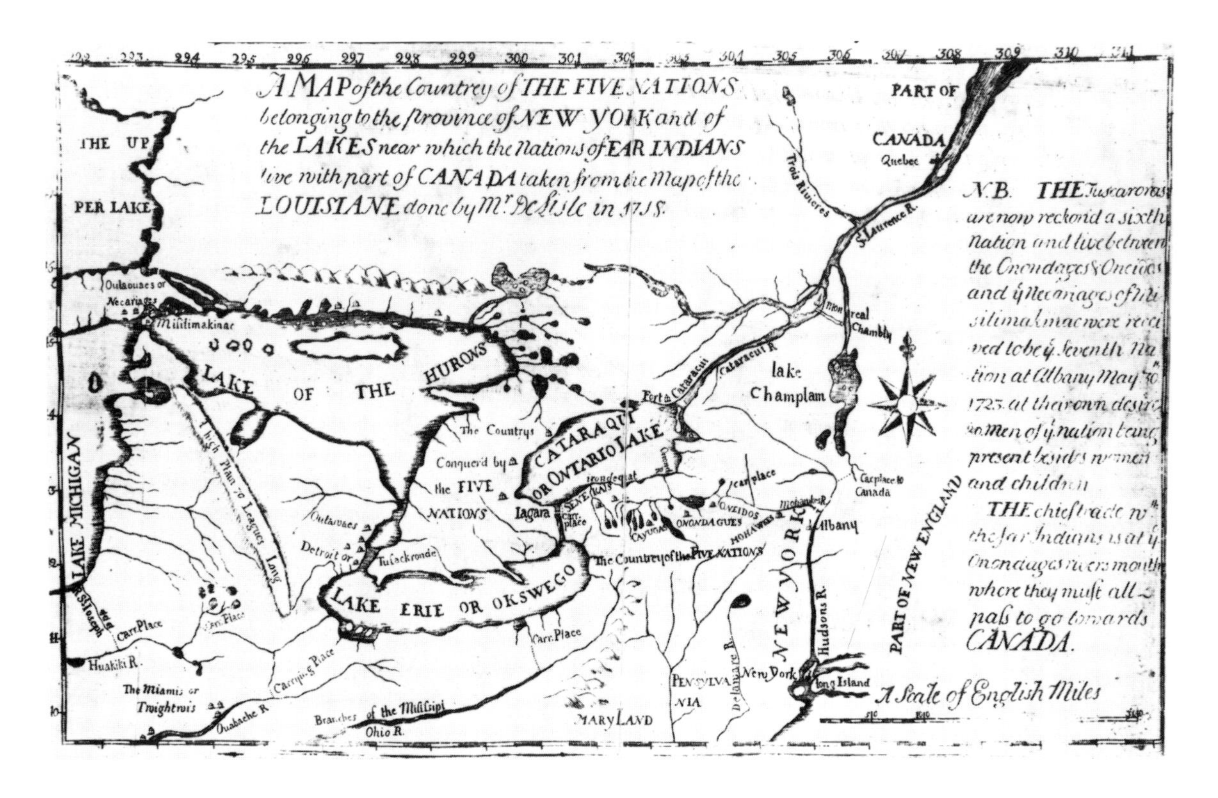

PLATE 88: Cadwallader Colden. "A Map of the Countrey of the Five Nations belonging to the province of New York." 1724. Engraving, 23 × 37 cm. Private collection. *Considered first map engraved in New York City. Distinguished by frequent appearance of phrase "carrying place," indicating portages. A note reports that the Tuscarora have joined as a sixth Iroquois nation, and the Necariage as a seventh. Published separately and also appeared in Colden's* Papers Relating to an Act of New York for Encouragement of the Indian Trade *(New York, 1724).*

PLATE 89: Cyprian Southack. "The New England Coasting Pilot from Sandy Point of New York, unto Cape Canso in Nova Scotia, And Part of Island Breton." c. 1718–34 (2nd state). Engraving, 107 × 252 cm. Private collection. *First marine atlas published in America; it consists of eight maps, which when joined make a single large sheet, as here. A channel runs through Cape Cod at Eastham. Along coastline are over 100 descriptive notes, discussing places named on map.*

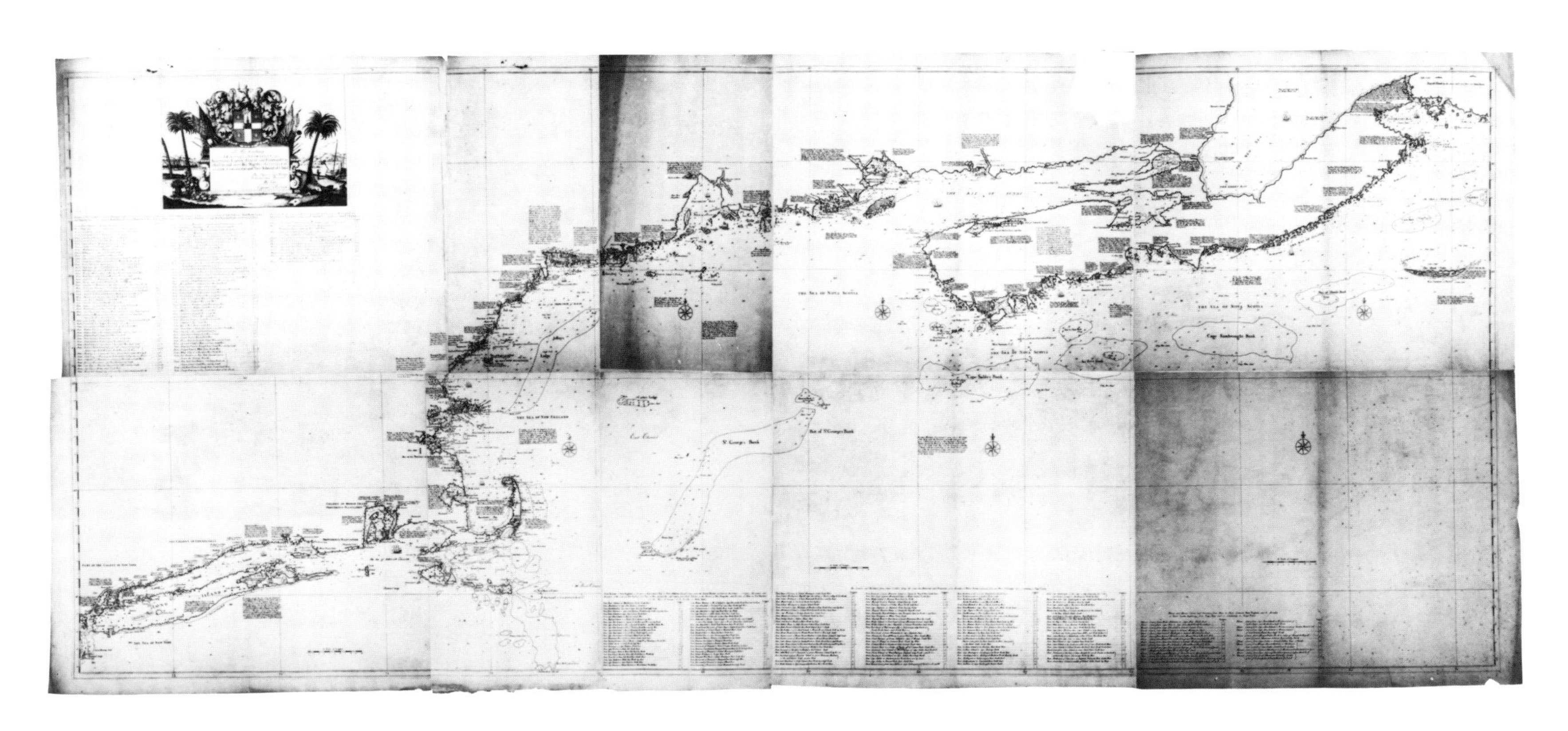

Library of Congress presents evidence (see *Imago Mundi* 11, 1954) that a more probable publication date was between 1729 and 1734.

During the first half of the century, events far to the northwest were unfolding that would change the mapping of that portion of North America. The Russians were expanding in an easterly direction, and by 1706 they had settled Kamchatka Peninsula. In 1728 Vitus Bering, a Danish explorer in Russian employ, traversed the strait now called by his name; sighting no land, he did not recognize the strait's importance. The first printed map of part of present Alaska, drawn by Bering, appeared in the fourth volume of *Description Géographique Historique Cronologique Politique et Physique de l'Empire de la Chine* (4 vols., Paris, 1735) by Jean Baptiste du Halde. On Bering's second voyage, in 1741, he and Aleksey Chirikov sailed to the east of Alaska and determined the peninsularity of that region (*see Plates 94, 95*).

Also in 1741 the British Admiralty dispatched an expedition of discovery to Hudson Bay; they wintered at Fort Churchill, and the following year explored the north and west coasts of the bay, discovering and naming the Wager River. Christopher Middleton's "Chart of Hudson's Bay and Straits," in his *A Vindication of the Conduct of Captain Christopher Middleton*, was published in London in 1743. This was the first attempt at an accurate survey of the Hudson Bay coast, depicting the present Wager Strait as a river and showing a tide in the bay's western portion. Henry Ellis's "Chart of the Coast Where a North West Passage was attempted," in his *A Voyage to Hudson's-Bay* (London, 1748), showed the Wager Strait as a closed bay and included the first map reference to Chesterfield Inlet.

Following the Queen Anne's War, a foreboding about future conflicts persisted among the great powers, and consequently the French continued to expand their North American holdings. The English took a defensive step in 1725 by establishing Fort Oswego on the eastern shore of Lake Ontario. Building a fort at Crown Point on Lake Champlain in 1731 was one of several strategic maneuvers by the French to control the southern approach to the St. Lawrence River. In 1732 powerful Fort Louisbourg was erected on Cape Breton Island to secure approaches to the St. Lawrence River, and Fort Niagara was constructed simultaneously to dominate Lakes Ontario and Erie and serve as a military base against the Iroquois. The French also continued to probe westward from Lake Superior. In 1731 Pierre Gaultier de Varennes, sieur de la Vérendrye, opened a new and easier route to Rainy Lake and the following year supervised the building of Fort Charles on the western shore of the Lake of the Woods. One year later, in 1733, the French secretary of state, the comte de Maurepas, was again honored when another fort was named for him, this one on the Red River south of Lake Winnipeg.

The scope of the cartographer's geographic awareness at the time is best noted on the first large-scale printed map of North America, "A Map of the British Empire in America with the French and Spanish Settlements adjacent thereto," published in London by Henry Popple in 1733 (*Plate 90*). The work was issued in atlas format, one sheet showing a reduction of the large map (239 by 229 cm) formed by joining together the other twenty sheets. Although the endorsement of the astronomer-scientist Edmund Halley appears as printed text on the map, it abounds with geographic distortions, errors, and omissions, all of these emphasized by its size. The English artist-naturalist Mark Catesby included a map—largely a derivative of Henry Popple's 1733 map—of Carolina and Florida and the Bahama Islands in his *Natural History of Carolina, Florida, and the Bahama Islands* (2 vols., London, 1731–43). During two visits, to Virginia from 1712 to 1719 and to the Carolinas from 1722 to 1725, Catesby made delightful drawings of the local flora and fauna from which he

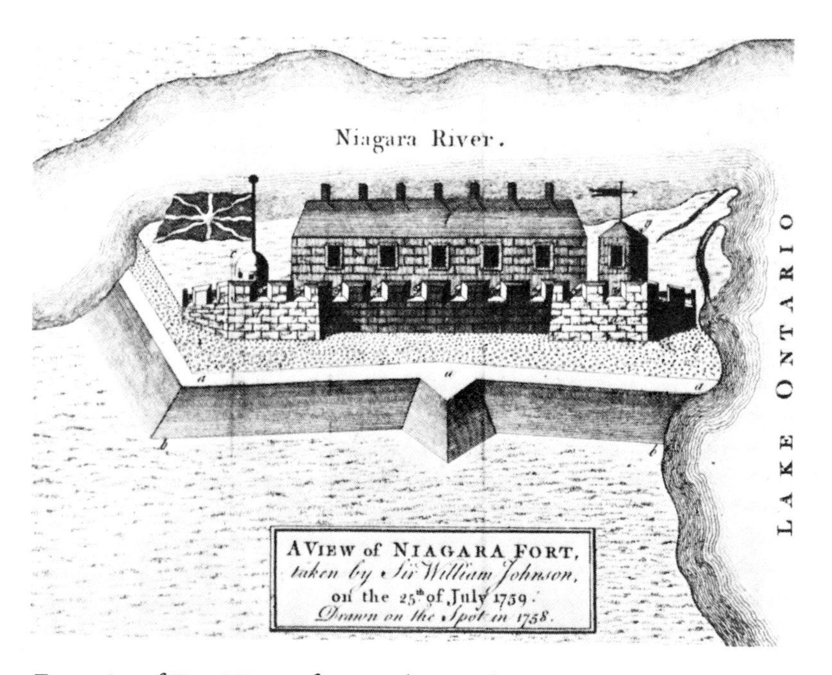

Engraving of Fort Niagara from on-the-spot drawing of 1758

PLATE 90: Henry Popple. "A Map of the British Empire in America with the French and Spanish Settlements adjacent thereto." 1733. Engraving, hand colored; 239 × 229 cm. Private collection. *The first large-scale printed map of North America. Published in atlas format with the first page a one-sheet reduction of the grand map that forms when remaining twenty sheets are joined. Its size magnifies contemporary errors and missing information. Insets of views of Niagara Falls, Quebec, New York, and of several harbors including Annapolis Royal, Boston, New York, Charles Town, St. Augustine, and Port Royal.*

later made engravings for his magnificent two-volume *Natural History*.

Another international conflict with North American implications erupted in 1739 when England declared war on Spain. English trading ships had abused certain privileges spelled out by an earlier treaty, and when Spanish trade thereby suffered, Spanish ships began attacking British trade vessels. In the course of these events an English smuggler, Robert Jenkins, had an ear cut off, and the English exploited this effrontery as a rallying point to declare war. The resultant conflict is commonly referred to as the War of Jenkins's Ear. At the outbreak of this war the Creek, Cherokee, and Chickasaw Indians in the Gulf coast region ceded most of their coastal lands to Georgia and joined the English in the campaign that wiped out Spanish posts in Florida, pushing the Spanish frontier back to the Altamaha River.

The War of Jenkins's Ear merged with the larger European

war, known as King George's War or the War of Austrian Succession, which was touched off in 1740 when Frederick II of Prussia invaded Silesia. France went to the aid of Prussia, and in 1743 a compact signed between France and Spain forced France to enter the war against England and its colonies. After the French unsuccessfully attacked Annapolis Royal in Nova Scotia in 1744, the New England militia under Sir William Pepperell, supported by a fleet commanded by Admiral Sir Peter Warren, captured Fort Louisbourg in 1745. Towns in Maine were overrun during the war and raids were launched on Albany and Saratoga. The Treaty of Aix-la-Chapelle in 1748 restored the status quo and returned Fort Louisbourg to France.

Peaceful expansion continued in North America despite the skirmishes of war. Bethlehem, Pennsylvania, evolved from a 1739 provincial government grant to German Moravian immigrants of land at the junction of the Delaware and Lehigh rivers in eastern Pennsylvania. This town was a point of departure for exploration of Pennsylvania's adjacent Wyoming and Ohio valleys. By mid-century there were about 300 traders living in the Ohio Valley, some as far north as the southern shore of Lake Erie.

Probing for a Northwest Passage persisted in the north. Significant inland exploration was conducted by Anthony Henday, an employee of the Hudson's Bay Company, who journeyed from York to the lower Saskatchewan River and then south to the Deer River, passing through the neighborhood of present Calgary, Alberta.

Expeditions also continued in warmer southern regions. John Peter Salley, a Virginia farmer, accompanied by John Howard, had received permission in 1737 from the Virginia Council to explore westward to the Mississippi, in return for which the two men would be granted land. They traveled in 1742 from Virginia to the Mississippi River, and Salley recorded the first description of the Natural Bridge in Virginia (a manuscript copy, made by Peter Jefferson, of Salley's *Brief Account* is preserved in the Public Record Office in London). Also in 1742 John Bartram, pioneer American botanist, traveled extensively on the eastern seaboard, from northern New York to Florida, in order to examine the country's flora and fauna. The journey was of broad scientific significance. During a part of his trip he was accompanied by America's greatest eighteenth-century cartographer, Lewis Evans, who made use in his maps of the geographic information he

King of the Yamacraw, a Creek tribe in Georgia, and his nephew, members of an Indian delegation sent by Oglethorpe to England, 1734

thereby acquired, particularly in his key map of 1755, "A general Map of the Middle British Colonies, in America" (*see Plate 98*).

Evans's first major work, "A Map of Pensilvania, New-Jersey, New-York, And the Three Delaware Counties" (*Plate 91*), appeared initially in 1749; in 1752 the second and third states were published. In addition to many textual details on the geography, this document includes a comprehensive description of the "Endless Mountains" and of regional weather conditions. These mountains, which belong to the Allegheny system, furnished Evans with evidence for his speculations about the creation of the world. Provocative comments on this map about lightning and electrical storms led Governor Thomas Pownall in his *A Topographical Description of Such Parts of North America* (London, 1776)

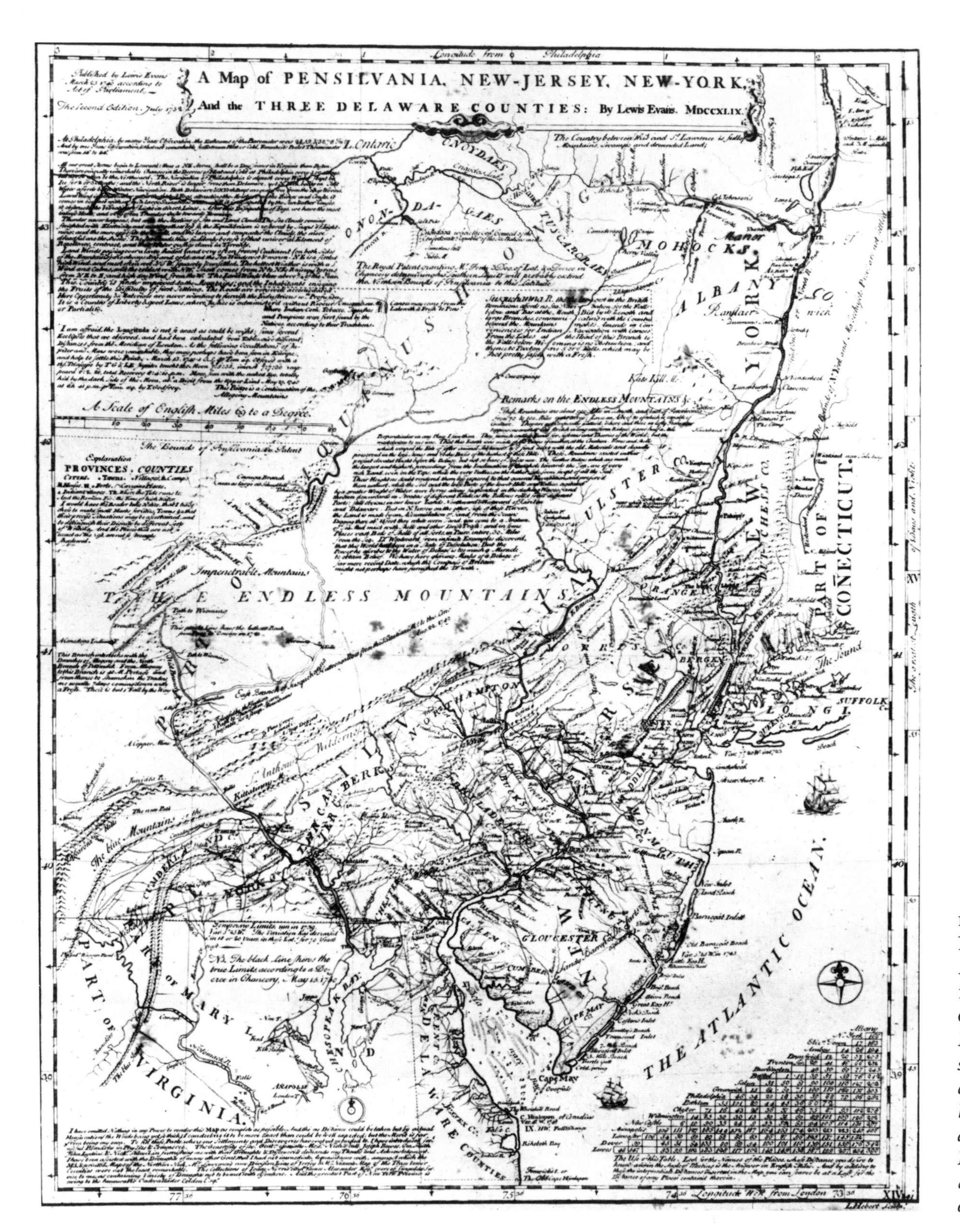

PLATE 91: Lewis Evans. "A Map of Pensilvania, New-Jersey, New-York, And the Three Delaware Counties." 1749. Engraving (3rd state, 1752), 64 × 48 cm. Private collection. *Prime meridian passes through provincial statehouse in Philadelphia, shown at a correct latitude. The first occurrence of a large area of colonies mapped in great detail. Text on map describes "The Endless Mountains," weather conditions, and relationship between lightning and electricity.*

to suggest that Benjamin Franklin's discoveries about electricity, published in *Experiments and Observations on Electricity, Made at Philadelphia in America, by Mr. Benjamin Franklin, and Communicated in Several Letters to P. Collinson* (2 vols., London, 1751–53), were derived from the earlier observations by Evans. The map encompasses both material personally gathered by Evans and information gleaned from previously published surveys. Furnishing the first detailed coverage of such a large colonial area, the map of course has great importance; for this reason, certain minor errors of location may be overlooked. Philadelphia is to be found on the almost exactly correct latitude, and the prime meridian, drawn through the spot situating the Pennsylvania provincial statehouse, provided a convenient point from which longitude of other places could be determined by actual measurement.

William Penn's second son, Thomas Penn, who arrived in the province in 1732 to organize the land system and sort out claims, was the major proprietor of the mapped region and a severe critic of the manner in which boundaries had been placed. The map's 1752 revised editions were in part rebuttals to his objections, but they also enumerated changes that had occurred during the intervening three years: the town of Easton as well as new counties are now named, and alterations of placenames are noted near the entrance to Delaware Bay. The southern boundary of Pennsylvania is clearly outlined and the western and southern boundaries of Delaware's counties have been added. The 1749 copperplate was used, but because additional land had been purchased by Penn from several tribes of regional Indians and because population spread had become significant, numerous revisions were made. Lancaster was moved west to the east side of the Susquehanna River, and the counties of York, Cumberland, Berks, and Northampton were included. At the time of first publication a black and white version of this now extremely rare map sold for one Spanish dollar, and a hand-colored version, advertised as being printed on superfine paper, for two Spanish dollars.

Toward 1750 the provincial governments developed great interest in pushing the frontier ever farther west. In 1748 Thomas Walker, the representative of the Loyal Land Company of Virginia, was sent on an exploratory mission to find desirable settlement sites west of the Blue Ridge Mountains. Walker, whose name would later be associated with a George Washington map (*see Plate 105*), traveled up the Holston River as far as Kingsport, Tennessee. He then went overland through Cave Gap, a divide in a long precipitous ridge; in 1749 he renamed the pass Cumberland Gap, honoring William Augustus, duke of Cumberland and commander in chief of the British army. Also in 1748 the Ohio Company, which had been granted by the provincial government of Virginia 200,000 acres bounded by the Ohio and Kanawha rivers and the Appalachian Mountains, dispatched Christopher Gist, a Maryland frontiersman and surveyor, to map the Ohio Valley as far as Louisville, Kentucky. In 1749 the Loyal Land Company secured a provincial grant of 800,000 acres north of the Carolina line and west of the Allegheny Mountains. Although the company's initial plans for development never materialized, by that year Virginia had established settlements as far west as the Watauga River in Tennessee.

At the end of the decade serious dispute over conflicting territorial demands between the French and the English was imminent. In order to strengthen the English claims, George Montagu Dunk, earl of Halifax and president of the Board of Trade and Plantations, in 1749 sent out 2,500 English settlers, most of whom were debtors, to organize a colony in Nova Scotia. The town of Halifax, founded in 1749 as a British stronghold to rival the French Louisbourg, was named in Dunk's honor. Although Nova Scotia had been in England's possession since 1713, the only European inhabitants at that time were several thousand French Acadians. In 1755 their hostile overtures impelled Colonel Charles Laurence, governor of Nova Scotia, to deport anyone who refused to pledge allegiance to the British crown. Some of these exiled French Canadians then resettled in Louisiana, which belonged to France. They kept much of their native language alive, and their dislodgment from Acadia led to the name Cajun—a corruption of the term Acadian—which came to be used for a member of this group.

7. The Emergence of the Nation

Here every portion of our country finds the most commanding motives for carefully guarding and preserving the union of the whole.... In contemplating the causes which may disturb our union, it occurs as matter of serious concern, that any ground should have been furnished for characterizing parties by geographical discriminations—Northern and Southern—Atlantic and Western.

George Washington
Farewell address to the people of the
United States, September 17, 1796

1750-1800

DURING THE first half of the eighteenth century there was evidence along the Atlantic seaboard of peaceful expansion by the colonial settlers. Connecticut and Massachusetts were so overpopulated that mass emigration to Pennsylvania, Vermont, New Hampshire, and Maine was initiated. Between 1750 and 1775 there were 74 new townships established in Vermont, 119 in New Hampshire, and 94 in Maine. During this quarter century, in the period preceding the American War of Independence, cartographers were more prolific than they had been during any comparable period subsequent to the European discovery of the New World, producing a large number of important North American maps.

Joshua Fry and Peter Jefferson, the father of Thomas Jefferson, drew "A Map of the Most Inhabited part of Virginia, containing the whole province of Maryland with Part of Pensilvania, New Jersey and North Carolina" (*Plate 92*) in 1751, but it was not engraved and printed until later, presumably in 1754. Only two copies of the first state are known, one in the New York Public Library and the other in the Alderman Library of the University of Virginia at Charlottesville. Multiple derivatives of this map were produced until 1800, drawn by men who personally surveyed many of the mapped areas. The revised 1755 edition is particularly impressive in the amount of detail shown in the Ohio Valley and the transallegheny west. A table of distances and the arteries of roads were extracted from a personal journal by John B. Dalrymple, captain of the Virginia regiment, and the information was incorporated into this edition.

Settlers were moving into many areas covered by the map. In 1751 John Robinson, president of the Virginia Council, was granted a large tract of land along the Greenbrier River. At the Treaty of Logstown in the following year, the Iroquois and Delaware Indians ceded land south of the Ohio River to the Virginia colony. This permitted the Ohio Company to build a fort on the Monongahela River, after which Christopher Gist enticed families from eastern Pennsylvania to settle near him at the junction of the Ohio and the Monongahela rivers. In 1752 the Ohio Company received another land grant along the upper Ohio River and built a trading post at present Cumberland, Maryland.

Philadelphia at this time was a commercial hub and the origin of several important commercial routes. One of the most important wagon trails during the colonial period extended from Philadelphia to the Yadkin River in North Carolina. Known as the Great Wagon Road, it developed after a group of German Moravians purchased 100,000 acres near the Yadkin River and encouraged settlement there. Twelve brethren of this sect left Bethlehem, Pennsylvania, in 1753 to found Bethabara, North Carolina, and in their diary of that year they provided a descriptive account of their route of travel.

The city of Philadelphia and its environs are best represented on a map at mid-century by "A Map of Philadelphia, and Parts Adjacent" by Nicholas Scull and George Heap (*Plate 93*). This 1752 plan of the city has become the most popular ever produced. The view of the statehouse is the earliest appearance in print of Independence Hall. The posthumously published 1753 "A Plan of the British Dominions of New England in North America" by William Douglass, a distinguished Boston physician, depicted that region in the prewar decades. This very rare map was the basis for the popular "Map of the Most Inhabited Part of New England" published two years later in London by Thomas Jefferys.

During this decade cartography of the Northwest also advanced. In 1752 the French geographer Philippe Buache's "Carte des Nouvelles Découvertes au Nord de la Mer du Sud" (*Plate 94*) reproduced geographic information gathered by his brother-

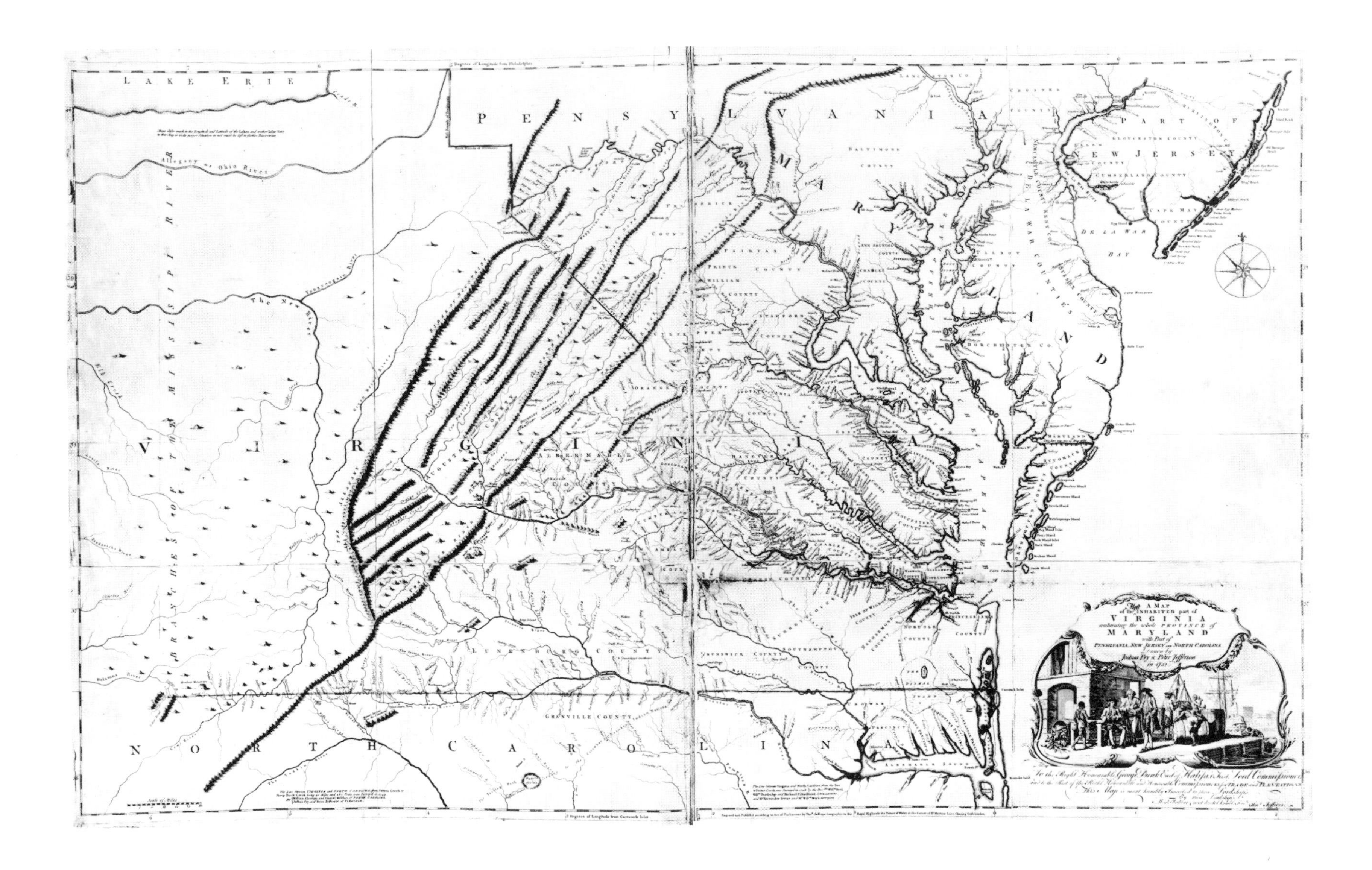

in-law Joseph-Nicolas Delisle, younger brother of Guillaume Delisle, during the twenty years he served as cartographer to the court of Russia. (Volume 24 of *The Gentlemen's Magazine*, published in London in 1754, includes a copy of the Delisle map dated 1750, indicating an earlier preparation of the work.) This key map of the Northwest also depicted the imaginary large northwestern inland sea known as Mer ou Baye de l'Ouest. It further incorporated information about a Northwest Passage from the Pacific to the Atlantic derived from the apocryphal voyages of the Spanish admiral Bartholome de Fonte and Juan de Fuca. According to legend, Bartholome de Fonte, sailing north from the Pacific coast of South America in 1640, discovered a large network of bays and rivers in the northwestern region of North America. It was reported that sailing inland he met a ship that had traveled west from Boston. Juan de Fuca in 1592 claimed the discovery of a large inland sea in the same part of the American Northwest, indicating it was connected to the North Sea by a strait. Both accounts were eventually rejected as overimaginative speculation.

John Green, under the pseudonym Bradock Mead, published in 1753 his "Chart of North and South America," a specific attempt at negating the French territorial claims in North Ameri-

(opposite) PLATE 92: Joshua Fry and Peter Jefferson. "A Map of the Most Inhabited part of Virginia, containing the whole province of Maryland with Part of Pensilvania, New Jersey and North Carolina." 1751. Engraving, 77 × 123 cm. Rare Book Division, New York Public Library; Astor, Lenox and Tilden Foundations. *The Fry-Jefferson map was drawn in 1751 but not published until 1754. Shows distances between Virginia cities and includes the great road from Yadkin River to Philadelphia as well as other major regional roads. First printed map to show parallel ridges and valleys in Appalachian Mountain range in correct direction. Cartouche at lower right, a Virginia wharf scene.*

ca that had been presented on the Delisle–Buache maps. This is the first English map that recorded the discoveries of Vitus Bering and Aleksey Chirikov in Alaska. Gerhard Friedrich Müller's "Nouvelle Carte des Decouvertes faites par des Vaisseaux Russiens Aux côtes inconnues de l'Amerique Septentrionale avec les Pais Adiacents" (*Plate 95*), showing these voyages and a distorted Alaskan peninsula, was prepared in 1754 but published in 1758.

The French and Indian War was prefaced in the early years of the decade by an increase in the number of forts constructed by the French along the Allegheny River and the upper Ohio. Fort LeBoeuf was built in 1753 at the junction of French Creek and the Allegheny River, and the following year Fort Duquesne, named for the area's French governor, was established at the site of what is now known as the Golden Triangle in Pittsburgh. The twenty-one-year-old George Washington was sent in 1754 to protest the building of a French fort in the Ohio Valley, to which the English claimed territorial rights. During that year, while surveying a route that later became a major highway in the Ohio Valley during the revolutionary era, he drew a series of manuscript maps showing the Cumberland area in Maryland, and Fort LeBoeuf at present Waterford, Pennsylvania. These manuscripts trace the route that Washington had taken with Christopher Gist from the Potomac to Fort LeBoeuf.

The political issue of English or French dominance in the Ohio Valley was one of the major causes of the French and Indian War, which eventually resolved territorial rights throughout the entire North American continent. This controversy also stimulated the production of numerous maps in 1755, some of which are so important that the year 1755 has commonly been designated the year of the great maps. The greatest of these is unquestionably "A Map of the British and French Dominions in North America with the Roads, Distances, Limits, and Extent of the Settlements" (*Plate 96*), regarded by most authorities as the most important map in the history of American cartography.

The author of this impressive document was an extraordinary, Renaissance-style man. Dr. John Mitchell was born in Virginia and educated at Edinburgh. For a while he practiced medicine in Virginia, in the course of which he described the symptoms and treatment of what was thought to be yellow fever, and presented a fascinating dissertation on the causes of black skin, relating it to environmental and developmental factors. As a biologist he studied the embryology of the opossum; as a chemist he researched methods for producing potash; as a botanist he corresponded with the eminent Swedish botanist and taxonomist Carolus Linnaeus. Mitchell established a new method for classifying plants and even has a species of the madder family (*Mitchella repens*, or partridgeberry) named for him. His emigration to England in 1746 was followed by a commission from the earl of Halifax, the president of the Board of Trade and Plantations, for a map to

Sitka, capital of Russian Alaska

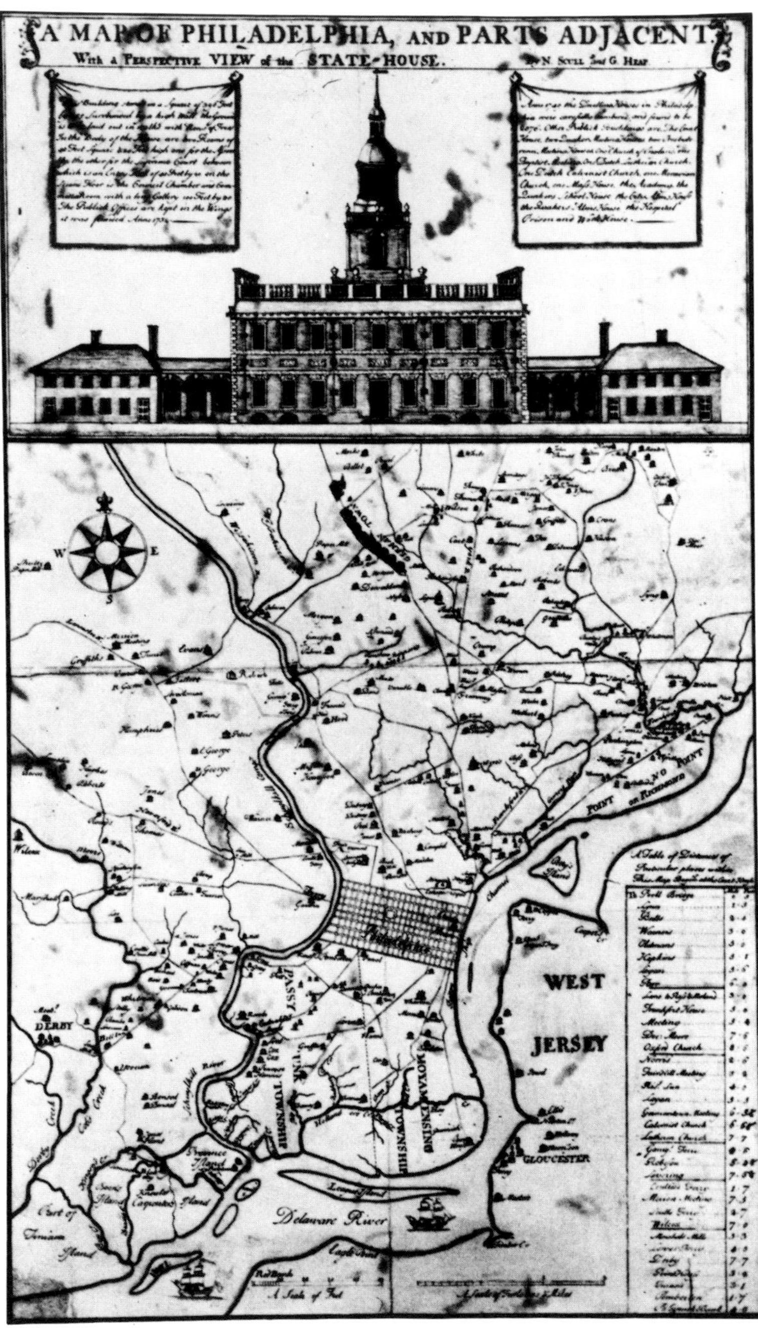

PLATE 93: Nicholas Scull and George Heap. "A Map of Philadelphia, and Parts Adjacent." 1752. Engraving, 52 × 30 cm. John Carter Brown Library, Brown University, Providence. *First map of Philadelphia printed in America and first print of the statehouse (Independence Hall). The most popular plan of Philadelphia ever issued; has been reproduced countless times. A summary of public buildings is included. Detailed representation of the six to eight miles of countryside, including townships, around the city. Date of publication established through a contemporary advertisement in* Pennsylvania Gazette *(June 4, 1752), stating map was "just published."*

define English territorial rights in North America. It was the only map that Mitchell is known to have drawn.

The map was devised as a conscious cartographic rebuttal to French boundary claims proposed on maps prior to the French and Indian War and it distinguishes British and French possessions in eastern North America and the administrative subdivisions of the British colonies. The boundaries of the Atlantic seaboard colonies are extended westward across the Mississippi River. In addition to specific cartographic information derived from contemporary maps of every North American province, supplied by the provincial governors, the document also incorporated geographic and cartographic knowledge stored in London's Public Record Office. Most of the methods of gathering geographic data were as sophisticated as possible for the time, with latitudinal determinations made with the quadrant, which had been invented in 1731 by John Hadley of London and Thomas Godfrey of Philadelphia, simultaneously. Longitudinal accuracy was limited and less precise, although John Harrison's invention of the chronometer in 1735 had allowed for some improvement.

Twenty-one editions and impressions of Mitchell's map appeared in four languages between 1755 and 1781, attesting to its importance. It is the primary political treaty map in American history. A copy of the third edition was used by John Jay during the negotiations for the 1783 Treaty of Paris. Jay, along with John Adams and Benjamin Franklin, had been appointed by Congress to negotiate the treaty, which ended the Revolution and definitively established the independence of the American colonies. A copy of the fourth edition was in the library of George III at the time. Whether it was consulted at Paris during the negotiations or simply held by the English monarch for personal reference has not been ascertained. The map was resorted to in boundary disputes throughout the eighteenth and nineteenth centuries, and even into the twentieth. It served as evidence for the Webster-Ashburton Treaty of 1842, the Quebec boundary definition of 1871, the Canada-Labrador boundary case of 1926, the Wisconsin-Michigan boundary case of 1926, and the Delaware-New Jersey dispute of 1932.

The French cartographers Jean Nicolas Bellin, Jean-Baptiste Bourguignon d'Anville, and Robert de Vaugondy, John Mitchell's contemporaries, adopted features from his map in their works but added their own conceptions of boundaries to counter

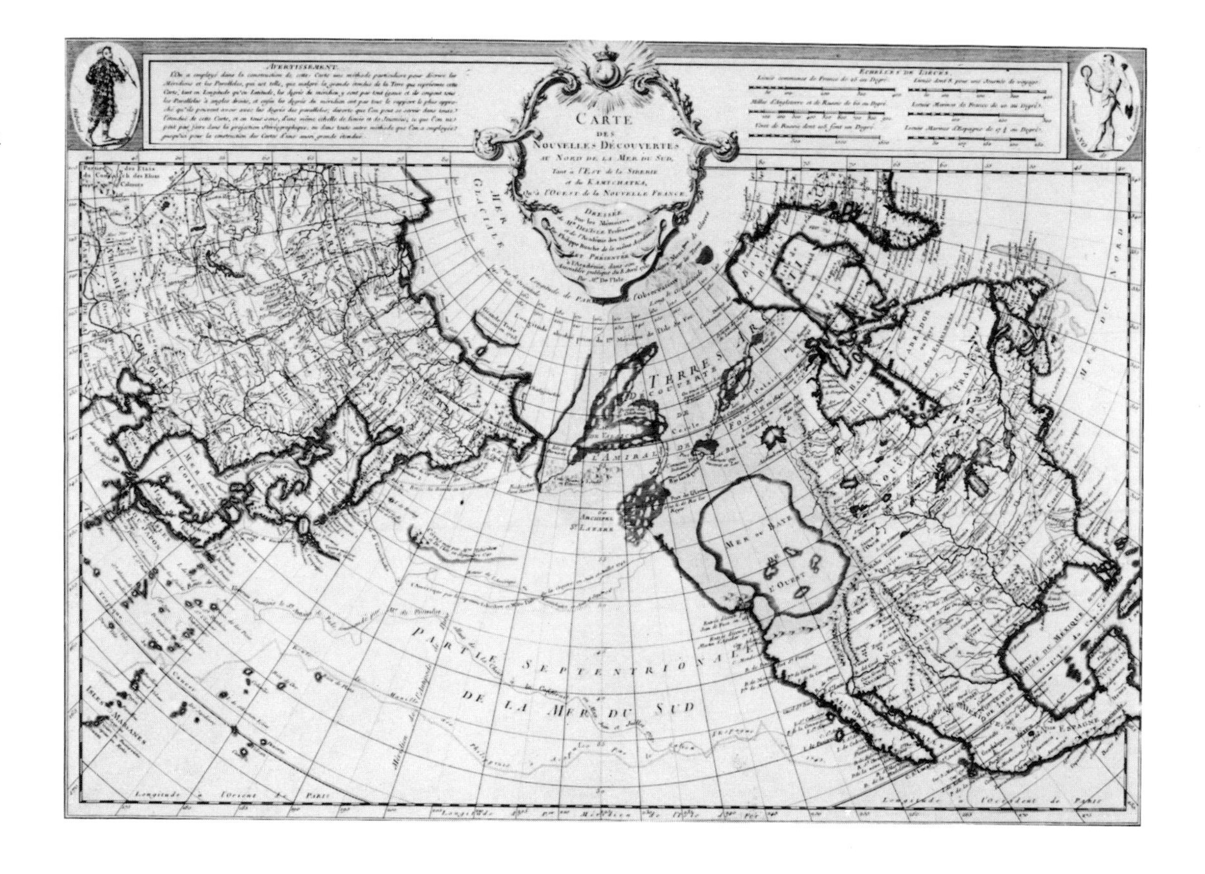

PLATE 94: Philippe Buache. "Carte des Nouvelles Découvertes au Nord de la Mer du Sud." 1752. Engraving, 46 × 63 cm. Private collection. *Cornerstone map of Alaska. Depicts Vitus Bering's first (1728–30) and second (1741–42, with Aleksey Chirikov) voyages for Russia. Fictitious 1,200-mile-long Mer ou Baye de l'Ouest in northwestern area of America is shown for first time. Cartographer was related by marriage to Delisle brothers.*

PLATE 95: Gerhard Friedrich Müller. "Nouvelle Carte des Decouvertes faites par des Vaisseaux Russiens Aux côtes inconnues de l'Amerique Septentrionale avec les Pais Adiacents." 1754. Engraving, 46 × 64 cm. Newberry Library, Chicago. *Prepared in 1754, includes statement that map was presented in 1758 to St. Petersburg's Imperial Academy of Sciences. Shows course of Vitus Bering's and Aleksey Chirikov's voyages. (Plate 94 Delisle map shows only Chirikov's ship reaching America.) The apocryphal Rivière de l'Ouest runs from Lake Winnipeg to the Pacific.*

British taking Quebec in 1759

the British claims. In 1755 Bellin, hydrographer to Louis XV of France, drew "Partie Occidentale de la Nouvelle France ou Canada" (*Plate 97*) focusing on the Great Lakes and the western frontier of the British colonies as well as France's inland empire. The document locates settlements, forts, and Indian villages and presents the four apocryphal islands in Lake Superior described by Pierre Francois Xavier de Charlevoix, French Jesuit explorer and historian, in his *Histoire et Description Générale de la Nouvelle France II* (Paris, 1744), for which other explorers for many years searched in vain. It was later demonstrated that these islands, named Philippeaux, Maurepas, Pontchartrain, and Ste. Anne, had been invented to honor Charlevoix's patron, Jean Frédéric Phélippeux, comte de Maurepas, whose family estate was named Pontchartrain, and whose patron saint was St. Anne.

John Huske, an enthusiastic admirer of Mitchell, produced a small map based on the large Mitchell map and included it in his book *The Present State of North America* (London, 1755), which clarifies British and French claims at the outset of the French and Indian War. Also in 1755 Thomas Jefferys, geographer to the prince of Wales, published in London John Green's map of New England and Canada, "A Map of the Most Inhabited Parts of New England," which took issue with some of the geographic coordinates on the first edition of Mitchell's map. This criticism induced Mitchell to add textual explanation on the 1757 edition, justifying his own conclusions.

Another important 1755 document was Lewis Evans's "A general Map of the Middle British Colonies, in America" (*Plate 98*), which, in addition to its depiction of the British colonies, included the Ohio Valley. It was published in eighteen editions between 1755 and 1814, and two other cartographers, Thomas Kitchin in 1756 and John Bowles in 1765, both published pirated versions. The map is considered by historians to be the most ambitious performance of its kind undertaken in America up to that time, and its publication was a milestone in the development of the printing arts in the colonial period. As might be expected, significant competition arose between the Mitchell and Evans maps. Evans wrote in a letter to the English map publisher Robert Dodsley in 1756: "Although we have many copies of Mitchell's map, nobody pretends to look into them for any places in our borders." By contrast, supporters of the Mitchell map denounced that of Evans because it had not been sanctioned by the Board of Trade in London. The Evans map is accompanied by an essay, *An Analysis of the Middle British Colonies* (Philadelphia, 1755), which was published by Benjamin Franklin, utilizing his own printing press.

Prior to the outbreak of the French and Indian War the French had begun to seize British forts on the Monongahela and Ohio rivers. Formal warfare commenced on July 4, 1755, when George Washington's troops were defeated at Fort Necessity, and five days later General Edward Braddock's troops were repelled at the battle of the Wilderness below Fort Le Quesne (Fort Duquesne). The Indians placed their allegiance with the French, giving the war the name by which it was called in North America. In 1756 this struggle merged into the Seven Years War in which France, Austria, Sweden, and certain German states banded together against Britain and Prussia. Fort Duquesne, the center of activities at the beginning of the war, eventually became Fort Pitt, then the nucleus of present Pittsburgh. The fort was first mapped in 1754 by Captain Robert Stobo, who drew his plan and smuggled it out while imprisoned in the fort. Four manuscript copies of Stobo's map are known, in addition to the 1755 engraving printed in London (*Plate 99*). In consequence of defeats at the British forts, the region's English settlers were evacuated to the Atlantic watershed.

In 1755 the British experienced some success in the Northeast; they captured Fort Beausejoux and the shores of the Bay of Fundy came under their control. Two engagements that halted the

French invasion of upper New York were depicted in 1755 by Samuel Blodget on "A Prospective Plan of the Battle fought near Lake George on the 8th of September 1755" (*Plate 100*). It was the first geographic representation of a battle plan published in America. By 1757 the fall of Forts Oswego and George and the abandonment of Fort William Henry forced settlers to flee to Schenectady and Albany. In the Southeast the British built a series of forts along the Potomac, James, and Roanoke rivers, beginning with Fort Cumberland, to circumvent attacks by Indians, who were allied with the French.

During this period William de Brahm's "A Map of South Carolina And a part of Georgia" (*Plate 101*) was published in London in 1757; for the first time a large area in the southern colonies was mapped accurately making use of scientific surveys. Settlements, lagoons, and coastal islands are correctly located. This key map was used as the basis for numerous maps throughout the century.

Familiar symbols of New World in cartouche of 1755 George Willdey map

Publication of maps by American presses continued during the French and Indian War, and in 1759 appeared the first map of the province of Pennsylvania printed on the North American continent (*Plate 102*). The author, Nicholas Scull, was the first member of a North American family to engage in cartography as a business.

William Pitt, first earl of Chatham, became secretary of state and prime minister in 1758. His principal objective for England was the conquest of Canada and the Ohio Valley. Lord Jeffrey Amherst was made commander in chief of the armed forces in America and captured Fort Louisbourg on July 26; Fort Duquesne was taken in November 1758, when it was renamed Fort Pitt. In July 1759, Fort Niagara, Crown Point, and Fort Carillon (Fort Ticonderoga) all fell to the British. The British master maneuver revolved around the capture of Quebec, and since they planned to overcome the city by sea, James Cook had been appointed in 1758 to take soundings as part of the naval tactics, which resulted in his charting the St. Lawrence River. Published in 1760, the large twelve-sheet "A New Chart of the River St. Laurence" (*Plate 103*), executed when Cook was a junior officer, established his reputation, and as a consequence he was made surveyor of Newfoundland. Later Cook became famed as the leader of English exploration in the Pacific.

In 1759, following the battle of the Plains of Abraham, French forces under General Louis Joseph Montcalm succumbed at Quebec to the English forces under Brigadier General James Wolfe. The battle was the most decisive of the French and Indian Wars and led to British supremacy in Canada. Four years later Major Robert Rogers, fighting for the English, took possession of Detroit and of other Great Lakes posts. In 1761 Spain formally joined France in an attempt to defeat the British, but in 1763 the Treaty of Paris ended the Seven Years War and spelled the end of French power on the North American continent. France was left with several islands: St.-Pierre and Miquelon off Newfoundland, and Dominique, Martinique, and Guadeloupe in the West Indies. England gained Canada, Acadia, Cape Breton, and several small inconsequential islands in St. Lawrence Bay and the St. Lawrence River. Spain ceded to Great Britain East Florida and West

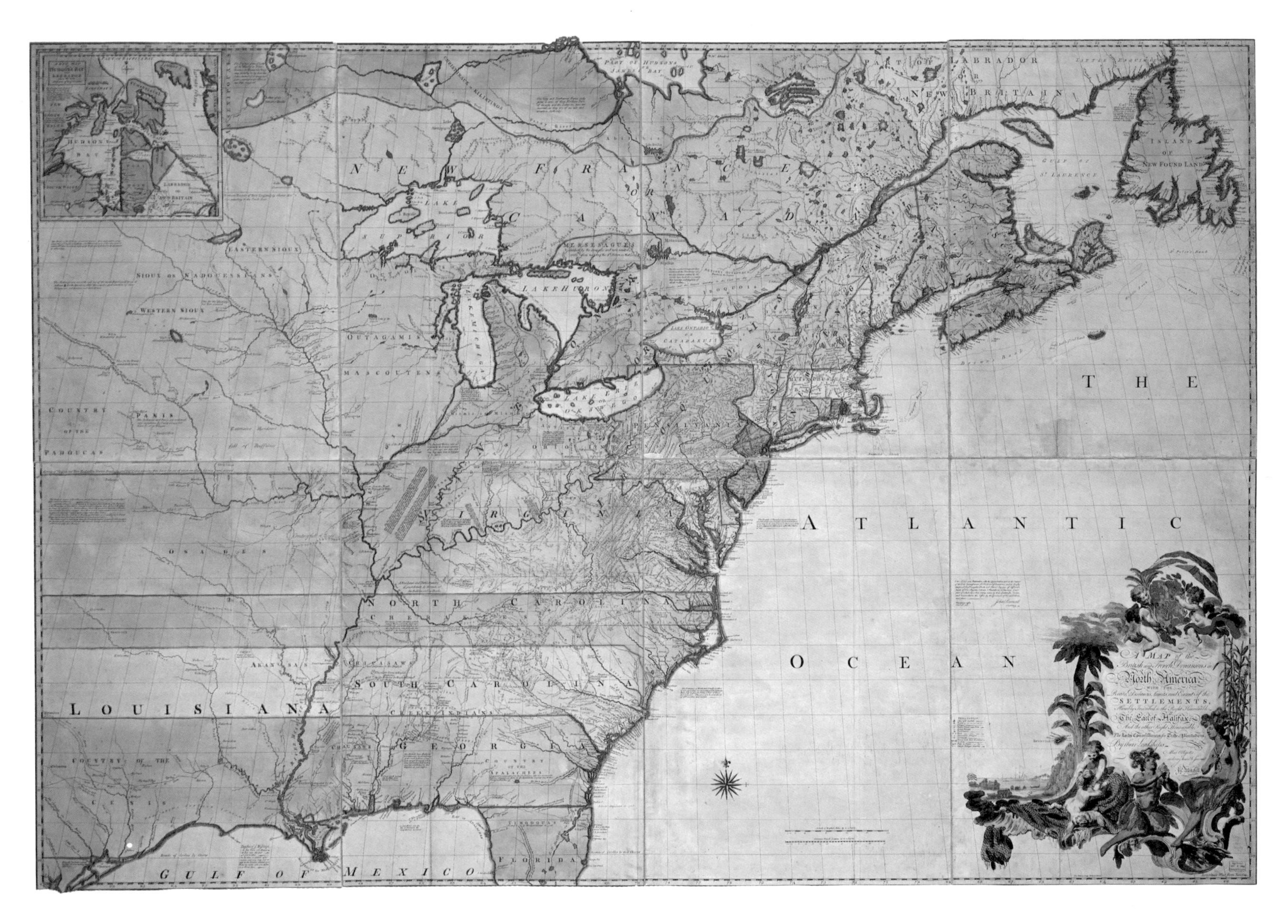

PLATE 96: John Mitchell. "A Map of the British and French Dominions in North America with the Roads, Distances, Limits, and Extent of the Settlements." 1755. Engraving, hand colored; 137 × 196 cm. Geography and Map Division, Library of Congress, Washington, D.C. *A copy of third edition consulted during 1783 Treaty of Paris negotiations to establish boundaries of the United States. Used to clarify boundary disputes throughout nineteenth century and as recently as 1932. Many historians regard it as the most important map in America's history.*

Florida, which thereby became England's sixteenth and seventeenth colonies in the Western Hemisphere. As compensation for aid during the war, France surrendered to Spain all territories west of the Mississippi formerly under French sovereignty, thus establishing the Mississippi River as a boundary between the English and Spanish empires in North America.

The year 1763 witnessed the posthumous publication of *A Set of Plans and Forts in America, Reduced from Actual Surveys* by

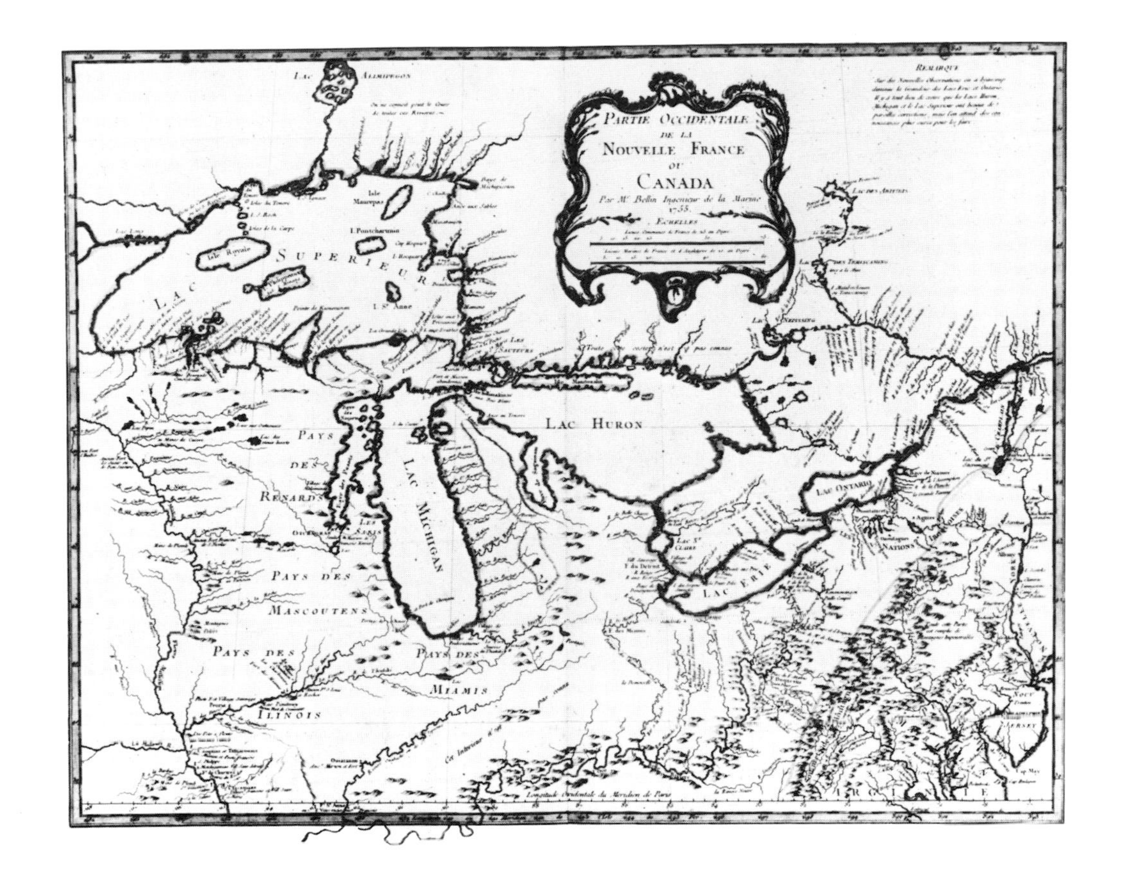

PLATE 97: Jean Nicolas Bellin. "Partie Occidentale de la Nouvelle France ou Canada." 1755. Engraving, hand colored; 48 × 61 cm. Private collection. *Shows strategic forts and areas claimed by French just before French and Indian War. Four legendary islands, described by French explorer Father Pierre de Charlevoix, appear in Lake Superior; they were vainly sought by explorers for many years.*

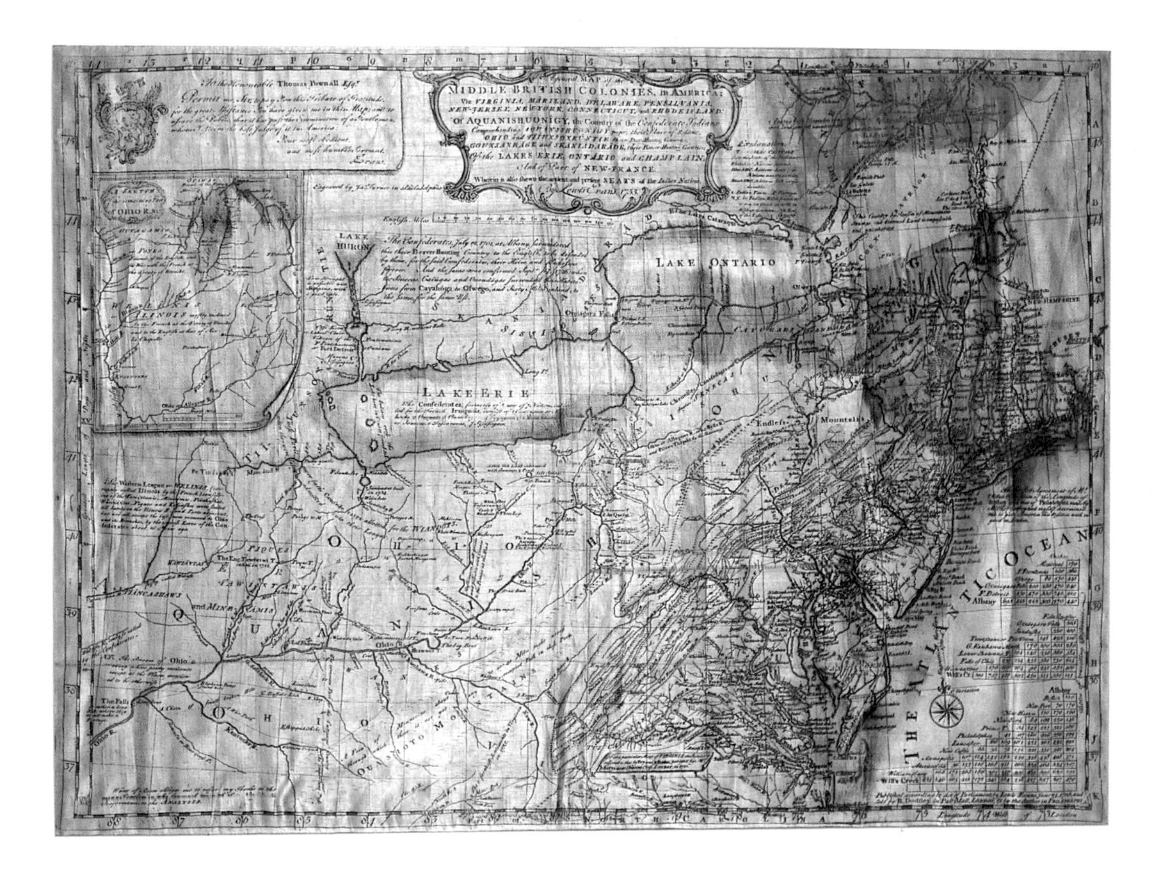

PLATE 98: Lewis Evans. "A general Map of the Middle British Colonies, in America." 1755. Engraving on silk, hand colored; 49 × 64 cm. Private collection. *One of the most important maps published in America before independence. Emphasizes Ohio Valley and French positions there. Inset shows sketch of Illinois country (presently Michigan). Mileage distances are charted (at right) west as far as Detroit, and the Falls of the Ohio (Louisville). Map reproduced is a rare printing on silk. Published separately in London and Philadelphia and also appeared in Evans's* Geographical, Historical, Political and Mechanical Essay *(Philadelphia, 1755).*

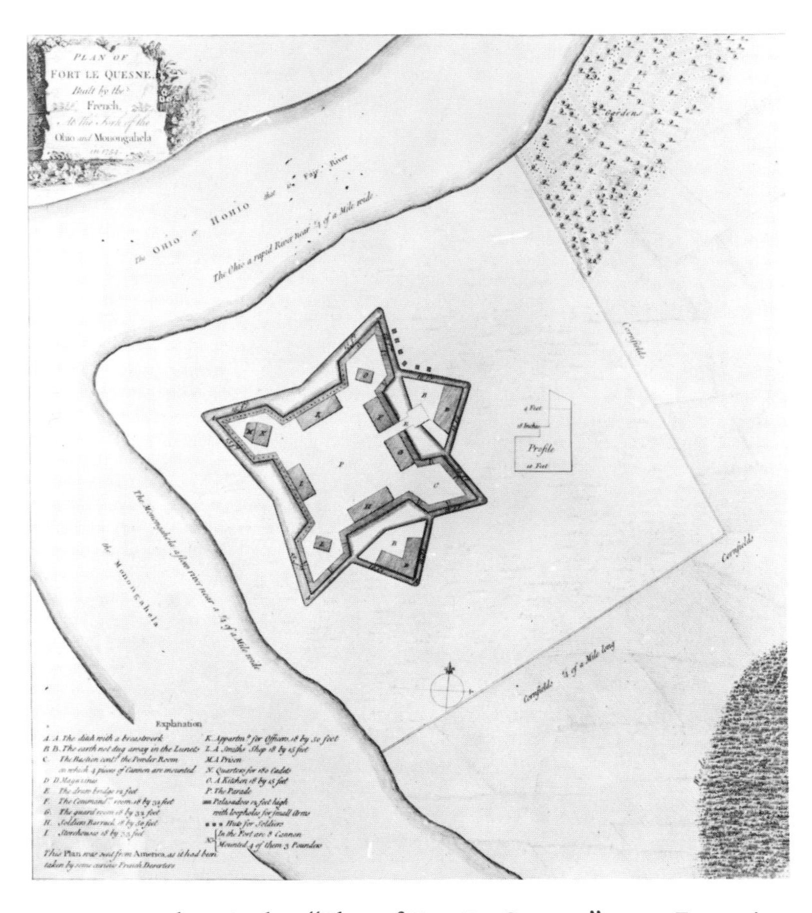

PLATE 99: Robert Stobo. "Plan of Fort Le Quesne." 1755. Engraving, 33 × 30 cm. Private collection. *First printed map of what later became the Golden Triangle in downtown Pittsburgh, drawn by Stobo in 1754 while prisoner in the French fort. It was smuggled out to George Washington and sent to England, where it was engraved and printed by Robert Sayer and John Bennett.*

Boston in 1722, engraved by William Burgis

John Rocque, geographer to George III of England. Included in this small and extremely rare volume are plans of New York City (*Plate 104A*), Quebec (*Plate 104B*), Montreal (*Plate 104C*), Louisbourg, Albany, and Halifax. Also shown are forts Ontario, Frontenac, Brewerton, Oswego, William Henry, Saratoga, George, Ligonier, Pitt, Bedford, Stanwix, Niagara (*Plate 104D*), Tienderoga (Ticonderoga) (*Plate 104E*), and Crown Poynt. The best eighteenth-century chronicle of the French and Indian War is Thomas Mantes's *The History of the Late War in North America* (1772), which includes many maps of the critical military areas and major battles.

In 1760 population estimates of several cities were made: Boston had 16,000 inhabitants; New York, 14,000; Philadelphia, 19,000; Newport, Rhode Island, 6,000; Marblehead, Massachusetts, 5,000; Salem, Massachusetts, 4,000; Charleston, South Carolina, 8,000. In 1763 Britain defined the organization of its North American empire. The Proclamation of 1763, issued on October 7, 1763, established four new colonies: East Florida, West Florida, Quebec, and Grenada, the latter including the newly acquired West Indian islands of Dominica, St. Vincent, the Grenadines, Grenada, and Tobago. Isle-St.-Jean (Prince Edward Island) and Cape Breton were annexed to Nova Scotia, while Anticosti Island and the Magdalen Islands in the Gulf of St. Lawrence were placed under Newfoundland's control. The proclamation established a line from East Florida to Quebec through the heads of rivers that terminated in the Atlantic. All colonists west of the line were to move east, and no land west of the line was to be granted or sold unless authorized in London. This edict was directed at preventing Indian wars.

The territorial grants of the Hudson's Bay Company and of the original British island colonies remained unchanged, including Jamaica, Bahamas, Bermuda, and the Leeward Islands. To settle a boundary dispute between Georgia and South Carolina, a small area north of East Florida was given to Georgia; otherwise the boundaries of the original thirteen colonies were unaltered. Yet boundary disputes between colonies, such as New York and New Jersey and New York and Massachusetts, persisted. That the proclamation line near Lake Champlain was not defined precisely only added to the confusion.

In the early 1760s the Susquehanna Company, in a move unrelated to the French and Indian War, began settlement of the Wyoming Valley, which overtly conflicted with Pennsylvania's

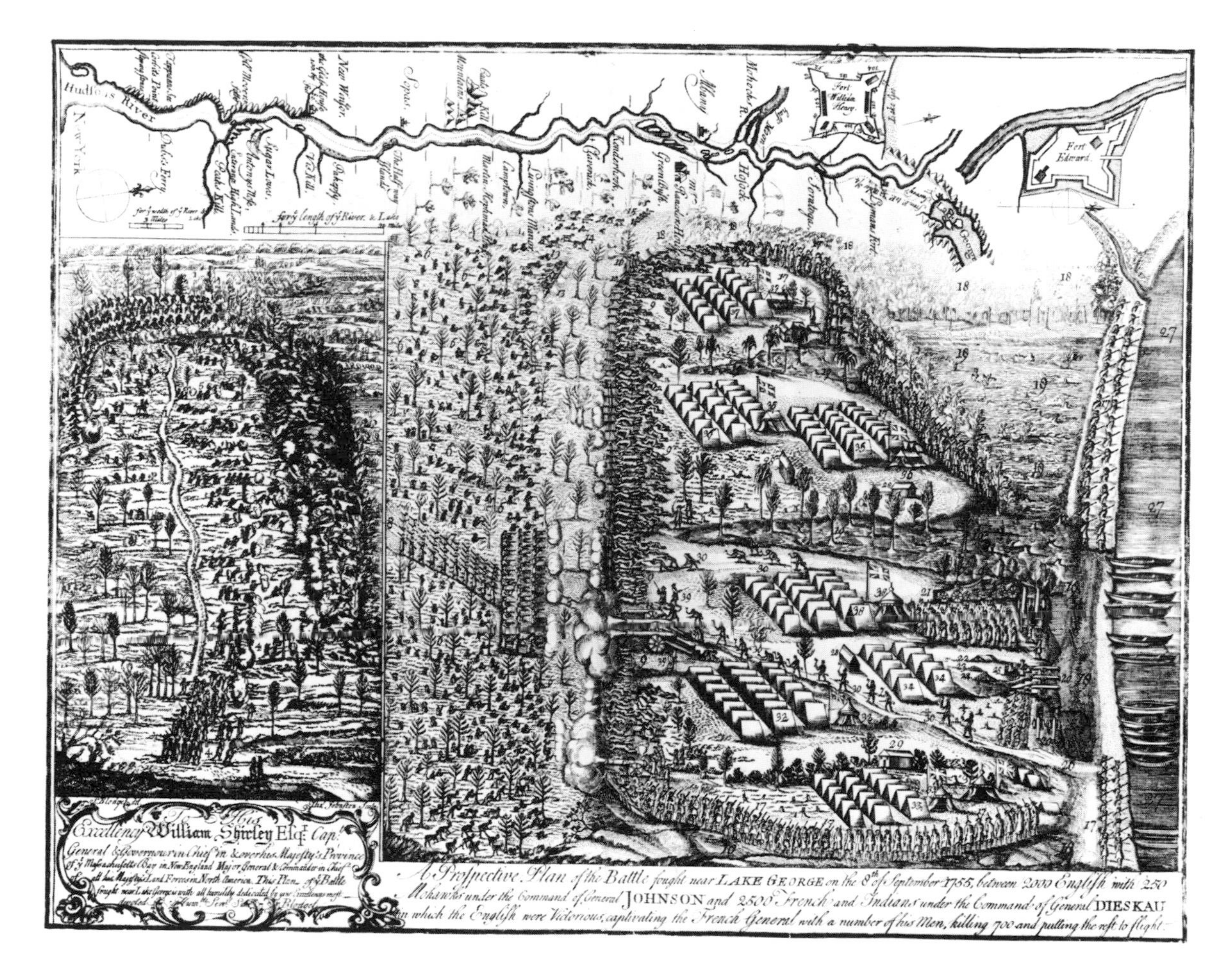

PLATE 100: Samuel Blodget. "A Prospectiye Plan of the Battle fought near Lake George on the 8th of September 1755." 1755. Engraving, 35 × 45 cm. John Carter Brown Library, Brown University, Providence. *Divided into two parts; at left of map proper is a view of first engagement and at right a view of second engagement. Insets show Hudson River, Fort Edward, and Fort William Henry. First battle plan printed in America. Published separately and also in Blodget's* A Prospective Plan of the Battle near Lake George *(Boston, 1755).*

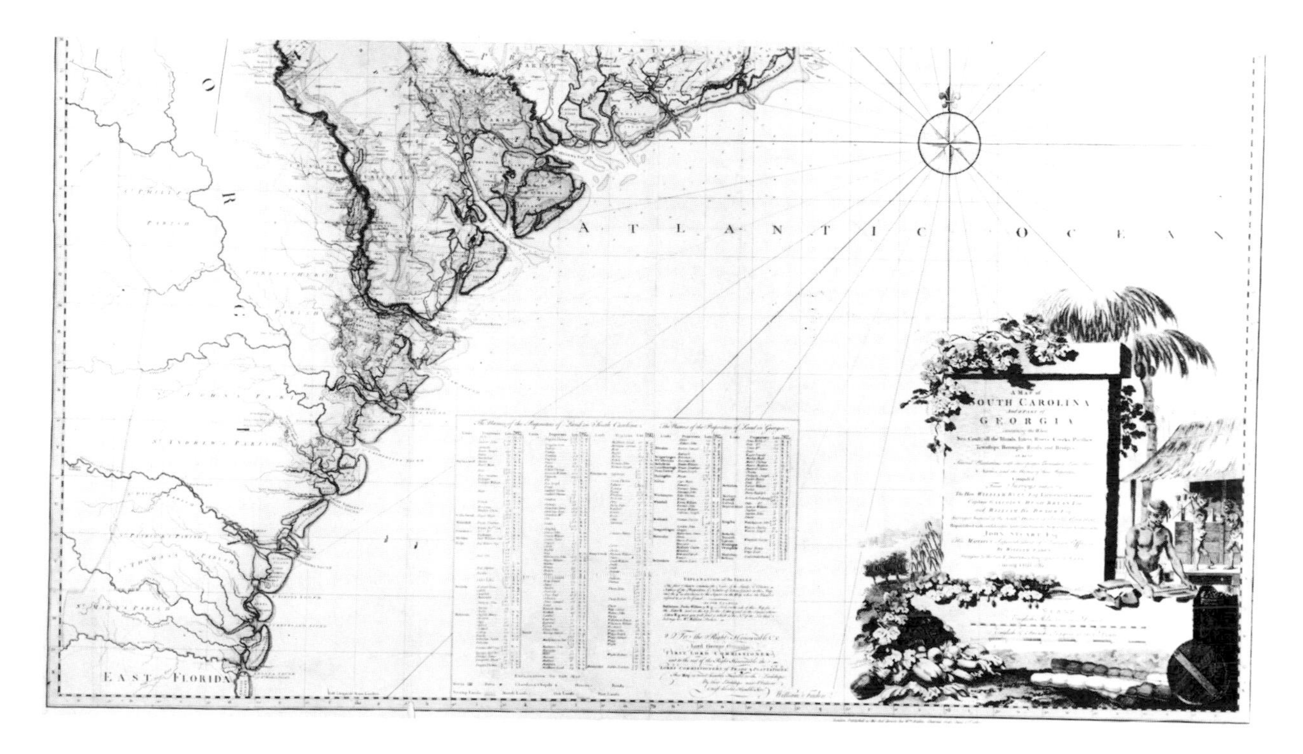

PLATE 101: William de Brahm. "A Map of South Carolina And a Part of Georgia" (detail). 1757. Engraving, hand colored; entire dimensions 134 × 122 cm. Newberry Library, Chicago. *First mapping of a large area in the southern colonies based on a scientific survey. Entire map (lower half is reproduced) extends from North Carolina's northern boundary to St. Marys River in Georgia. Legend lists names of landholders. Separate publication as first state in 1757; also appeared in Thomas Jefferys's* A General Topography of North America and the West Indies *(London, 1768).*

Benjamin Franklin's historic slogan of 1754

expansionist interests. Shortly after the war, in order to satisfy an earlier claim, the Mississippi Company, headed by George Washington, petitioned for 2.5 million acres at the junction of the Ohio and Mississippi rivers. During his survey of the Little Kanawha and the Great Kanawha rivers, Washington apparently used a holograph manuscript that is now among the George Washington Papers in the Manuscript Division of the Library of Congress (*Plate 105*). Known as the "Walker-Washington Map," it was copied by Washington from an earlier map by Thomas Walker. The original Walker map accompanied Walker's presentation to the Virginia House of Burgesses in 1769 which focused on the boundary between western settlements and Indian lands. The "Walker-Washington Map" defines the boundary line proposed by the Lords of Trade and Plantations as well as that by the London-based superintendent of Indian affairs; it also sketches the regional rivers as they were ascertained in 1769, the year the document was drawn.

There was great activity involving land speculation in the second half of the eighteenth century. The governor of New Jersey planned a colony in the Illinois region and requested sixty-three million acres extending from Lake Erie to the Mississippi River. Successful colonial expansion during this period was frequently contingent upon establishing friendly relations with the local Indians. In 1761 and 1762 Lieutenant Henry Timberlake set out from Williamsburg, Virginia, and traveled down the Holston River on a peace mission to the Cherokee. His 1765 "A Draught of the Cherokee Country" (*Plate 106*), the first map specifically devoted to that area, follows the Tennessee River from the Great Smoky Mountains to Fort Loudon. It shows Cherokee towns, and also provides the names of Indian chiefs and a census of warriors.

In 1764 Colonel Henry Bouquet led an English army west of the Ohio River in an attempt to pacify Pontiac, the Ottawa Indian chief, and his supporters and thus facilitate trade and settlement. Thomas Hutchins accompanied Bouquet and mapped the route along the Ohio River from Fort Pitt to the neighborhood of present Dennison, Ohio, as shown on "A General Map of the Country on the Ohio and Muskingham," which with "A Topographical Plan of that part of the Indian-Country through which the Army under the Command of Colonel Bouquet marched in the year 1764" constitutes one map (*Plate 107*); this combination map was engraved in 1765.

In 1766 the first American imprint map of Connecticut (*Plate 108*), drawn at the request of the British government by Moses Park in order to improve postal service, depicted that colony in great detail.

One of the most famous American boundary lines, the Mason-Dixon Line, was illustrated cartographically in 1768. "A Plan of the Boundary Lines between the Province of Maryland and the Three Lower Counties on Delaware with Part of The Parallel of Latitude which is the Boundary between the Provinces of Maryland and Pennsylvania" (*Plate 109A*) is the first graphic expression of any part of the Mason and Dixon survey, which was completed in 1767. This landmark map incorporates the measurement of a degree of latitude; coupled with its companion chart, "A Plan of the West Line or Parallel of Latitude, which is the Boundary between the Provinces of Maryland and Pensylvania" (*Plate 109B*), it completes the representation of the Mason-Dixon Line as surveyed by the English astronomers Charles Mason and Jeremiah Dixon.

The Mason-Dixon Line, which ran 244 miles west of Delaware in latitude 39°43′18″ north, was established as a compromise for a geographical blunder in the description of the original charter. When William Penn had received his charter, the status of what was referred to as the Three Lower Counties, the future

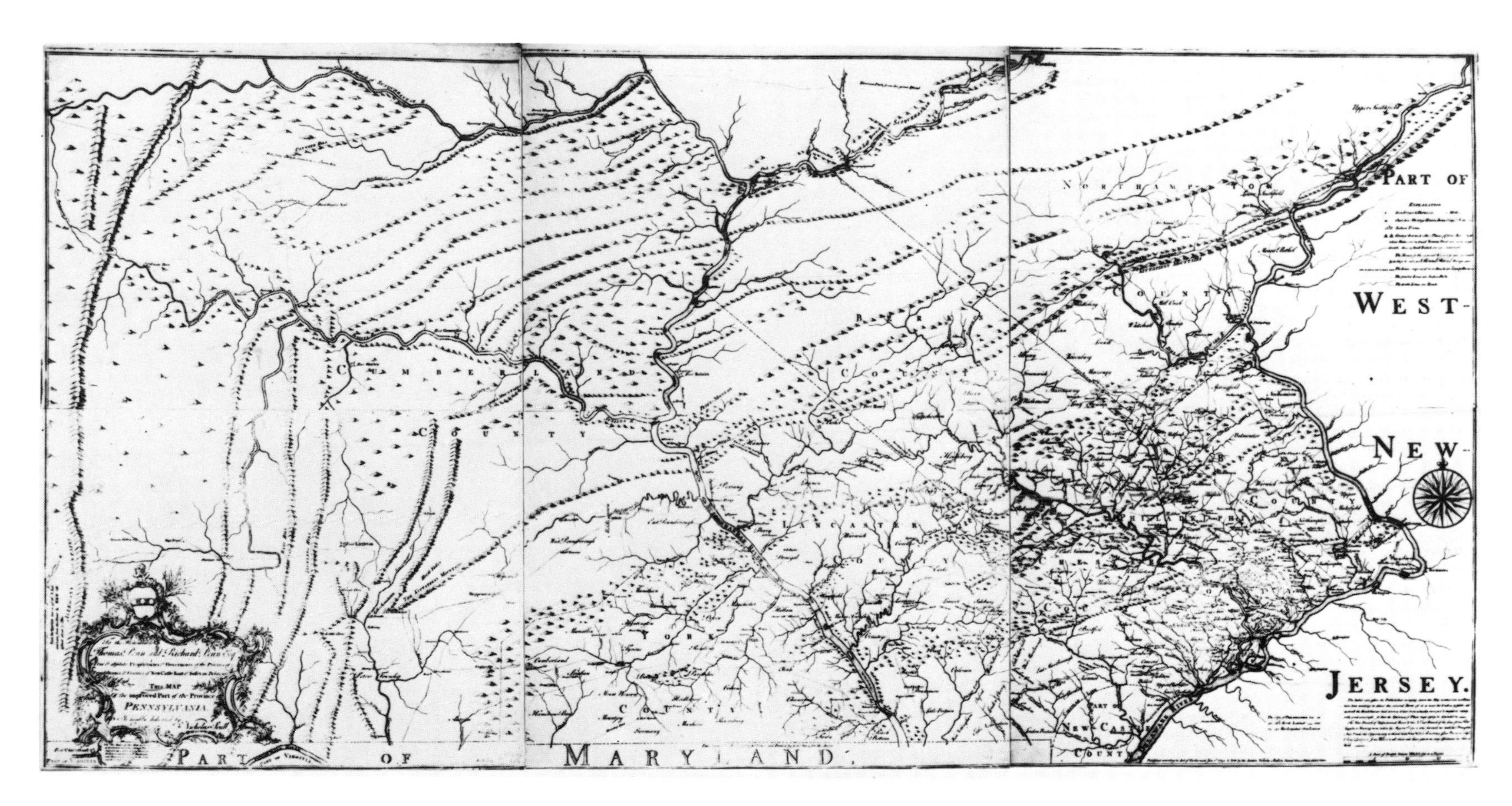

PLATE 102: Nicholas Scull. "Map of the improved Part of the Province of Pennsylvania." 1759. Engraving, 76 × 151 cm. Private collection. *First map of province published in America (in Philadelphia). Philadelphia located both longitudinally and latitudinally. Road through Allequippy's Gap and distance to Fort Duquesne are shown.*

Title page of Rocque's book of fort plans (see Plates 104A–104E)

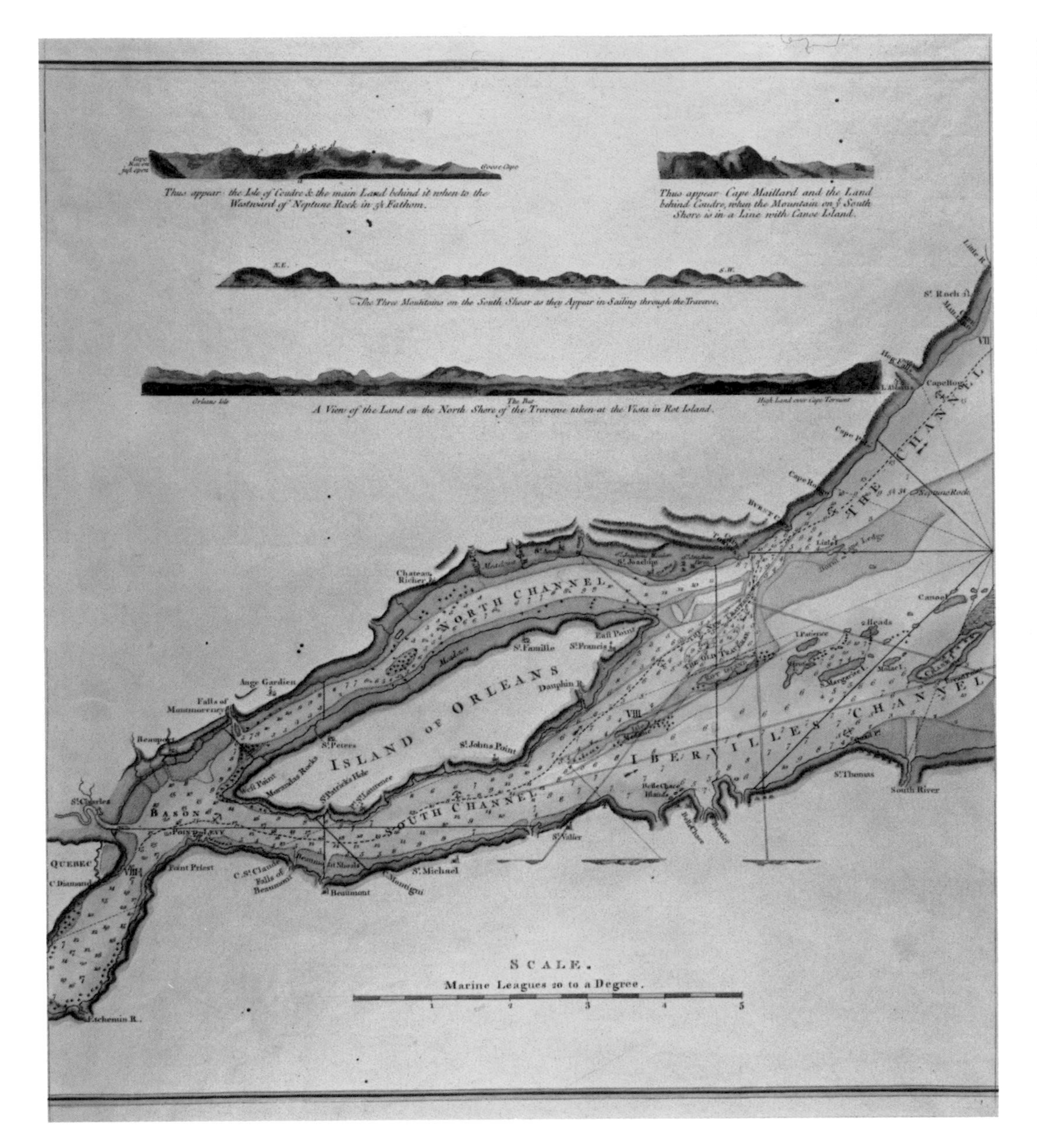

PLATE 103: James Cook. "A New Chart of the River St. Laurence" (detail). 1760. Engraving, hand colored; entire dimensions 172 × 117 cm. National Library of Australia, Canberra. *Entire map comprises twelve sheets (each 43 × 39 cm) and covers area from Richelieu Falls to Anticosti Island; it identifies all islands and shoals and provides soundings for navigation. Cook executed map as a junior officer in the British navy, and it led to his appointment as surveyor of Newfoundland. This sheet shows area just east of Quebec.*

state of Delaware, was overlooked, and a boundary dispute developed between Penn and Lord Baltimore. The Mason-Dixon Line permitted Pennsylvania to include Philadelphia within its borders and to include land that gives access to Delaware Bay and allowed Maryland to retain Baltimore within its province.

The rare 1770 "Map of the Province of Pennsylvania" by William Scull (*Plate 110*) shows "the whole line run by Messrs. Mason & Dixon." This map locates the site of General Edward Braddock's defeat at the battle of the Monongahela River east of Fort Pitt during the French and Indian War. Also depicted are several important roads, including the routes the French had used from Lake Erie to the Ohio River and the Pennsylvania State Road (also known as Forbes Road), which was the main highway from the East to the Mississippi Valley. In the same year Captain John Collett, commandant of Fort Johnston, North Carolina, published "A Compleat Map of North-Carolina from an actual

PLATE 104A: John Rocque. "A Plan of the City of New-York, Reduced from an actual Survey." 1763. Engraving, 26 × 42 cm. Private collection. *In upper right all churches, schools, marketplaces, and government houses are keyed to map. Separate cemeteries for blacks (Negros Burial Ground) and Jews located. All wharves and slips are on East River. Plates 104A–104E all appeared in Rocque's* A Set of Plans and Forts in America: Reduced from an Actual Survey *published posthumously in London in 1763 by Rocque's wife, Mary Ann.*

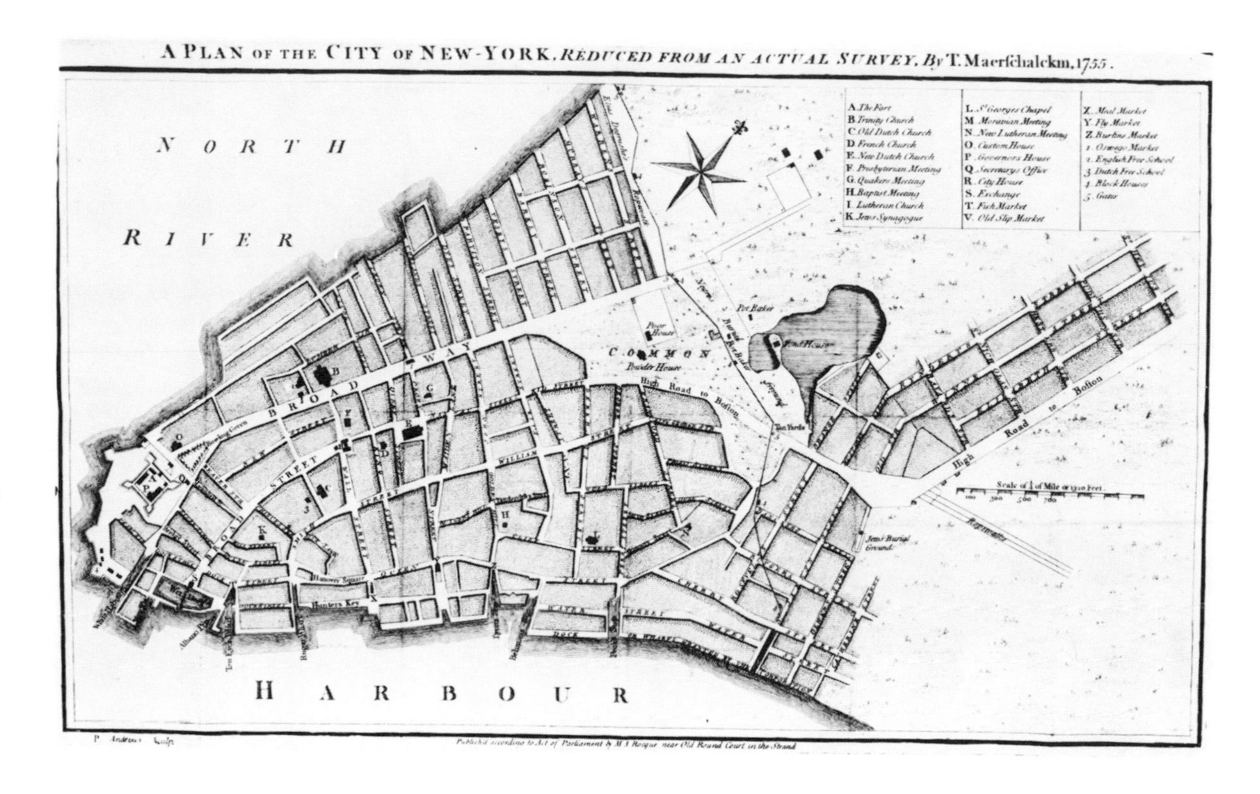

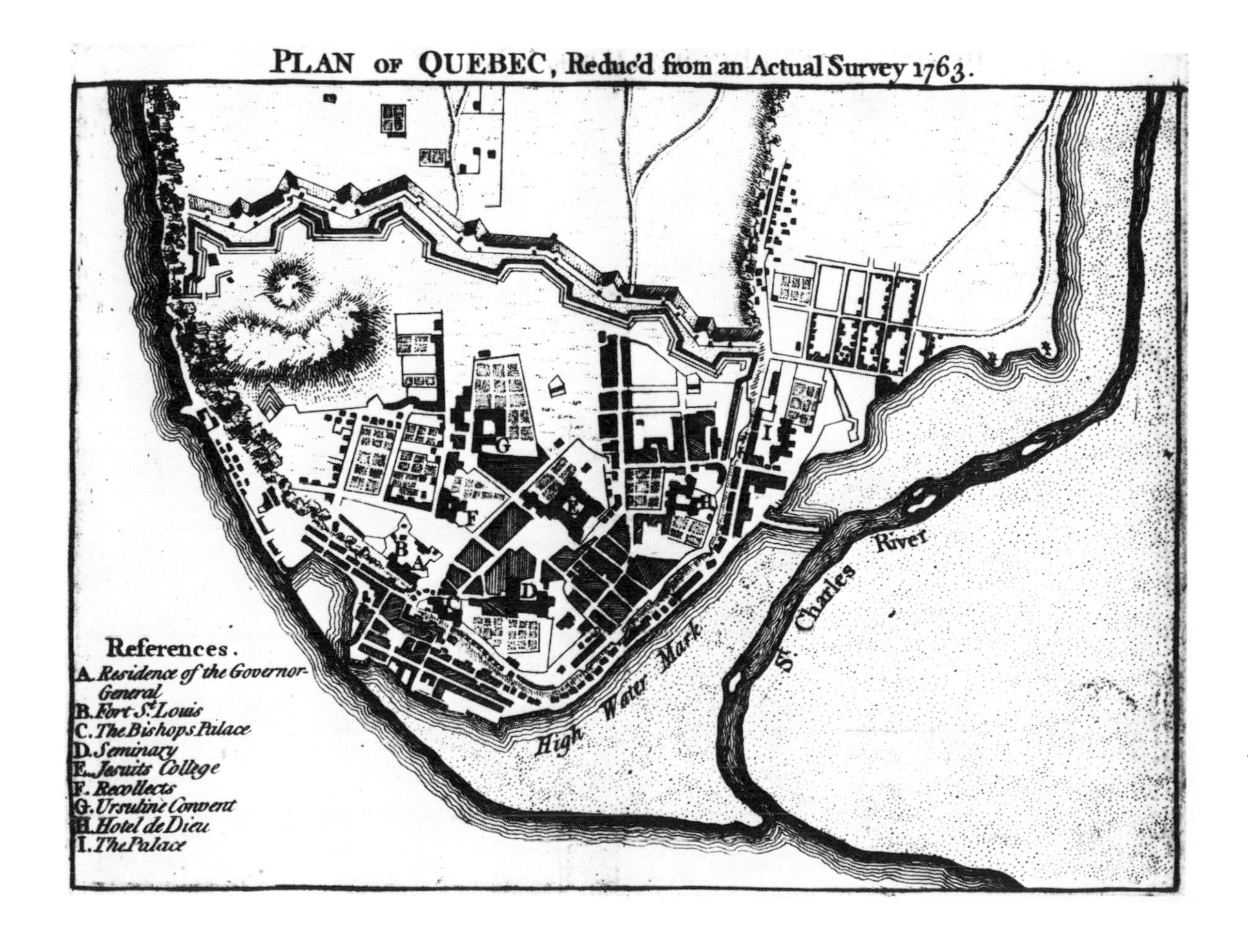

PLATE 104B: John Rocque. "Plan of Quebec, Reduc'd from an Actual Survey 1763." 1763. Engraving, 14 × 18 cm. Private collection. *Keyed for governor general's house, Fort St. Louis, church house, and Hôtel de Dieu, the oldest hospital extant in North America.*

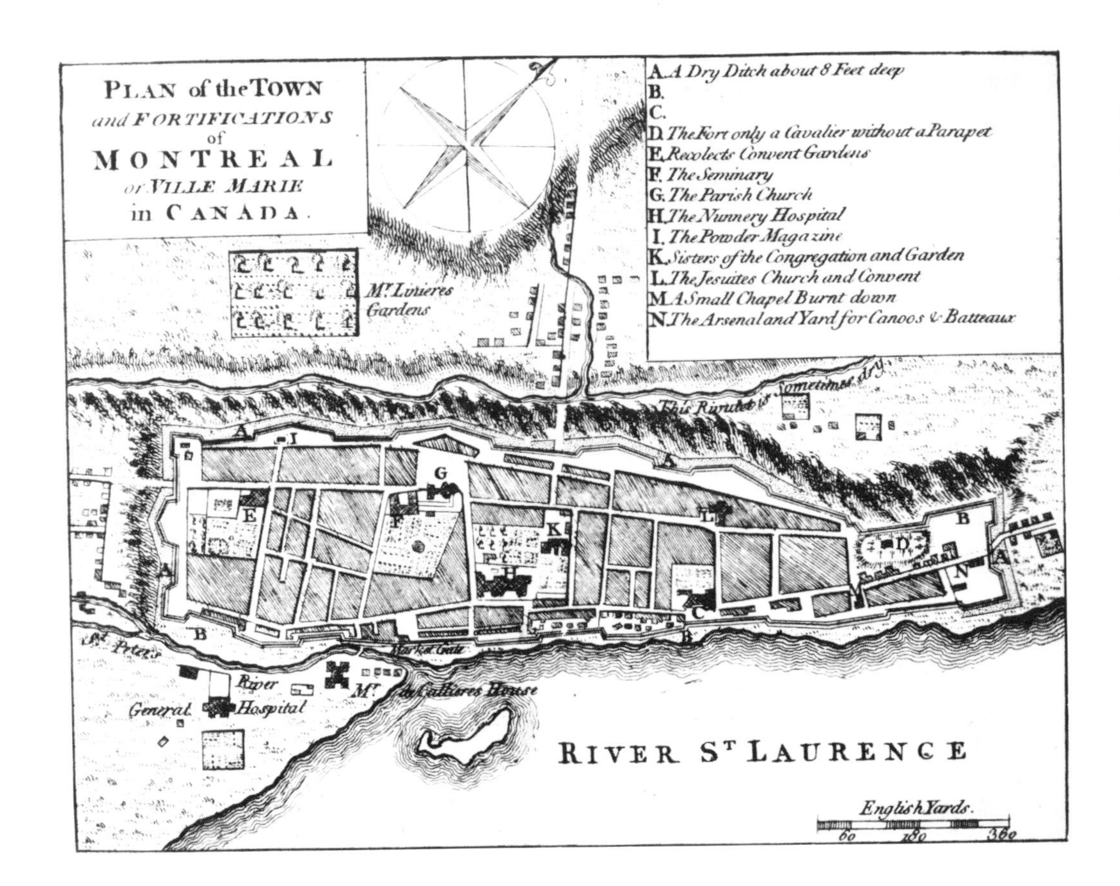

PLATE 104C: John Rocque. "Plan of the Town and Fortifications of Montreal or Ville Marie in Canada." 1763. Engraving, 14 × 18 cm. Private collection. *Keyed for fortifications, arsenals, churches, and hospitals. Two hospitals were General Hospital and Nunnery Hospital.*

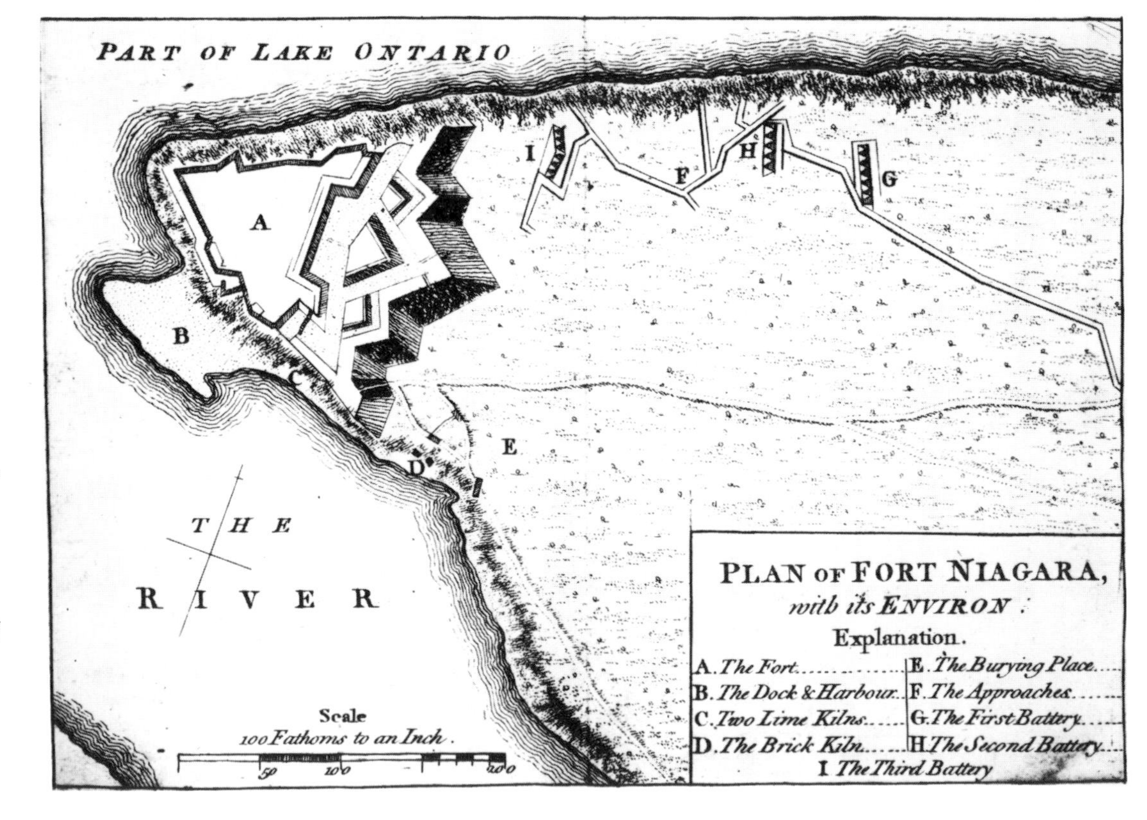

PLATE 104D: John Rocque. "Plan of Fort Niagara, with its Environ." 1763. Engraving, 14 × 18 cm. Private collection. *A typical layout for a fort and its protective batteries. Fort Niagara is on a point overlooking junction of Niagara River and Lake Ontario. It fell to British forces on July 25, 1759, preventing American access to west from the St. Lawrence. Now a popular tourist attraction.*

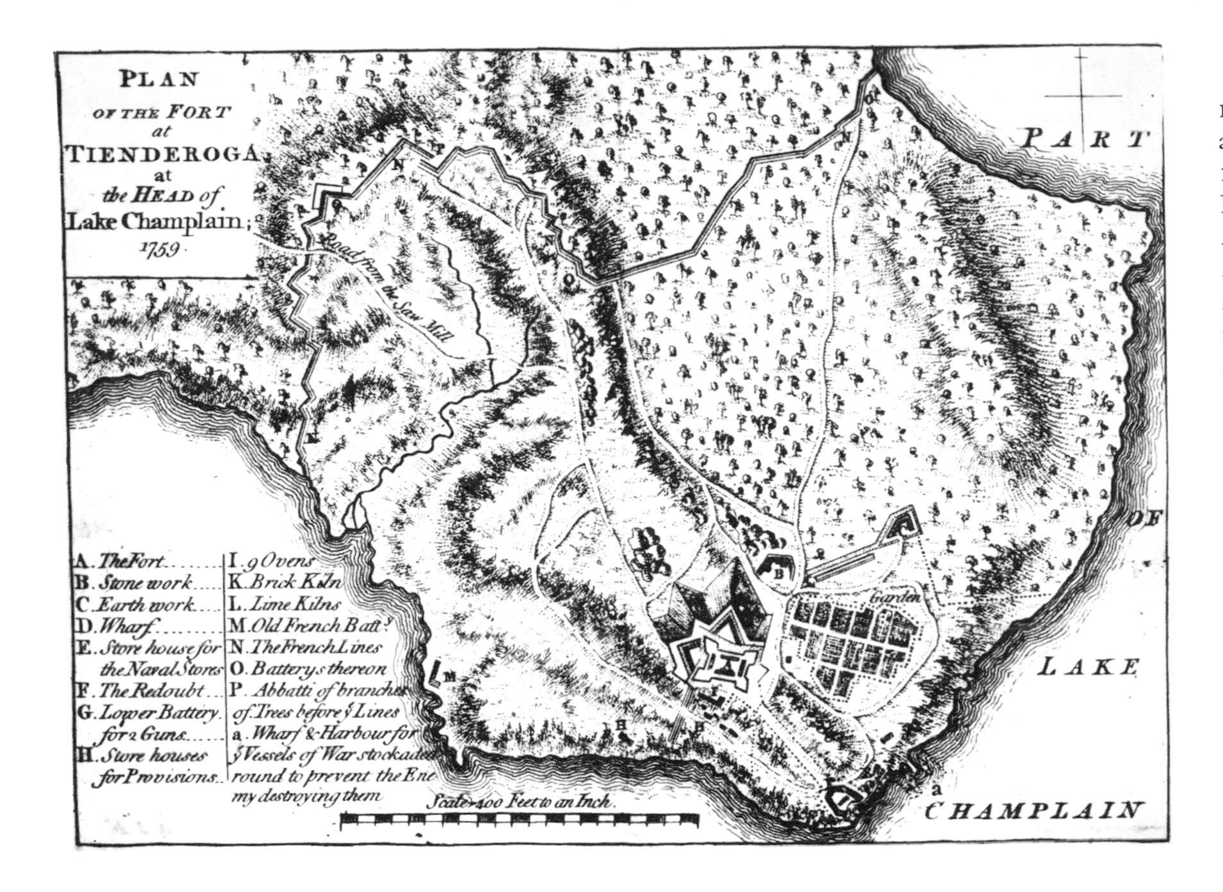

PLATE 104E: John Rocque. "Plan of the Fort at Tienderoga at the Head of Lake Champlain; 1759." 1763. Engraving, 14 × 18 cm. Private collection. *Fort was built to protect Lake Champlain, the major waterway to St. Lawrence Valley. Fort withstood an attack by the British in July 1758. In 1759, when the French realized they were outnumbered by Lord Jeffrey Amherst's attacking forces, they blew it up.*

Survey" (*Plate 111*). Its northern portion reflected a twenty-year survey by William Churton; Collett himself surveyed the southern and coastal regions. Throughout the remainder of the eighteenth century this accurate map was the basis for many subsequent maps of North Carolina.

The longest journey during the period following the French and Indian War was taken by Jonathan Carver between 1766 and 1768. He left Boston and, taking Mackinac Island as a jumping-off point, explored the Wisconsin and upper Mississippi rivers as far north as the St. Francis River. Carver was the first person to refer in print (in *Travels Through the Interior Parts of North America in the Years 1766, 1767 and 1768*, London, 1778) to a large mountain range that was a barrier to explorers seeking the Pacific Ocean from the east, probably a reference to the Rocky Mountain system. In 1767–68 Daniel Boone made his first excursion to the trans-Appalachian region, having been preceded a year earlier by at least four hunting parties. Boonesboro, Kentucky, was established in 1775 when Boone, acting as an agent for the Transylvania Company, induced settlers to accompany him. Harrodsburg had been founded the previous year by James Harrod, making it the oldest city in Kentucky.

The prerevolutionary period was also marked by acquisition of large segments of Indian lands by the English colonizers. In 1768 the Treaty of Fort Stanwix secured from the Iroquois all land east of a line near the fort and extending south as far as the Tennessee River and west as far as Oswego, New York. A 1771 manuscript map, "The Country of VI Nations," was drawn by Colonel Guy Johnson, who served under Jeffrey Amherst and became superintendent of Indian affairs in 1774. The original was destroyed by fire, but an engraved copy, which appeared in the fourth volume of Edmund B. O'Callaghan's *A Documentary History of the State of New York* (4 vols., Albany, 1849–51), shows the proclamation line, or boundary, between Indian territory and that of the American settlers, as established by the Treaty of Fort Stanwix. Also depicted on the Johnson map is the route from the Hudson River to Lake Ontario, beginning with a wagon road

Cartouche of the 4th state of 1755 Mitchell map, showing change in map title (see Plate 96)

from Albany to Schenectady and continuing along the Mohawk River to Fort Stanwix (present Rome, New York) and then to Lake Oneida and finally along the Onondaga River (Oswego River) to Fort Ontario.

In 1768 the Indiana Company purchased from the Iroquois 1.8 million acres south of the Ohio River, extending from the southern border of Pennsylvania to the Little Kanawha River. Between 1769 and 1771 western Pennsylvania's population doubled from 5,000 to 10,000 and new settlements developed in the West Virginia area. In 1770 a grant was made to the Grand Ohio Company to establish the proprietary colony of Vandalia in the Ohio Valley. The 1770 Treaty of Lochaber between the Cherokee and the English settlers, led by John Stuart, an Indian trader in Charles Town, South Carolina, who became superintendent of Indian affairs in 1763, added 9,000 square miles to Virginia, including most of the lands claimed by the Greenbrier and Loyal companies. By still another treaty, with the Creek Indians in 1773, the western boundary of Georgia was moved farther west to the Oconee River, while the Quebec Act of 1774 extended the boundaries of the colony of Quebec to the Ohio and Mississippi rivers, encroaching upon Virginia's western claims. With these various boundary changes and land acquisitions, new boundaries and placenames would be displayed on certain contemporary American maps and then disappear almost immediately on subsequent maps.

During the period between the French and Indian Wars and the American Revolution exploration continued in the politically detached western section of the continent. The Jesuits were deported in 1767 from New Spain and the region of California by the regional viceroys and were replaced by the Franciscans, who immediately began to establish a series of missions ranging from Baja California as far north as Monterey. In 1768 José de Gálvez, the viceroy general of New Spain, went to the California peninsula, where he drew up a master plan to prevent the Russians from taking possession of the western coast of North America. Attempting to bring northern California, known as Alta California, under Spanish control, Gálvez enlisted the aid of Junípero Serra, father-president of the Franciscan mission, and the cooperation of Spanish soldiers and sailors. In order to fulfill Spanish political aims in this region, a combination of coastal voyages and inland journeys was initiated in 1769 with the intention of establishing a colony at Monterey Bay. Captain Gaspar de Portolá, governor of Alta California, and the Franciscan friar Juan Crespi set forth in a northerly direction overland from San Diego, where they had founded a mission on July 16, 1769. It was during this journey that they camped at the site of Los Angeles, giving it its present name. Traveling up the San Fernando Valley, they eventually reached the Santa Clara Valley; a manuscript map by Miguel Costansó emanating from these explorations suggests that their journey extended north as far as the Golden Gate. A mission was finally established at Monterey in 1770.

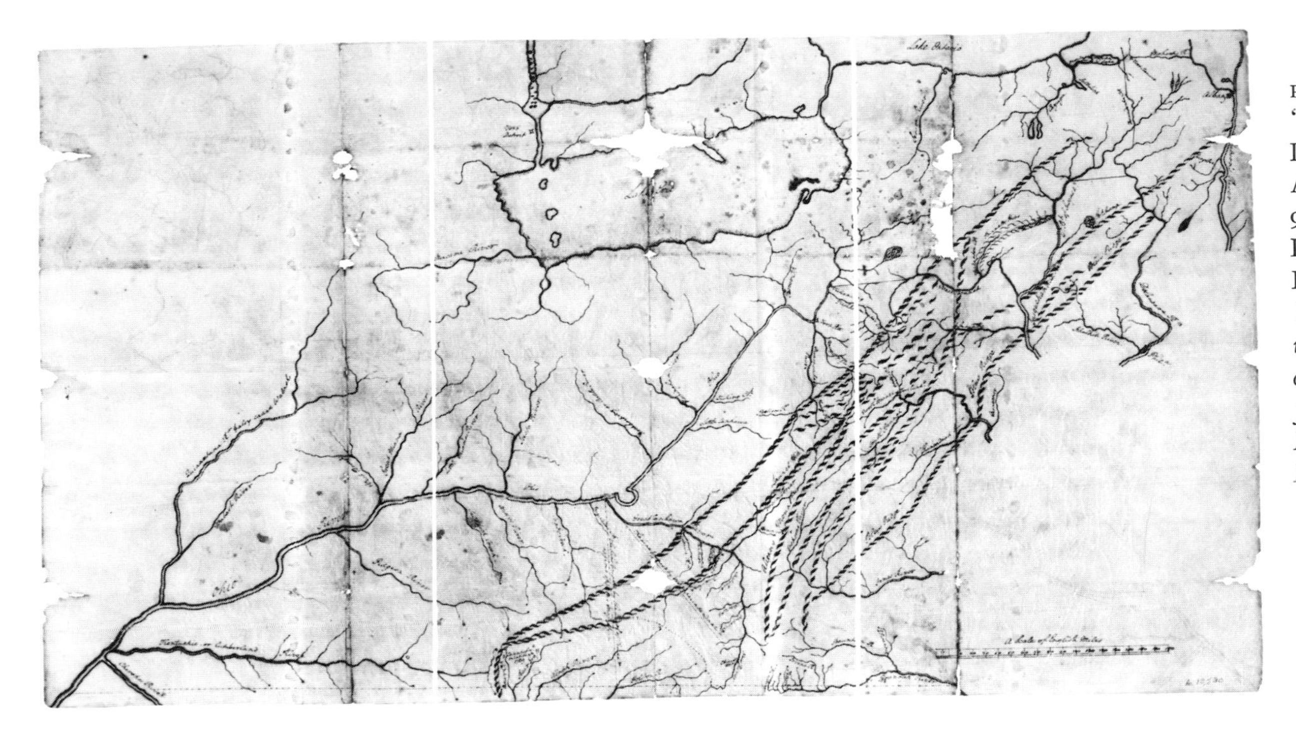

PLATE 105: George Washington. "Aligany. Copied from a Map of Doctor Walkers laid Before the Assembly." 1769. Manuscript, 52 × 97 cm. Manuscript Division, Library of Congress, Washington, D.C. *Known as the "Walker-Washington Map," this manuscript was drawn by Washington and based on Walker's survey west of Virginia as far as the headwaters of the Cumberland River. Extends west of the Wabash River.*

Sir New york 3d March 1762
You are hereby notified of a Meeting of the
Hand-in-Hand Fire Company at the House
of Mr. Crawley, at the City Arms on
Thursday next at Seven o'Clock in the Evening
To The Rt. Honble The Earl of Sterling.
Isaac Roosevelt Clerk

Scene from the Hand-in-Hand Fire Company certificate, New York, 1762

In 1772 Father Crespi, having returned to San Diego, set out with the explorer Pedro Fages, and reached the lower edge of San Francisco Bay. They continued north to San Joachim, passing through the area that was later named Berkeley. The first relatively accurate map of the bay, drawn by Crespi, was a consequence of this expedition. The manuscript "Carta del Puerto y Rio de Sn Francisco," now in the Ministerio del Ejército in Madrid, identifies the Golden Gate Channel as Baya de San Francisco, and the bay itself is reduced in width and shown as part of a larger river. Representation of San Francisco Bay earlier had appeared on Miguel Costansó's "Carta Reducida Del Oceano Asiático, Ó Mar Del Súr" published in 1771 in Madrid.

In 1774 Juan Pérez, a colonial sea pilot, voyaged as far north as Vancouver Island, and the following year the Spanish sea captain Juan de Ayala navigated the first recorded passage through the Golden Gate. As a consequence of his journey, Yerba Buena and Alcatraz islands were mapped on the 1775 "Plano del Puerto de San Francisco" by José de Cañizares. This manuscript, owned by the Archivo General de Indias in Seville, gives the name Alcatres to Yerba Buena Island, while the present Alcatraz Island is correctly positioned but unnamed. Also in 1775 a land route from Sonora to Alta California was discovered by Juan Bautista de Anza and the explorer and Franciscan missionary Father

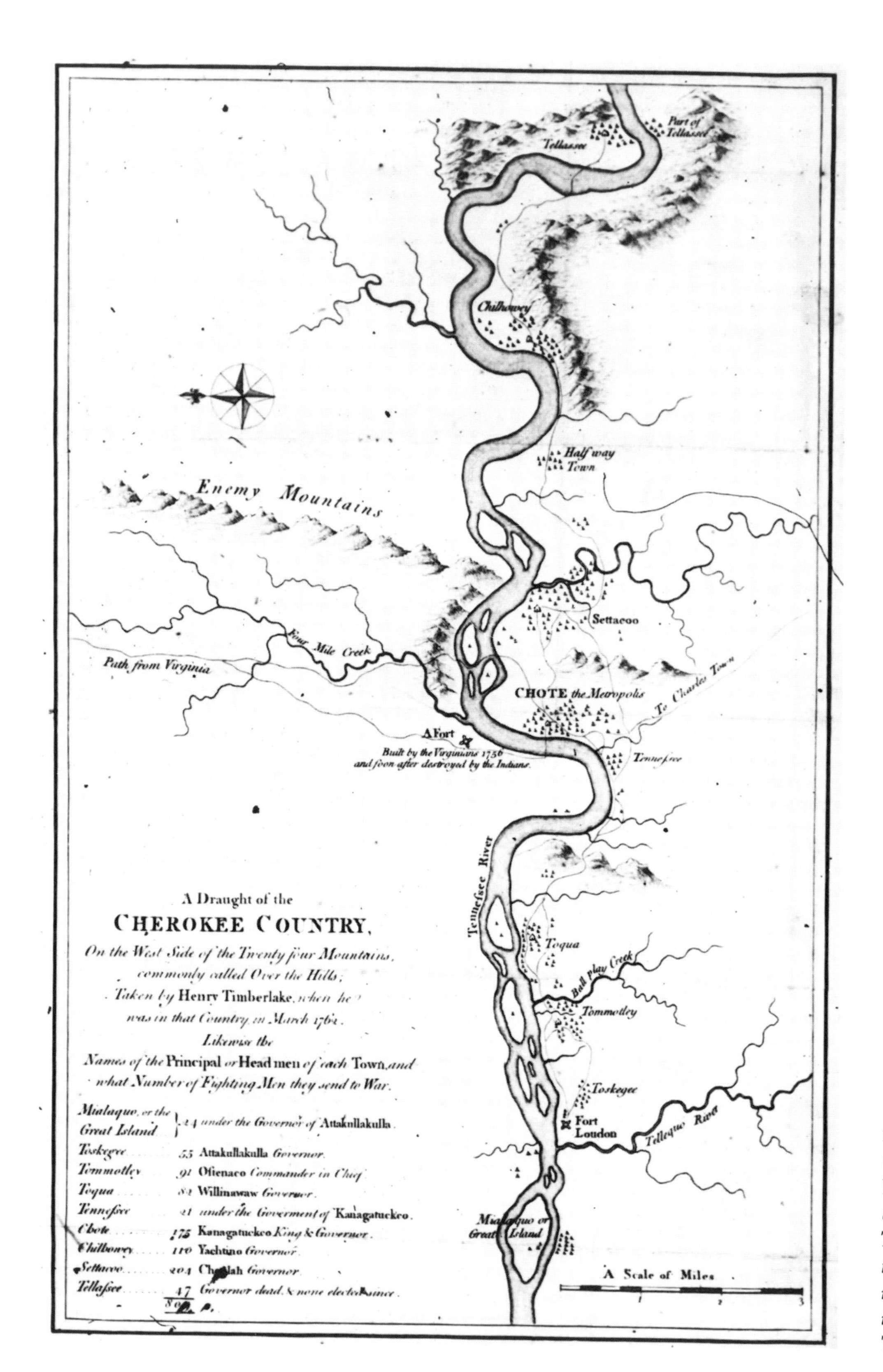

PLATE 106: Henry Timberlake. "A Draught of the Cherokee Country." 1765. Engraving, 39 × 24 cm. Private collection. *The first map of Tennessee region by an observer, who fought there in French and Indian War. Tennessee River is followed from Great Smoky Mountains to Fort Loudon and Great Island. Map is a memorial by naming for each town the chief and number of men who fought in the war. In Timberlake's* Memoirs of Lieut. Henry Timberlake *(London, 1765).*

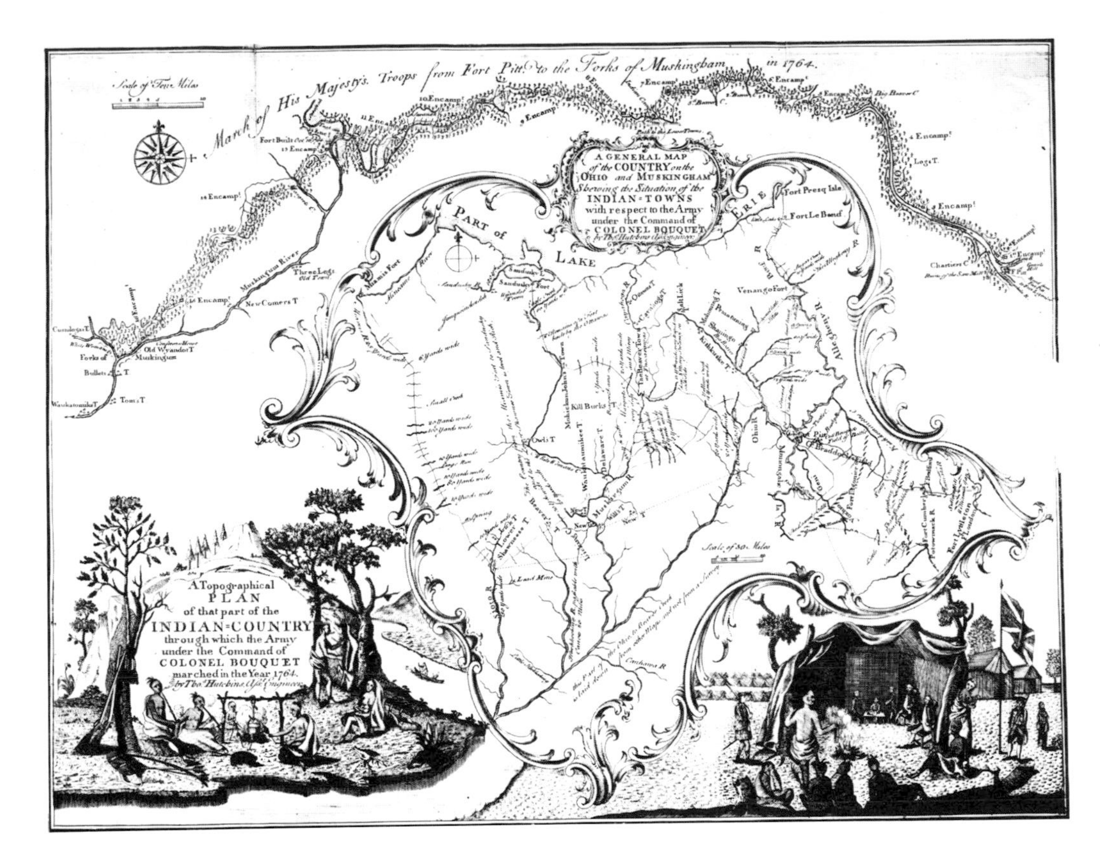

PLATE 107: Thomas Hutchins. "A Topographical Plan of that part of the Indian-Country through which the Army under the Command of Colonel Bouquet marched in the Year 1764." 1765. Engraving, 37 × 48 cm. Newberry Library, Chicago. *Actually combines two maps since "A General Map of the Country on the Ohio on Muskingham Shewing the Situation of the Indian-Towns with respect to the Army under the Command of Colonel Bouquet" is also included. First map published in America of what in eighteenth century was considered the Northwest. Shows route from Fort Pitt (Pittsburgh) to Old Wyandot Town near present Dennison, Ohio. Many rivers and Indian towns are located. Cartouches depict scenes of Indian life. Published in William Smith's* An Historical Account of the Expedition under the Command of Henry Bouquet Against the Ohio Indians *(Philadelphia, 1765).*

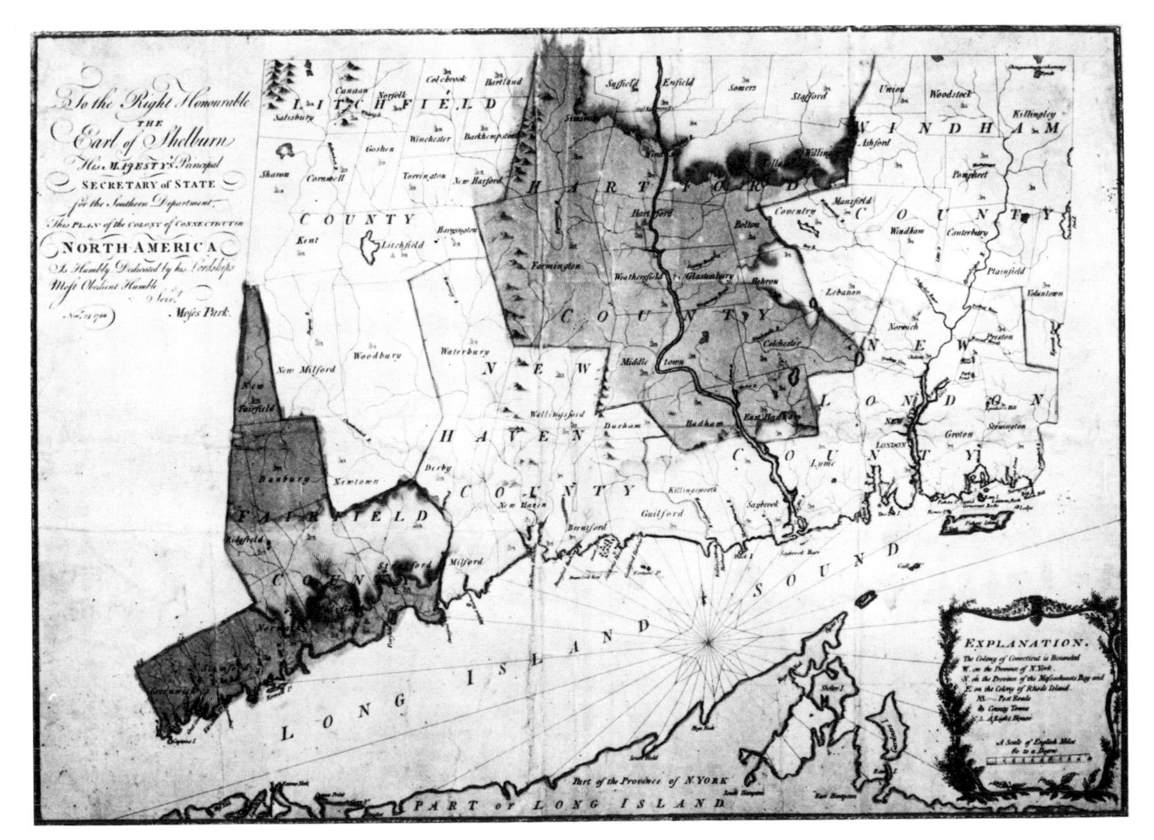

PLATE 108: Moses Park. "Plan of the Colony of Connecticut in North-America." 1766. Engraving, hand colored; 53 × 73 cm. William L. Clements Library, University of Michigan, Ann Arbor. *First map designed, engraved, and published in Connecticut. Map was requested by the earl of Halifax to improve postal service. Engraved by Abel Buell.*

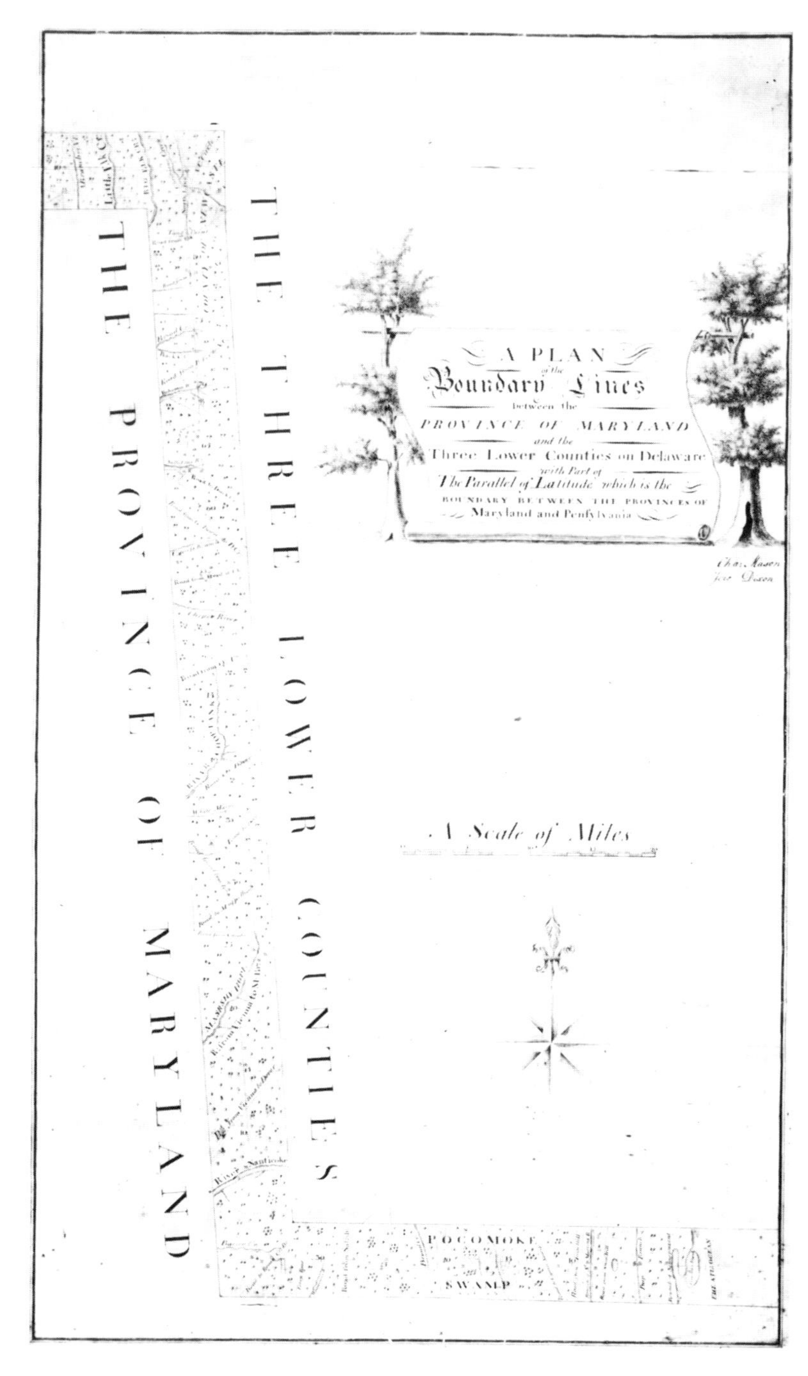

PLATE 109A: Cartographer unknown. "A Plan of the Boundary Lines between the Province of Maryland and the Three Lower Counties on Delaware with Part of The Parallel of Latitude which is the Boundary between the Provinces of Maryland and Pennsylvania." 1768. Engraving, 37 × 67 cm. Rare Books and Special Collections, Princeton University Library, Princeton. *Map represents a part of the Mason and Dixon survey (1763–67), which was ordered by the provincial government of Maryland to solve long-standing boundary dispute between Pennsylvania and Maryland. Incorporates Mason and Dixon's famous measurement of a degree of latitude.*

Francisco Garces. Garces's first route, in 1774, passed through the Colorado Desert into the San Jacinto Valley. Garces became the first European to enter the Great Basin, which stretched east from the Sierra Nevada Mountains to central Utah, and he was also the first known European since Coronado to reach the Grand Canyon.

The mapping of the Pacific Northwest was significantly affected when French scientists in 1769 ascertained the correct location for Cape San Lucas at the southern tip of Baja California, which became a reference point for calculating longitude farther north. Inland, far to the north, the British fur trader Samuel Hearne, commissioned by the Hudson's Bay Company, traveled west in 1771 from Hudson Bay and became the first European to sight the northern coastline of the North American continent. On this expedition Hearne discovered the Coppermine River and a few years later the entire region was scientifically surveyed by cartographers, including Philip Turnor, Peter Fidler, and David Thompson.

The third quarter of the eighteenth century witnessed the appearance of two maps by Bernard Romans, both now extremely rare: one of these, only two copies of which survive, is actually a two-part chart of East Florida and West Florida (*Plates 112A, 112B*). Engraved by Paul Revere and Abel Buell, to accompany Romans's *A Concise Natural History of East and West Florida* (New York, 1774), they are the first maps of the Florida area published in America. The second rare Romans map is an untitled manuscript generally known as "The Colony of New York and Its Surroundings" (*Plate 113*); ascribed to 1774, it is autographed by the cartographer. It covers an area between Detroit and Cape Cod, from Lake Nipissin and the mouth of the St. Lawrence to northern New Jersey. The colony of New York encompasses the northern half of Lake Erie, all of Lake Ontario, and part of the present Canadian province of Ontario. The northern boundary is fixed according to the "King's Order 20 July 1764." The old colony of New Hampshire, assigned to John Mason in 1621, and the enlarged province of New Hampshire, to Benning Wentworth in 1742, are outlined. Also shown are two sections of New York east of the Hudson River: one "will belong to Massachusetts Bay Province," the other "now a part of the Colony of Connecticut."

The 1770s and 1780s were dominated by the American Revolution. The American War of Independence was accompanied

PLATE 109B: Cartographer unknown. "A Plan of the West Line or Parallel of Latitude, which is the Boundary between the Provinces of Maryland and Pensylvania." 1768. Engraving, 50 × 64 cm. Rare Books and Special Collections, Princeton University Library, Princeton. *Continuation of Mason and Dixon survey, part of which appears in Plate 109A, to make up the Mason-Dixon Line. The two maps do not join but were separate publications.*

Boston's North Battery, built 1646; engraved by Paul Revere, 1770

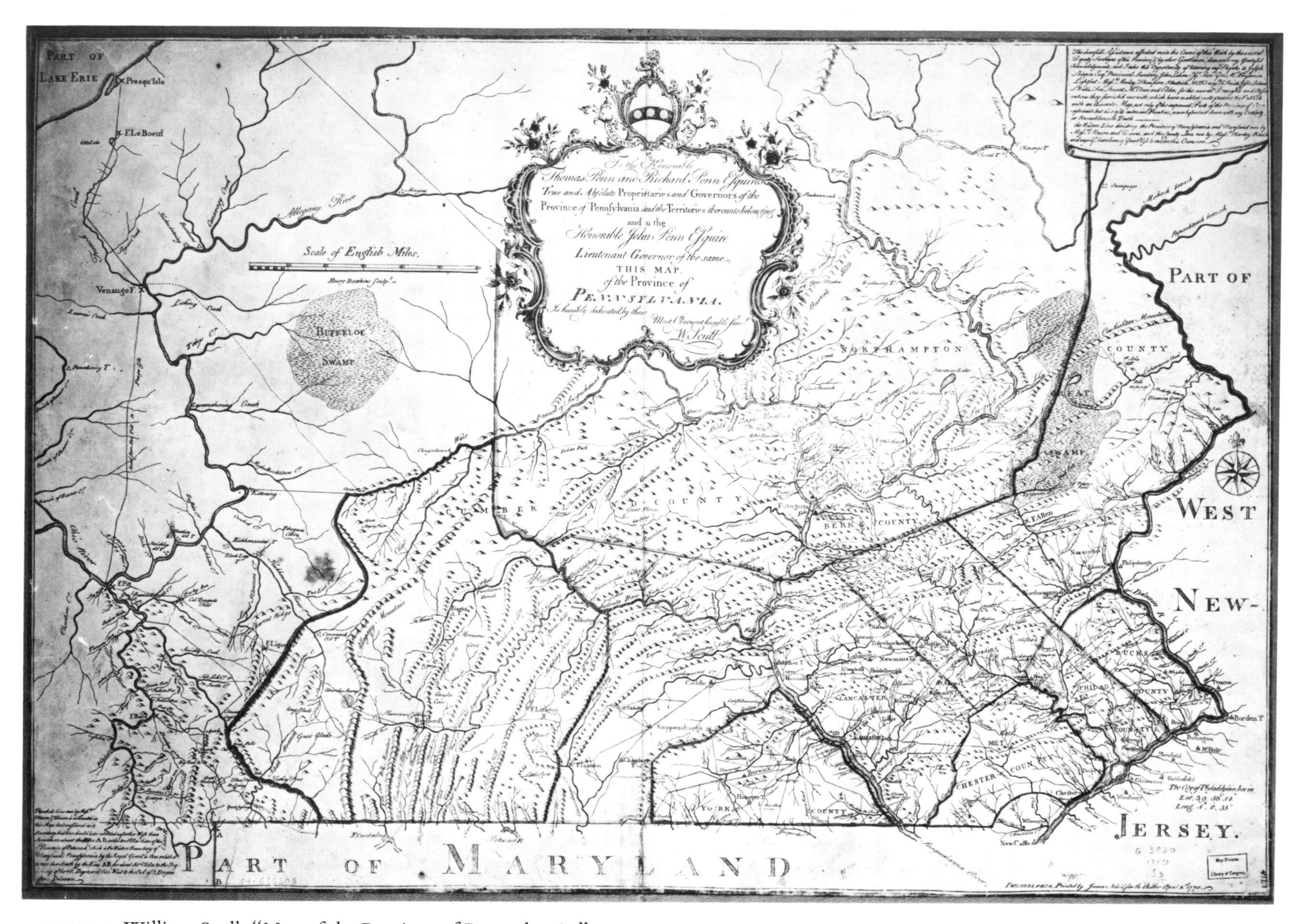

PLATE 110: William Scull. "Map of the Province of Pennsylvania." 1770. Engraving, 69 × 81 cm. Geography and Map Division, Library of Congress, Washington, D.C. *"The whole line run by Messrs. Mason & Dixon is delineated in this map" (noted on lower left of map). The routes of French from Lake Erie to Ohio River are shown; also roads built by General Edward Braddock (1755) and General John Forbes (1758). Roads from Lancaster, York, and Carlisle were routes used in southwestern migration. Location of Braddock's defeat east of Fort Pitt is indicated.*

(opposite) PLATE 111: John Collet. "A Compleat Map of North-Carolina from an actual Survey." 1770. Engraving, 73 × 110 cm. Geography and Map Division, Library of Congress, Washington, D.C. *Includes almost the entire present state; it remained the definitive map of the area for the rest of the century. Detail of the northern part of map is based on William Churton's survey.*

by a plethora of cartographic records, which is characteristic of most wars. Maps were produced to detail more precisely areas of potential strategic importance. Battle plans were published after the fact to keep the public informed on the latest military maneuvers, and they were eagerly sought by England, whose troops were in combat an ocean's distance from their homeland.

Several important strategic maps were published just before, or shortly after, the onset of the war. The former were clearly in anticipation of the conflict. In 1775 the first edition of "A Map of the Province of New York, with Part of Pensilvania, and New England" (*Plate 114*) was issued in London. The map was drawn by the well-known British military engineer, John Montresor, who also had surveyed the region. The mapped area emphasizes the Hudson Valley and extends westward from Connecticut to the Mohawk Valley and south from Crown Point to Burlington, New Jersey. Large insets depict the upper Connecticut Valley

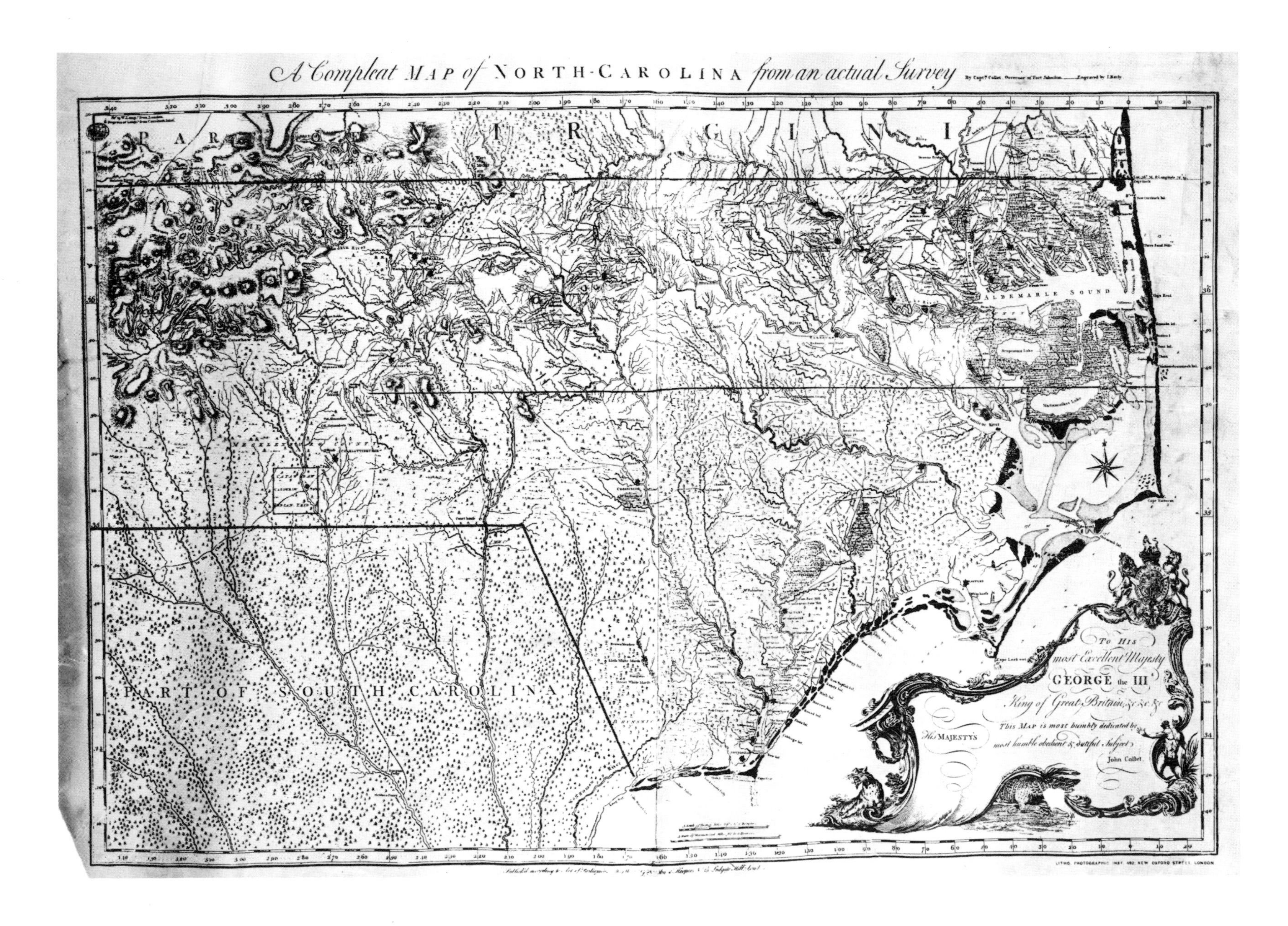

PLATE 112A: Bernard Romans. "Part of The Province of East Florida." 1774. Engraving, 62 × 221 cm. Geography and Map Division, Library of Congress, Washington, D.C. *One of the two whole-sheet maps that comprise a famous chart of part of the east and west coasts of Florida (see Plate 112B). Detailed representation of the coastline and immediate interior. Two insets: one a view of Fort St. Marks, showing a squall rising over the land; the other a view of the mouth of St. Marys River. Engraved by Paul Revere and Abel Buell. Only other extant copy of the two-part map is at Historical Society of Pennsylvania in Philadelphia. Two-part map published to accompany Romans's* A Concise Natural History of East and West Florida *(New York, 1774).*

and Lake Champlain. The map's first state is identified by the appearance of Ticonderoga as Carillon Fort on the west bank of Lake Champlain and Tienderoga on the east bank, since these names were altered on subsequent editions.

Another 1775 map is of interest mainly because of its artist, John Trumbull, the portrait and history painter whose later work adorns the Capitol rotunda in Washington, D.C. Trumbull drew a manuscript map of "A Part of the Colony of Connecticut," now in the Massachusetts Historical Society in Boston. Its main geographic value is its documentation of the Connecticut colony's claims in its dispute with Pennsylvania over title to the Wyoming Valley in the region of present Wilkes-Barre. In 1782 a New Jersey court decided in favor of Pennsylvania.

The status of the southern colonies at the beginning of the revolutionary war was depicted on several British maps. The Fry and Jefferson map (*see Plate 92*) was updated to provide new cartographic information on the Ohio Valley. The London map firm of Robert Sayer and John Bennett, which had acquired a substantial share of Thomas Jefferys's business following his bankruptcy in 1766, published in 1775 an important topographical map, "An Accurate Map of North and South Carolina With Their Indian Frontiers" by Henry Mouzon and others (*Plate 115*). This map, which incorporated cartographic data from William de Brahm's map of 1757 (*see Plate 101*), was the archetype for plotting out that region for almost fifty years. A series of large wall maps, each about six feet square (183 by 183 cm), the first of

(opposite) PLATE 112B: Bernard Romans. "Part of the Province of East Florida." 1774. Engraving, 147 × 169 cm. Geography and Map Division, Library of Congress, Washington, D.C. *In second of Romans's two whole-sheet maps (see Plate 112A) a strip of Florida peninsula from Tampa Bay region on the west coast to an area north of Cape Canaveral on the east is represented. Map dedicated "To all Commanders of vessels round the Globe." A second dedication "To the Honble. the Planters in Jamaica and all Merchants Concerned in the trade of that Island." Engraved by Paul Revere and Abel Buell.*

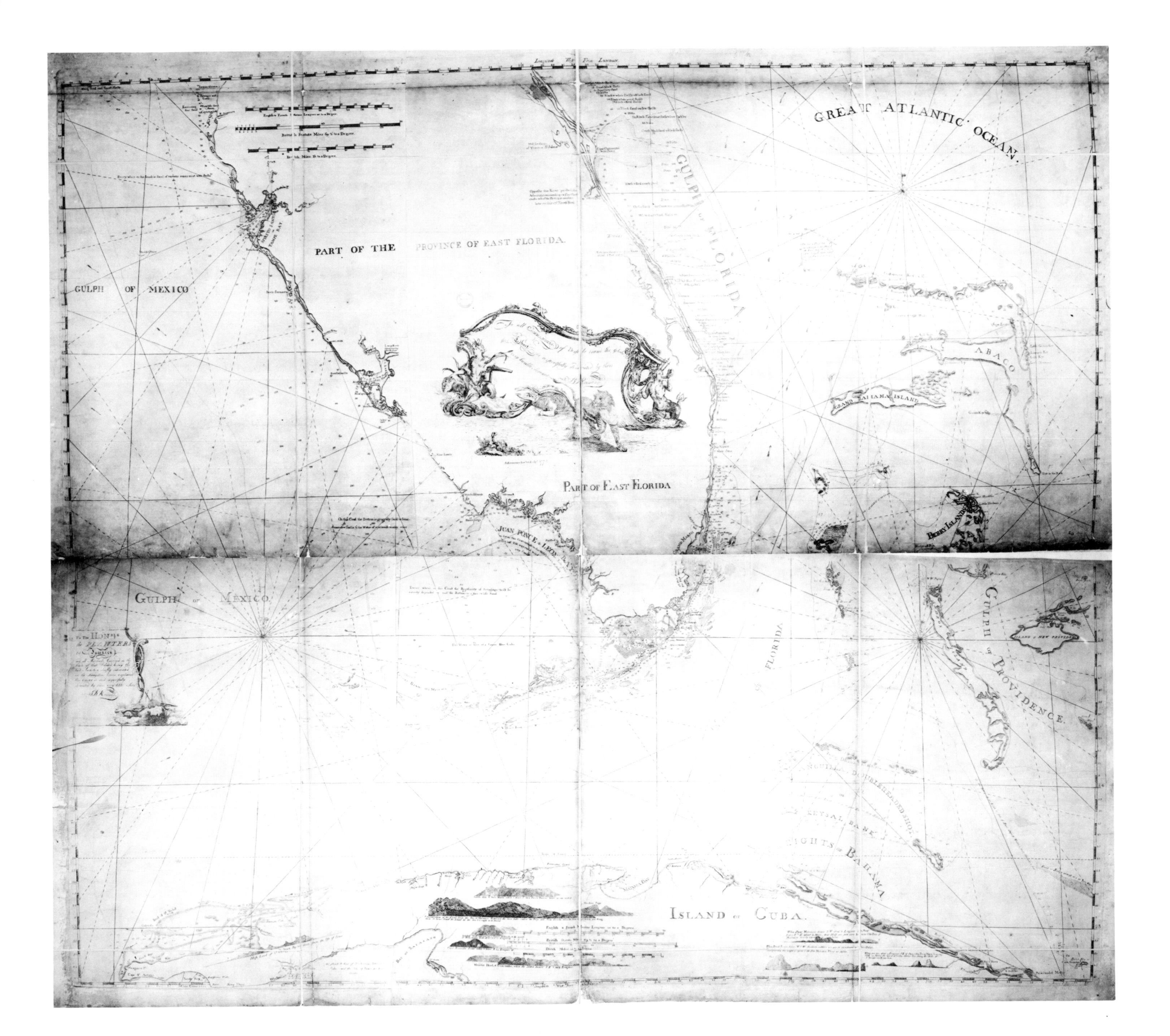

GREAT ATLANTIC OCEAN.
GULPH OF FLORIDA
PART OF THE PROVINCE OF EAST FLORIDA
GULPH OF MEXICO
PART OF EAST FLORIDA
ABACO
GRAND BAHAMA ISLAND
BERRY ISLANDS
JUAN PONCE de LEON
GULPH OF MEXICO.
FLORIDA
GULPH OF PROVIDENCE.
ISLAND of NEW PROVIDENCE
ISLAND of CUBA.

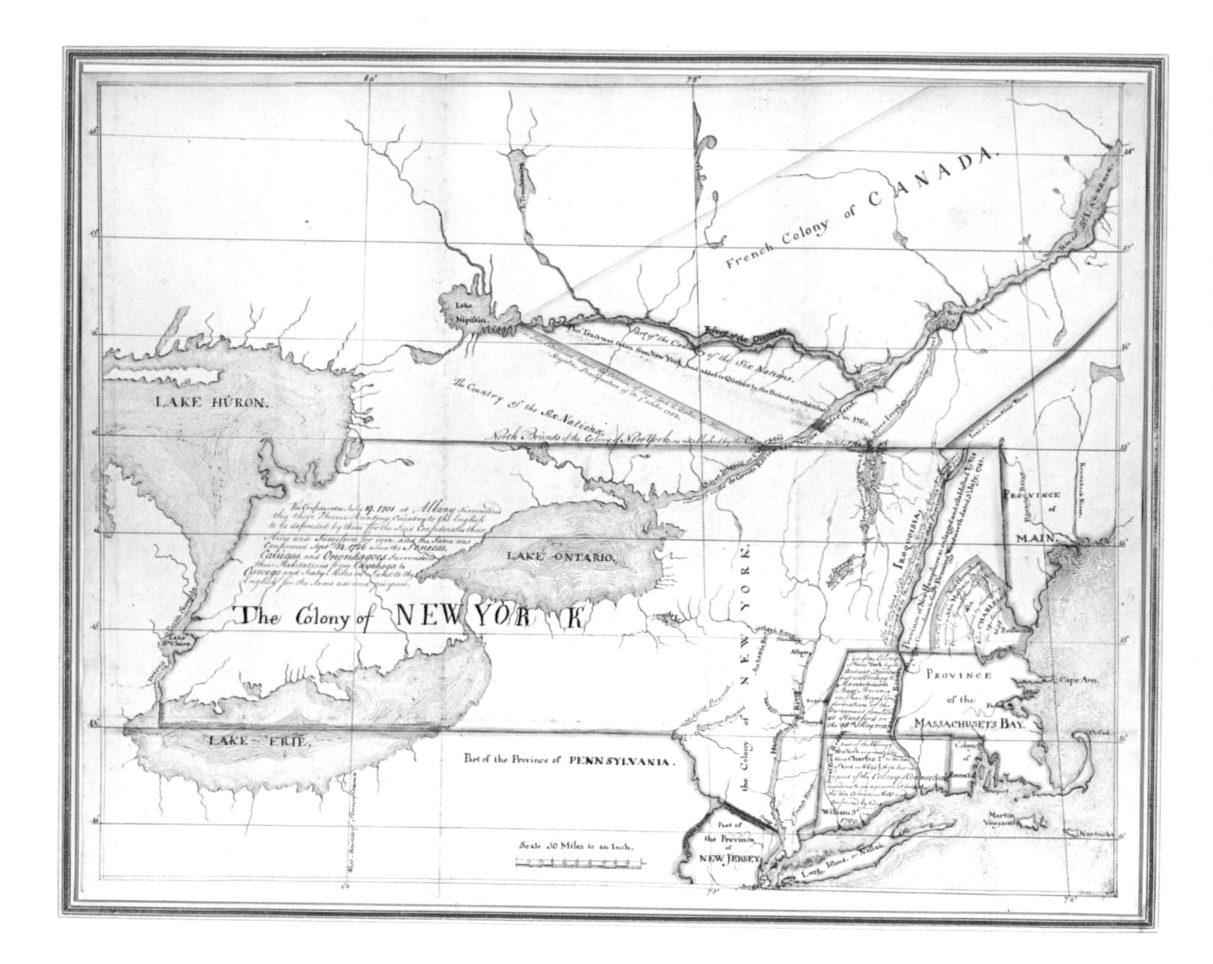

PLATE 113: Bernard Romans. "The Colony of New York and Its Surroundings." 1774. Manuscript, pen and ink and watercolor; 46 × 59 cm. Private collection. *Manuscript maps by this major American cartographer are extremely rare. Colony of New York, based on the proclamation of 1764 (as stated on map), encompasses present Vermont and southern part of Ontario. Extensions of provinces of Massachusetts Bay and New Hampshire are defined according to specific decrees.*

which was completed in 1775, also provided geographic knowledge about this region. John Stuart, the superintendent of Indian affairs, and John Purcell, that department's most talented cartographer, collated information on the Southeast that had been included on various earlier surveys made by others. Their first wall map, in manuscript, is entitled "A Map of the Southern District of North America."

April 19, 1775, marks the beginning of the War of Independence, when the British marched on Lexington; the following day British troops seized stores at Concord. In May the Americans directed their initial efforts at gaining control of the Lake Champlain waterways. During this venture the combined efforts of Ethan Allen and Benedict Arnold led to the capture of Fort Ticonderoga and Crown Point. In the following month, on June 17, the British troops, which were concentrated in Boston, defeated the recently assembled American troops at Breed's Hill in an episode that has come to be known as the battle of Bunker Hill.

"A Plan of the Town and Harbour of Boston" (*Plate 116*) by I. De Costa, published in London on July 29, 1775, is the first map depicting a battle of the revolutionary war. It was designed to show the action at Lexington and Concord and includes references to the battle of Bunker Hill, which had taken place only forty-three days prior to the map's being printed. This speedy publication is impressive since information detailing the battle had to be dispatched by ship to England. Recently the historian and cartography specialist William P. Cumming has suggested in *British Maps of Colonial America* (1974) that a manuscript map belonging to the Percy Collection at Alnwick Castle, England, may be the original on which De Costa's map was based.

One of the maps detailing comprehensively the battle area in Massachusetts was published by Robert Sayer and John Bennett

The Boston Tea Party *(1773), from* Kalender für 1784, *Berlin*

on September 2, 1775. "The Seat of War, in New England, by an American Volunteer" (*Plate 117*) shows troops converging on Boston from New Hampshire, Connecticut, and Rhode Island. The most meticulous representation of the battle of Bunker Hill appears on a map by Thomas Hyde Page based on an actual survey by Captain John Montresor and published between 1775 and 1778 (*Plate 118*). The first separate American imprint dedicated to this battle was executed by Bernard Romans and published in Philadelphia in 1775. It bears the title "To The Hone. Jno. Hancock Esqre., President of the Continental Congress, This Map of the Seat of Civil War in America is Respectfully Inscribed By His Most Obedient Servant B. Romans," interesting for its mention of John Hancock.

The events of the remainder of the first year of war were centered on the Canadian theater. These culminated on December 31 when American forces under General Richard Montgomery and Benedict Arnold, following an unsuccessful attack on Quebec, laid siege to that city. "Plan of the City and Environs of Quebec," published September 1776 in London by William Faden, depicts the American artillery positions and British fortifications as well as the deployment of Arnold's troops on the adjacent Plains of Abraham. The year 1776 was ushered in by the British burning and occupation of Norfolk, Virginia, on New Year's Day. A month later American forces reoccupied the city. In the North the British were forced to evacuate Boston on March 17. In the same month the field of battle extended as far as the Bahamas, where a naval engagement took place at Nassau. In June the British made their first attempt to capture Charleston, South Carolina, which was guarded by Fort Moultrie on Sullivans Island in Charleston Harbor. The effort failed and put an end to active British operations in the southern theater for two years. Also in March the Americans discontinued their siege of Quebec and retreated in stages to Fort Ticonderoga.

British forces landing in the Jerseys

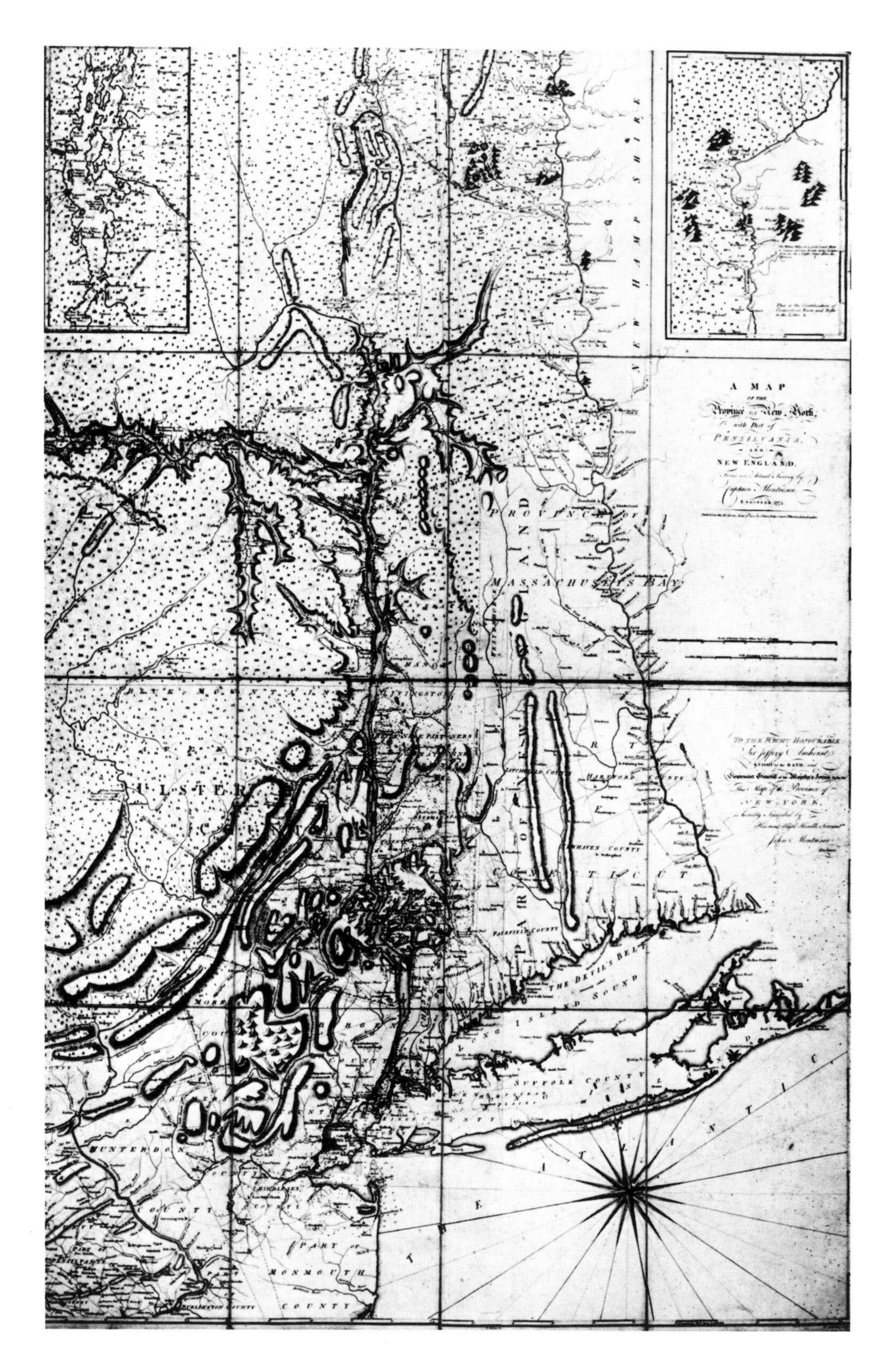

PLATE 114: John Montresor. "A Map of the Province of New York, with Part of Pensilvania, and New England." 1775. Engraving, 147 × 93 cm. Private collection. *First of four editions of a topographical map by an important British military engineer. One of the most detailed maps of New York region issued during the revolutionary era. Inset on right shows White Hills east of Connecticut River; that on the left shows Lake Champlain.*

(opposite) PLATE 115: Henry Mouzon *et al.* "An Accurate Map of North and South Carolina With Their Indian Frontiers." 1775. Engraving, 101 × 144 cm. Private collection. *Most important topographic map of the region for ensuing fifty years. Besides details of natural features, it depicts forts, parishes, bridges, roads, Indian paths, and boundaries. Insets show Charleston and Port Royal harbors. Published in Thomas Jefferys's* American Atlas *(London, 1775).*

The major military activity during 1776 was focused on New York and New Jersey. Bernard Ratzer had two of his earlier maps of New York City republished. The smaller map, known as the "Ratzen Plan" due to a misspelling of the cartographer's name, first published in 1769, was incorporated into the second and larger map, first published in 1770, called the "Ratzer Plan" (*Plate 119*), which pictures the lower half of Manhattan and Brooklyn Heights. The bottom portion shows a view of New York from Governors Island. The map has been cited by I. N. Phelps Stokes in *Iconography of Manhattan Island, 1498–1909* (1915–28) as "one of the most beautiful, important and accurate plans of New York." Also in 1776 Ratzer collaborated with Claude Joseph Sauthier on the separately published "A Map of the Province of New York. Which Included New Jersey." "The

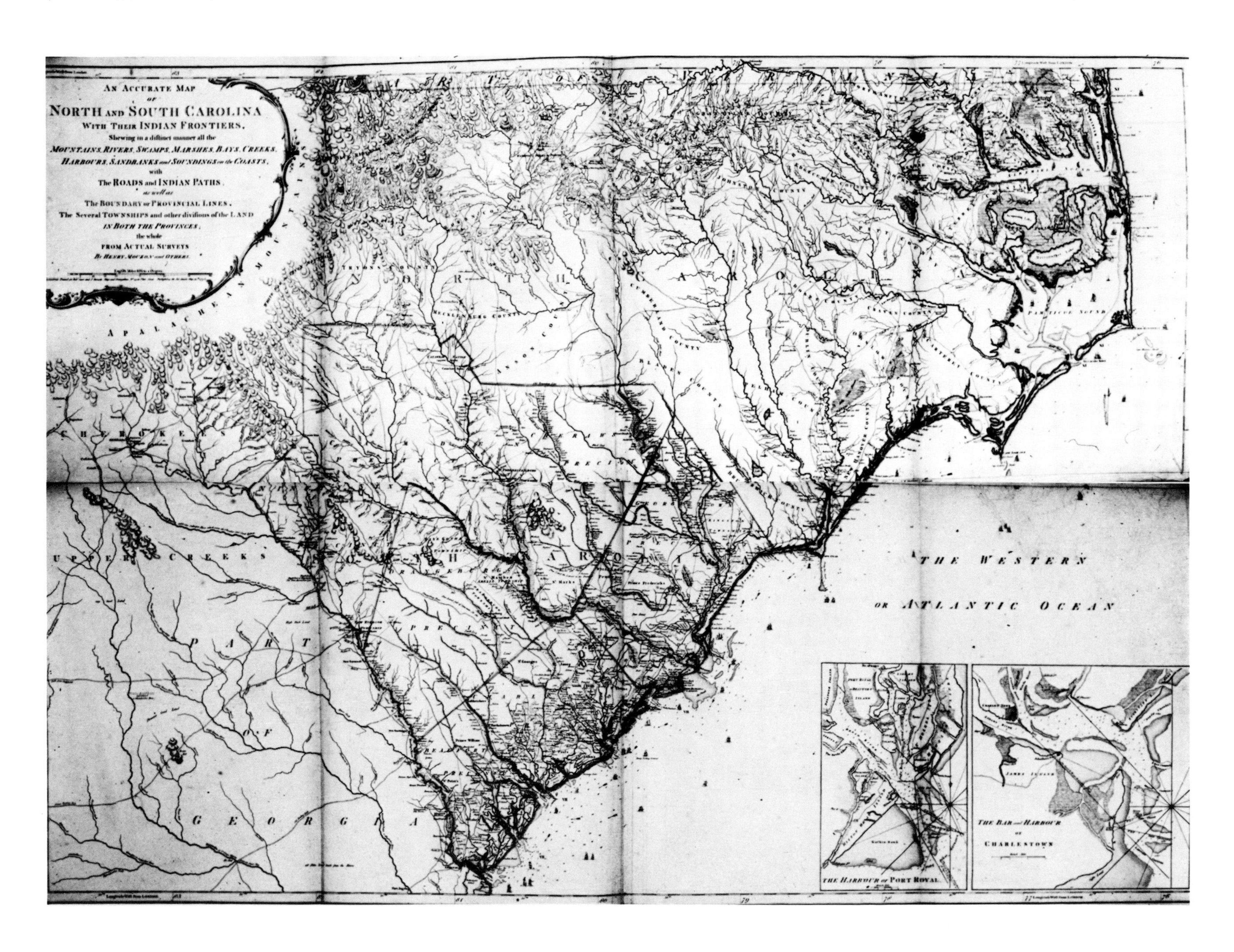

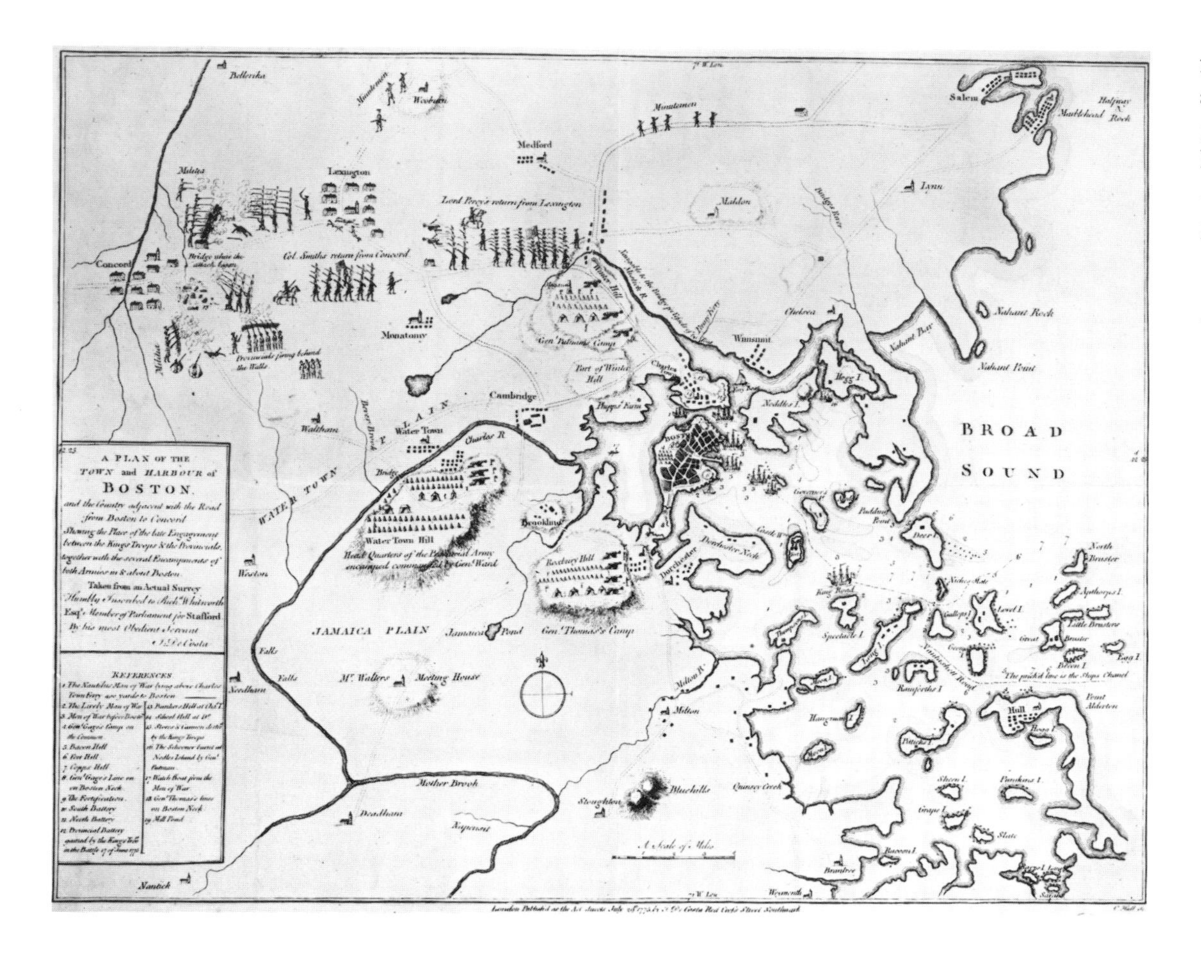

PLATE 116: I. De Costa. "A Plan of the Town and Harbour of Boston." 1775. Engraving, 37 × 49 cm. Geography and Map Division, Library of Congress, Washington, D.C. *First printed map of first battles of the Revolution, published in London. Shows troops fighting at Concord and Lexington and indicates site near Charlestown of battle of Bunker Hill only six weeks after it was fought.*

Province of New Jersey, Divided into East and West, commonly called The Jerseys" (*Plate 120*), by Ratzer alone, was published in 1777. This was a more detailed chart of the area and was drawn from a survey made in 1769; it is often regarded as the most important general map of New Jersey during the revolutionary period.

In the spring of 1776 Washington had moved his troops from Boston to New York, fortifying Brooklyn Heights and the northern part of Manhattan Island. On August 25 the British, under General William Howe, landed on Long Island. They were victorious at Brooklyn Heights, forcing Washington to withdraw his troops from Manhattan to White Plains. Claude Joseph Sauthier's "Topographical Map of the North Part of New York Island" published in early March 1777 shows the area through which Washington passed. A more inclusive map of the northern colonies during the beginning of the revolutionary war was Bernard Romans's "A Chorographical Map of the Northern Department," published in New Haven in 1777, and designed to accompany Romans's "A General Map of the Southern British Colonies in America."

There were further British victories on Long Island and in Manhattan and White Plains. The battle of Long Island on August 27, 1776, was reported in England within seven weeks on "A Plan of New York Island with Part of Long Island, Staten Island & East New Jersey," published as a separate map by William Faden. The British capture of Fort Lee and Fort Washington (renamed Fort Knyphausen) led to an American retreat from New York, first to New Jersey and then across the Delaware River into Pennsylvania. Major battle activity at the end of 1776 occurred on the evening of December 27 when the American troops launched a successful surprise attack on Trenton, New Jersey. The New Jersey campaign of General Washington was the subject of a Wil-

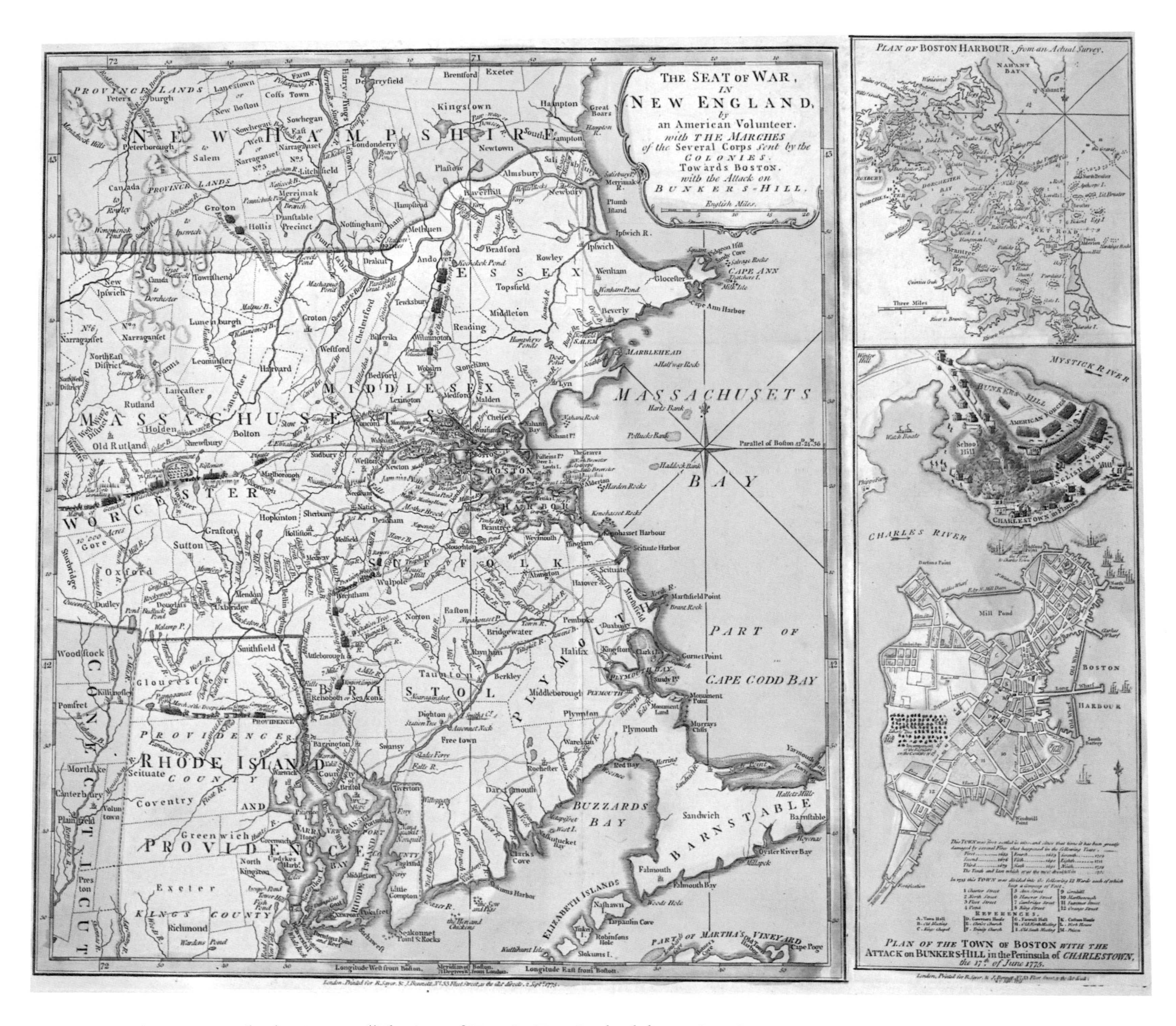

PLATE 117: Robert Sayer and John Bennett. "The Seat of War, in New England, by an American Volunteer." 1775. Engraving, hand colored; 46 × 54 cm. Private collection. *Troops from New Hampshire, Connecticut, and Rhode Island are converging on Boston. Two insets show Boston harbor and town of Boston with the attack on Breed's Hill (battle of Bunker Hill) in the peninsula of Charlestown on opposite shore of Charles River.*

Fort at Boonsborough, Kentucky, 1775

liam Faden map, "Plan of the Operations of General Washington, against the King's Troops in New Jersey," published in April 1777; it depicted the approach to Trenton, the battle action in the town, and the subsequent troop movements.

The maps that the British high command regarded as providing essential topographical information in the most convenient form were collated in *The American Military Atlas* published by the firm of Robert Sayer and John Bennett in 1776. The book, known as the Holster Atlas because during the war it was carried by British officers in their holsters, included six large folding maps. The subjects of these were (1) North America, by Samuel Dunn; (2) the northern colonies, by Samuel Holland and Thomas Pownall; (3) the middle colonies, after Joshua Fry and Peter Jefferson, and Lewis Evans; (4) the southern colonies, after William De Brahm, Henry Mouzon, John Collett, and Bernard Romans; (5) the West Indies, by Samuel Dunn; and (6) a survey of Lake Champlain and Lake George, drawn by William Brassier in 1762.

To the north of the activities of Washington's troops, General Arnold engaged British troops led by Sir Guy Carleton on October 11, 1776, in a delaying action at the battle of Valcour Island on Lake Champlain. Although the British were victorious in this first naval battle of the revolutionary war, the American

King of the Siminoles, *from William Bartram's* Travels, *1791*

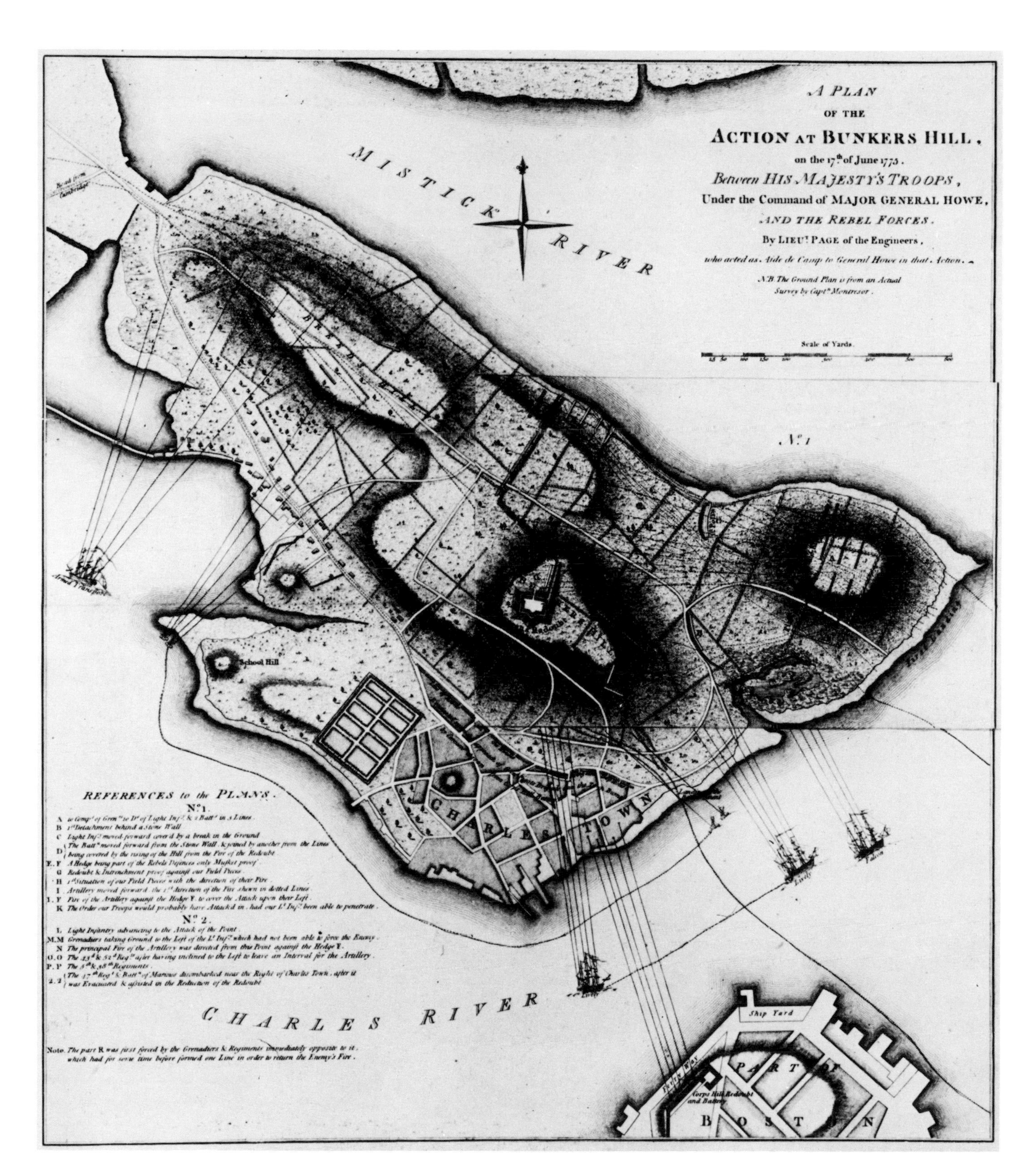

PLATE 118: Thomas Hyde Page. "A Plan of the Action at Bunkers Hill." c. 1775–78. Engraving, 49 × 43 cm. Private collection. *Most detailed representation of the famous battle. Names of Bunker Hill and Breed's Hill are transposed on map. An overlay permits viewer to follow various phases of the battle.*

PLATE 119: Bernard Ratzer. "Plan of the City of New York, in North America." 1770. Engraving, 122 × 91 cm. Private collection. *One of the most beautiful and accurate early plans of New York. Locates churches, estates, markets, and barracks, and names streets and roads. View in lower vignette is from Governors Island. First published in 1770; second state, 1776, more frequently encountered.*

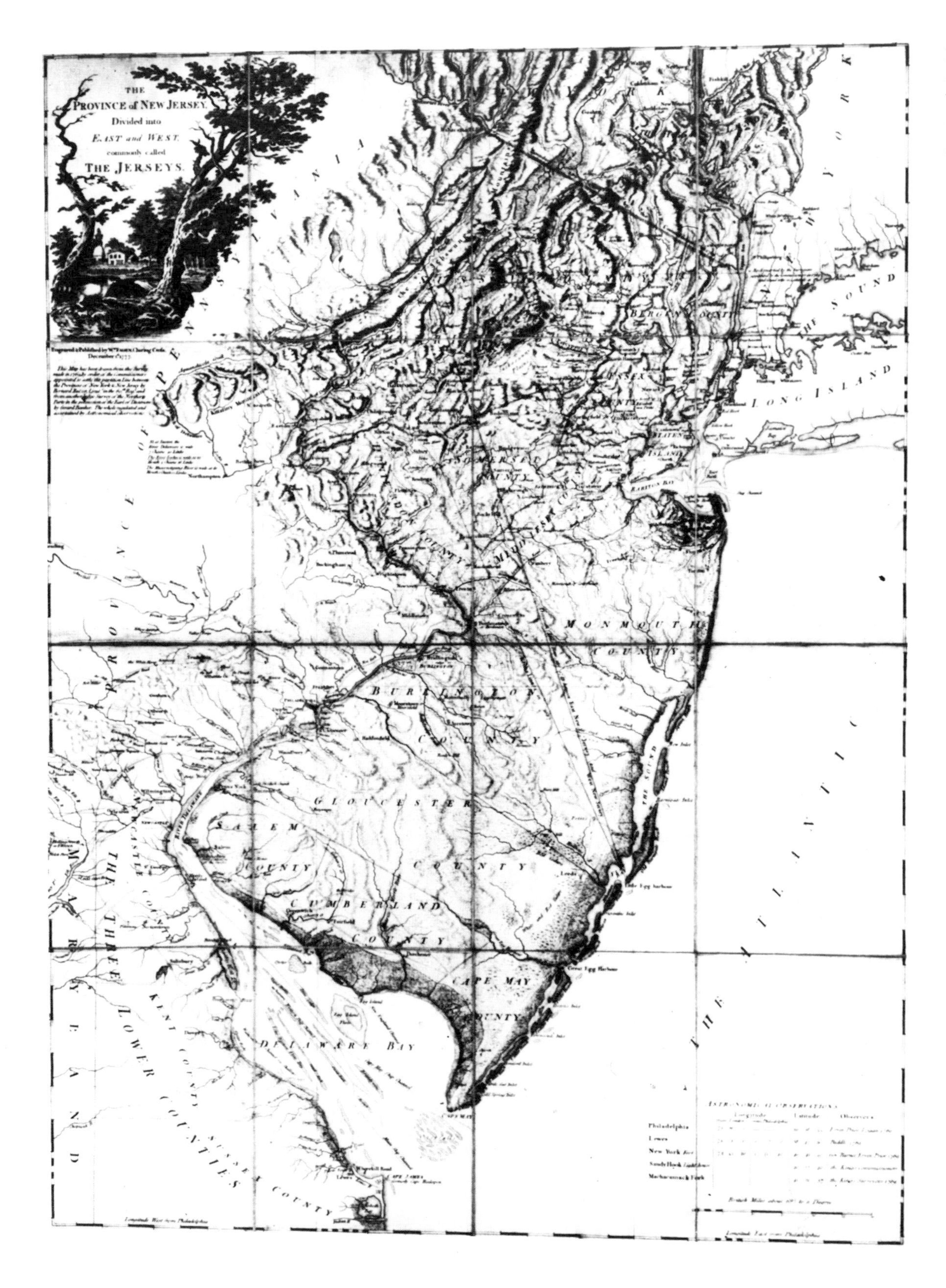

PLATE 120: Bernard Ratzer. "The Province of New Jersey, Divided into East and West, commonly called The Jerseys." 1777. Engraving, 79 × 57 cm. Private collection. *Most important general map of New Jersey during the Revolution; it was published in London. Shows northern boundary with New York, established in 1769. Depicts area known to George Washington prior to battle of Monmouth and shows fortified Valley Forge. Raccoons are pictured in cartouche.*

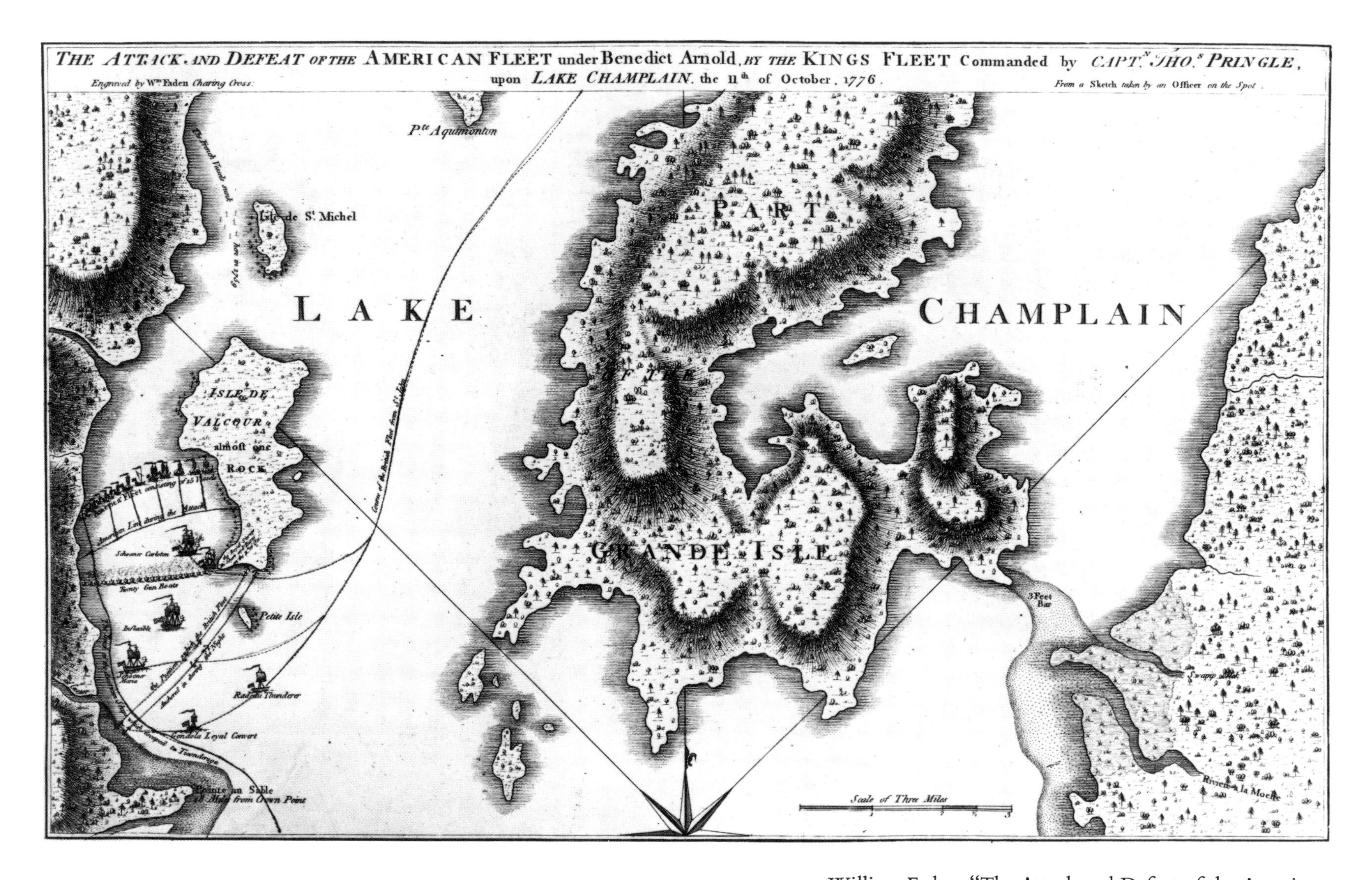

PLATE 121: William Faden. "The Attack and Defeat of the American Fleet under Benedict Arnold." 1776 (2nd state). Engraving, 26 × 42 cm. Private collection. *First naval battle of revolutionary war. Movement of British and American squadrons on Lake Champlain shown as well as locations of opposing naval forces at Valcour Island and the shore of New York. Published separately and also in Faden's* North American Atlas *(London, 1777).*

efforts had a definite strategic effect by aborting the British attempt to cut off the northern colonies. Two months later the map "The Attack and Defeat of the American Fleet under Benedict Arnold" by William Faden (*Plate 121*) represented this battle. At the end of 1776 the British occupied Newport, Rhode Island, which became the major base for their fleet, and this area was emphasized on a number of contemporary maps (*see Plate 126*).

The year 1777 burst forth with Washington's success at Princeton, New Jersey, on January 3. In June British troops under General John Burgoyne began their march south from Crown Point toward Albany in an attempt to isolate the New England

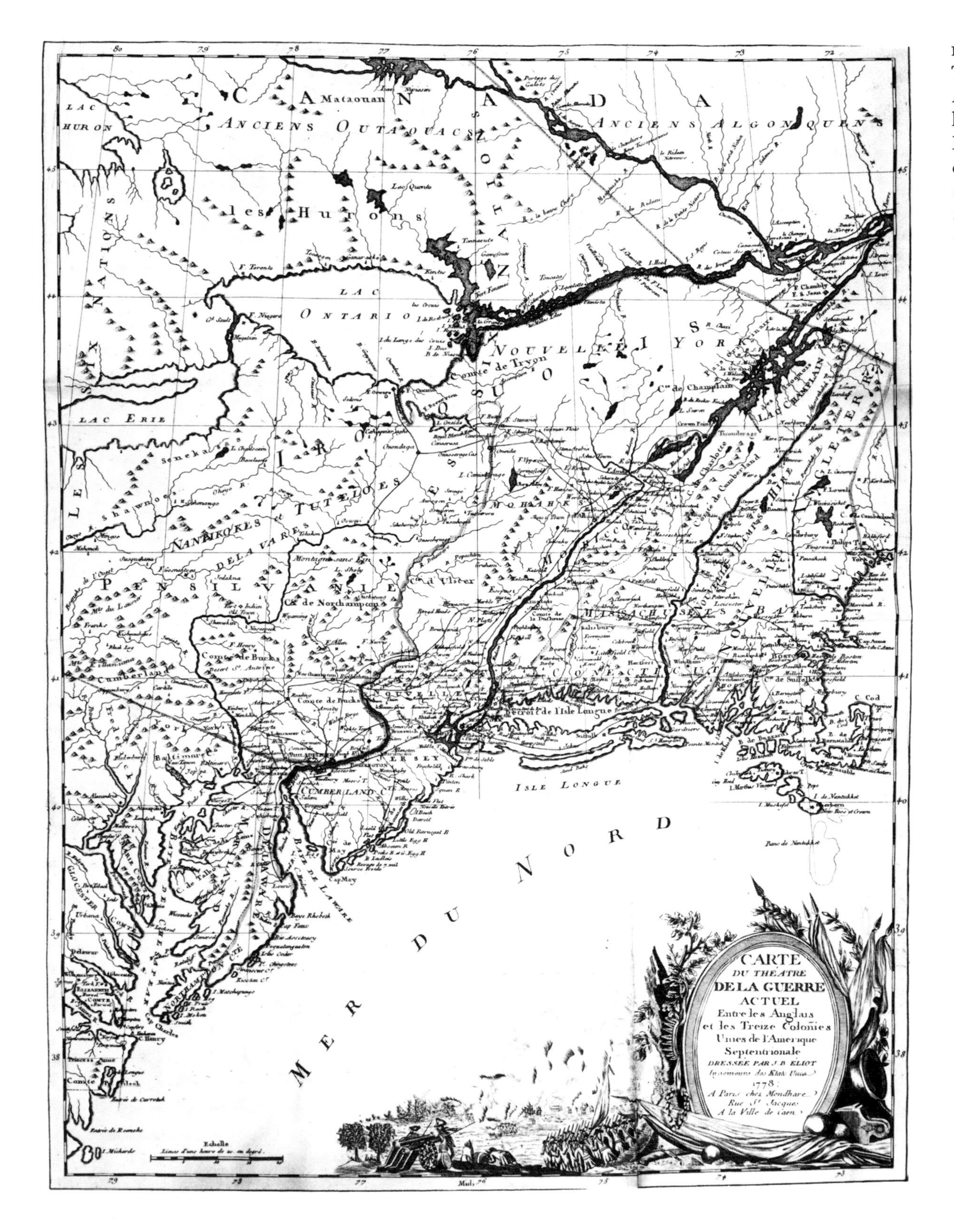

PLATE 122: J. B. Eliot. "Carte du Théatre de la Guerre Actuel Entre les Anglais et les Treize Colonies Unies de l'Amerique Septentrionale." 1778. Engraving, 70 × 51 cm. Private collection. *Drawn by an American engineer but published in Paris; first map to present the name United States (in its French version, États Unis, in the cartouche). Cartouche also includes a battle scene.*

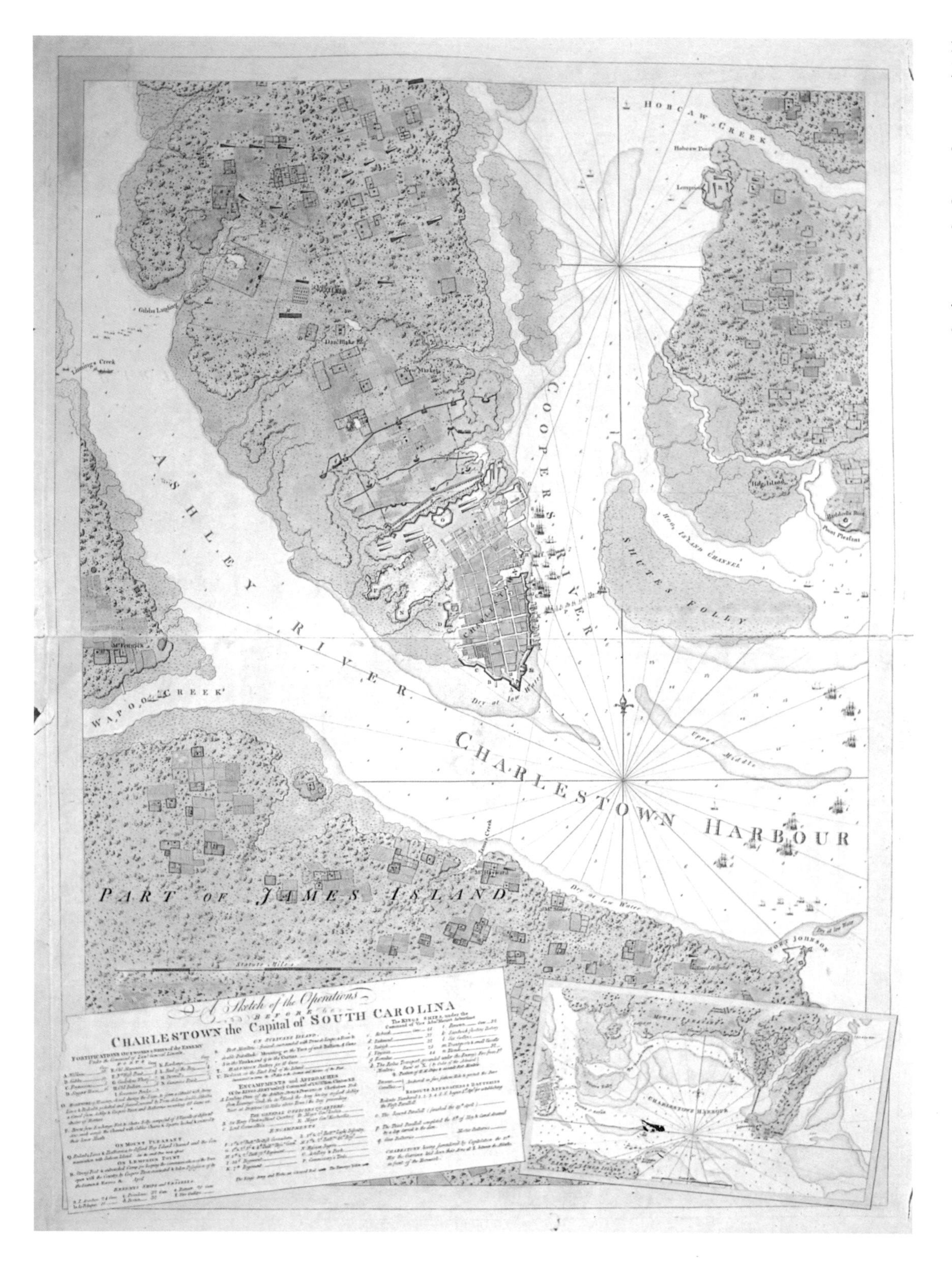

PLATE 123: Joseph Frederick Wallet Des Barres. "A Sketch of the Operations Before Charlestown the Capital of South Carolina." 1780. Engraving, hand colored; 104 × 77 cm. Private collection. *The best plan of this 1780 campaign. Sir Henry Clinton's siege is detailed and British and American troops located as well as investment and defense lines and ships of both fleets. These illustrations indicate names of ships and their gun complement. Published separately in 1780 and also in Des Barres's atlas* The Atlantic Neptune *(London from 1774 to 1782).*

(opposite) PLATE 124: William Faden. "A Plan of the Entrance of Chesapeak Bay, with James and York Rivers." 1781. Engraving, hand colored; 41 × 52 cm. Private collection. *First printed map of the final battle of the American Revolution at Yorktown, Virginia. Published November 26, 1781, in London approximately six weeks after the action. British had surrendered before map was issued.*

area. By July they had captured Ticonderoga. In October 1777 a series of engagements terminating in the battle of Saratoga on October 17 resulted in Burgoyne's surrender of the British troops to the northern American army. The defeated general's book, *A State of the Expedition from Canada*, was published in London in 1780 and contains six maps documenting the campaign which ended in his capitulation. During the second half of 1777 the British also failed in an attempt to capture Fort Stanwix in the Mohawk Valley, while the Americans were defeated in an ambush by the British and Indians at Oriskany.

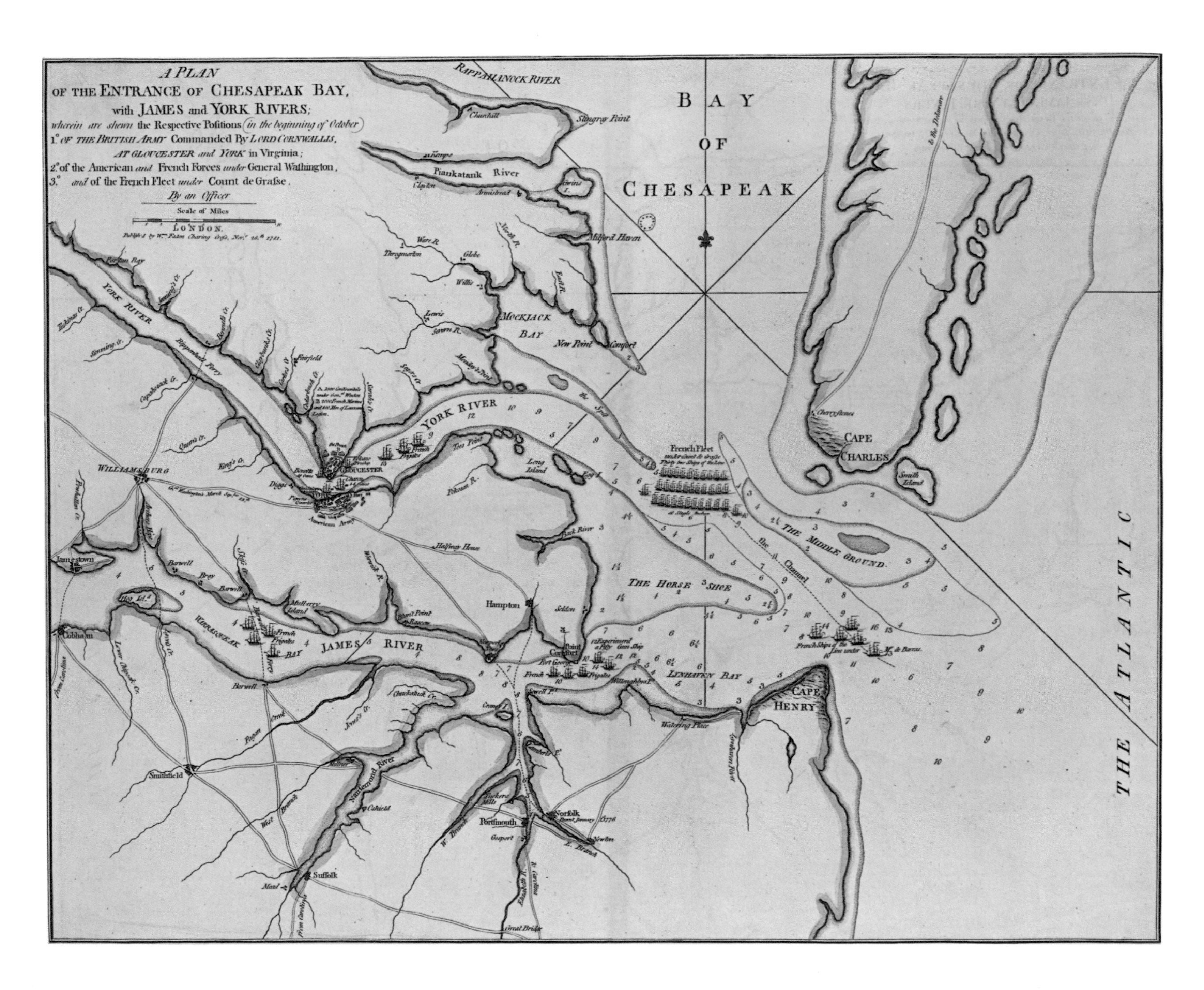

Sketch of reception at Mission Carmel in Monterey, by artist of visiting expedition, 1792

During early autumn 1777 the British were mobilizing forces in order to occupy Philadelphia. This campaign was initiated with the battle of Brandywine on September 11, 1777, and by the end of the month Philadelphia was occupied by General William Howe and his British forces. After Washington's unsuccessful attack on Germantown, Pennsylvania, in October, the American troops spent their severely miserable winter at Valley Forge.

A highlight of 1778 was the French declaration of alliance with the Americans on May 4. This led immediately to French mapping of the American War of Independence, and that year "Carte du Théatre de la Guerre Actuel Entre les Anglais et les Treize Colonies Unies de l'Amerique Septentrionale" (*Plate 122*) by J. B. Eliot, an American engineer, was published in Paris. It is the earliest known map to include the name United States (appearing in French in the cartouche: "Dressée par J. B. Eliot, Ingénieurs des Etats Unis"). There were few major battles in 1778. Indian attacks in the frontier land of the Illinois country were described by Thomas Hutchins, who personally explored the area and published a representative map, "A Plan of the several Villages in the Illinois country with Part of the River Mississippi &c," in his book *A Topographical Description of Virginia, Pennsylvania, Maryland, and North Carolina* (London, 1778). In more formal warfare the British evacuated Philadelphia on June 8 and retreated in the direction of New York City. Washington's troops followed from Germantown along a parallel line, and the two forces met on June 28, 1778, at Monmouth Court House, New Jersey (now Freehold), in the last major battle of the northern sector.

Beginning in 1779 to the final surrender in 1781, the major activity of the war was localized in the southern colonies. The principal political event of 1779 was Spain's entry into the war against Great Britain. At the beginning of April 1780 the British initiated an assault against Charleston, South Carolina; on April 6, 1780, Fort Moultrie in Charleston Harbor capitulated, and five days later Charleston was under British control. This campaign accounted for the greatest loss of American troops during the war. The map that best presents an appreciation of the battles associated with Charleston was published by Joseph Frederick Wallet Des Barres in 1780 (*Plate 123*). Battle lines and naval positions are well defined, and an insert depicts the strategic fort on Sullivans Island. In August 1780 at the battle of Camden in South Carolina the Americans suffered heavy losses, and the American defeat at Fishing Creek led to General Charles Cornwallis's invasion of North Carolina in September.

The turning point in the southern campaign occurred during the first half of 1781. At the beginning of the year British forces controlled most of the Carolinas and Georgia. General Nathanael Greene replaced General Horatio Gates and led the patriot troops in a series of battles that included: (1) the battle of Cowpens, South Carolina, in January; (2) the battle of Guilford Courthouse near present Greensboro, North Carolina, in March; and (3) the battle of Hobkirk's Hill near Camden, South Carolina, in April. Although most of these battles ended indecisively, the cumulative effect was the significant weakening of Cornwallis's forces, which were compelled to retire from the field into Virginia and fortify Yorktown. The war's final battle was a combined land and sea operation in which French forces took a significant role. In early September the French fleet gained control of the Chesapeake Bay area, and at the end of the month combined French and American troops set out from Williamsburg for Yorktown. On September

PLATE 125: Sebastian Bauman. "Plan of the investment of York and Gloucester." 1782. Engraving, hand colored; 65 × 46 cm. Private collection. *First American publication of a map of battle of Yorktown, final battle of War of Independence. Drawn in 1781, shortly after the battle, at Washington's request, and published the following year at Philadelphia. American and French units, ships, and batteries are located. Successive positions during battle also detailed.*

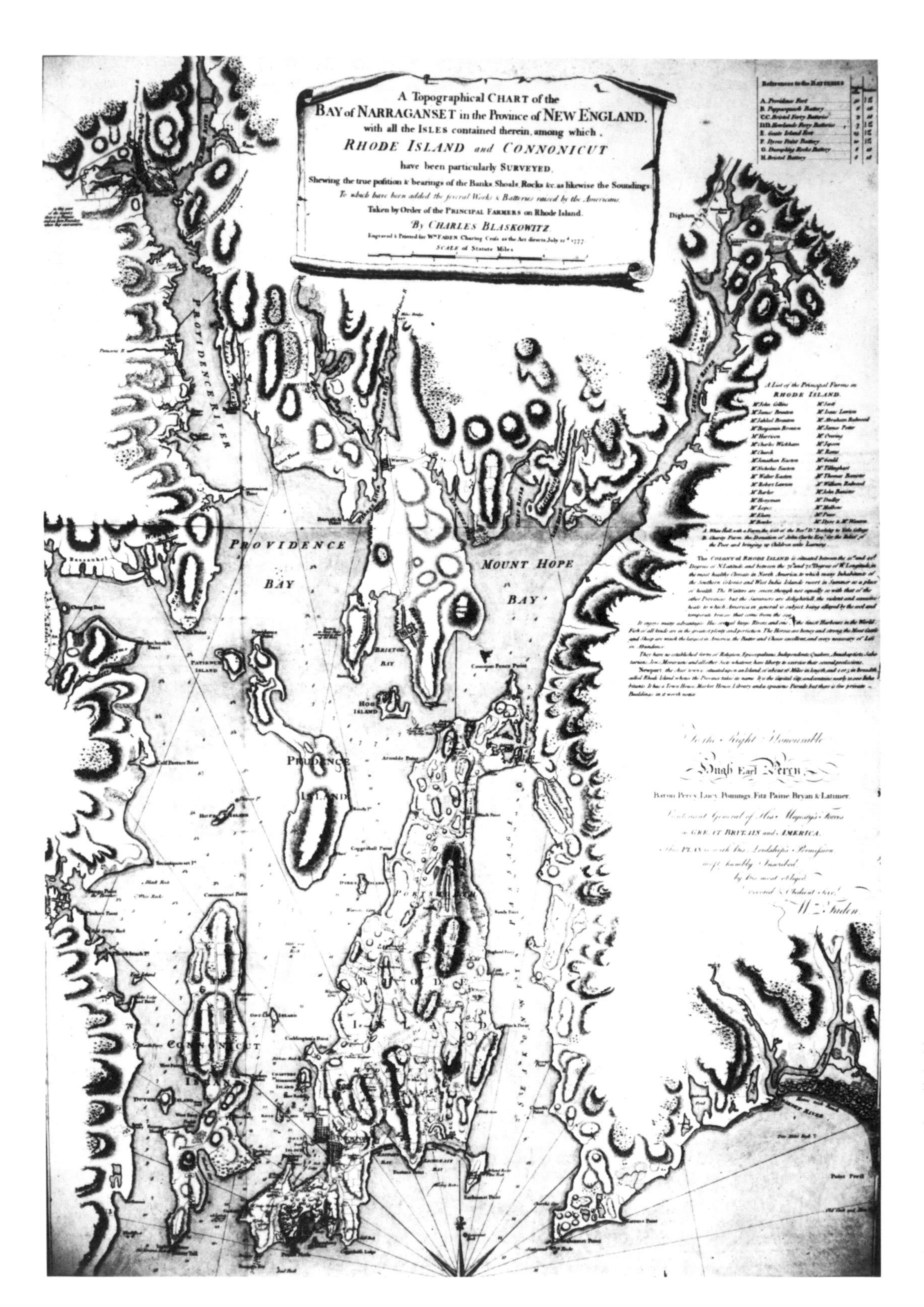

PLATE 126: Charles Blaskowitz. "A Topographical Chart of the Bay of Narraganset in the Province of New England." 1777. Engraving, 93 × 64 cm. Private collection. *Locates forts, batteries, and principal farms in Rhode Island; Brown College in Providence; and Newport, where British fleet was based during that period. Also shows soundings and hazards of Narragansett Bay. Published separately and also in William Faden's* North American Atlas *(London, 1777).*

29 the siege of Yorktown was initiated, and on October 9 the actual bombardment began. Ten days later Cornwallis surrendered.

Three significant maps document this final battle at Yorktown. "A Plan of the Entrance of Chesapeak Bay, with James and York Rivers" by William Faden (*Plate 124*) was published in London on November 26, 1781. It was the first map depicting the battle, and when it was issued in England, the native population there could not have known that their overseas troops had surrendered. "Carte de la Partie de Virginie," published in Paris in 1782, testifies to the major role played by the French fleet and army in the campaign. The third map under discussion is particularly important because it is the first printed in America to represent the battle of Yorktown. This extremely rare map, "Plan of the investment of York and Gloucester" by Sebastian Bauman (*Plate 125*), was published in Philadelphia in 1782 and dedicated to George Washington.

The American War of Independence was recorded in several contemporary histories in which cartographic illustrations complemented the text. The works of John Burgoyne, David Ramsay,

PLATE 127: Abel Buell. "A New and correct Map of the United States of North America Layd down from the latest Observations and best Authority agreeable to the Peace of 1783." 1784 (2nd state). Engraving, hand colored; 109 × 122 cm. New-York Historical Society, New York. *First map of the United States compiled, engraved, and printed by an American, published separately in New Haven. Derived primarily from maps of John Mitchell and Lewis Evans (see Plates 96, 98). American flag, in cartouche, appears for first time on a map printed in America.*

Banastre Tarleton, John D. Simcoe, and Charles Stedman are rich sources for maps of the war. *A State of the Expedition from Canada* (London, 1780) by Lieutenant John Burgoyne describes his Hudson Valley campaign, which ended in defeat at Saratoga; it contains a large folding map and five battle plans. David Ramsay's *History of the Revolution of South Carolina*, published in Trenton in 1787, includes five maps of battles in the Carolina region. Banastre Tarleton's *A History of the Campaigns of 1780 and 1781 in the Southern Provinces of North America*, published in London in the same year, contains five maps of a broader scope. A third book, also published in London in 1787, John D. Simcoe's *A Journal of the Operations of the Queen's Rangers,* presents ten order-of-battle plans. Undoubtedly the most significant contemporary history of the Revolution was published in London in 1794. Charles Stedman's *The History of the Origin, Progress, and Termination of the American War* uses fifteen derivatives of previously published maps that cover various campaigns, from Bunker Hill to Yorktown.

Not only did maps documenting the American Revolution proliferate, atlases were also becoming popular; these atlases emphasized the evolving nation, particularly the rapidly changing political subdivision of the North American continent. Although atlases were not yet published in America, French and British compilations were common.

The major French production was the *Atlas Ameriquain Septentrional* issued in Paris by Georges-Louis Le Rouge in 1778. It contains about twenty-five French versions of maps published originally by William Faden and Thomas Jefferys. Included are the great John Mitchell map (*see Plate 96*), William Scull's "Pennsylvania," Joshua Fisher's "Delaware Bay," Joshua Fry and Peter Jefferson's "Virginia and Maryland," Henry Mouzon's "North and South Carolina," William de Brahm's "South Carolina and Georgia," and Thomas Jefferys's "Florida." An elegantly engraved frontispiece pictures William Penn in colloquy with the Indians. In the same year Le Rouge also published *Pilote Americain Septentrional.* The official reference for major United States and Canadian harbors used by the French navy was the 1778 *Neptune Americo-Septentrional* with twenty-five engraved hydrographic charts in fine detail showing soundings, shoals, and pertinent topographic features.

The comparable atlas produced in England was the *Atlantic Neptune* by Joseph Frederick Wallet Des Barres, issued in several printings in London between 1774 and 1782. Historical consensus has it that this atlas is the handsomest collection of hydrographic maps ever published, and, according to Lester J. Cappon, editor in chief of the *Atlas of Early American History* (1978), it is "one of the most remarkable products of human industry which has been given to the world through the arts of printing and engraving."

George Washington after the battle of Princeton *(1777), painting by Charles Willson Peale*

The work is a folio collection usually comprising ninety-five sea and harbor charts and views. Included among the many rivers and harbors represented, there are several delineations of Boston Harbor, Plymouth, and Narragansett Bay; also included in this treasury is one of the most accurate charts covering the lower Hudson River valley and Long Island. It depicts the battle between the ships *Phoenix* and *Rose,* based on the painting by Dominick Serres. Another collection of sea charts, *The North Atlantic Pilot for Newfoundland, Labradore, and the Gulf and River St. Laurence,* was published in London in 1778–79. It did not specifically refer to the revolutionary battle areas, but sixty-five contemporary charts and plans were drawn from original surveys and then engraved by Thomas Jefferys.

The Jefferys firm continued to publish the *American Atlas,*

PLATE 128: John Filson. "Map of Kentucke, Drawn from actual Observations." 1784 (7th state). Engraving, 50 × 45 cm. Private collection. *Eastern and western portions of map are distorted but central area is accurate. Towns, forts, and trails, as well as James Harrod's town (first settlement in Kentucky), are displayed. First map of Kentucky locates Daniel Boone's house southeast of Lexington; also Louisville, with fourteen houses, and Clarksville, with eleven. Although published in Philadelphia, it accompanied Filson's book* The Discovery, Settlement, and Present State of Kentucke *(Wilmington, 1784).*

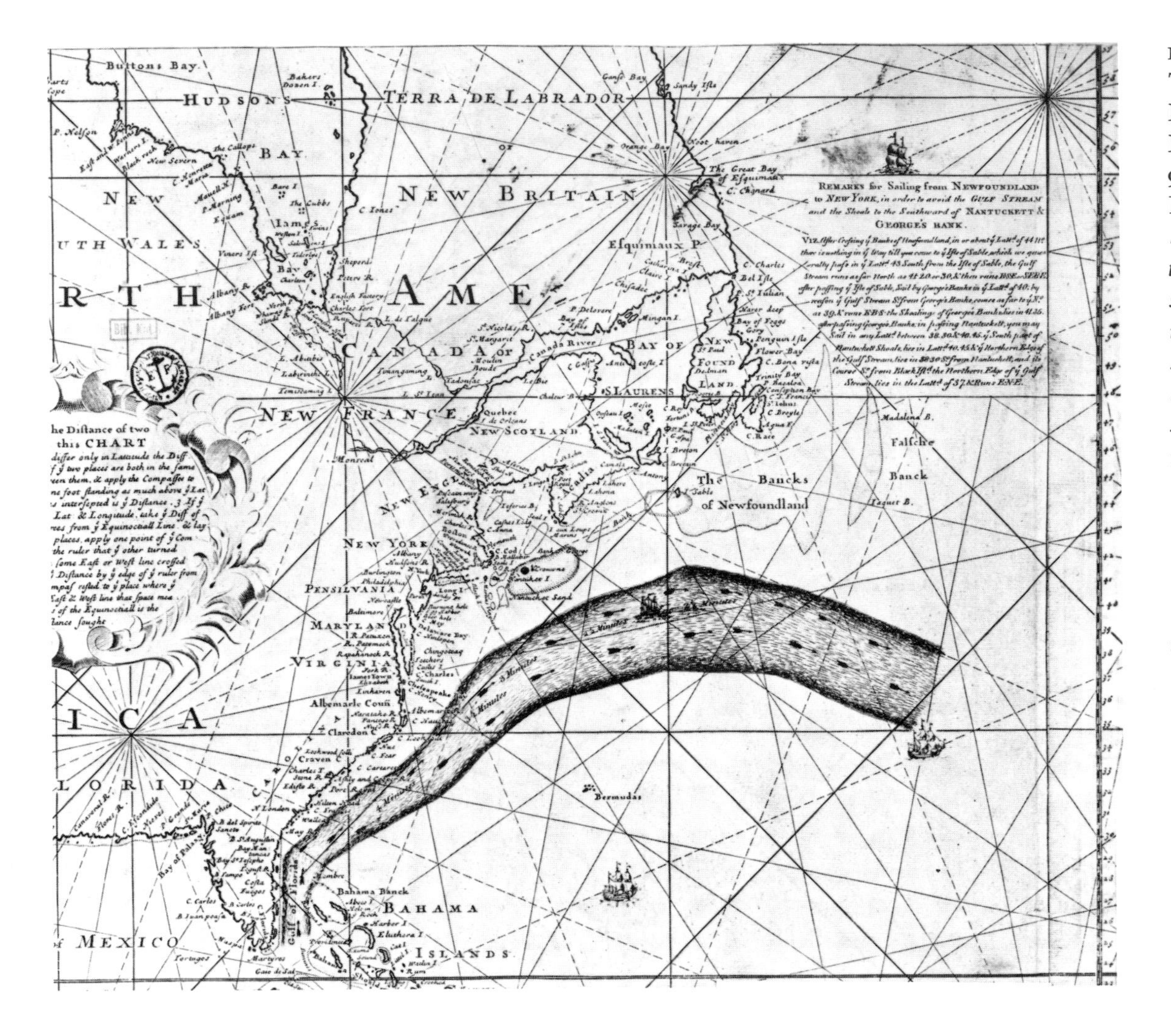

PLATE 129: Benjamin Franklin and Timothy Folger. "A New and Exact Chart" (detail). 1769 or 1770. Engraving, entire dimensions 86 × 96 cm. Bibliothèque Nationale, Paris. *Commonly known as "Gulf Stream Chart," this is oldest chart of the Gulf Stream; its precise charting sponsored by Benjamin Franklin from information supplied by the Nantucket sea captain Timothy Folger. Mapping the current was stimulated because mail shipment from Europe was slower than reverse trip. Franklin states in a letter published in 1786 that he had Gulf Stream engraved on an old chart of the Atlantic, but no copy was uncovered for nearly 200 years until 1978 when two prints were found in Paris.*

issued with minor revisions during and after the Revolution by Sayer and Bennett, who had taken over the firm after Jefferys's death in 1771. The first edition appeared in 1775 and consisted of twenty-nine important maps made by the most renowned cartographers of the day. This is one of the most authoritative and most comprehensive atlases covering the revolutionary period. It was the primary cartographic publication consulted by both contestants in planning strategy, and after the war it was valuable in settling boundary disputes.

The rarest and most important atlas treating the events of the American Revolution was *The North American Atlas* published in London by William Faden in 1777. The total number of maps in this atlas varies with the specific edition, but twenty-seven were always present. Although the great regional maps of the period were represented, the atlas's major historical contribution is the series of detailed battle plans drawn by eyewitness observers. Here can be found two engravings by the British military surveyor Charles Blaskowitz. One of these, "A Topographical Chart of the Bay of Narraganset in the Province of New England" (*Plate 126*), was used by the British after their occupation of Newport, and that city was the subject of the second, "A Plan of the Town of Newport." Other military plans in the atlas are the battles of Bunker Hill and Lake Champlain, and the New York, New Jersey, and Pennsylvania campaign battles.

The Treaty of Paris was signed on September 3, 1783, whereby Great Britain formally acknowledged the independence of the

United States and the warring European powers effected a large-scale peace settlement. One of the treaty's most dramatic results was the transference of land between the Allegheny Mountains and the Mississippi River from English sovereignty to the new nation. Specific boundaries were also established. The St. Croix River was designated the boundary between Maine and Nova Scotia but was in dispute for many years. A line of demarcation dividing the newly formed United States from Canada was defined by the St. Lawrence–Atlantic watershed, through the Great Lakes, and along the 45th parallel. A line through the Mississippi River to the 31st parallel became the boundary between the United States and Spanish Louisiana, while the 31st parallel, the Apalachicola River, and the St. Marys River defined the boundaries between the United States and Spanish Florida. In consequence of the treaty, Spain claimed an area that was east of the Mississippi River, south of the Tennessee River, and west of the Flint River in Georgia. France retained political sovereignty over only the islands of St.-Pierre, Miquelon, and Tobago.

When the guns of war were silenced and peace finally became a reality, the colonists directed their energies toward structuring a central government and settling innumerable interstate boundary disputes. There was a short hiatus between the peace settlement and the appearance of maps depicting the new nation. In 1784 Abel Buell of New Haven, Connecticut, published the first map of the original thirteen states that comprised the United States. "A New and correct Map of the United States of North America Layd down from the latest Observations and best Authority agreeable to the Peace of 1783" (*Plate 127*) was advertised at the time as the "first [map] ever compiled, engraved and finished by one man and an American." It is a crude incorporation of the boundary definitions established by John Mitchell (*see Plate 96*) and Lewis Evans (*see Plate 98*), and contains errors of commission and omission that are apparently the result of Buell's zeal to publish before his competitors. "An Accurate Map of the State and Province of New-Hampshire in New England" by Colonel Joseph Blanchard, and revised by Samuel Langdon, was published in Boston in 1784. This was the second state of the first printed map of New Hampshire and is unusual insofar as the plate was originally engraved in England and then brought to America to be reengraved. Evart Banker's map of New Jersey, also published in 1784, was the first map of that state to be produced in the state.

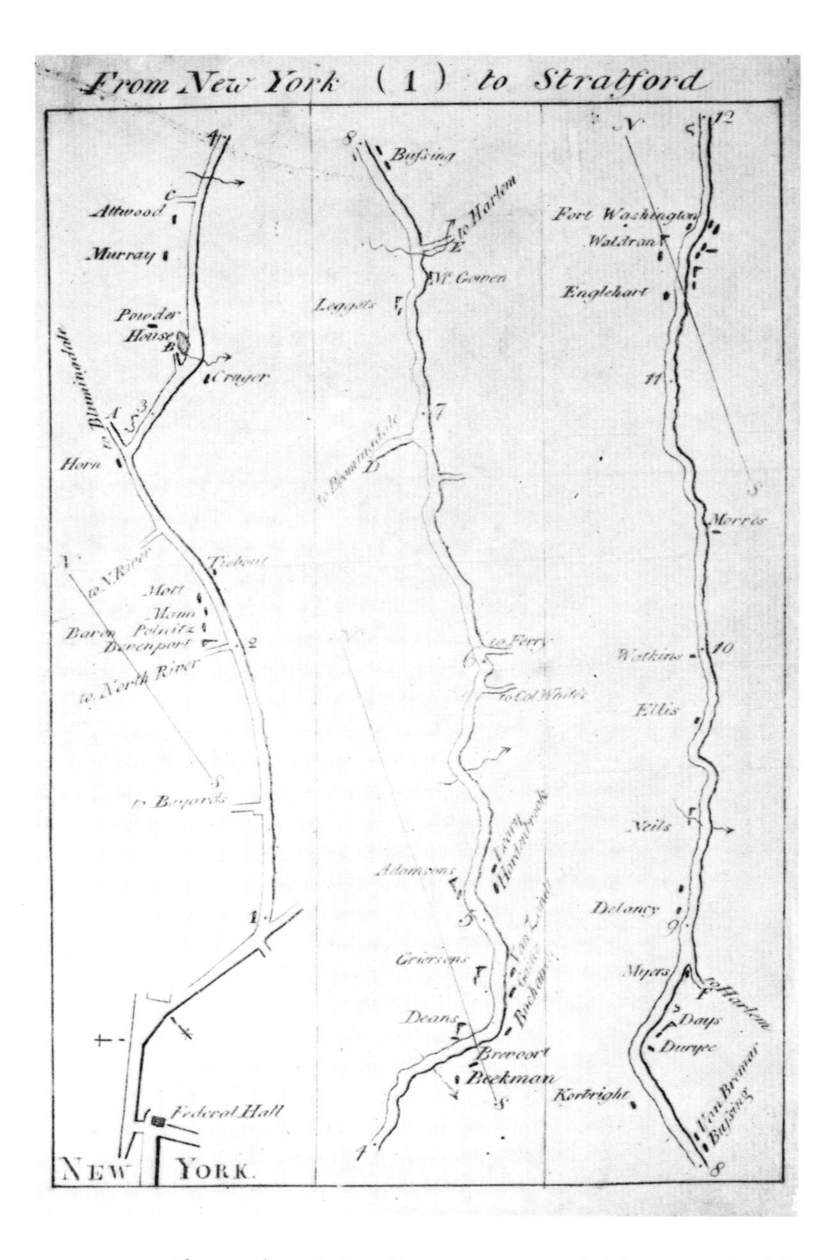

PLATE 130: Christopher Colles. "From New York (1) to Stratford." 1789. Engraving, 18 × 11 cm. Geography and Map Division, Library of Congress, Washington, D.C. *First map in the earliest systematic series of road maps. Survey consists of eighty-three maps, all drawn to same scale (1 inch = $\frac{4}{7}$ mile). Map shows road running twelve miles north from Federal Hall in Manhattan past Fort Washington. Included in Colles's compilation* A Survey of the Roads of the United States of America *(New York, 1789).*

PLATE 131: I. Norman. "The United States of America laid down From the best Authorities Agreeable to the Peace of 1783." 1791. Engraving, hand colored; 82 × 114 cm. Private collection. *Shows Phelps-Gorham land sale in western New York east of Genesee River, the Seven Ranges west of the Ohio River, and new townships between the Penobscot River and the Scioto River (Schodic on map)—all for first time on an inclusive map of United States. "A Map of the Lakes and Rivers Between Lake Superior and the North Sea" included as inset.*

One of the rarest American maps—a striking accomplishment of American mapmaking in the eighteenth century—was published in 1784. This document, "Map of Kentucke, Drawn from actual Observations" by John Filson (*Plate 128*), was published in Philadelphia to accompany his book *The Discovery, Settlement, and Present State of Kentucke* (Wilmington, 1784). Although the map's peripheral areas are somewhat distorted, the middle

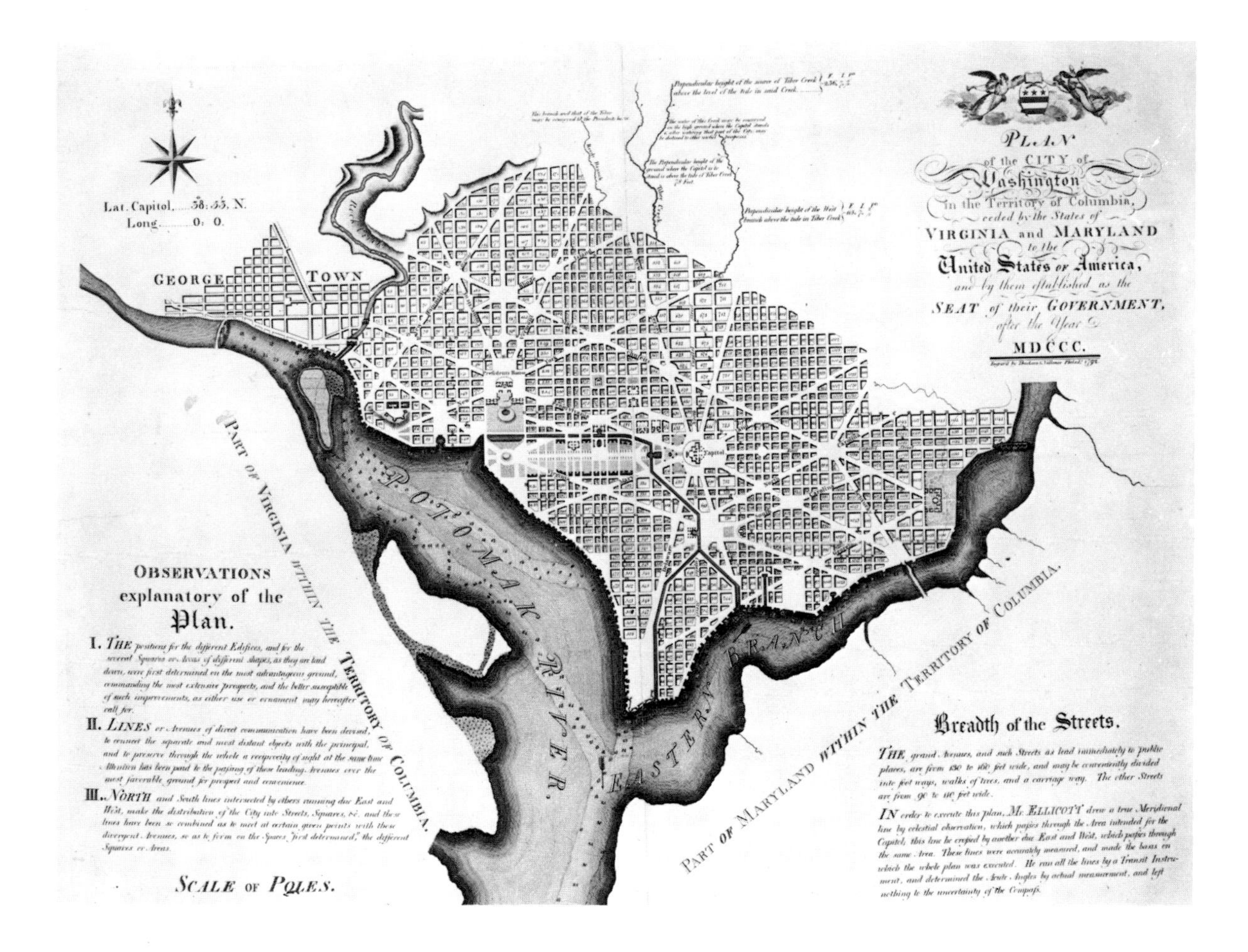

PLATE 132: Andrew Ellicott. "Plan of the City of Washington in the Territory of Columbia, ceded by the States of Virginia and Maryland to the United States of America and by them established as the Seat of their Government, after the Year MDCCC." 1792. Engraving, 51 × 69 cm. Geography and Map Division, Library of Congress, Washington, D.C. *Published in Philadelphia, map generally considered first official plan of Washington, D.C.; based on Pierre Charles L'Enfant's original design. Soundings and channel marked in the Potomac (Potomak on map) and streets in Washington and Georgetown depicted.*

accurately presents Fayette, Jefferson, and Lincoln counties. Filson's map, which went through nine states, includes the author's statement of appreciation to Daniel Boone and James Harrod, the two famous frontiersmen of that region who furnished details on which the map is based. In 1784 cartographic attention was also focused on the western coast when "A General Chart Exhibiting the Discoveries Made by Capt. James Cook" was published; the map was drawn by Henry Roberts as part of an official account of Cook's last voyage in 1778. The erroneous delineation on this map of the Northwest coast was due to the misconception that Cook's two ships, *Resolution* and *Discovery*, were traveling along the coast, not off an island chain, as they proceeded north from Nootka Sound at Vancouver Island.

In 1769 or 1770 John Mount and Thomas Page printed in London a map of interest today not so much because it is a significant representation of North America but because a famous American of the revolutionary period was responsible for its genesis. The earliest printed chart of the Gulf Stream (*Plate 129*), it came about through the efforts of Benjamin Franklin. In London, as deputy postmaster general for the American colonies, Franklin received numerous complaints that the mails between England and New England took two weeks longer in the westerly direction. He consulted with his cousin Timothy Folger, a Nantucket whaling captain, who informed him that the warm ocean current of the North Atlantic was the reason for the discrepancy of delivery time and that the British packet captains were ignorant of this current, frequently stemming it. Folger sketched the current on a chart, and Franklin had it printed. Although Le Rouge published a nearly exact copy of the chart in Paris, traditionally dated 1785 but now believed printed as early as 1778, the earlier

From Patrick Campbell' Travels in the Interior *1793*

Franklin-Folger chart became extremely rare; no copy had been uncovered until 1978, when two prints were found in the Bibliothèque Nationale in Paris (see Philip L. Richardson, "Benjamin Franklin and Timothy Folger's First Printed Chart of the Gulf Stream," *Science*, February 8, 1980).

Once the new government of the United States was firmly established, several Indian tribes ceded land to the state and Federal governments. Land companies accelerated settling of the area between the Allegheny Mountains and the Mississippi River. Individual states also ceded land to the United States; yet Connecticut retained three million acres in Ohio, the region becoming known as the Western Reserve.

In the second half of the eighteenth century the Northwest, as a geographic designation, referred to the northern Ohio Valley region. After the Treaty of Paris several proposals were made for purchasing land in the western territories and organizing

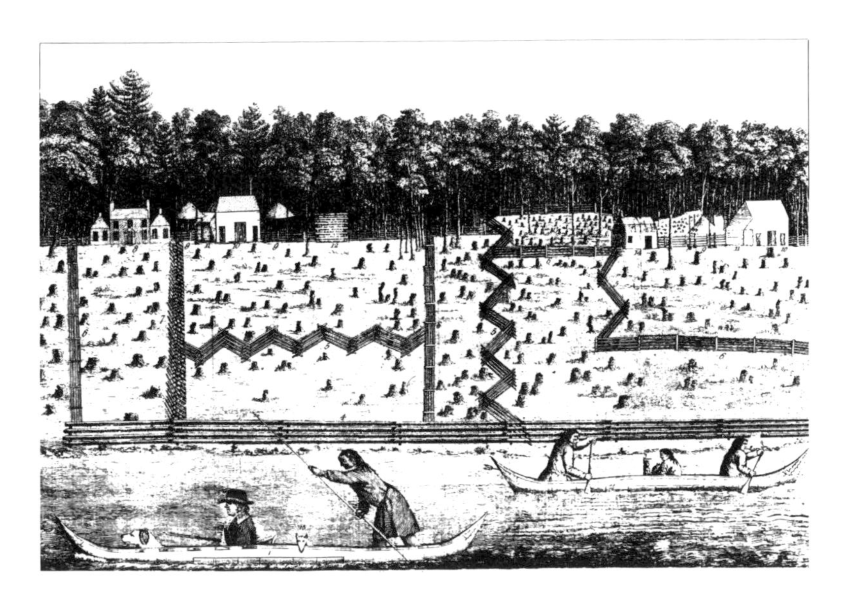

New cleared farm, from Travels in the Interior, *1793*

The Alegator of St. Johns, *watercolor by William Bartram, c. 1774*

new settlements there. The landmark Northwest Ordinance, which created the Northwest Territory, was passed in 1787. This ordinance, which marked the beginning of western expansion of the United States, stipulated the creation of a territorial assembly under an appointed governor as soon as a district's population included 5,000 voting citizens (that is, free males) and statehood when the citizen population reached 60,000. The states of Ohio, Illinois, Indiana, Michigan, and Wisconsin were created out of the Northwest Territory. The 1787 "A Map of the Federal Territory from the Western Boundary of Pennsylvania to the Scioto River," often credited to Manasseh Cutler, was the first printed map to show the Seven Ranges of Townships, the name of the tiers of townships proposed by the Federal government in the area west of Pennsylvania. The Geographer's Line, which would establish the northern boundary of the townships, is shown and the tract purchased by the Ohio Company also appears. "Plat of the Seven Ranges of Townships" by William Barker reflects the famous survey made by Thomas Hutchins, geographer of the United States, to implement the Ordinance of 1785, which divided public land into townships of six square miles, having three sections each, which established a standard of measurement for future land division.

Notes on the State of Virginia by Thomas Jefferson, published in Paris and London in 1787, described the geography, climate, population, communities, laws, colleges, manners, and commerce of Virginia. It included the only map attributed to Jefferson, "A Map of the Country Between Albemarle Sound and Lake Erie" and is a composite of Lewis Evans, Thomas Hutchins, and Fry and Jefferson maps. In 1788 Joseph Purcell's "A Map of the States of Virginia, North Carolina, South Carolina and Georgia" was engraved by Amos Doolittle. It was initially published separately but later appeared in Jedidiah Morse's *American Geography* (Elizabeth Town, N.J., 1789) which included many small maps. Purcell's map is of interest today because it documents the proposed State of Franklin between present Tennessee and North Carolina, and outlines the boundaries claimed by the Indian Nations at the time. Purcell was one of several British cartographers active in America during the Revolution who became American citizens and continued their work in the United States.

A move toward sophistication in American mapmaking at the end of the eighteenth century is evidenced in a systematic series of American road maps begun in 1789. *A Survey of the Roads of the United States of America* (New York, 1789), was published that year by Christopher Colles, who is also credited with the proposal of a system of canals to connect the Hudson River with Lake Erie, an idea that eventually resulted in construction of the

From Bartram's Travels, *1791*

PLATE 133: Abraham Bradley, Jr. "Map of the United States, Exhibiting the Post-Roads, the situations, connections & distances of the Post-Offices, Stage Roads, Counties, Ports of Entry and Delivery for Foreign Vessels, and the Principal Rivers." 1796 (4th state). Engraving, hand colored; 86 × 93 cm. Private collection. *Defines route of mail carriers from Brewer, Maine, along eastern seaboard to Charleston, South Carolina, including all designated mail stations. One of the first maps of United States designed specifically for commercial purposes.*

Erie Canal. The *Survey*, of which fifteen copies are extant, consists of eighty-three small maps bound in book form. (The route from New York to Stratford is represented in *Plate 130*.) Twelve miles of road are shown on each page with a scale of 1 inch to $\frac{4}{7}$ mile. Precise measurement of distance was expedited by Colles's invention of a perambulator, a device that measures mileage by adding up the revolutions of a wheel trailed behind a carriage. On Colles's maps, which cover the area from Albany to Annapolis, the names of inhabitants, houses contiguous to or in view of the road, churches and other public buildings, taverns, blacksmith shops, mills, crossroads, and streams are all detailed. In 1794 Colles began work on *A Geographical Legend and Systemized Atlas*, but only five segments of the atlas have been located, and it must be assumed that this ambitious project was never completed.

Development of the frontier—the land west of the original thirteen states—along with changes in boundaries and ownership continued at an accelerated rate until the end of the century. In 1787 the Ohio Company purchased a large area in present southern Ohio, and the Scioto Company acquired adjacent land to

New York No 145
These are to Certify that Lawrence Sink was by
a Majority of Votes regularly admitted a Member of the New
York Mechanick Society at a Meeting held the 3 day of
April A. D. 1793 Given under my hand and the Seal
of the Society this 4 day of March AnnoqueDomini 1795
Gabriel Furman, President
Gardiner Baker, Sec.

A certificate of the New York Mechanick Society, c. 1785

the west. Marietta, Ohio, and Gallipolis, Ohio, were founded by French immigrants in 1788 and 1790, respectively. In 1788 Oliver Phelps and Nathaniel Gorham bought from Massachusetts and the Seneca Indians land which jointly encompassed the western half of New York State. They retained for development the land east of the Genesee River. The land west of the Genesee River reverted to Massachusetts and was then purchased first by Robert Morris in 1791, who in turn sold his land in 1792 and 1793 to Dutch bankers who in 1796 organized themselves as the Holland Land Company. In 1795 the Connecticut Land Company was formed and purchased land in the Western Reserve, in the Ohio Valley. Moses Cleaveland, one of the company's directors and a surveyor, took a party of men to the mouth of the Cuyahoga River, where he planned to develop the main settlement. The surveyors gave the name Cleaveland to this site, which it bore until about 1830 when it was changed to Cleveland. In 1798 the Mississippi Company was established to advance settlement of the Southwest Territory. In all states as well as in the territories land was reserved for veterans of the American Revolution, who had first choice to buy.

Before the end of the eighteenth century three states were added to the developing nation—Vermont in 1791, Kentucky in 1792, and Tennessee in 1796. In 1791 the English navigator and explorer George Vancouver set out from Tahiti and the Hawaiian Islands in the Pacific Ocean for the Northwest coast of America and explored inlets of the Pacific Northwest coast, in 1792 naming Vancouver Island for himself and Puget Sound for his second lieutenant, Peter Puget, who led an exploring party in a small boat and discovered the sound. At the close of the century it was simply a matter of time before the fever of expansion would drastically change the tenor and shape of the country. The Louisiana Purchase and detailed exploration of this vast expanse, encompassing an area extending as far as the Pacific Northwest, would establish the United States as a transcontinental nation, eagerly mapped by native cartographers who understood the practical reasons for a precise representation of the land.

In 1791 the large map "The United States of America laid down From the best Authorities Agreeable to the Peace of 1783" (*Plate 131*) was published by I. Norman in Boston. The importance of this rare map is the specific delineation of newly surveyed regions that were being developed. The Phelps-Gorham land sale in western New York is outlined, New England is shown in great detail, and fifty townships sold by lottery between the Penobscot and Scioto rivers are noted. The lands of the Ohio Company in the Northwest Territory are mapped, and those claimed by the Wabash Company, the New Jersey Company, and the Illinois Company are also located. The Norman firm also published in 1791 the first edition of *The American Pilot*, a handy book of charts for navigation of the eastern coast of North America.

The major cartographic activity during the last decade of the eighteenth century was the mapping of states and cities. In 1789 the first map of the first state added to the original thirteen was published. "A Topographical Map of the State of Vermont" by William Blodget was engraved and printed in New Haven by the well-known engraver Amos Doolittle. And the first map of the state of Pennsylvania published in that state—important primarily for its delimitation of exact state boundaries—appeared in 1792. Donation lands, counties, townships, and settlements are clearly shown.

Two significant maps of cities in the adjacent region were also published in 1792. "Plan of the Town of Baltimore and It's [sic] Environs," the first map of that city to be published in America, was, surprisingly, drawn by a French geographer, A. P. Folie.

PLATE 134A: Charles Williamson. "A Map of the middle states, shewing the situation of the Genesee Lands and their connection with the Atlantic coast." 1798. Engraving, 26 × 24 cm. Private collection. *Three maps (Plates 134A–134C) give a synoptic view of detailed mapping of same area over three years' time. Map extends from Baltimore to northern region of Lake Ontario and from eastern Lake Erie in west to east of Hudson River. Only two cities named: Baltimore, Maryland, and Bath, New York. Genesee lands located as well as navigation route to Albany from Finger Lakes. Published in Williamson's* Description of the Genesee Country, Its Rapidly Progressive Population and Improvements: In a Series of Letters from a Gentleman to His Friend *(Albany, 1798).*

(opposite) PLATE 134B: Charles Williamson. "A Map of the Middle States of North America." 1799. Engraving, 37 × 40 cm. Private collection. *Morris's Purchase, Phelps-Gorham tract, land granted to the American army, and settlements in Canada along St. Lawrence River appear. Lakes are named, forts are identified, and river systems defined. Published in Williamson's* Description of the Settlement of the Genesee Country, in the State of New-York *(New York, 1799).*

Unquestionably the most important urban area to be mapped that year was the city of Washington, which later became the District of Columbia. The city was designed by the engineer and architect Pierre Charles L'Enfant, who refused to release a map for fear of land speculation. Andrew Ellicott, an assistant to L'Enfant, spent a year surveying the land, which George Washington had set aside by a proclamation of March 30, 1791, and he devised the first official plan of Washington (*Plate 132*), published in 1792. A reduced version of Ellicott's survey first appeared in March in *The Universal Asylum and Columbian Magazine.* The earliest folio plan of Washington was engraved by Samuel Hill in 1792, and later that year the original engraving of Ellicott's survey by James Thackara and John Vallance was issued as a separate folio in Philadelphia in November; it is this issue that is usually designated the official plan. It was reproduced widely, and commercial enterprise produced the so-called handkerchief

REFERENCES
Of the Principal Villages in Ontario & Steuben Counties.
H. Canandarque, the County Town.
I. Geneva.
K. Lyons.
L. Sodus.
P. Hope Town.
D. Williamsburgh.
E. Geneseo.
F. Hartford.
G. Athens.
West of the Genesee River
N. Gansons Tavern.
X. Town and Mills at the falls of the Genesee River.
M. Caledonia, a Scotch Settlement.
O. Station in the Big Plains.
B. Bath, the County Town.
A. Painted Post.
C. Dansville.
Q. Fredericks Town.
UPPER CANADA
SETTLEMENTS
ALEXANDER MACOMB & Co.
TOTTEN & CROSFIELD
LAKE ONTARIO
ROSEVELTS PURCHASE
ONEIDA L.
Great Genesee Road
Mohock River
PART of LAKE ERIE
MORRIS'S Purchase
Lands Granted to the American Army
Seneca Lake
NEW YORK
Newtown
Tyoga Point
Pennsylvania Line
Albany
MANOR of RENSELAR
VERMONT
NEW HAMPSHIRE
DARTMOUTH COLL.
MASSACHUSET
CONNECTICUT
UNITED STATES
THE SOUND
LONG ISLAND
West Branch of the
North East Branch of the
Susquehanna River
Northumberland
PENNSYLVANIA
Fort Pit
JERSEY
NEW
PHILADELPHIA
Haver de Grace
Baltimore
MARYLAND
CHESAPEAK BAY
DELAWARESTATE
DELAWARE BAY
VIRGINIA
A Map OF THE Middle States of North America

A Map of the Middle States of North America.
Shewing the Position of the Genesee Country comprehending the Counties of Ontario & Steuben as laid off in Townships of Six Miles square Each.
REFERENCES
Of the Principal Villages in Ontario & Steuben Counties.
H. Canandarque, the County Town
I. Geneva.
K. Lyons.
L. Sodus.
P. Hope Town
D. Williamsburgh.
E. Genesee.
F. Hartford.
G. Athens.
West of the Genesee River
N. Gansons Tavern.
X. Town and Mills at the falls of the Genesee River.
M. Caledonia, a Scotch Settlement.
O. Station on the Big Plains.
B. Bath, the County Town.
A. Painted Post.
C. Dansville.
Q. Fredericks Town.
UPPER CANADA
SETTLEMENTS
Montreal
45 North Latitude
N
LAKE ONTARIO
ALEXANDER MACOMB & Co
TOTTEN & CROSSFIELD
ROSEVELTS PURCHASE
PART of LAKE ERIE
MORRIS'S Purchase
Proposed Road.
NEW YORK
ONTARIO CO.
Lands Sold in 1791 by the State of New York
Granted to the American Army
CHMUNG
Lackhartsburg
Tyoga Point
Pennsylvania Line
Mohawk River
Black River
Albany
MASSACHUSETTS
Massachusetts Line
VERMONT
NEW HAMPSHIRE
DARTMOUTH COLL.
UNITED STATES
CONNECTICUT
Connecticut Line
Jersey Line
THE SOUND
LONG ISLAND
ATLANTIC OCEAN
PENNSYLVANIA
NEW JERSEY
PHILADELPHIA
MARYLAND
CHESAPEAK
DELAWARE STATE
DELAWARE BAY
VIRGINIA
Ohio River
Alligany River
Fort Pitt
West Branch of the Susquehannah
Delaware River
Hudsons River
Trenton
Burlington
Baltimore
Annapolis
Lancaster
York
Carlisle
Reading
Easton
Scale of Miles

(*opposite*) PLATE 134C: Charles Williamson. "A Map of the Middle States of North America Shewing the position of the Genesee Country comprehending the Counties of Ontario & Steuben as laid off in Townships of Six Miles square Each." 1800 (3rd state). Engraving, 37 × 40 cm. Private collection. *Numerous land grants and developments and many small streams are added, and state lines are specified. Previously unnamed and undefined expanses of area now filled in throughout New York State and adjacent states. Published in Williamson's* Observation of the Proposed State Road *(New York, 1800).*

maps, with the plan printed in red ink on cloth.

The first map published in America of Virginia after statehood, "The State of Virginia from the Best Authorities" by Samuel Lewis, has an inscription indicating that it was engraved for Mathew Carey's American edition of the popular contemporary textbook, Guthrie's *Geography Improved.* "A Map of the Tennessee Government" by Joseph T. Scott was included in the same work. These two maps along with maps of the other states, most of them drawn by Samuel Lewis, appeared in Carey's *American Atlas* (Philadelphia, 1795), the first atlas published in America. The year 1795 witnessed the publication of yet more state maps. "An Accurate Map of the District of Maine" by Osgood Carleton depicted towns, rivers, lakes, roads, mills, iron works, and public buildings; distances from Boston and from the county seat are given for each town. Carleton was also responsible for "An Accurate Map of the Commonwealth of Massachusetts," the most inclusive eighteenth-century map of that area. Caleb Harris's "A Map of the State of Rhode Island" is the classic map of that state, and a separate issue of the best eighteenth-century map of Maryland, drawn by Dennis Griffith, also appeared in 1795. In 1796 Mathew Carey published in Philadelphia his *American Pocket Atlas,* a pocket atlas showing each state. In the same year John Reid issued in New York the second atlas printed in the United States, *The American Atlas,* which was designed to accompany William Winterbotham's *An Historical, Geographical, Commercial, and Philosophical View of the United States* (4 vols., New York, 1796) and comprises twenty-two maps. Reid's atlas enjoys the priority of being the first atlas to include a plan of the city of Washington, a copy of the classic Ellicott plan of 1792.

Pennsylvania-German birth certificate of 1789

Stagecoach travel, from Weld's Travels through . . . North America, *1799*

American commercial and transportation interests at the end of the eighteenth century are cartographically represented by Abraham Bradley, Jr.'s "Map of the United States, Exhibiting the Post-Roads, the situations, connections & distances of the Post-Offices, Stage Roads, Counties, Ports of Entry and Delivery for Foreign Vessels, and the Principal Rivers" (*Plate 133*), published in 1796. The mail system along the main line from Brewer, Maine, to Charleston, South Carolina, with mileages between post offices and arrival and departure times for the mail, appears in an inset.

Two significant maps treating the Midwest were published in 1798. "A Map of the Connecticut Western Reserve from Actual Survey" by Seth Pease, engraved by Amos Doolittle, showed surveys east and west of the Cuyahoga River to the Vermilion River, naming thirty-two townships. Two years later the region was ceded by Connecticut to the Ohio Land Company. A detailed plan of the United States military district, reserved for veterans of the revolutionary war, is depicted on the "Plat of that Tract of Country in the Territory Northwest of the Ohio Appropriated for Military Services." Twenty ranges of five-mile townships are numbered from east to west, and the map also shows the region's northernmost limit, established by the Greenville Treaty, which was signed by twelve Indian tribes in August 1795 and demarcated the boundaries between Indian lands and those available to United States settlers. Three newly settled Moravian towns are also identified.

A comprehensive view of the progressive mapping of just one area reveals the cartographer's interest at the end of the century in filling empty spaces. The first of three maps exemplifying this tendency was published as part of a 1798 promotional book by Charles Williamson to attract settlers to that part of western New York known as the Genesee Country. Williamson's "A Map of the middle states, shewing the situation of the Genesee Lands and their connection with the Atlantic coast" (*Plate 134A*) names only two cities—Bath, New York, and Baltimore, Maryland. A slightly expanded text, accompanied by "A Map of the Middle States of North America" (*Plate 134B*), was published a year later. The same area shown in the 1798 map now has seventeen villages in Ontario and Steuben counties referenced in New York. Finally the same basic map, which appeared in Williamson's book *Observations on the Proposed State Road* (New York, 1800) under the inclusive title "A Map of the Middle States of North America Shewing the position of the Genesee Country comprehending the Counties of Ontario & Steuben as laid off in Townships of Six Miles square Each" (*Plate 134C*), appeared with names of dozens of rivers and towns added. Numerous land grants and developments and many small streams are indicated, and state lines specified. The originally unlisted and undefined expanses are now filled in throughout New York State and even in adjacent states. The cartographic progression in these three maps, all covering the same area, expresses the trends in mapping at the end of the eighteenth century, anticipating the sophistication of the maps produced in the following century. Concurrently with the political confidence gained by American independence, detailed mapping was coming of age.

PART TWO

SINCE 1800

RALPH E. EHRENBERG

8. *Mapping an Expanding Nation*

On [the ideal] map should be delineated the *Actual Courses* of the Rivers and Water Courses within its bounds. . . . The Map should likewise shew the Face of the Country, such as the Hills, gentle slopes, Valleys, Marsh Grounds and Morrasses. These should be so far accurate as to give a Stranger a just idea of the Country. . . . But such my Dear Sir are not the American Maps. Four lines of about an inch and half in length include a thousand Acres, and a waved line through it with a pen, is to represent a River, a Brook or a Run, as you may happen to find it!

NICHOLAS KING
Diary, September 18, 1794
Manuscript Division, Library of Congress

1800-1840

AN INDIGENOUS cartography sprang up and eventually flourished during the nineteenth century in response to nationalism, exploration, settlement, war, rising literacy and mobility, and finally, the exploitation of natural resources. The initial or formative period lasted until about 1840, at which time commercial companies and government agencies began large-scale systematic mapping programs. During these first four decades domestic mapping skills and printing techniques were developed and the economic and social conditions were laid for a burgeoning trade in domestic maps. At the same time European fascination with the New World continued to be reflected in the issuance of a significant number of important maps.

One of the forces behind the development of an indigenous cartography was the demand for accurate maps for administrative purposes. For the region east of the Mississippi these took the form of city, state, and national maps. Most uniquely American were the state maps: as we have already seen (see page 211), William Blodget published the first state map, Vermont, in 1789. Blodget's map was followed by some thirty other separate state maps by various cartographers over the next fifty years, most of which have been described by Walter W. Ristow (see Bibliography). These were generally prepared at a medium scale of two to eight miles per inch, and were detailed enough to provide useful information on internal boundaries, routes, and settlements. They represent an important milestone in the development of American cartography.

At the turn of the century, state maps existed for Vermont, Connecticut, Pennsylvania, and Maryland. In 1801, a large state map of Massachusetts was issued. Osgood Carleton, with the assistance of the Massachusetts Historical Society, prompted the Massachusetts State Legislature to pass a resolution in 1794 directing each town to prepare an accurate town map. These large-scale maps—some 265 for Massachusetts and 100 for Maine, which until 1820 was administered by Massachusetts—were incorporated into state maps by Carleton for Massachusetts in 1801 and the District of Maine in 1802 (*Plate 135*). They show the counties and towns, principal roads, rivers, mountains, mines, islands, shoals, falls, mills, and manufacturing plants by various symbols.

In the same year that Carleton's map of Maine was engraved, Simeon DeWitt completed one of the earliest state-subsidized maps. DeWitt served as Surveyor-General of New York State for fifty years, beginning in 1784 when he resigned his position as Geographer of the Continental Army. His large map of New York State, which measures 66 by 53 inches, was engraved on six plates. It includes the surveys he directed of lands in the western part of the state which had been set aside for Revolutionary War veterans, to encourage long-term enlistments. The New York State Senate directed that one copy of each map be distributed to all other state governors, an action which probably encouraged the preparation of other state maps. DeWitt's map laid the groundwork for all successive maps of New York State.

Both Abraham Bradley, Jr., and Aaron Arrowsmith issued revisions of their large maps of the United States in 1804 (*Plate 136; see Plate 133*). Bradley's map notes that the region "the French call . . . Louisiana" has been ceded to the United States, but it fails to show more than a few rivers on the eastern periphery of the Louisiana Territory. Both maps are limited in coverage to the country east of the Mississippi River. A derivative of the Arrowsmith map was prepared in Boston by Carleton in 1806 and published by John Sullivan. This is one of several derivative maps generated by Arrowsmith's United States map in England, France, and the United States during the next fifteen years.

During this decade the first coastal navigational charts were

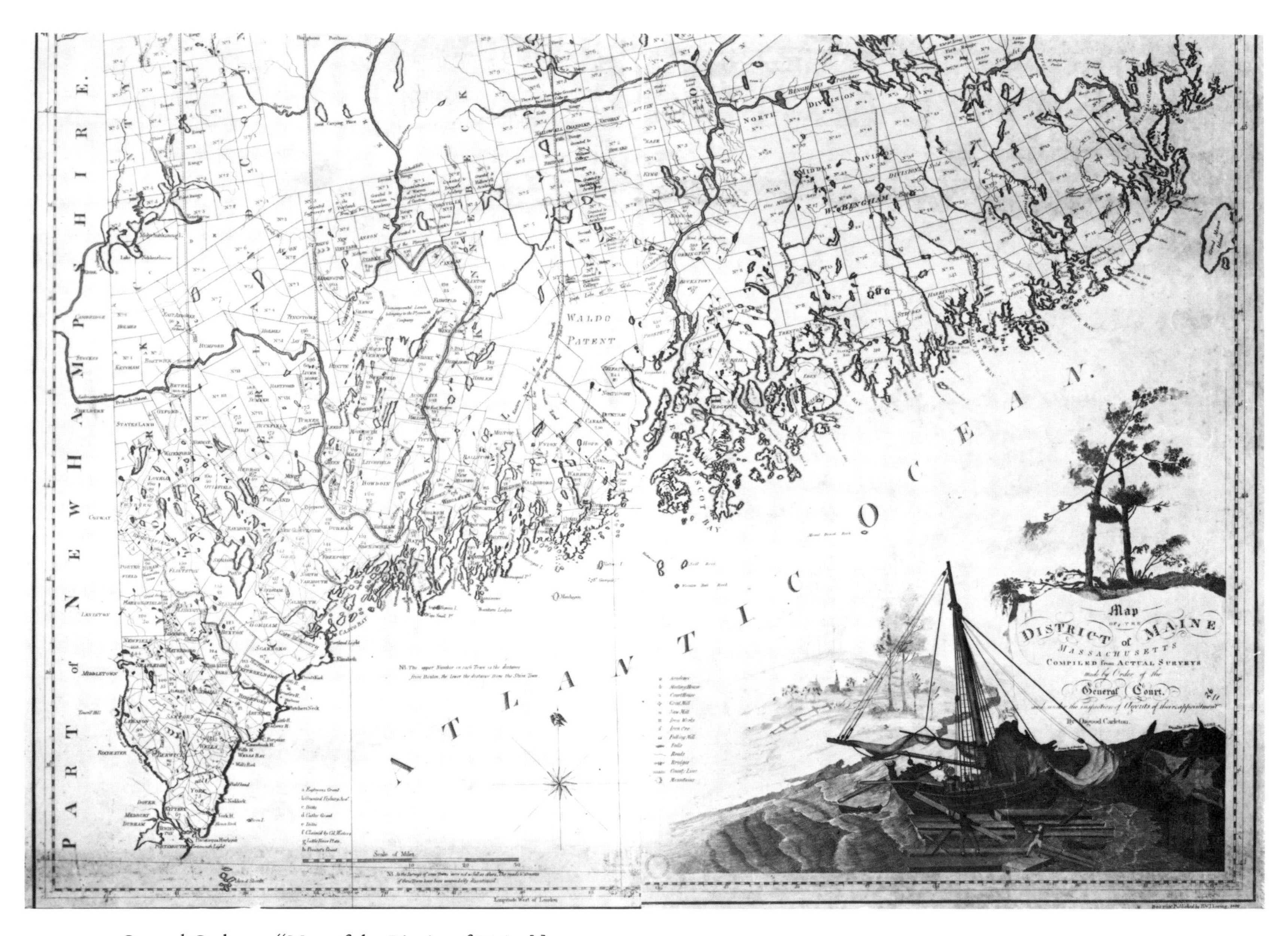

PLATE 135: Osgood Carleton. "Map of the District of Maine[,] Massachusetts Compiled from Actual Surveys made by Order of the General Court, . . ." (portion). 1802. Engraving, entire dimensions 134 × 91.5 cm. Reference Map Collection, National Archives, Washington, D.C. *Southeast quadrant of representative state map depicting county and town divisions, locations of academies, meeting-houses, courthouses, gristmills, sawmills, ironworks, iron ore deposits, falls, roads, and bridges. Drawn by G. Graham; engraved by J. Callender and S. Hill, Boston; published by B. & J. Loring, Boston.*

produced by American firms. In London the publishers R. Laurie and J. Whittle revised their *North-American Pilot* in 1800 and 1807, but the Laurie and Whittle charts were gradually replaced by Edmund March Blunt's *The American Coast Pilot*; first published in 1796, Blunt's work did not include charts until the fourth edition in 1804. From 1809 onward, many of the charts published by Blunt were engraved by William Hooker, an engraver later associated with the production of pocket guides of New

York City. The demand for navigational aids of the inland waterways prompted Zadok Cramer, advantageously located in Pittsburgh, the gateway to the Ohio Valley, to publish the *Ohio and Mississippi Navigator*. While the first edition issued in 1801 contained only directions and notes, the 1806 edition, renamed *The Navigator*, included thirteen page-size charts.

One other important contribution to coastal cartography was made in 1806 with the compilation of "A Chart of the Coast of North Carolina between Cape Hatteras & Cape Fear." This chart was prepared by civilian surveyors Jonathan Price and Thomas Coles from personal surveys requested by President Thomas Jefferson and the U.S. Congress because of the dangers that the Outer Banks presented to American shipping. Jefferson's concern with the safety of coastal shipping led to the founding of the U.S. Coast Survey one year later.

The Far West continued to interest mapmakers, particularly after the transfer in 1803 of French Louisiana to the United States. Aaron Arrowsmith's "Map exhibiting all the new discoveries in the interior parts of North America," first published in London in 1795, was reissued there with "Additions to 1802." Inscribed to "The Honorable Governor and Company of Adventurers of England trading into Hudson Bay," this map was compiled largely from information and from Indian maps supplied to Arrowsmith by the Hudson's Bay Company. It was considered to be the most accurate representation of the trans-Mississippi West up to that period, and was used by Thomas Jefferson, Meriwether Lewis, and William Clark in planning the Lewis and Clark expedition. Arrowsmith's map reveals a single unbroken chain of mountains stretching north–south between the 112th and 115th meridians of longitude. The upper Missouri River is highly generalized west of the Mandan villages. Running in an east–west direction to its source near the headwaters of the Rio Grande and Colorado rivers, the course of the Missouri as delineated on this map led Jefferson and the expedition's leaders to the erroneous belief that the Missouri River provided a shorter and more direct route to the Pacific coast than was actually the case.

A French map of the same year was compiled by François Perrin du Lac and included information from the explorations of James Mackay in present-day Nebraska. The lower course of the Missouri River is delineated rather accurately, but the headwaters of both the Missouri and Mississippi rivers are greatly

BOSTON,

Plymouth & Sandwich

MAIL STAGE,

CONTINUES TO RUN AS FOLLOWS:

LEAVES Boston every Tuesday, Thursday, and Saturday mornings at 5 o'clock, breakfast at Leonard's, Scituate; dine at Bradford's, Plymouth; and arrive in Sandwich the same evening. Leaves Sandwich every Monday, Wednesday and Friday mornings; breakfast at Bradford's, Plymouth; dine at Leonard's, Scituate, and arrive in Boston the same evening.

Passing through Dorchester, Quincy, Wyemouth, Hingham, Scituate, Hanover, Pembroke, Duxbury, Kingston, Plymouth to Sandwich. *Fare,* from Boston to Scituate, 1 doll. 25 cts. From Boston to Plymouth, 2 dolls. 50 cts. From Boston to Sandwich, 3 dolls. 63 cts.

N. B. Extra Carriages can be obtained of the proprietor's, at Boston and Plymouth, at short notice.—
☞STAGE BOOKS kept at Boyden's Market-square, Boston, and at Fessendon's, Plymouth.

LEONARD & WOODWARD.

BOSTON, *November* 24, 1810.

The Boston–Sandwich mail stage, 1810; announcement of schedule

elongated in a northwesterly direction. Entitled "Carte du Missouri levée et rectifiée dans toute son Etendue," it was based on Perrin du Lac's visit to Louisiana in 1802 but not published until 1805 when it appeared in his *Voyage dans les deux Louisianes.*

Beginning in 1803, Jefferson and other advocates of Federal expansion authorized the preparation of a series of maps of the newly acquired lands beyond the Mississippi River. Andrew Ellicott's map of the Mississippi River, which was reproduced in his

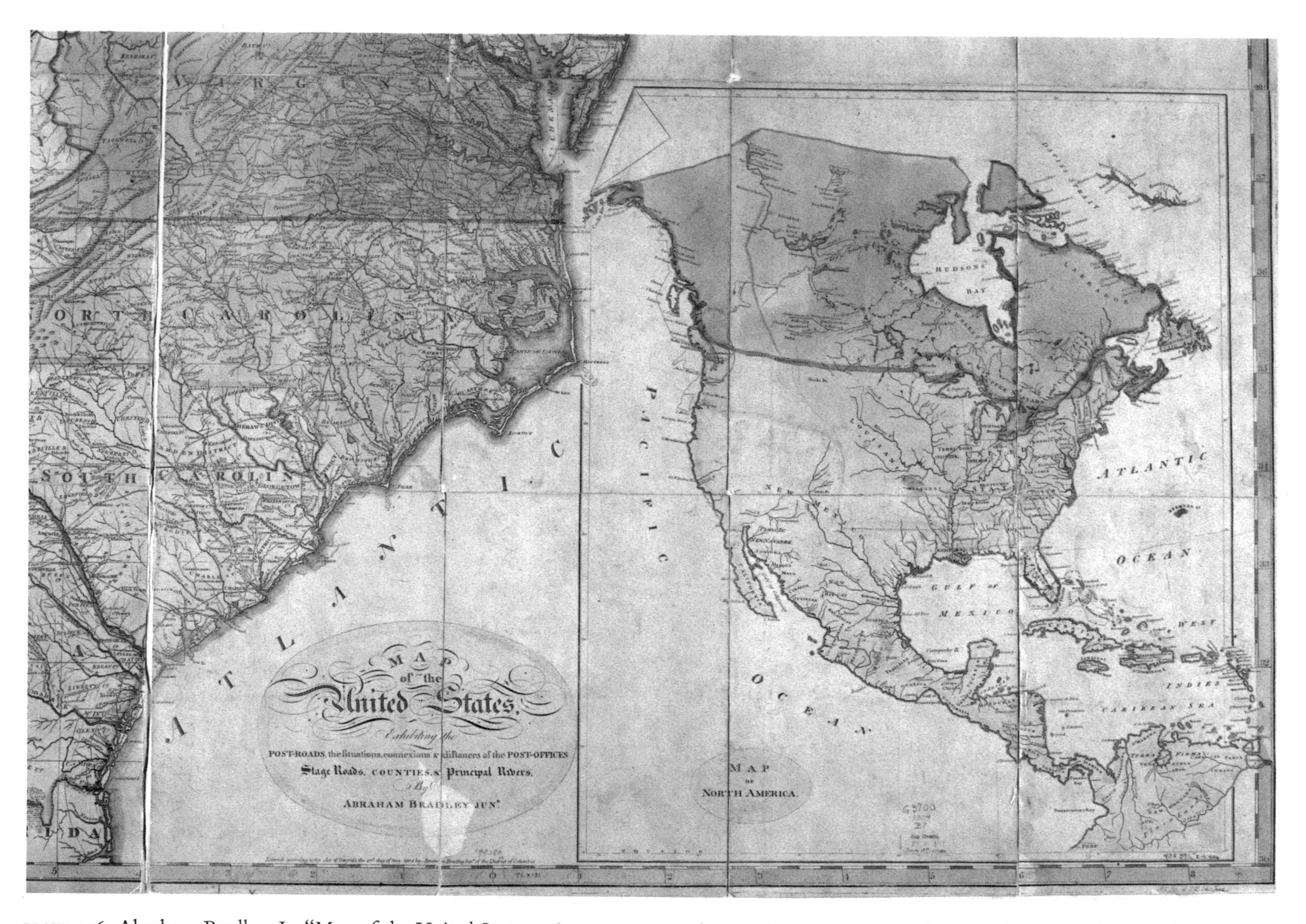

PLATE 136: Abraham Bradley, Jr. "Map of the United States, Exhibiting the Post-Roads, the situations, connexions & distances of the Post-Offices, Stage Roads, Counties, & Principal Rivers" (portion). 1804. Engraving, hand colored; entire dimensions 96.5 × 134 cm. Geography and Map Division, Library of Congress, Washington, D.C. *Southeast quadrant of the United States east of the Mississippi River on the eve of the Lewis and Clark expedition. Large inset, "Map of North America," reveals a remarkable absence of geography for much of the northern hemisphere.*

(opposite) PLATE 137: Nicholas King. "A Map of part of the Continent of North America, Between the 35th and 51st degrees of North Latitude, and extending from the 89° degrees of West Longitude to the Pacific Ocean. Compiled from the Authorities of the best informed travellers, by M. Lewis." 1805–6. Manuscript, pen and ink; 80 × 117 cm. Records of the Office of the Chief of Engineers, National Archives, Washington, D.C. *First official map of the trans-Mississippi West compiled from data furnished King by William Clark, of the Lewis and Clark expedition. Grossly misrepresents the terrain features and drainage patterns of the Far West, beyond the Great Bend of the Missouri River.*

Journal in 1803, provided a reasonably correct delineation of the Mississippi River south from its confluence with the Missouri River, and it located the mouth of the Missouri more accurately than on any previous map.

At the request of Jefferson and Albert Gallatin, Secretary of the Treasury, Nicholas King prepared a manuscript map of the western part of North America in 1803 which graphically summarized the existing geographical information on the West before Lewis and Clark left Washington. In the critical upper Missouri region, King depicted the headwaters of a "conjectural" river running directly eastward from the mouth of the Columbia River on the Pacific coast. The delineation of this river reflects the cartographer's belief that a direct water route to the Pacific coast existed, one which lay well within U.S. territory. It was this erroneous route which became the major objective of the Lewis and Clark expedition.

This was the first of several maps of the trans-Mississippi West that King prepared between 1803 and 1806 at the direction of Jefferson and the War Department for distribution to Congress. King, a native of England and Surveyor of the City of Washington from 1803 until his death in 1812, was one of the outstanding cartographic craftsmen at this time in the United States. In 1804 or 1805 he compiled a "Map of the Washita River in Louisiana from the Hot Springs, to the confluence of the Red River with the Mississippi . . ." which was based on the journal and survey of William Dunbar. The map, engraved by William

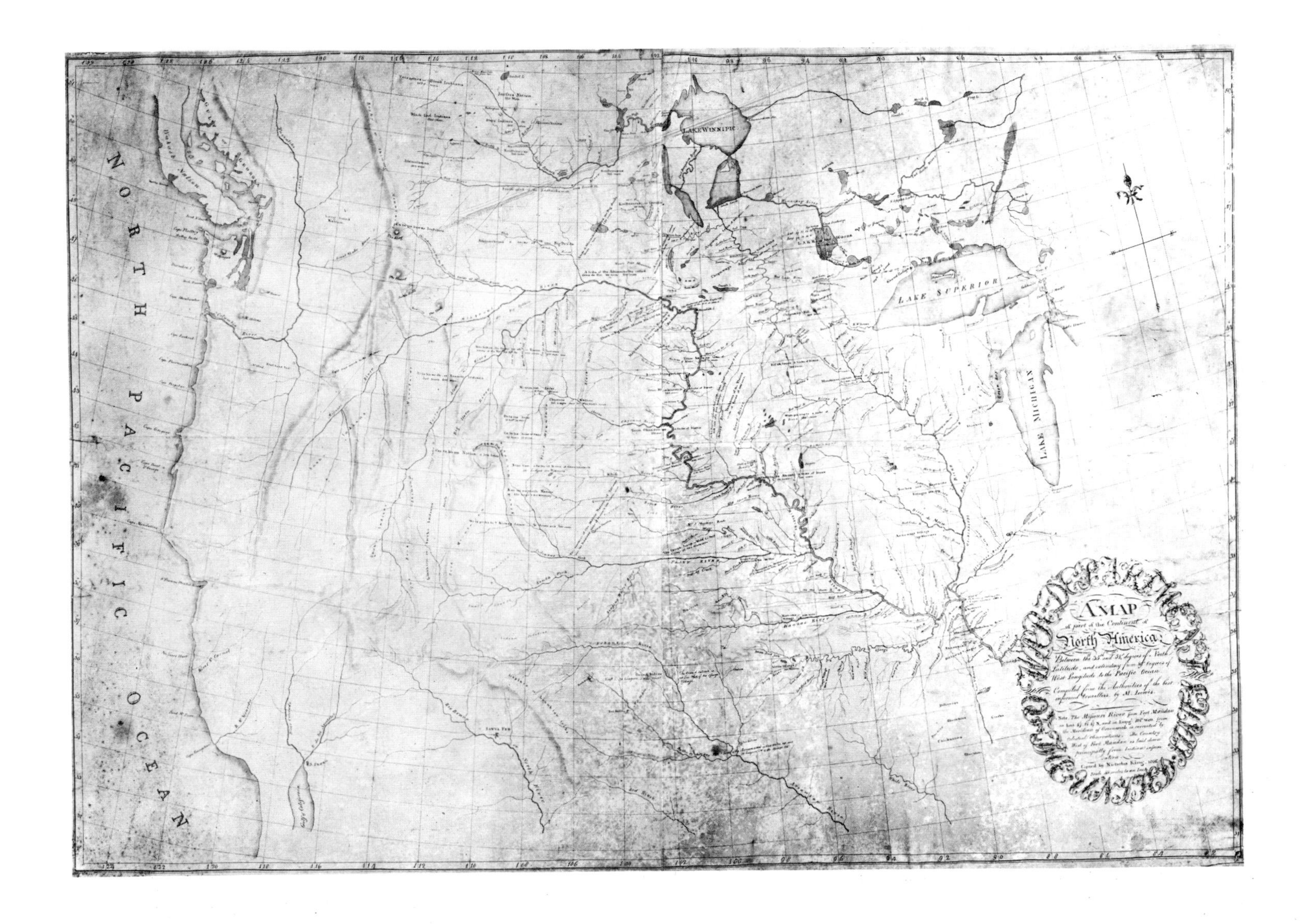

Captain William Clark and his men shooting bears, from Patrick Gass's Journal of . . . Lewis & Clark, *1812*

Kneass in Philadelphia, was described in the leading scientific journal of the day, *The Medical Repository,* as "a substantial addition to American geography."

In late 1805 and early 1806 King compiled four copies of the map sketched by William Clark while the Lewis and Clark expedition wintered at Fort Mandan on the large bend of the Missouri River in 1804–5 (*Plate 137*). For the first time the Missouri River was accurately delineated as far north as the Mandan villages; the Far West, still to be explored, remained distorted, particularly west of the Rocky Mountains. On February 19, 1806, Jefferson presented King's maps of the Lewis-Clark and Dunbar-Hunter expeditions to both houses of Congress in an effort to keep the members informed and interested in the newly acquired Louisiana Territory. Later in the same year King reworked and reduced Antoine Nau's dramatic large-scale maps of Zebulon Montgomery Pike's Mississippi River expedition to a manageable size for engraving and printing; Pike's expedition had just surveyed the Mississippi River from St. Louis northward beyond modern-day Minneapolis in search of its headwaters. King also authored a condensed narrative out of Pike's journal, and published it along with the reduced map for distribution to members of Congress in the spring of 1807. King's final work on western exploration was the compilation and publication of a "Map of the Red River in Louisiana" based upon the Freeman-Custis expedition of 1806. These maps and reports prepared by King represent the earliest official geographical image of the trans-Mississippi West.

The preparation of state maps shifted from the northeast to the southeast in 1807 with the publication of Virginia's first state map. It was prepared under the direction of Bishop James Madison (president of William and Mary College, and a cousin of President James Madison), by William Prentis and William Davis from data received from local surveyors. Unable to secure financial aid from the state, Bishop Madison had the map engraved privately on nine plates by Frederick Bossler. Madison's map was redrawn in 1818 by Davis and remained the most accurate map of Virginia until 1826. Also privately produced was the first state map of North Carolina. Compiled by Jonathan Price from surveys undertaken by Price and John Strother as early as 1789, the entire preparation and production of the map was financed by subscribers (*Plate 138*). It was engraved by William Harrison in Philadelphia in 1808. An error of omission of one degree of longitude in the western part of the map, however, led to distortions of natural features in this region on general maps of the United States until corrected by Henry S. Tanner in his *New American Atlas* of 1823. These and other state maps of the

State Capitol, Richmond, Va., built 1789; architect, Thomas Jefferson

southeast are described by Walter W. Ristow in his article of that title (see Bibliography).

The first decade of the new century drew to a close with the revision of Mathew Carey's *American Atlas*, first engraved in 1795 for Carey's American edition of Guthrie's *Geography*. The 1809 edition contained twenty-six maps, including one of the United States by Samuel Lewis "compiled chiefly from State maps, and other Authentic information." This map contained an inset map of East Florida (then still under Spanish control) which was characterized by a single line of hills dissecting the peninsula lengthwise and labeled the "Great Sandy Ridge."

In 1809 William Maclure also prepared his geological map of America which appeared, along with his "Observations on the Geology of the U.S.," in the *Transactions* of the American Philosophical Society. The first geological map of the region east of the Mississippi River, it was imprinted over a topographic map by Samuel Lewis and hand colored to show geological information. Maclure, a native of Scotland who settled in the United States, was said to have visited nearly every state and territory in the Union and to have traversed the Allegheny Mountains more than fifty times in the preparation of this map. His five-color classification of rock formations was based on the English stratification scheme. Republished in 1817, it eventually led to modifications of contemporary geological theories of classification. This map represents the emergence of an indigenous, special purpose or thematic cartography in the United States.

At the beginning of the second decade several important maps of the American West provided new information about the region recently purchased from France. Pike's expeditions southwestward across the high plains to Santa Fe resulted in the publication of three maps in 1810. The two most significant were titled "The First Part of Captn. Pike's Chart of the Internal Part of Louisiana" and "A Chart of the Internal Part of Louisiana, including all the hitherto unexplored Countries, lying between the River LaPlatte of the Missouri on the N: and the Red River on the S: the Mississippi East and the Mountains of Mexico West: with a part of New Mexico and the Province of Texas." Engraved by Francis Shallus and published in 1810 by Fielding Lucas, Jr., in Baltimore along with Pike's *An Account of Expeditions to the Sources of the Mississippi and through the Western Parts of Louisiana*, these two maps were compiled by Antoine Nau, a French draftsman who had served as a sergeant on General James Wilkinson's

Seals of the first sixteen states, surrounding a portrait of President John Adams, engraving by Amos Doolittle, 1803

staff in St. Louis. They are the first published maps to depict graphically the geographical knowledge of the entire southwest derived directly from exploring parties, and the earliest to reveal a practical route from St. Louis to Santa Fe. Pike's report and maps, however, perpetuated the concept of the "height-of-land" theory, which hypothesized that the headwaters of the major rivers of the West were located within a day's march from one another.

Pike's third map in this *Account*, of New Spain, was plagiarized directly from Baron Alexander von Humboldt's significant "Carte Générale du Royaume de la Nouvelle Espagne." Pike, or his copyist, apparently obtained a preliminary copy of Humboldt's map which the latter had left at the State Department during his

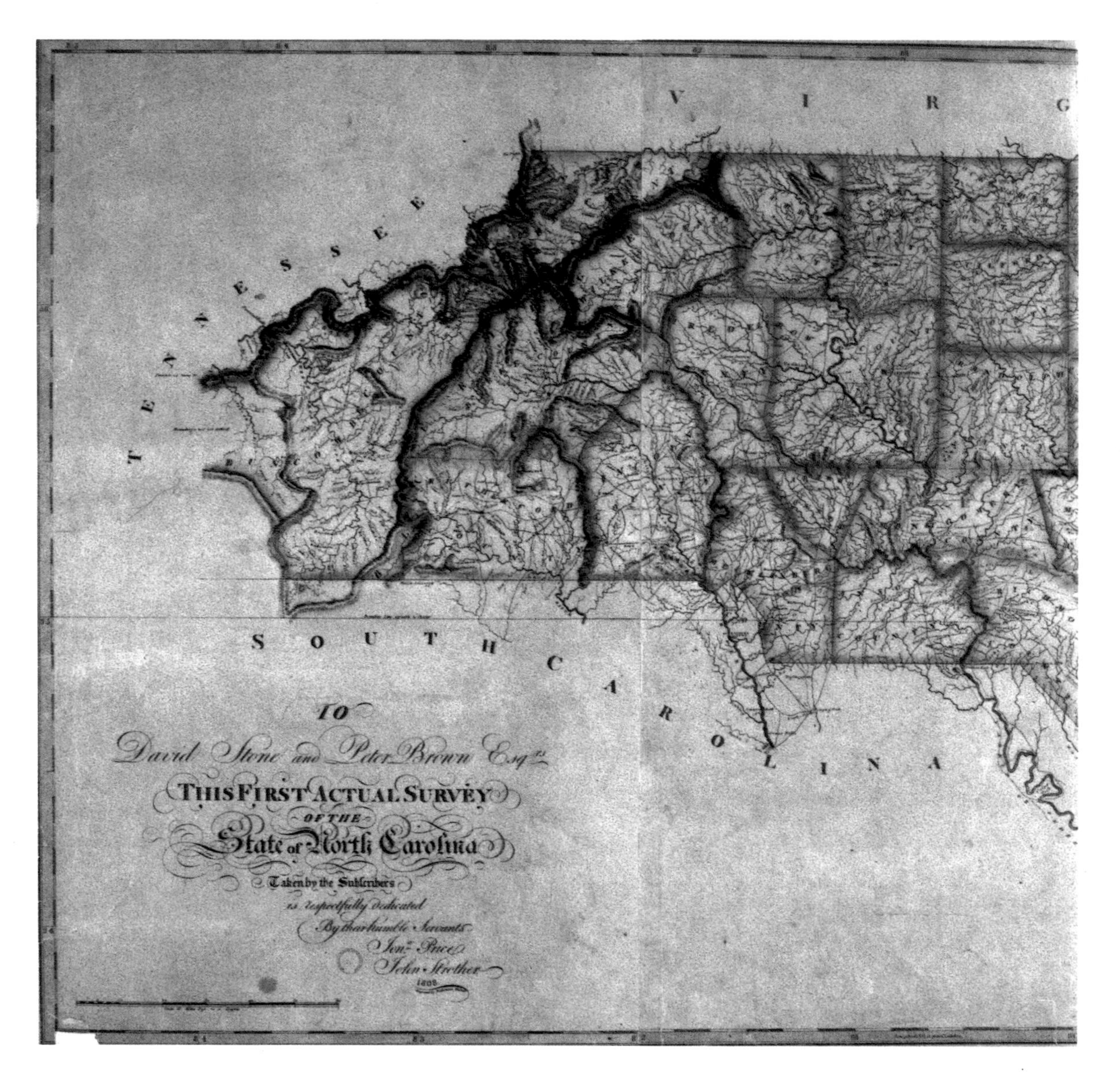

PLATE 138: Jonathan Price and John Strother. ". . . First Actual Survey of the State of North Carolina Taken by the Subscribers . . ." (western portion). 1808. Engraving, hand colored; entire dimensions 72 × 148 cm. Records of the Office of the Chief of Engineers, National Archives, Washington, D.C. *Published by William Harrison, Philadelphia. The title section of an early, privately produced state map showing county boundaries, roads, courthouses, drainage system, ironworks, towns, and selected private residences.*

(opposite) PLATE 139: Alexander von Humboldt. "Carte Générale du Royaume de la Nouvelle Espagne depuis le Parallele de 16° jusqu'au Parallele de 38° (Latitude Nord) Dressée Sur des Observations Astronomiques et sur l'ensemble des Matériaux qui existoient à Mexico, au commencement de l'année 1804" (northern portion). 1811. Engraving, entire dimensions 108.5 × 74 cm. Records of the Office of the Chief of Engineers, National Archives, Washington, D.C. *Northern half of important source map; shows the American southwest, based on information gathered by Spanish exploring parties during the eighteenth century. Perpetuates the myth of the Rio de San Buenaventura, believed by the Spanish authorities to drain the region south of the Columbia River. Engraved by Barrière, in Paris.*

visit to Washington in 1804. Pike's unauthorized version of the Humboldt map is of interest because it appeared in print one year earlier than Humboldt's original map, which was published in 1811 in his *Atlas Géographique et Physique du Royaume de la Nouvelle Espagne* (*Plate 139*). Humboldt's map of New Spain was drawn in 1803 while the German geographer was staying at the Royal School of Mines in Mexico City, where many Spanish maps were available to him for consultation. Humboldt, through Pike's map, reproduced for the first time in printed form the geographical features discovered by Spanish exploring parties that had reached as far north as present-day Utah. Humboldt inadvertently perpetuated several geographical misconceptions borrowed from his Spanish sources: notably the inclusion of the Rio de San Buenaventura, a mythical river that Spanish explorers believed drained the region south of the Columbia River, and the depiction of the source of the Red River in the mountains east of Taos.

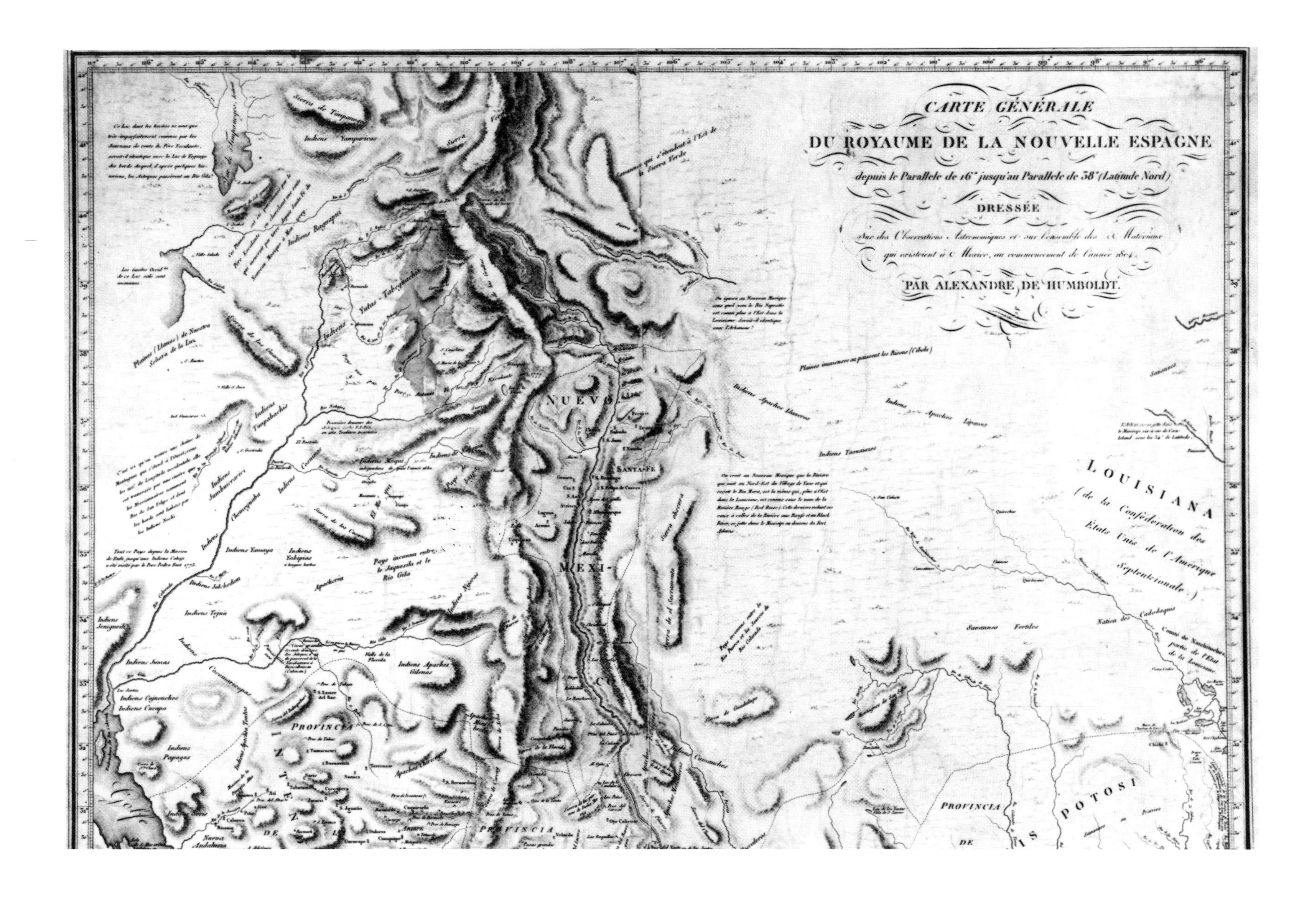

Despite these errors Humboldt's map remained the standard map of the Great Basin region until Frémont's expeditions thirty-five years later (*see Plate 171*).

The region traversed by Lewis and Clark was depicted by William Clark's monumental manuscript map of the region west of the Great Lakes (*Plate 140*). Begun sometime after the return of the two explorers in 1806, Clark worked on the manuscript until late in 1810, when it was copied and reduced for engraving by Samuel Lewis for inclusion in Nicholas Biddle and Paul Allen's history of the expedition. The map was published in 1814 by Bradford and Inskeep in Philadelphia. More accurate than any previous western map, it rapidly became the source for a new generation of western maps. The narrow single chain of mountains that characterized many earlier maps was replaced by a complex system of ranges, and the courses of the Missouri and Snake rivers were shown for the first time in their approximately correct

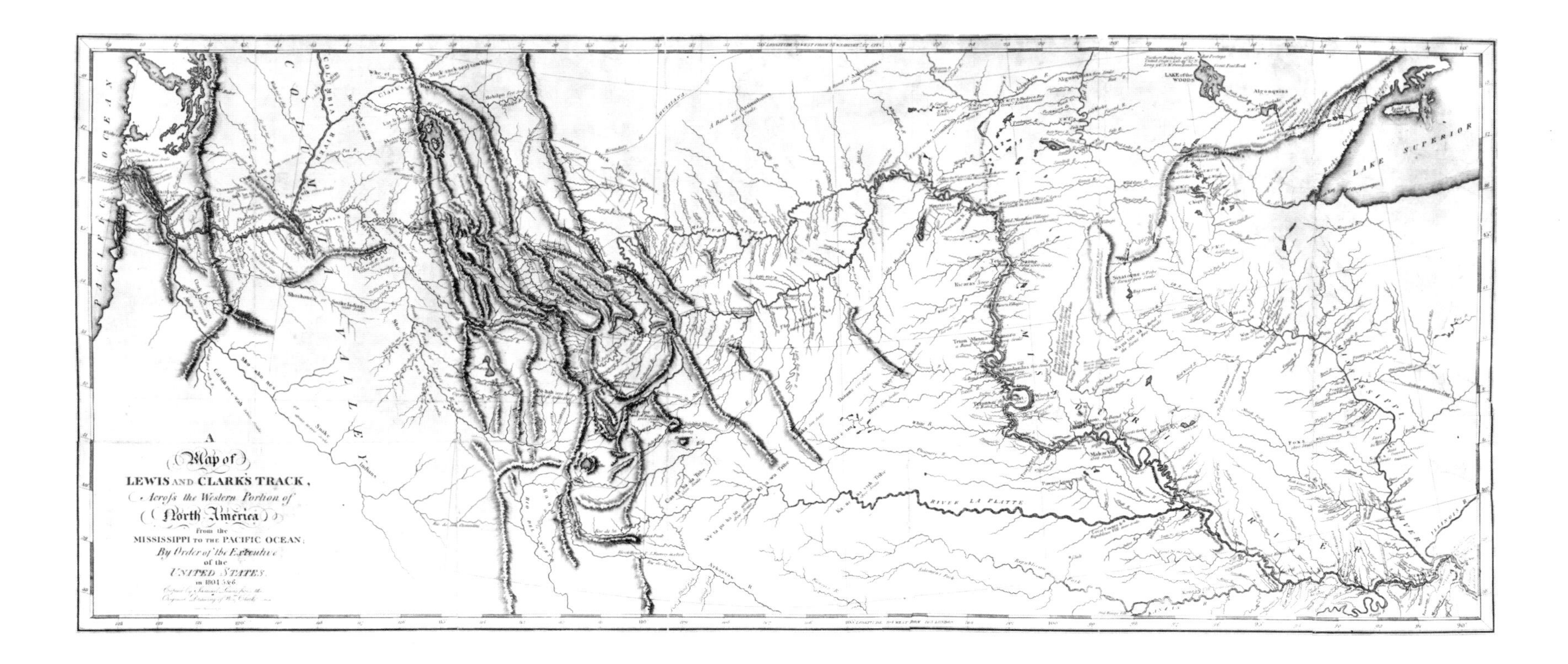

position. The Far Southwest, however, still remained grossly inaccurate, with the atavistic Rio de San Buenaventura reappearing as the Multnomah River, and the headwaters of the Yellowstone, Platte, Rio Grande (Rio del Norte), and Multnomah rivers converging at a mythical height-of-land located in the Colorado Rockies.

In 1812 the second war with England diverted cartographic interest back to the East. In Connecticut the General Assembly authorized the preparation of a state map by Moses Warren and George Gillet. By February 1812 it had been engraved by Abner Reed and published in Hartford by Hudson and Goodwin, some three months before hostilities began with the British. Thirty-six different symbols showed roads, townships, counties, and manufacturing establishments. In September 1812 William Watson completed the first large-scale state map of New Jersey.

John Melish's military and topographical atlas of the United States was published a year later by G. Palmer in Philadelphia. Melish, a native of Scotland, became the first publisher in the United States to specialize in geographical and cartographical works. His atlas included a general map of "the seat of war" and seven other colored maps and plans of strategic and military significance. Most of these maps were engraved by Henry S. Tanner, who eventually succeeded Melish as the leading cartographic publisher. In response to the success of Melish's atlas, an enlarged edition was reissued in 1815 containing twelve colored maps.

After-battle maps of selected campaigns were prepared by both the Quartermaster General's Office of the British Army and by U.S. Army mapmakers to illustrate troop movements. Included were maps of the British capture and destruction of Washington and their unsuccessful adventure in New Orleans, which resulted in the greatest American land victory of the war and propelled General Andrew Jackson toward the presidency. These British maps were printed from stone and represent perhaps the earliest lithographic maps devoted to the United States (*Plate 141*). Over the next several decades lithography was to revolutionize mapmaking. Invented in Germany by Aloys Senefelder about 1798, it was cheaper and faster than laboriously engraving and printing from copperplates; lithography also lent *(opposite)* PLATE 140: Samuel Lewis. "A Map of Lewis and Clark's Track, Across the Western Portion of North America From the Mississippi to the Pacific Ocean; By Order of the Executive of the United States, in 1804, 5 & 6." 1814. Engraving, 31 × 72 cm. Geography and Map Division, Library of Congress, Washington, D.C. *Engraved by Samuel Harrison; published by Bradford and Inskeep, Philadelphia. First published map to incorporate the geographical information obtained from Lewis and Clark's trans-Mississippi exploration from St. Louis to the mouth of the Columbia River on the Pacific coast, shortly after the United States acquired this vast region from France. Copied from William Clark's original manuscript map and published in Nicholas Biddle's* History of the expedition under the command of Captains Lewis and Clark . . ., *Philadelphia, 1814.*

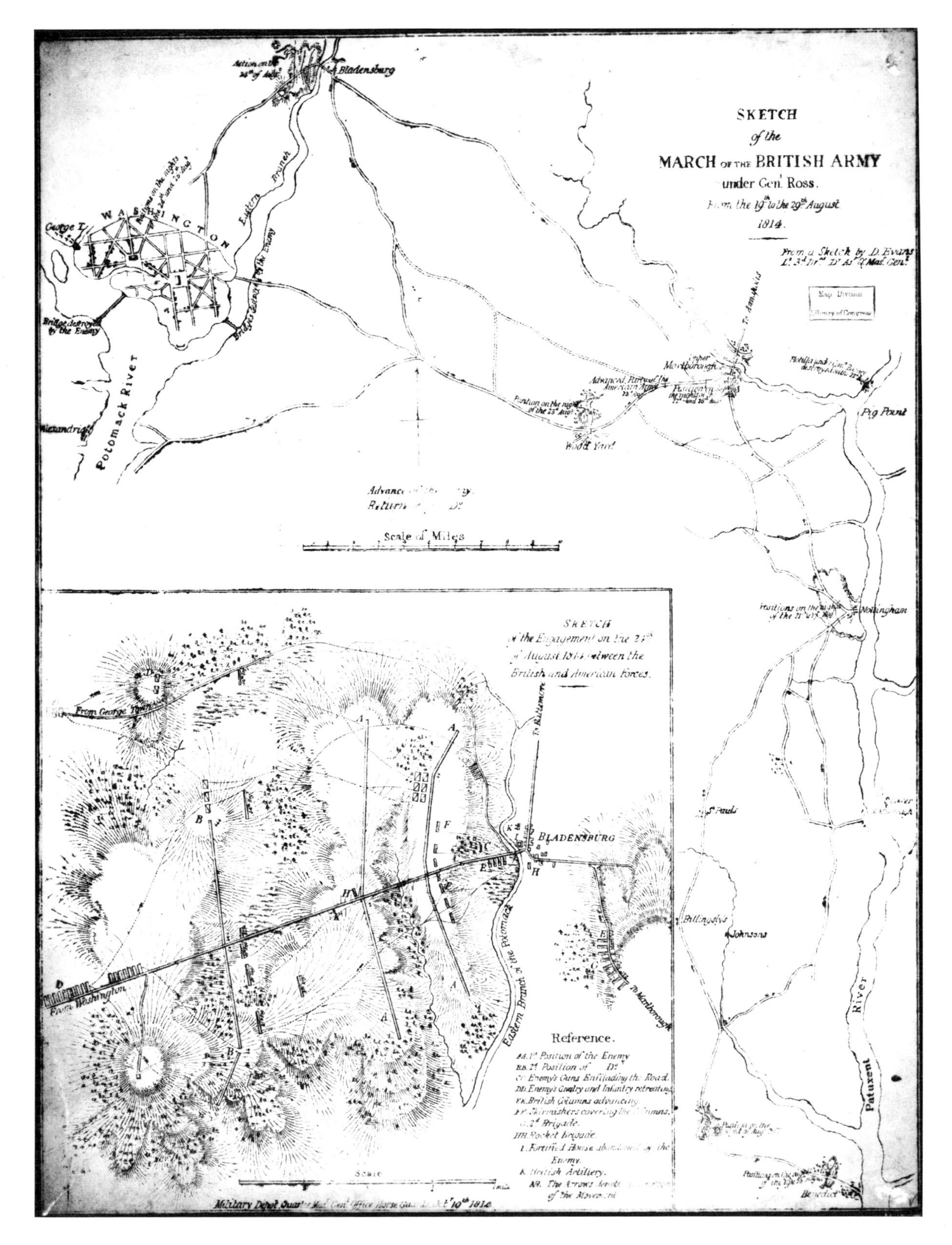

PLATE 141: British Military Depot. Quartermaster Central Office. Horse Guards. "Sketch of the March of the British Army under Genl Ross. From the 19.th to the 29.th August. 1814. From a Sketch by D. Evans L^{t}. 3^{d}. Drn^{s}. D^{y}. As^{t}. Q^{r}. Mas^{r}. Genl." 1814. Lithograph, 47 × 34.5 cm. Geography and Map Division, Library of Congress, Washington, D.C. *Order-of-battle map showing the British attack on Washington, D.C., during the War of 1812; inset map of the battle of Bladensburg, Maryland, on August 24. One of the earliest lithographed maps of a portion of the United States.*

PLATE 142: Cartographer unknown. "General Jackson's campaign against the Creek Indians 1813 & 1814." c. 1814. Manuscript, pen and ink; 85.5 × 56 cm. Records of the Office ot the Chief of Engineers, National Archives, Washington, D.C. *Map showing permanent and temporary military posts and Indian villages in Alabama, some of which were destroyed by United States military units under General Andrew Jackson's command during the War of 1812.*

(*opposite*) PLATE 143: General Land Office. "[Plat of] Township No. V. North, Range No. IX West of the 3rd [Principal] Meridian." Nov. 18, 1815. Manuscript with watercolor wash, 39.5 × 32.5 cm. Records of the Bureau of Land Management, National Archives, Washington, D.C. *A typical township plat prepared by surveyors of the General Land Office during the early decades of the nineteenth century at a scale of 2 inches to the mile. Each township plat covered thirty-six square miles and was subdivided into sections one mile square. In addition to defining the exterior and interior boundary lines of the rectangular land survey system, township plats depicted existing cultural and physical features, such as private land claims that predated the survey. Several of these private land claims are seen in this plat. Federal township plats were prepared for all territories and states carved out of the public domain and were used extensively by commercial map publishers such as John Melish to compile territorial and state maps. Three original copies of each township plat were prepared: one was deposited with the local land office; one with the territorial or state government; and one with the General Land Office in Washington, D.C.*

itself to color printing. American efforts to map the campaigns were less sophisticated; the majority were never printed (*Plate 142*).

In 1814 the fourth edition of Mathew Carey's small *American Pocket Atlas* was issued in Philadelphia. First printed in 1796, it now contained twenty-three general and state maps, a number of them drawn by Samuel Lewis and Amos Doolittle. Of particular interest is one map headed "Missouri Territory formerly Louisiana." Drawn by Samuel Lewis, it incorporates data from the Lewis and Clark expedition. Arrowsmith's map of North America was also revised in London in 1814 in order to incorporate the newly available Clark and Pike materials. The cartographer added new information from the discoveries of the British ex-

Zebulon Montgomery Pike, *1808, painting by Charles Willson Peale*

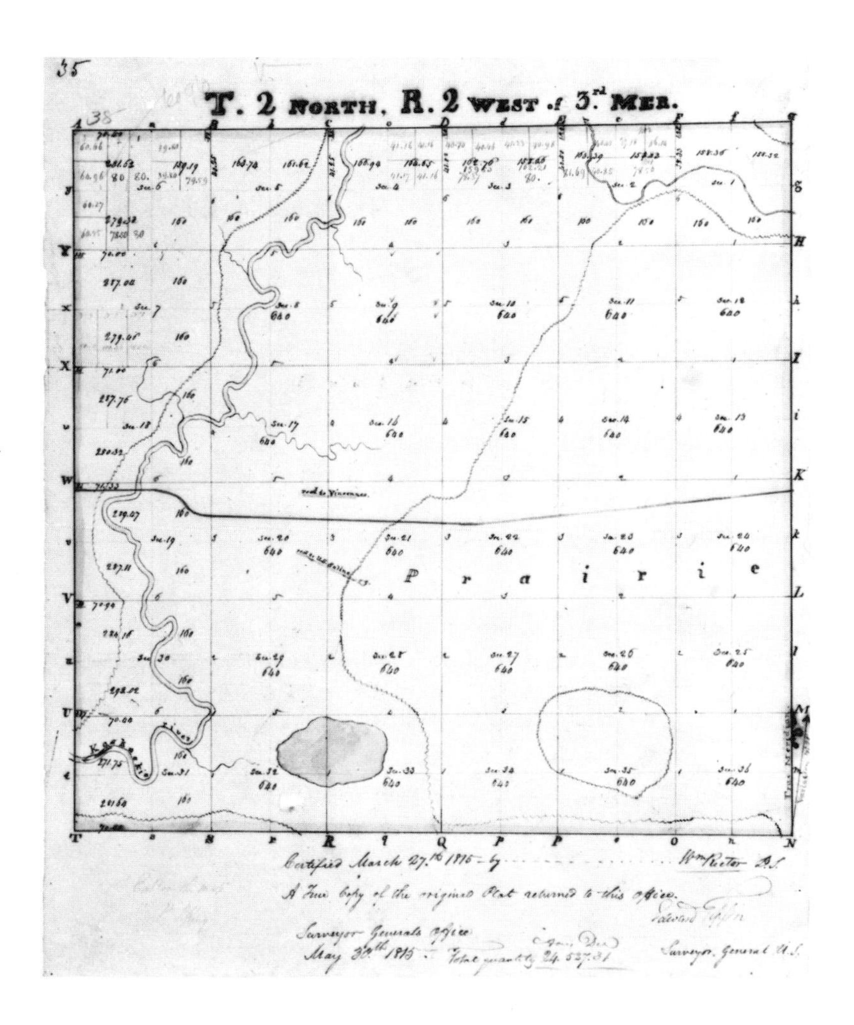

plorer David Thompson, and thus his delineation of the upper Columbia River system is more accurate than Clark's map.

Fielding Lucas, Jr., one of the few map publishers then residing outside of Philadelphia, published his first atlas in Baltimore in 1814. Entitled *A New Elegant General Atlas Containing Maps of Each of the United States*, it consists of thirty-one maps drawn by Samuel Lewis and engraved by Henry S. Tanner. The rapid settlement of the midwestern and southern states during this period resulted in several variant editions, new atlases being often made up for binding as improved maps were obtained.

Into Ohio, Indiana, and Illinois, the General Land Office extended the rectangular land survey westward along the Ohio River and undertook special surveying and mapping projects in

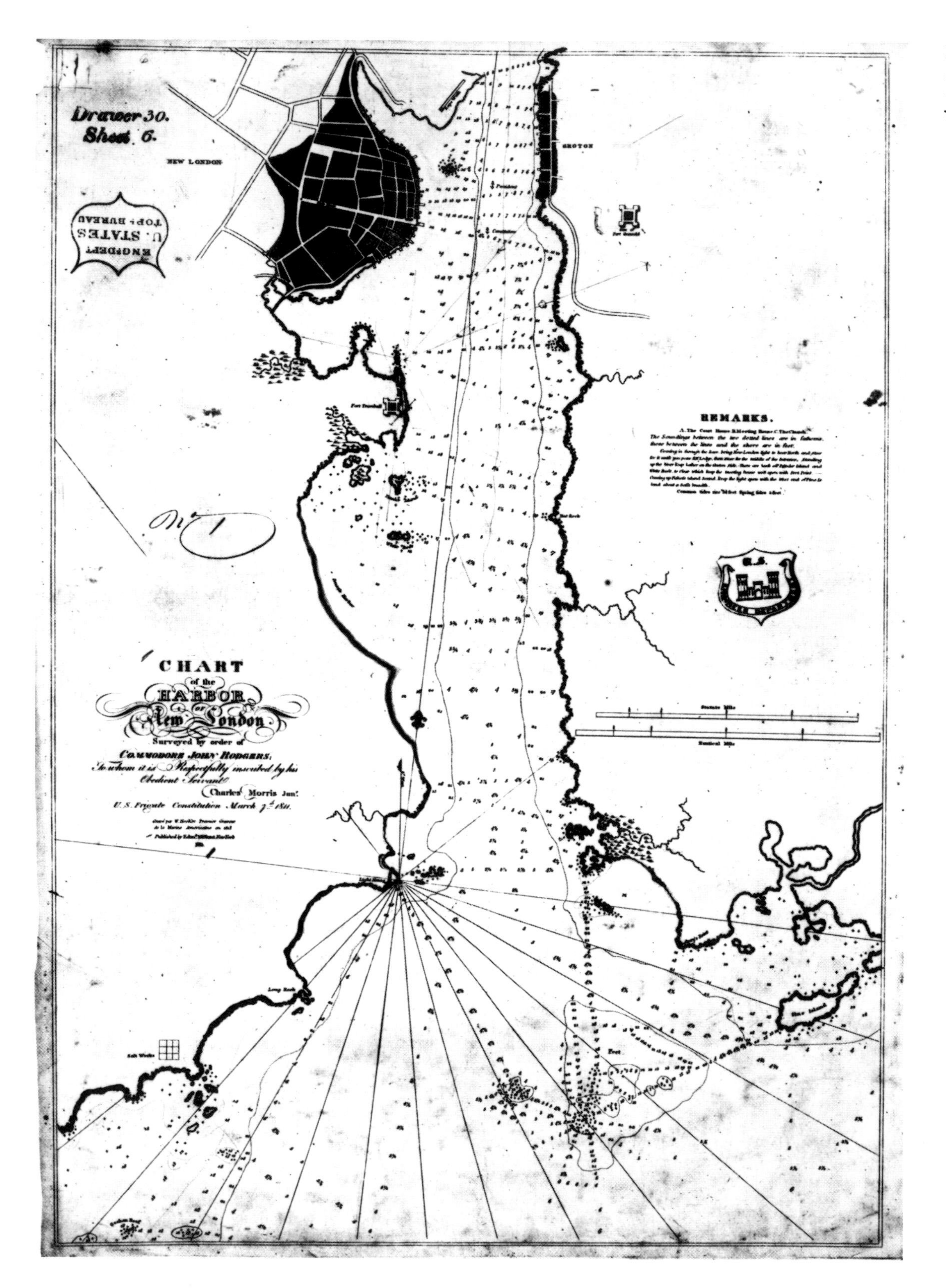

PLATE 144: Charles Morris, Jr. "Chart of the Harbor of New London Surveyed by order of Commodore John Rodgers; To whom it is Respectfully inscribed by his Obedient Servant Charles Morris Junr. U.S. Frigate Constitution. March 7th 1811." 1811 (published 1815). Engraving, 66 × 45.5 cm. Records of the Office of the Chief of Engineers, National Archives, Washington, D.C. *Early American coastal chart showing the plans of New London and Groton, Connecticut, and Forts Griswold and Trumbull guarding the port on the Thames River. Soundings are given in both fathoms and feet. Engraved by W. Hooker; published by Edmund M. Blunt, New York City.*

(opposite) PLATE 145: John Melish. "Map of the United States with the contiguous British and Spanish Possessions Compiled from the latest & best Authorities." 1816. Engraving, hand colored; 89 × 141.5 cm. Geography and Map Division, Library of Congress, Washington, D.C. *First American-produced wall map depicting the country from coast to coast. The geography of the unexplored Southwest remains greatly distorted; the legendary San Buenaventura River is portrayed as draining the Great Basin of present-day Utah and Nevada. Printed from six copperplates engraved by John J. Vallance and Henry S. Tanner, and published by John Melish, Philadelphia.*

other sections of the public domain during this period. The General Land Office, established in the Treasury Department in 1812 as an outgrowth of the Land Ordinance Act of 1785, controlled the disposal of public land throughout the nineteenth century. Under the direction of Federally appointed Surveyors General, all public land west of the Ohio and Mississippi rivers was divided into townships measuring six miles square (*Plate 143*). Referred to as the Rectangular Land Survey because of the rectangular shape of these townships, the survey began in eastern Ohio in 1785 under the direction of Thomas Hutchins in an area known as the Seven Ranges. The standard township plat, a planimetric base map that laid down legal subdivision lines in each township, did not assume its characteristic form until after 1815, when instructions from the General Land Office standardized its format and content. Modifications were issued in 1831. These instructions required that the plats, which were to be drawn to a scale of two inches to a mile on durable paper of the "best quality and of uniform size," were to represent courses and distances of township, section, and subdivision lines in black ink, swamps by "slightly shaded black lines and dots," and prairies by "slightly

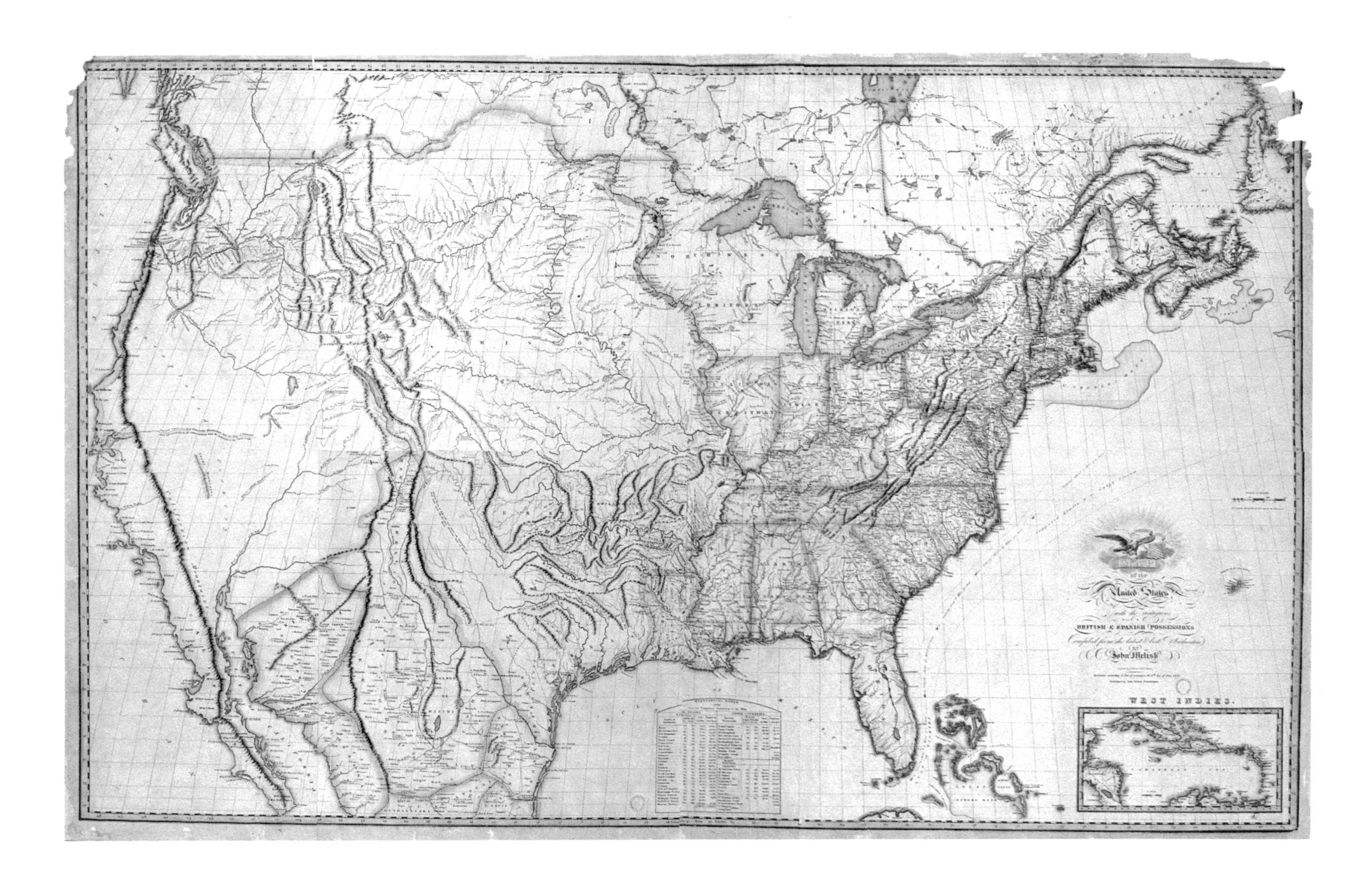

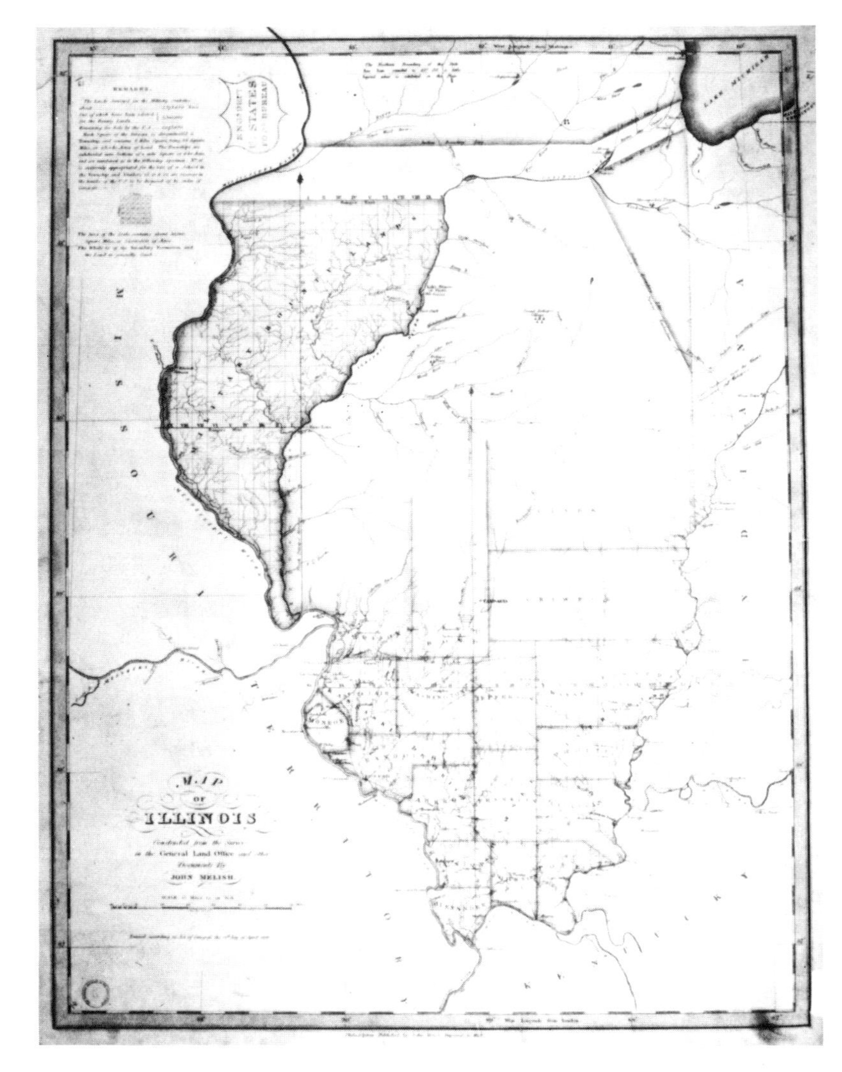

PLATE 146: John Melish. "Map of Illinois Constructed from the Surveys in the General Land Office and other Documents . . ." 1818, improved to 1819. Engraving, hand colored; 69.5 × 53 cm. Records of the Office of the Chief of Engineers, National Archives, Washington, D.C. *Portrayal of a frontier state shortly after its admittance to the Union. The disposition of public lands is depicted by rectangular land survey lines, a system of land subdivision which characterizes many of the middle and western states and territories. East of the Illinois River, Indian towns and boundary lines are shown in the unsettled area; "Military Bounty Lands" have been surveyed in the northwest of the state, between the Illinois and Mississippi rivers.*

Captain Oliver Hazard Perry's victory on Lake Erie during War of 1812

shaded green lines and dots." In addition the surveyors were required to indicate cultural features such as roads and Indian trails. Departing from contemporary mapping practice, field surveyors were ordered not to furnish new or original names for landscape features but to retain "the *received* names of all rivers, creeks, lakes, swamps, prairies, hills, mountains and other natural objects."

Reflecting the resumption of settlement in the Great Lakes region north of the Ohio River after the War of 1812, R. Paul prepared a map of the Indiana and Illinois territories in 1815 for Governor Edwards of the Illinois Territory, and B. Hough and A. Bourne compiled a large map of Ohio. Both were based principally upon the General Land Office surveys. (A smaller map of Ohio by John F. Mansfield was probably the first to be compiled from the returns of the Federal land surveyors; measuring 30 by 22½ inches, it was engraved in Philadelphia by William Harrison in 1806.) Henry S. Tanner, writing in 1823, observed that the General Land Office surveyors provided "a degree of correctness seldom attained by any other mode, and, when carefully combined, exhibit a very exact representation of the country."

Also in 1815, Moses Greenleaf completed a state map of the District of Maine, and Samuel Lambert compiled a chart of the coasts of Connecticut, New York, and Delaware which was engraved by Wightman of Salem, Massachusetts. Greenleaf's map, the second major map of Maine in little more than a decade (*see Plate 135*), paid particular attention to the coastal region, laid down from celestial observation. It was revised in 1819.

Despite the establishment of the Coast Survey in 1807 by Jefferson, no actual charting had been accomplished by 1815. As a result, both the Navy and War departments initiated limited charting operations. The earliest extant chart of the American coast by the U.S. Navy is a chart of New London Harbor by Charles Morris, Jr., of the U.S. frigate *Constitution* (*Plate 144*). Compiled in 1811 from surveys "by order of Commodore John Rodgers; To whom it is respectfully inscribed," it was published by Edmund M. Blunt in 1815.

Log house, 1796, from Voyage dans L'Amérique Septentrionale, *1826*

The Capitol, Washington, early 1800s, watercolor by Charles Burton

A flurry of cartographic activity took place during the remainder of the second decade. The War of 1812 caused the War Department to undertake a program of surveying and mapping the strategic waterways and coasts. Major Stephen H. Long, a member of the U.S. Topographical Bureau that was established in 1813 and remained responsible for all military mapping until the Civil War, conducted extensive topographic reconnaissances of the northwest part of the United States in 1815 and 1819. Long's surveys resulted in a large-scale ten-sheet map.

In the northeast a special purpose map by John H. Eddy was prepared to illustrate the potential value of the proposed Erie Canal that was to link the interior agricultural regions with the coastal emporium, New York City. An official map of New Hampshire was compiled under the direction of Philip Carrigain, Secretary of State, and engraved by William Harrison in 1816. Extremely detailed, it shows counties, townships, roads, ferries, bridges, county seats, post towns, churches, academies and colleges, iron foundries, cotton factories, and mills, and population figures of individual townships from the 1810 census.

The most noteworthy cartographic activity during 1816 and 1817, however, was the production of several large wall maps. Samuel Lewis, in 1816, prepared a mammoth map of the United States measuring about six feet square. Engraved by William and Samuel Harrison and published by Emmor Kimber in Philadelphia, this map was limited to that part of the United States east of the Mississippi River, but it included the so-called Northwest Territory, opened to general settlement in 1815 as Indian resistance was terminated. Shown in minute detail are roads, towns, county boundaries, and names, and a complex system of Appalachian mountains and hills depicted by profiles. The revision in 1819 includes an inset map of East Florida, ceded by Spain to the United States according to the Adams-Onis treaty of that year. A slightly smaller but similar wall map was prepared in 1816 by Shelton and Kensett, and engraved by Amos Doolittle; it shows

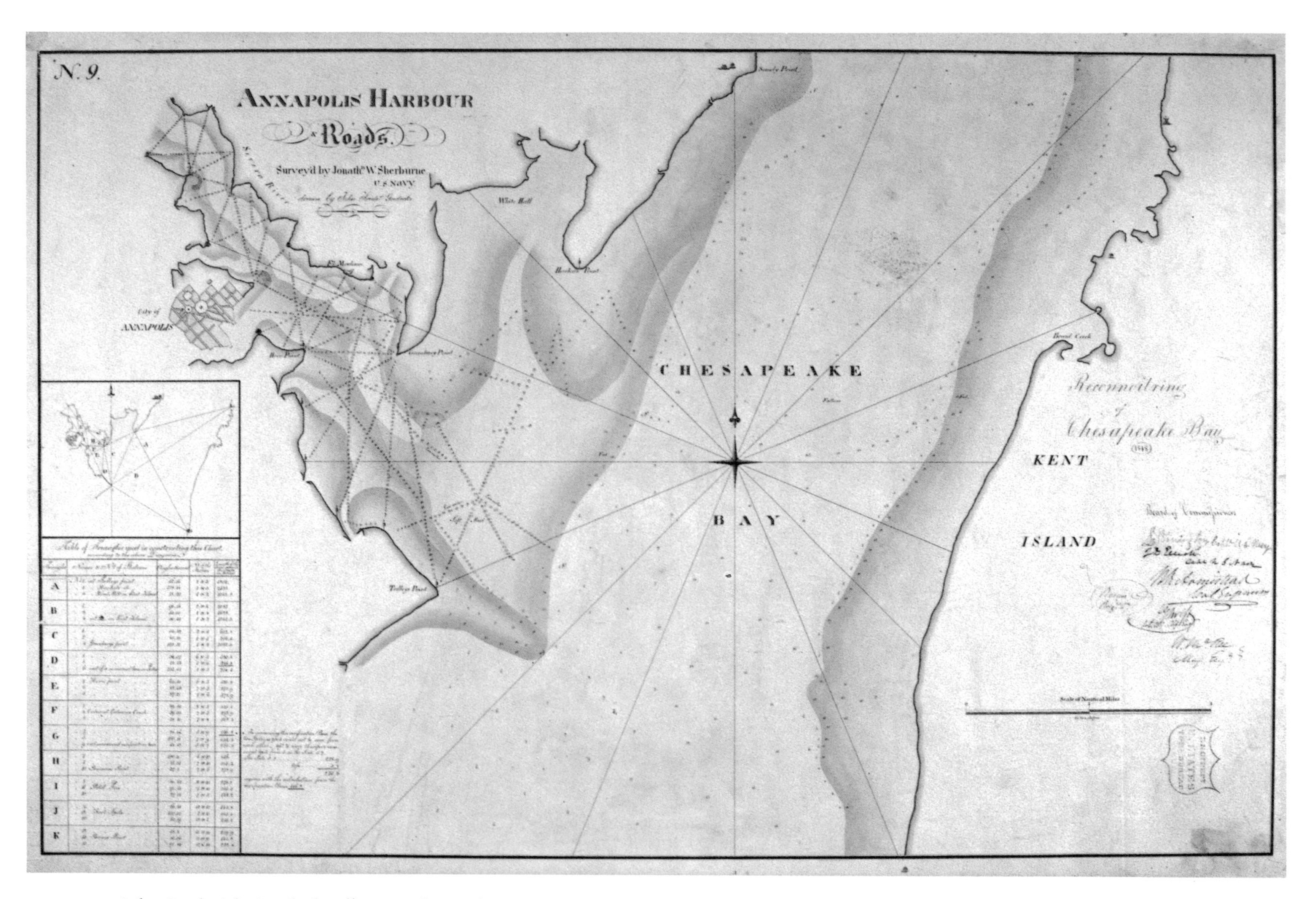

PLATE 147: John Frederick Goedecke. "Annapolis Harbour & Roads. Survey'd by Jonathn. W. Sherburne. U.S. Navy." 1818. Manuscript, pen and ink with watercolor wash; 60.5 × 93 cm. Records of the Office of the Chief of Engineers, National Archives, Washington, D.C. *One of several charts of strategic coastal areas prepared for the Board of Commissioners investigating the defense of the Atlantic coast following the War of 1812. Illustrates an early use of color tints and bathymetric contour lines to depict harbor depth.*

(opposite) PLATE 148: Stephen Harriman Long, Major, U.S. Topographical Engineers. "Map of the Country situated between the Meridian of Washington City and the Rocky Mountains exhibiting the route of the late Exploring Expedition commanded by Maj. Long, together with other recent surveys and explorations by himself & others . . ." 1820. Manuscript, pen and ink with watercolor wash; 139 × 125 cm. Records of the Office of the Chief of Engineers, National Archives, Washington, D.C. *Dedicated to John C. Calhoun, Secretary of War, this composite wall map illustrates the general geography of the United States and its frontier on the eve of its semicentennial. Served as an important source map for commercial map publishers during the 1820s.*

JOHN C. CALHOUN
THIS MAP OF THE
COUNTRY SITUATED BETWEEN THE MERIDIAN OF
WASHINGTON CITY and the ROCKY MOUNTAINS
exhibiting the route of the late Exploring Expedition commanded by Maj.
Long, together with other recent surveys and explorations by himself & others
is most respectfully inscribed, by his most obedient and humble servant
A CARD
Scale of Miles

The steamboat commanded by Major Stephen H. Long, at Council Bluffs, sketch by Titian Peale, who accompanied Long in 1819–20 as naturalist

additional information, particularly in the Ohio Valley and the Gulf plains. Like many other American maps published at this time, the prime meridian of Shelton and Kensett's map passes through the city of Washington rather than Greenwich, England. Such displays of "cultural patriotism" in mapmaking lasted for several more decades and were not limited to the nation's capital. Map projections were based also on prime meridians located in Boston, Philadelphia, and New Orleans.

A third wall map was published a year later by Charles Varlé, a refugee from the French Revolution and a trained engineer. Shortly after arriving in the United States in 1794 Varlé had published a plan of Philadelphia, and in 1808–9 he prepared the first two county maps to be printed in the United States. Varlé's 1817 six-sheet map of the United States is noteworthy primarily for its detail, and for the large number of symbols he employed to denote features. It is described, along with other Varlé maps, by Richard Stephenson (see Bibliography). Ten classes of towns are depicted, ranging in size from 3,000 to 110,000 inhabitants. A large inset map of North America, measuring 18 by 23 inches, incorporates some of the data from the Clark-Lewis map of 1814 (*see Plate 140*), but other parts of the West are grossly inaccurate. Across the bottom of the map are two profiles which illustrate the relative topographic relief along a line running from Washington, D.C., to the Columbia River, and from Acapulco to Vera Cruz. Varlé's map, which took five years to compile, was engraved by J. H. Young of Philadelphia and offered to subscribers for eight dollars. A hand-colored copy with canvas backing cost the purchaser an additional three dollars.

While these three wall maps represent important contributions to an indigenous cartography, they were derived from Arrowsmith's earlier British maps and their coverage was limited to the eastern portion of the United States. More noteworthy was Melish's fundamental six-sheet "Map of the United States with the contiguous British & Spanish Possessions," the first large wall map to show the new nation from coast to coast (*Plate 145*). An exquisite map, it distinguished Melish as the leading American map publisher of the second decade and placed American maps on equal footing with those produced by the prestigious firms in London and Paris. Incorporating data from state and military maps as these became available, Melish frequently revised and corrected the plates, limiting each printing to 100 copies. Walter W. Ristow, in his excellent analysis of this work (see Bibliography), has identified twenty-four different states of the map, issued between 1816 and 1823 in six separate editions. The early editions were engraved by John Vallance and Henry S. Tanner. A small booklet entitled *A Geographical Description of the United States* accompanied and elucidated the map.

The Melish firm also published in 1816 a large state map of Louisiana, which had been admitted to the Union four years earlier. Surveyed and drawn by William Darby and engraved by Samuel Harrison at a scale of one inch to ten miles, this map shows parish boundaries, roads, drainage patterns, and the location of mills. Darby, a former deputy surveyor of the U.S. General Land Office, served as a topographical officer under General Andrew Jackson during the British invasion of the South in 1814–15. Darby's Louisiana map was utilized by Melish to compile that portion of his 1816 wall map of the United States, which in turn was used as the basis for the boundary delineation of Florida in the Adams-Onis Treaty of 1819 between the United States and Spain. Arrowsmith in England reprinted Darby's map in 1817, an indication of the increased reliance that established European mapping firms were now placing on American maps.

In 1817 Melish initiated the project of an atlas of the United States to complement his wall map and his large state maps. It was to consist of reduced state maps on separate sheets, "uniform in plan and size, so that the possessors may bind them, or any number of them into an atlas." Before his death in 1822, Melish had completed maps of most of the frontier states: Indiana (1817), Illinois (1818; *Plate 146*), Tennessee (1817), Alabama (1818), Mississippi (1819), and Louisiana (1820). Based primarily on General Land Office surveys, these maps measured on the average about 20 by 28 inches, with a scale of one inch to fifteen or eighteen miles. Several were revised by Melish. They depict existing settlements, military posts, county names and boundaries, extent of public surveys, Indian villages and lands, and trails and roads. Although Melish's untimely death prevented the completion of his atlas, his work established a new tradition of transmitting geographical information in atlas format with maps of uniform scale and size.

The black-tailed deer, *by Titian Peale, 1819–20*

Two other official state maps were completed in 1818. Luke Munsell's six-sheet map of Kentucky, which measures 38 by 91 inches, was "compiled principally from returns in the surveyor general's office" and locally printed in Frankfort by the author. Along the Atlantic seaboard, Daniel Sturges's map of Georgia was engraved by Samuel Harrison; it was published by Eleazer Early in Savannah, and by John Melish and Samuel Harrison in Philadelphia. This map was compiled from manuscript copies of county maps submitted to Sturges over a fourteen-year period while he was Surveyor General of Georgia. Melish had a copy of Sturges's map in manuscript form by 1816 and used it with the author's consent in preparing his own map of the United States. Both of these state maps were useful to officials in developing internal improvement programs, particularly in Georgia where a series of treaties with Indians were opening up the central region to settlement.

Of more direct use to settlers was William Darby's map of the United States that accompanied his emigrant's guide; both map and guide were published in 1818 by Kirk and Mercein in New York City.

Two noteworthy coastal charts were compiled in 1818. The first was a manuscript chart of Annapolis Harbor by John Frederick Goedecke based on a survey by Jonathan W. Sherburne, U.S. Navy (*Plate 147*). It was prepared for the Board of Commissioners investigating the defense of the Atlantic coast. The Board, composed of both Army and Navy officers, undertook a number of surveys along the east coast during that decade. A visually attractive work on which color tints and contour lines

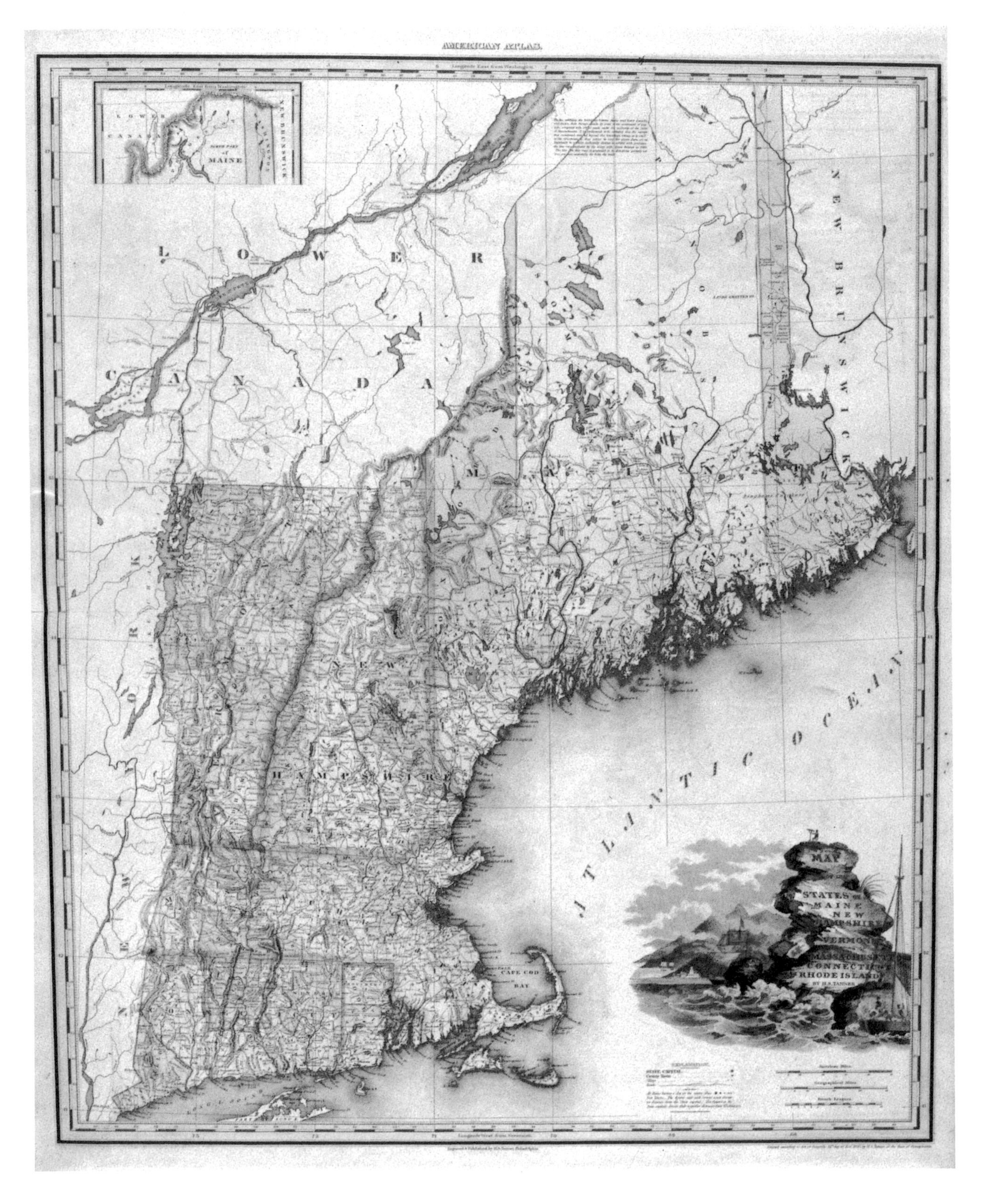

PLATE 149: Henry S. Tanner. "Map of the States of Maine New Hampshire Vermont Massachusetts Connecticut & Rhode Island." 1822. Engraving, with watercolor wash; 67.5 × 55 cm. Records of the Office of the Chief of Engineers, National Archives, Washington, D.C. *Map of New England depicting county and state boundaries, roads, and towns. The controversial and ill-defined international boundary line between Canada and the United States is shown as claimed by Maine, incorporating some 12,000 square miles of disputed territory. From Tanner's* New American Atlas *(1818–23), one of the first comprehensive atlases of the United States produced by an American publisher.*

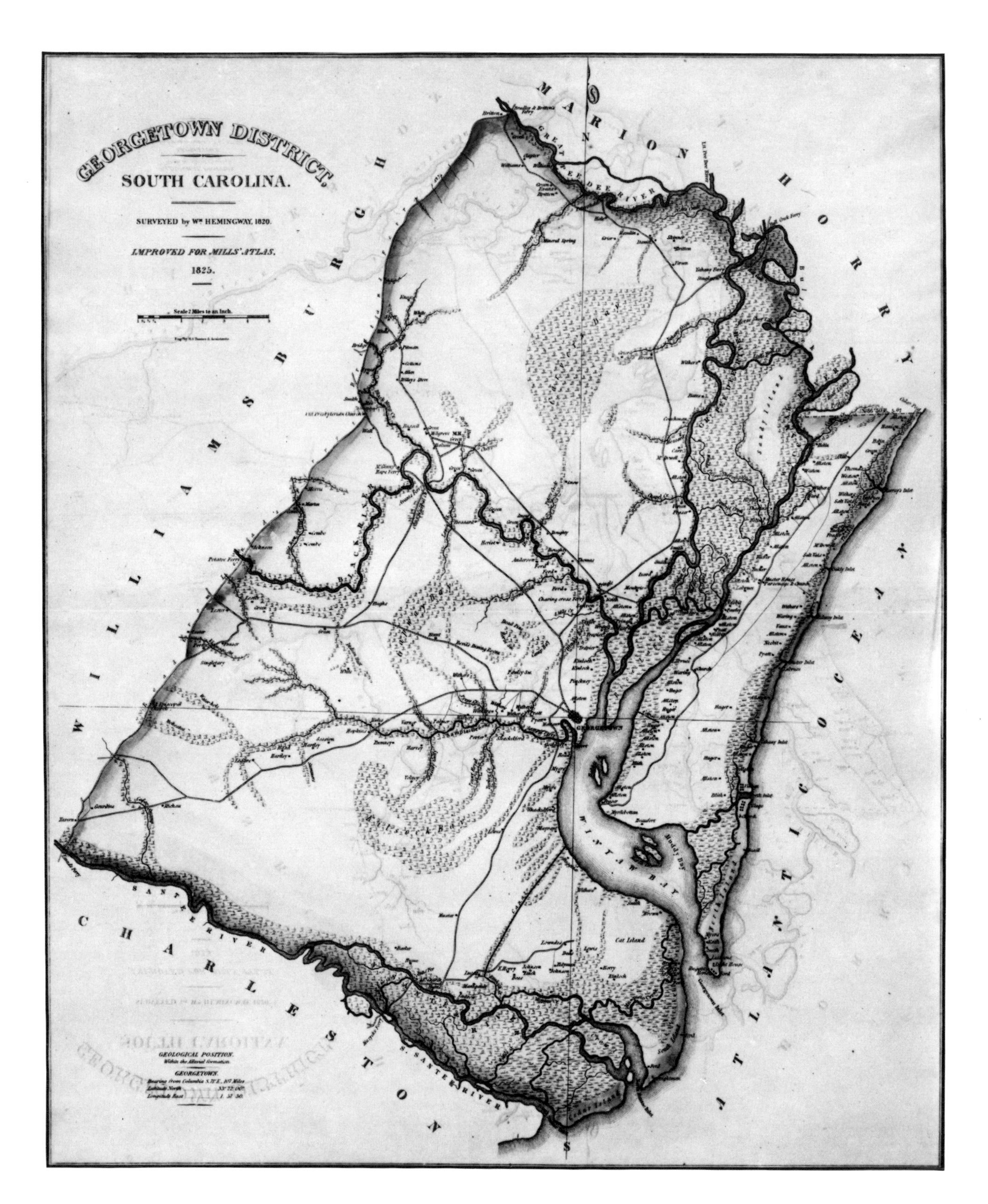

PLATE 150: Robert Mills. "Georgetown District, South Carolina." 1825. Engraving, hand colored; 66 × 53 cm. Records of the Office of the Chief of Engineers, National Archives, Washington, D.C. *Engraved by Henry S. Tanner, Philadelphia; printed by Fielding Lucas, Jr., Baltimore. Detailed map depicting drainage, roads, churches, stores, and taverns. The distribution of plantation names bordering on tidal and inland swamps reveals the early reliance upon indigo and sea-island cotton as an agricultural crop during the Colonial period and the initial decades of the nineteenth century. One of twenty-eight maps in Mills's* Atlas of the State of South Carolina, *the first state atlas produced in the United States.*

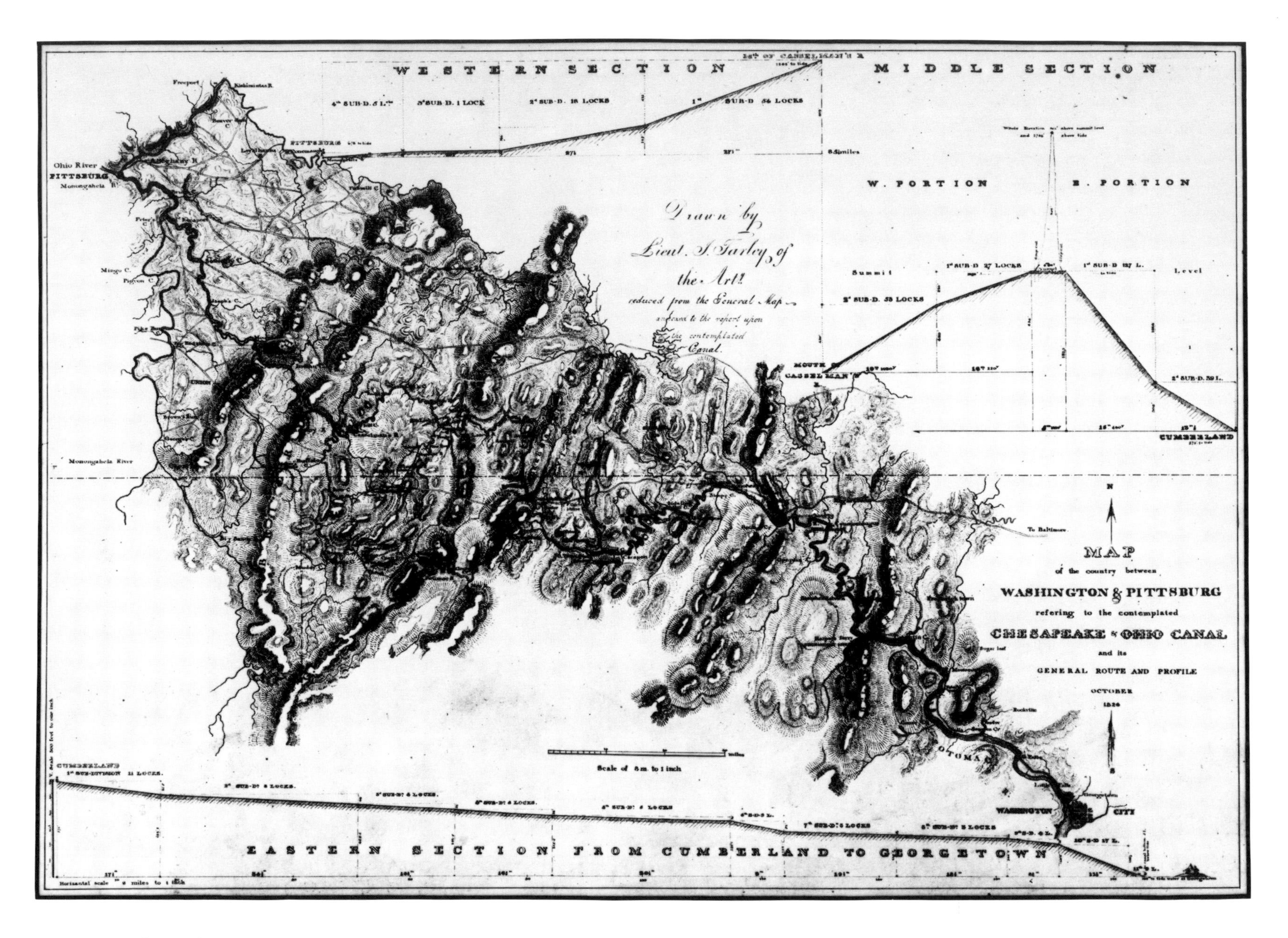

PLATE 151: John Farley, Lieutenant, First Regiment of Artillery, U.S. Army. "Map of the country between Washington & Pittsburg refering to the contemplated Chesapeake & Ohio Canal and its General Route and Profile." 1826. Manuscript, pen and ink; 47 × 65.5 cm. Records of the Office of the Chief of Engineers, National Archives, Washington, D.C. *Representative of an internal improvement map; shows the proposed route of the Chesapeake and Ohio Canal, designed to link the rich Ohio Valley with the ports of Georgetown and Alexandria on the Potomac River in an abortive effort to divert commerce from the Erie Canal, the emerging trade route completed in 1825 between New York City and the interior.*

(opposite) PLATE 152: George Washington Whistler. "A Plan of West Point. State of New-York." 1818. Manuscript, pen and ink with watercolor wash; 66 × 100 cm. Records of the Office of the Chief of Engineers, National Archives, Washington, D.C. *Specimen drawing by a young cadet at the U.S. Military Academy, later the father of the celebrated nineteenth-century painter and etcher, James Abbott McNeill Whistler.*

are combined to depict depths below mean sea level, Goedecke's chart was incorporated as an inset a year later on a larger chart of the Chesapeake Bay and the Patapsco River, commenced by the Marine Insurance Companies of Baltimore under the direction of Lewis Brantz, and published by Fielding Lucas, Jr.

The second major chart of 1818 is less significant for what it represents than for its technique and its portent for the future. It is a published chart of the triangulation network that Ferdinand R. Hassler established as a basis for further hydrographic surveys along the New York coast. Hassler, one of the originators of the Geodetic Survey of Switzerland and later a professor of mathematics at West Point, was appointed the first Superintendent of the U.S. Coast Survey when it was founded in 1807. Delayed by the war and by difficulties in obtaining adequate surveying instruments, actual surveying of the coasts did not get underway until 1816, when Hassler began his work on the New York triangulation network. His objective was to place coastal charting on a scientific basis by first undertaking carefully planned surveys that were interconnected through triangulation networks. These networks were to be controlled by geodetically determined points

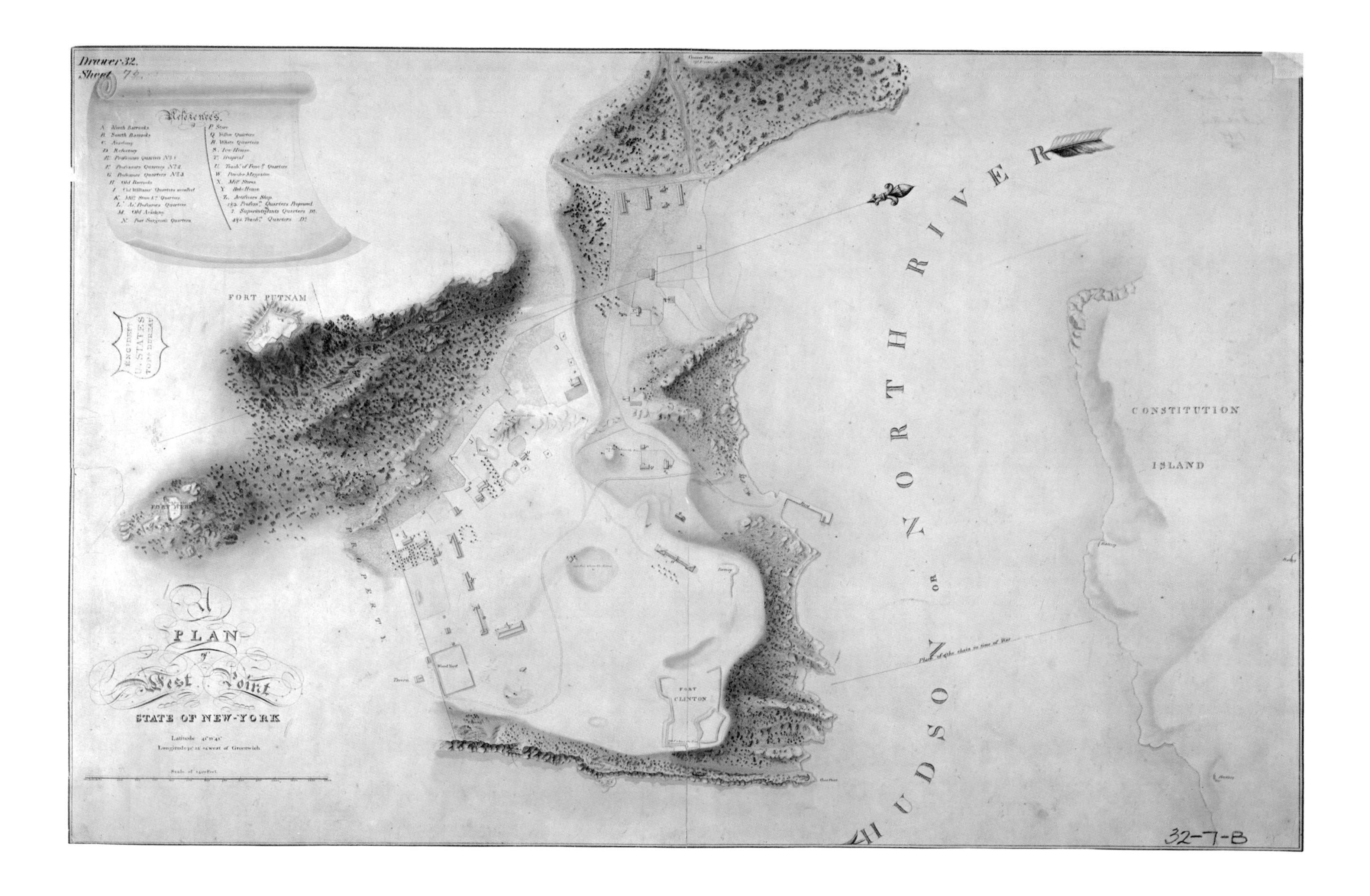

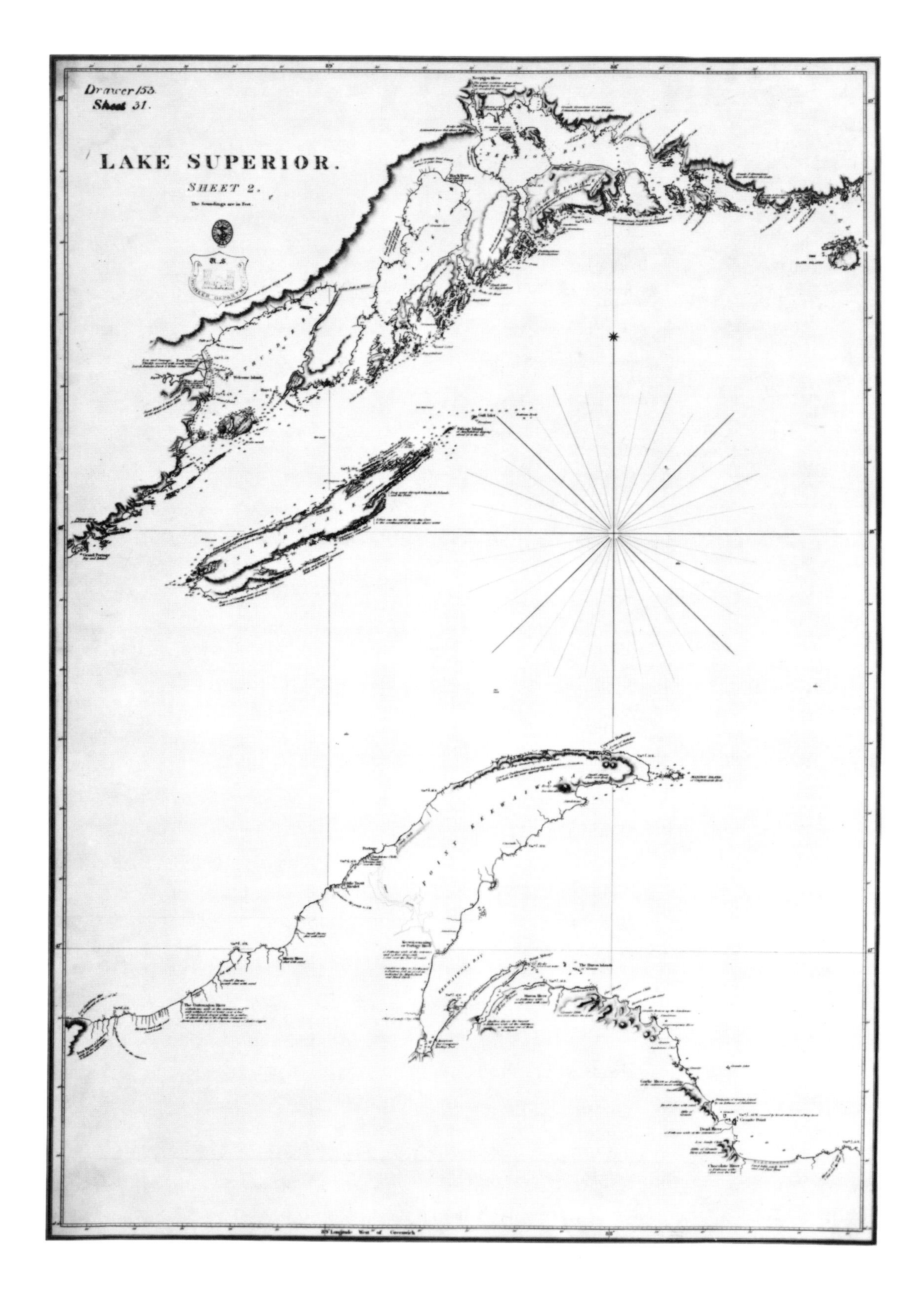

PLATE 153: Henry W. Bayfield, Lieutenant, Royal Navy. "Survey of Lake Superior . . . between the Years 1823 & 1825." 1828. Engraving, 100 × 68 cm. Records of the Office of the Chief of Engineers, National Archives, Washington, D.C. *Engraved by J. & C. Walker, London; sheet 2 of a three-sheet set, the first hydrographic chart of Lake Superior. Depicts the American Fur Company's trading post at the head of Keewaiwona Bay on the southern shore of the lake, and the British outpost, Fort William, on Thunder Bay on the northern shore.*

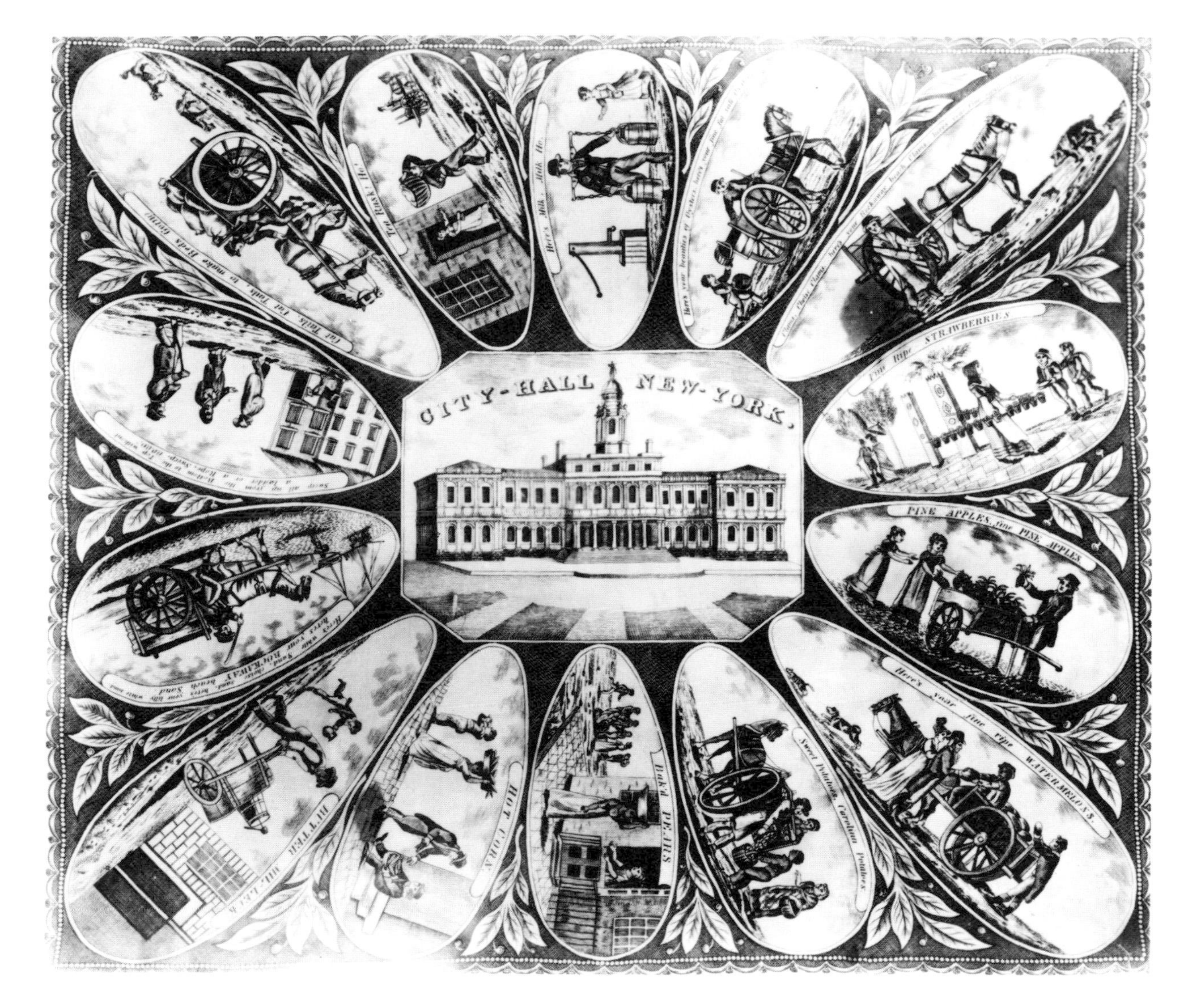

The cries of street vendors, about 1814, are printed around City Hall, New York, on a toile scarf or handkerchief

located along the coasts. Although the Coast Survey was temporarily discontinued shortly after Hassler's first triangulation chart was published, surveying activities resumed under his direction in 1832.

The next year 1819, a distorted visual image of the geography of the south and west was published by John H. Robinson, a medical doctor who had traveled with Zebulon Pike throughout the southwest and who later served as a brigadier general in the Mexican Revolutionary War. Robinson's map, which Carl Wheat characterizes as "more a curiosity than a contribution to western cartography," measures some six by five feet (see Bibliography). The western portion was derived in part from an 1810 map of the Pacific coast by Don Juan Pedro Walker that delineated three legendary rivers draining the great interior basin of Nevada and Utah. Robinson adopted these mythical rivers: the "Tinpanogos" River, which is shown to flow from Lake Timpanogos (depicted in the 1769–79 journal of the Spanish explorer Escalante and located in the general vicinity of present-day Great Salt Lake) to the port of San Francisco; the Rio de San Buenaventura, whose destination is near the mission San Antonio; and the Rio de San Felipe, which empties into the Pacific Ocean near San Luis Obispo. In the northwest a vestige of Lewis and

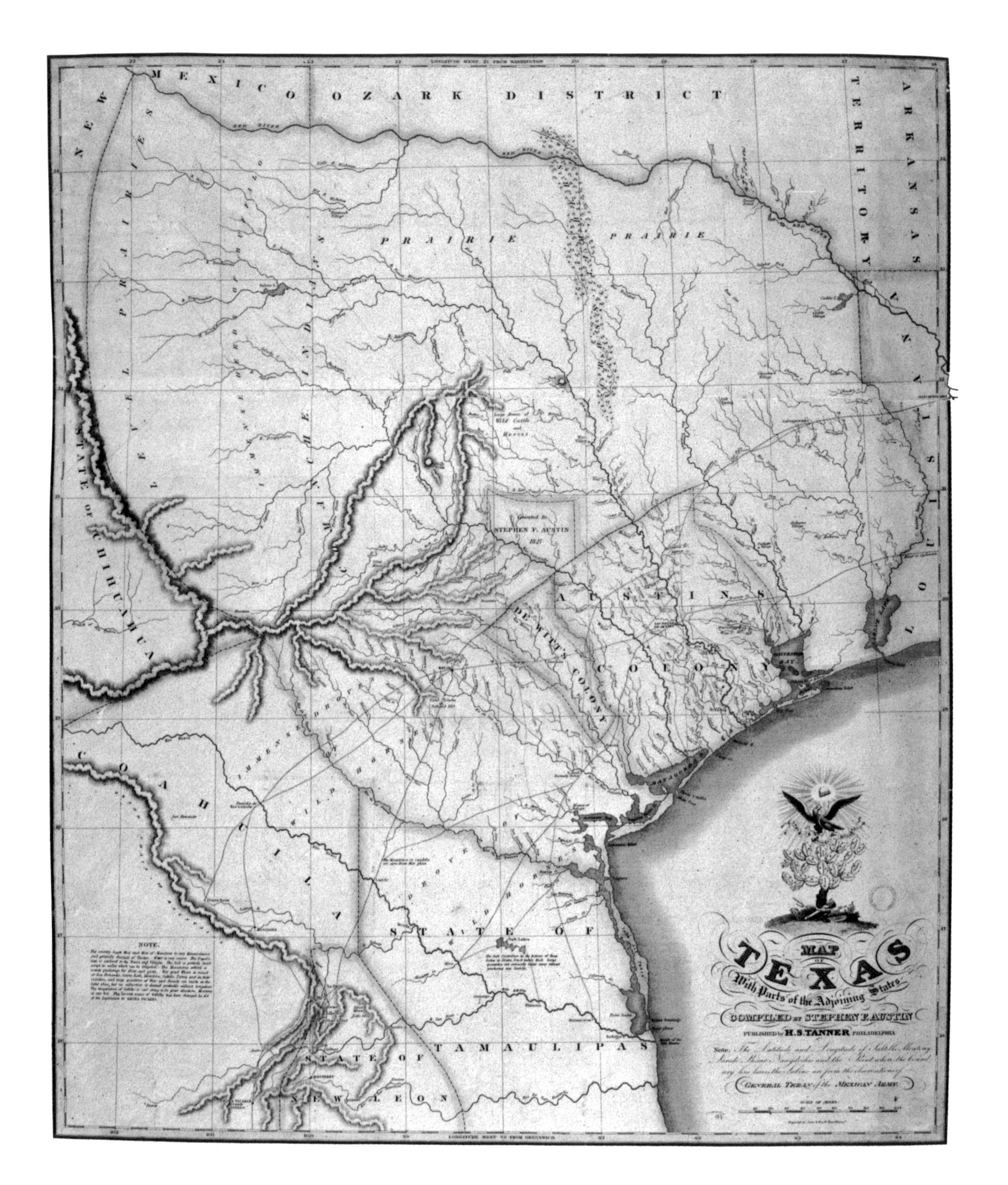

PLATE 154: Stephen Fuller Austin. "Map of Texas With Parts of the Adjoining States." 1830. Engraving, hand colored; 75 × 61.5 cm. Records of the Office of the Chief of Engineers, National Archives, Washington, D.C. *Map prepared to encourage American immigration to the Mexican province of Texas. Depicts the American colonies of Austin and DeWitt along the Gulf Coast, and a land grant to Stephen F. Austin in the interior. Inscribed in south and west are "immense droves of wild horses" and "immense herds of buffalo."*

PLATE 155: John Arrowsmith. "British North America" (portion). 1832. Engraving, hand colored; entire dimensions 55 × 63 cm. Geography and Map Division, Library of Congress, Washington, D.C. *Southwest quadrant of the first map to show accurately the relative positions of the Columbia and Snake rivers. Published by J. Arrowsmith, London; based on geographical information obtained from the intrepid Peter Skene Ogden, veteran Canadian fur trader.*

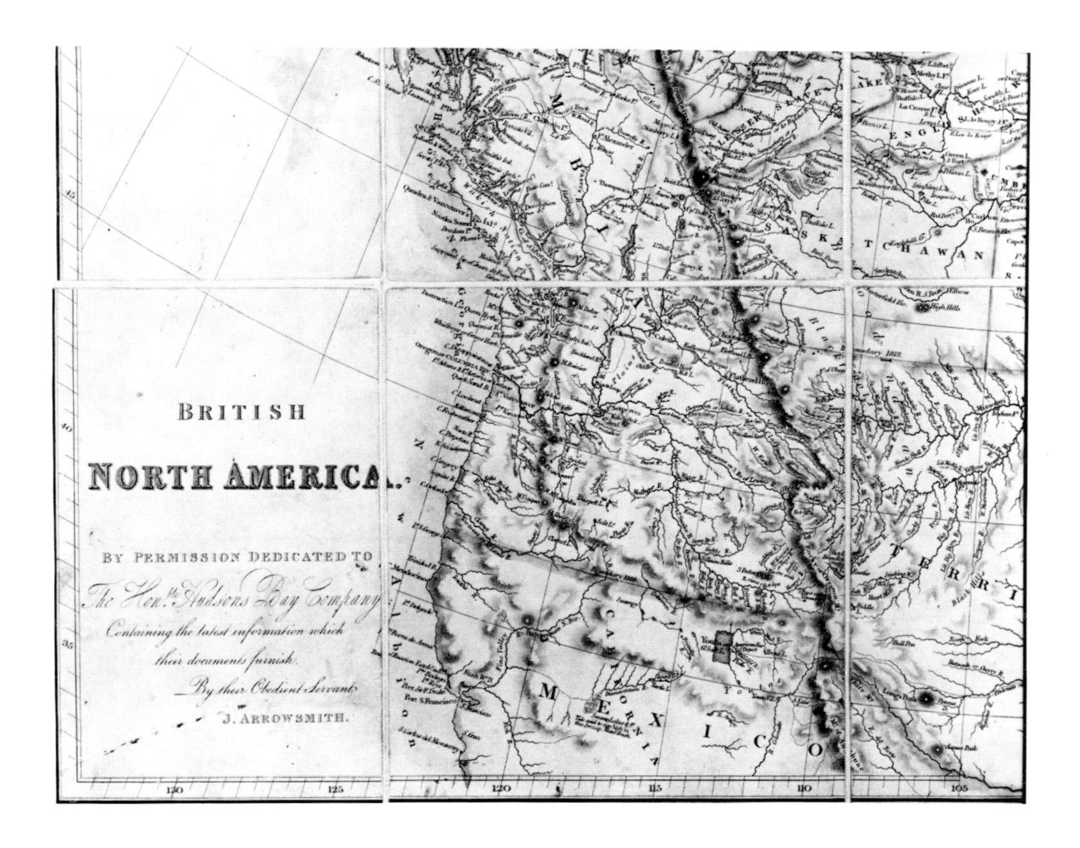

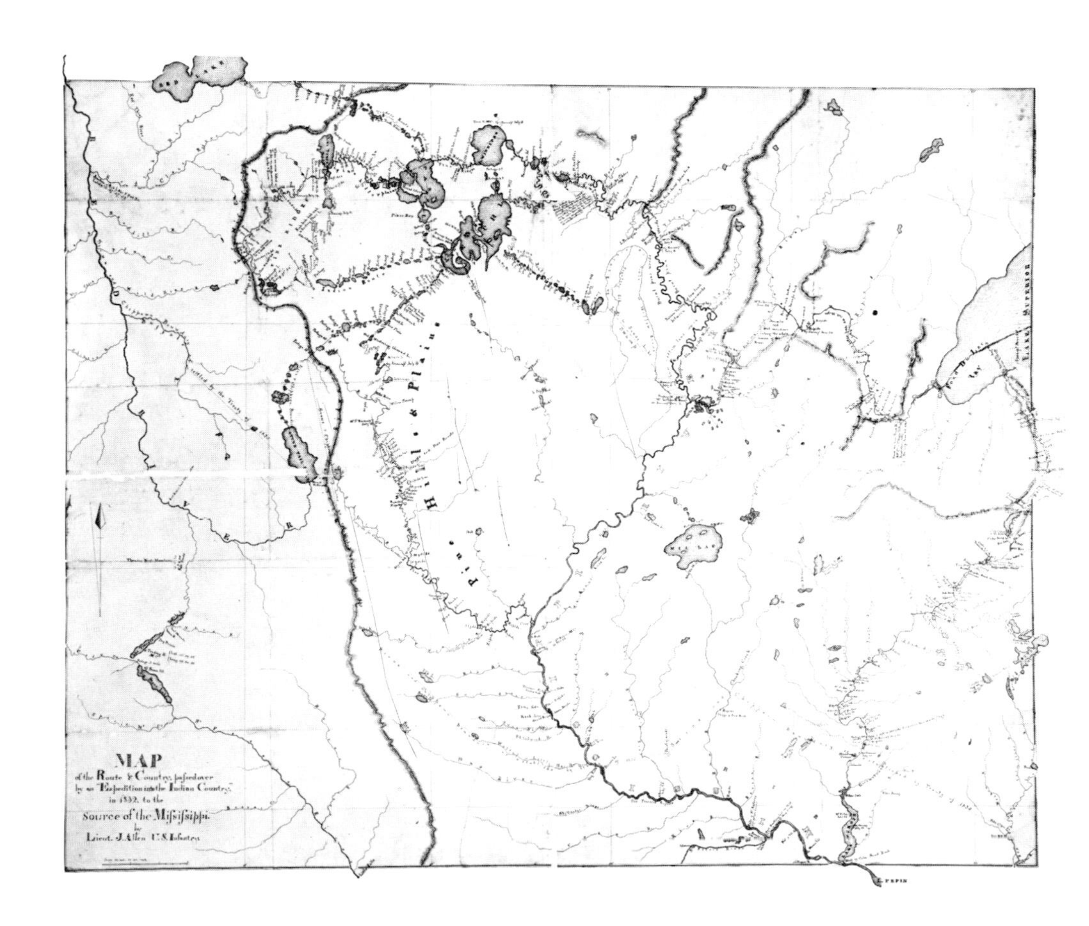

PLATE 156: James Allen, Lieutenant, U.S. Infantry. "Map of the Route & Country, passed over by an 'Expedition into the Indian Country,' in 1832, to the Source of the Mississippi." 1832. Manuscript, pen and ink; 76 × 92 cm. Records of the Office of the Chief of Engineers, National Archives, Washington, D.C. *Earliest map of the true source of the Mississippi River. Depicts Sioux and Chippewa boundary lines as established by the Treaty of 1825; Indian villages, towns, and placenames; trading posts and portages; the route of Lieutenant Allen. The dividing ridge separating the watersheds of the Mississippi and Red rivers is illustrated by a continuous chain of hills.*

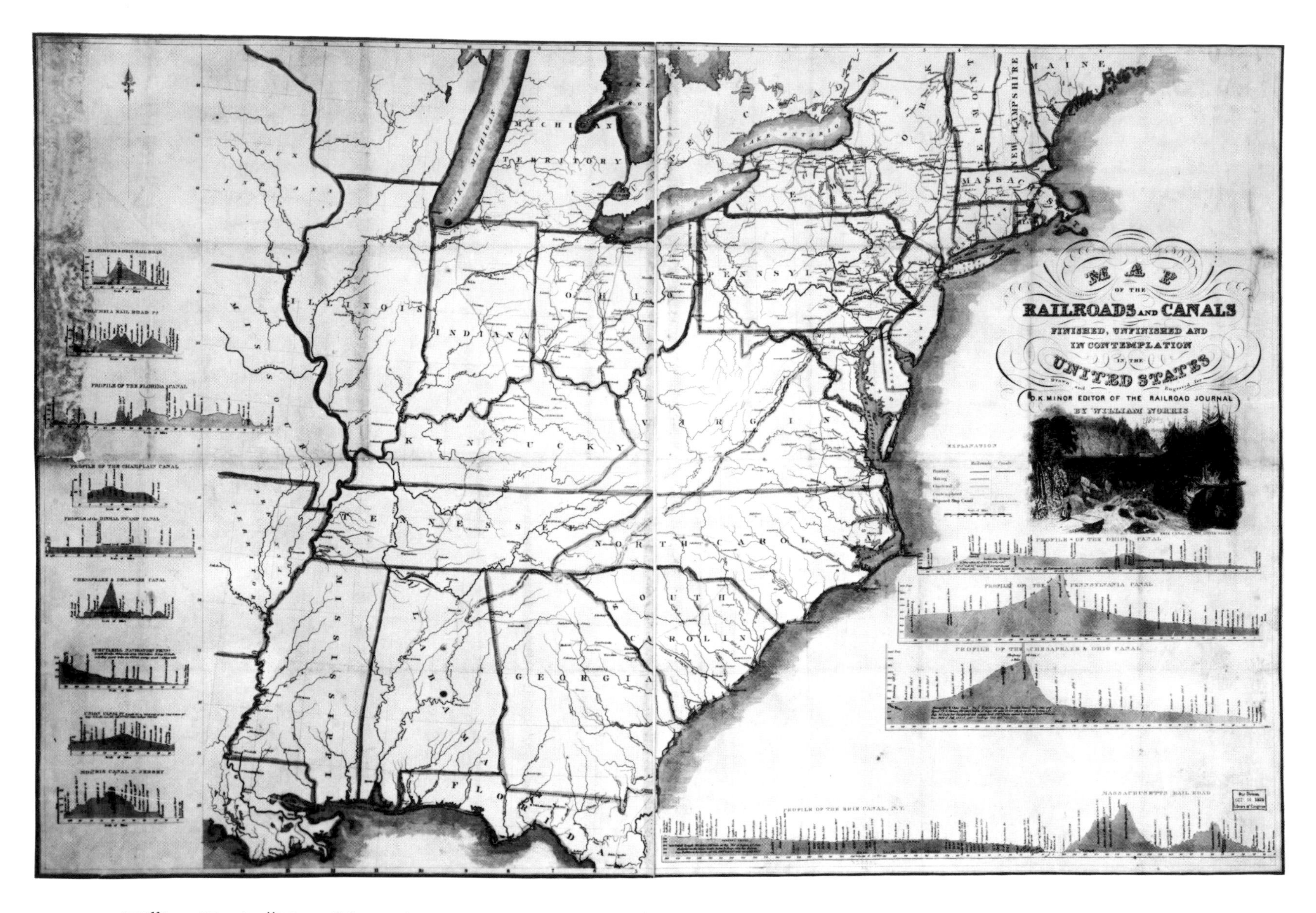

PLATE 157: William Norris. "Map of the Railroads and Canals Finished, Unfinished and In Contemplation in the United States." 1834. Engraving, hand colored; 62 × 94 cm. Geography and Map Division, Library of Congress, Washington, D.C. *Prepared for D.K. Minor, editor of the* Railroad Journal. *Important map depicting many early railroad lines and canal routes, as well as fourteen significant railroad and canal profiles in the eastern United States. Includes a vignette of the Erie Canal at Little Falls, near Herkimer.*

Clark—the Multnomah River—is delineated with its source near Lake Timpanogos. Robinson's imaginative excursion into western geography had numerous followers.

The third decade, according to Erwin Raisz, initiated "the golden age of American cartography." For the next twenty years the mapmaker's art flourished, as Federal and state governments undertook expanded roles in surveying and mapping projects, and commercial firms refined engraving techniques and introduced new formats.

Mouth of Timpanogos River Canon, *watercolor by J. J. Young, member of Captain James Harvey Simpson's expedition*

A large manuscript map graphically chronicled the reconnaissance of the Missouri River and the front ranges of the Rocky Mountains by Major Stephen H. Long in 1819–20 (*Plate 148*). Now in the National Archives, this manuscript map measures 54 by 49 inches and covers the interior region of the United States from Washington, D.C., to the headwaters of the Missouri in the northwest and to Santa Fe in the southeast. Long's map strengthened the myth of the "Great American Desert" in the southwest, first introduced by Pike. Persisting in later maps, this concept hindered settlement of this region for decades. But Long's map is the first to show the true course of the Canadian River, which Pike and others had confused with the Red River. A profile depicting surface relief along the 38th parallel, from Atlantic tidewater to the Rocky Mountains, is shown along the bottom of the map. Commercial mapmakers such as Henry S. Tanner relied heavily upon Long's work for two decades. An engraved version of it was published in two parts for inclusion in the official journal of Long's expedition, *Account of an Expedition from Pittsburgh to the Rocky Mountains,* written by Edwin James and published in 1823.

While cartographers showed a renewed interest in the West, graphic representation of the eastern states continued. John Wilson, a Scotsman who served as civil and military engineer in South Carolina, compiled a map of that state based on district surveys carried out from 1817 to 1821 under the aegis of the South Carolina Board of Public Works. The state legislature appropriated $60,000 for its preparation and publication. Measuring 44 by 58 inches, Wilson's map was engraved by Henry S. Tanner in 1822. In the same year John Melish published his impressive map of Pennsylvania, which was based on county maps each prepared by a deputy surveyor according to specifications provided by Melish at the request of the state government. More than six years were spent in compiling the four-by-six-foot map at an expense of $30,000. The Melish map was engraved on six plates by Benjamin Tanner, brother of Henry, and sold for $9.00 to $12.50, depending on format, coloring, and mounting. This map of Pennsylvania, which was revised in 1824, 1826, and 1832, became a standard model for other state maps. It has been described, notes Walter W. Ristow, as Melish's "greatest published work" (see Bibliography).

Several other state maps were issued during the decade. In the southeast Charles Vignoles, a civil and topographical engineer, compiled a map of Florida in 1823 at a scale of one inch to twenty miles; in 1826 Herman Böyë, a German engineer living in Richmond, compiled a large map of Virginia based on county surveys at a scale of one inch to five miles. Requiring nine separate copperplates and measuring 60 by 93 inches, the Böyë map served as the standard map of Virginia for more than a quarter of a century. Both of these state maps were engraved and published by Henry S. Tanner. In the northwest James Farmer compiled his map of the surveyed region of the territory of Michigan at a scale of eight miles to the inch, which was first engraved in Utica, N.Y., in 1826 by V. Balch and S. Styles. Farmer's map was revised periodically over the next ten years and was widely distributed in the east, where it helped promote extensive immigration to Michigan from 1825 to 1840.

Returning to 1822, the first map to be printed in the United States using the revolutionary technique of lithography appeared in the fourth issue of the *American Journal of Science and Arts.* Under the terse title, "Barton on the Catskills," the page-size map accompanied an article by a Mr. D. W. Barton of Virginia on the geology of the small mountain chain bordering the west bank of the Hudson River in southeast New York. The editor, Benjamin Silliman, observed with pride that all of the drawings in this issue were "printed on stone" by William A. Barnet and Isaac

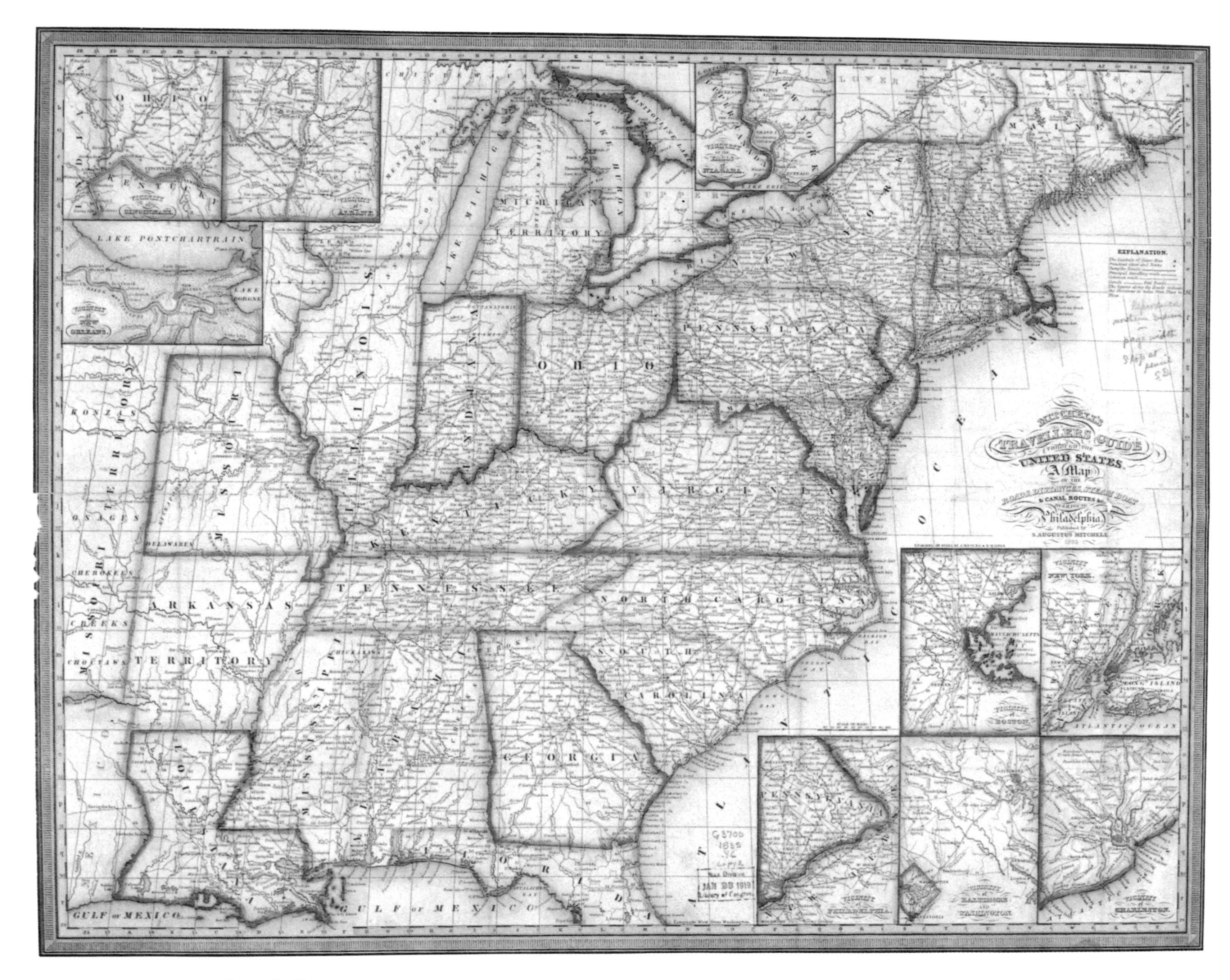

PLATE 158: J. H. Young. "Mitchell's Travellers Guide Through the United States. A Map of the Roads, Distances, Steam Boat & Canal Routes &c." 1835. Engraving on steel, hand colored; 46 × 58 cm. Geography and Map Division, Library of Congress, Washington, D.C. *Engraved by J. H. Young and D. Haines; published by S. Augustus Mitchell, Philadelphia. Typical traveler's guide for the eastern half of the United States; inset maps of the vicinities of Boston, New York City, Philadelphia, Baltimore and Washington, Charleston, Cincinnati, Albany, Niagara Falls, and New Orleans.*

Doolittle, whom he identified as "artists in this comparatively new department." "Having availed themselves in Paris of a regular course of practical instruction," Silliman continued, "they have brought to this country, not only the skill but the peculiar materials and press necessary to the execution of the art, and are now establishing themselves in New-York." For its first decade in America the lithographic printing of maps was limited primarily to those illustrating journal articles or official reports, but the Pendleton printing firm in Boston lithographed some twenty-five separate plans of New England towns and cities between 1829 and 1836, foreshadowing the explosive expansion of map production after 1846 that this technical innovation would bring about.

Samuel Cumings's *The Western Pilot* was first issued in 1822 and contained more charts of the Ohio and Mississippi rivers than did Cramer's *The Navigator*, which ceased publication two years later. Cumings's navigational aid was in direct response to the rapidly increasing domestic trade that resulted from the introduction of the steamboat on western waters in 1815 and the development of New Orleans, St. Louis, Cincinnati, and Louisville as principal shipping points. Ten editions of *The Western Pilot* were issued over the next thirty-two years. Also in 1822 the War Department printed a sixty-six-sheet chart based on a reconnaissance of the Mississippi and Ohio rivers by Captains H. Young and W. T. Poussin of the Corps of Engineers, initiating a series of large-scale charts and maps prepared by the military for planning internal improvements in the 1820s.

During the four-year period beginning in 1822, six large atlases were published in the United States by Carey and Lea, Fielding Lucas, Jr., Sidney E. Morse, Henry S. Tanner, Anthony Finley, and J. Conrad. Lucas and Morse were located in Baltimore and New Haven, respectively; the other firms were situated in Philadelphia.

All six atlases represented solid cartographic workmanship, but the most remarkable was Henry S. Tanner's *New American Atlas*, a landmark in American cartography. Walter Ristow, the foremost authority on U.S. commercial mapping, notes that the "Tanner atlas raised U.S. commercial map production to a new level of excellence." Borrowing Melish's plan, Tanner prepared an atlas of maps of uniform size and scale depicting individual states or state groups based on the latest available state and Federal maps (*Plate 149; see Plate 145*). A map of the United States from coast to coast was also included which showed the four legendary rivers of the west, but with a qualifying statement doubting their existence. An accompanying memoir described in detail the source material used in the preparation of this work, which took "nearly ten years of unremitted application and research." Tanner's *Atlas* represents the first comprehensive analytical compilation of existing cartographic and geographic data for the United States as a whole.

Two major advances in the cartography of the United States were the development of the official state map and of the large atlas format. Robert Mills integrated these two forms of geographical expression in his *Atlas of the State of South Carolina* (*Plate 150*). It was based on the original county surveys prepared for John Wilson's 1822 map of South Carolina (see page 249), which Mills redrafted at a scale of two miles to one inch. The twenty-eight district maps were engraved by Henry S. Tanner and printed by Fielding Lucas, Jr., in 1825. A revision was issued in 1838. Mills, a native of Charleston and a pupil of the architect Benjamin Henry Latrobe, is best known as the designer of the Washington monuments in Washington and Baltimore and of the Treasury Building in Washington. In 1829 David Burr compiled a state atlas of New York under the direction of Simeon DeWitt, and in the same year Moses Greenleaf's atlas and statistical survey of Maine was published by Shirley and Hyde in Portland, Maine. Not until after the Civil War was another state atlas published.

The impetus behind the publication of Mills's *Atlas of the State of South Carolina* was the need of a large-scale map for planning

Indian trio, by Samuel Seymour, employed by the Long expedition, 1819–20, to document landscape and record likenesses of Indians

roads, canals, and harbor and river improvements. Similarly, the establishment by Congress in 1824 of the Board of Engineers for Internal Improvements resulted in a variety of important maps based on direct surveys at the national level. Beginning in 1825 and extending over the next sixteen years, some 180 internal improvement maps were prepared by the Army topographical engineers. These were assembled and published collectively in 1843 by order of Congress. During this same period large strip maps were published separately, depicting contemplated post routes such as between Baltimore and Philadelphia or Washington and New Orleans. Other national projects included mapping the Cumberland Road from Washington to Vandalia, Illinois, and charting the Chesapeake and Ohio Canal (*Plate 151*).

In 1825 John Ogden Day of Albany improved and printed D. H. Vance's map of the western part of the state of New York, delineating the route, canal locks, and geological profile of the Erie Canal, which formally opened in October 1825. Vignettes of canal scenes decorate the map.

Far to the southwest Joseph C. Brown undertook in 1825–27, at the direction of President John Quincy Adams, the first actual survey of the Santa Fe trail. His manuscript map, made with chain and compass corrected by astronomical observations, is now in the National Archives. Although Brown's map was never published, it was consulted by other cartographers who retained many of the placenames that first appeared on this map.

Railroad maps made their appearance shortly after John Stevens demonstrated the practicability of steam locomotion on his experimental track in Hoboken, New Jersey, in 1826. According to Andrew Modelski in his *Railroad Maps of the United States*, the earliest railway map in the Library of Congress was prepared by James Haywood and published in 1828 by the Massachusetts Board of Commissioners of Internal Improvements. It is a topographical strip map of the proposed Boston and Providence Railway, which was originally designed for horse-drawn railcars.

In the same year Lieutenant George Washington Whistler, a graduate of West Point, authored eight maps of the northern and northwestern boundary between the United States and Canada as far west as Lake Superior. These maps were prepared for the commissioners under the Treaty of Ghent (1814), and were published by the Washington firm of Gales and Seaton in 1828. They represent the first large-scale international boundary maps based on the resurveys of arbitrated boundary lines between the

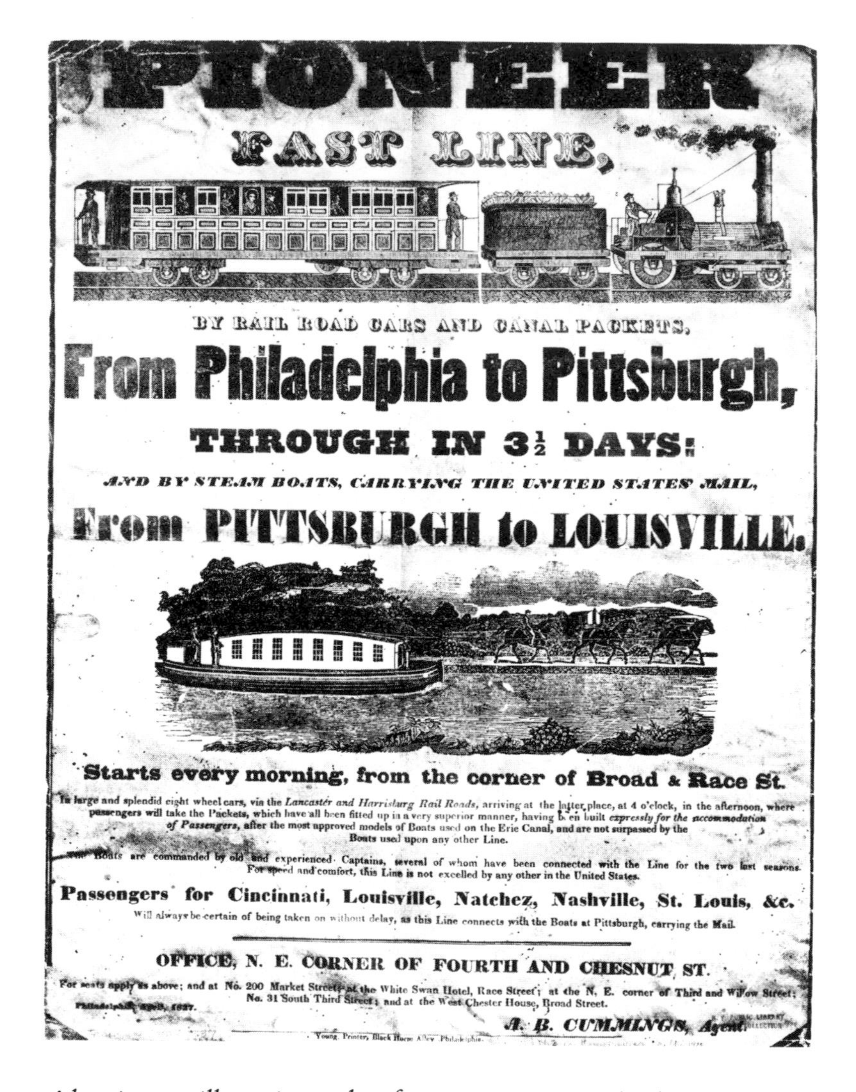

Advertisement illustrating modes of passenger transportation in 1837

United States and one of its neighbors. Another cartographer connected with the Canadian boundary surveys was Ferdinand Hassler; following the suspension of the U.S. Coast Survey in 1818, he briefly worked on the northeast boundary survey in 1818–19. Hassler graphically defined the practical impact of the effect of ellipticity on latitudes, which influenced the eventual settlement of the boundary question in 1842.

Whistler later became a leading American railroad engineer. From 1842 to 1849 he designed and constructed the first Russian railway connecting St. Petersburg with Moscow. His remarkable artistic talent was already evident while a young cadet in 1818, in a map he drew of the academy at West Point (*Plate 152*); in 1834 he became the father of James McNeill Whistler, who was subsequently expelled from West Point and the U.S. Coast Survey and went to Paris in 1855, to become the famous portrait painter and etcher.

British Admiralty charts of the Great Lakes were published in 1828, based on rapid reconnaissances made by Lieutenant Henry W. Bayfield of the Royal Navy (*Plate 153*). These remained the most accurate charts of the Lakes' coastlines until the 1850s but showed few depths, reefs, and shoals, and were consequently less valuable as hydrographic charts.

The third decade closed as it began, with the publication in 1829 of an important wall map of the United States. Compiled and engraved by Henry S. Tanner, it provided, in the words of W. L. G. Joerg, "a synoptic view of the whole country." Twice as detailed as Melish's map of 1816, Tanner's map measured 64 by 50 inches and was drawn at a scale of one inch to 32 miles. It included both internal improvements undertaken during the previous ten years and insets of plans of the major cities (Boston, New York, Philadelphia, Baltimore, Washington, Albany, Charleston, and New Orleans). The map, accompanied by a small booklet containing statistical data and information on the United States, was reprinted several times through 1844. In 1830 Tanner copyrighted a map specifically designed to show the number and extent of operating and proposed canals and railroads in the eastern United States. Engraved by J. Knight, this map was reduced from the author's large wall map.

To encourage American settlement in Texas, Stephen F. Austin compiled a map of Texas and parts of adjoining Mexican states (*Plate 154*). It was published by Henry S. Tanner and copyrighted March 17, 1830, about one month before the Mexican Federal congress prohibited further immigration from the United States. Austin's map, on which are mentioned wild horses, cattle, and buffalo, depicts land grants, colonies, towns, roads, Indian villages, and mines, and information about the characteristics of the land. It was reprinted in 1835 and 1845.

In 1831 graphic representation of the east coast reached another milestone when Rhode Island brought out its own state map, the last of the original thirteen states to do so. Compiled and published by J. Stevens of Newport, it was titled "A Topographical Map of the State of Rhode Island and Providence Plantations, surveyed Trigonometrically and in Detail."

Launch of the steam frigate *Fulton the First* at New York, October 29, 1814, *engraving after drawing "taken on the spot"*

Geographic expression of the West was also advanced in 1831 with the work of the explorer and trapper Jedediah Smith. In the previous decade, while Government exploratory efforts were limited to the high plains of the Missouri and the headwaters of the Mississippi River, bands of intrepid fur trappers had explored extensively in the Far West. Before Smith died at the hands of Comanche Indians in May 1831, he had broken the southwestern trail to California and explored the Great Basin, the Sierra Nevada, and the Pacific coast, from the Mexican settlements to as far north as Oregon, in search of furs ("brown gold"). Smith prepared a manuscript map in the winter of 1830–31 with the help of Samuel Parkman, a young surveyor; this map has not been found, but some twenty years later George Gibbs transferred data from it onto Frémont's printed map of 1845 which is now in the American Geographical Society. Smith's map delineated for the first time the essential features of the continental divide south of Yellowstone; accurately located the headwaters of the Colorado, Rio Grande, and Arkansas rivers, which Pike had depicted erroneously; and showed the Great Basin to be an interior drainage system without the four legendary rivers.

The geographic concepts of another trapper, Peter Skene Ogden, a Canadian who was associated with the Hudson's Bay Company, found expression in John Arrowsmith's 1832 map of "British North America" (*Plate 155*). John succeeded his brother

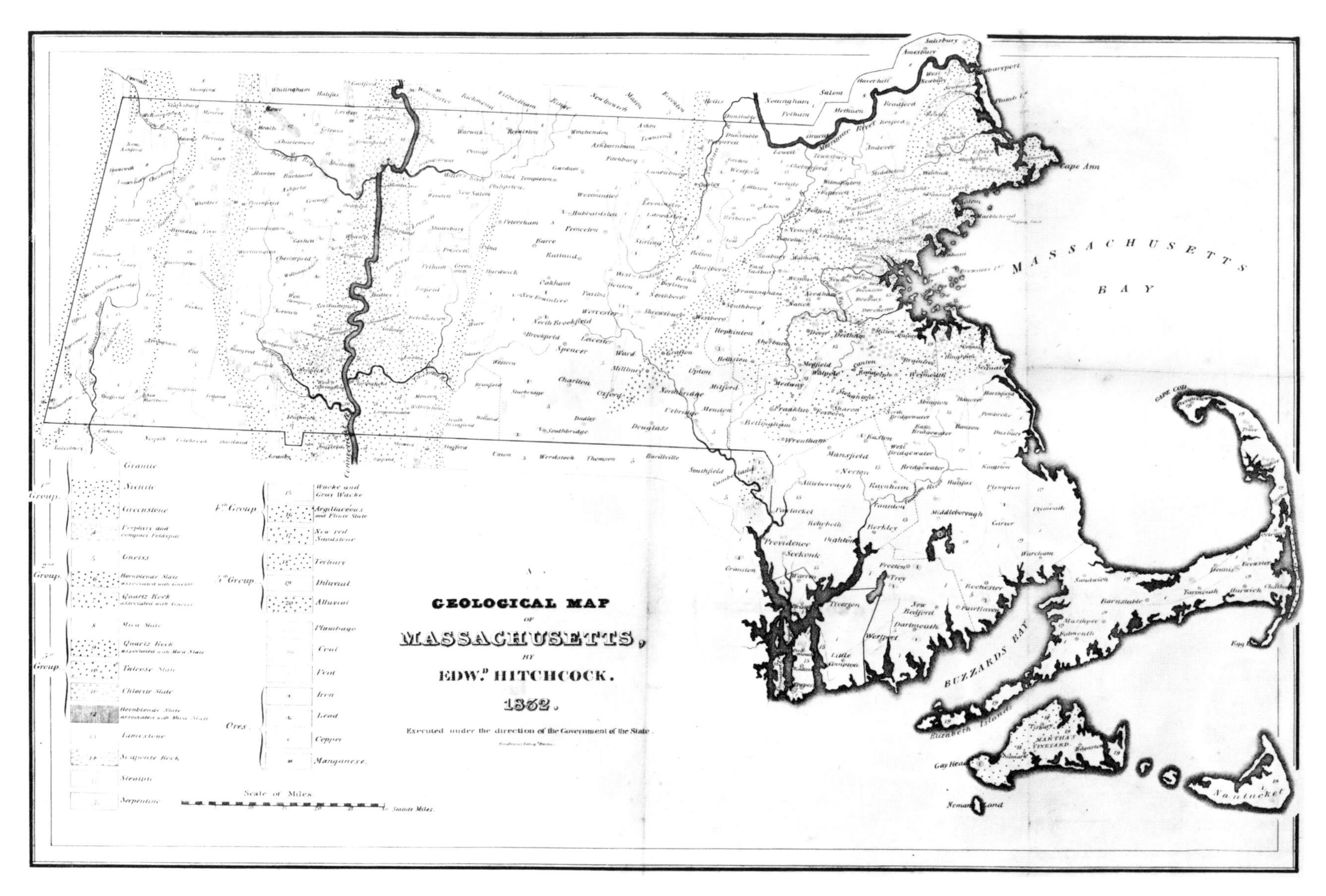

PLATE 159: Edward Hitchcock. "A Geological Map of Massachusetts." 1832. Lithograph, 46 × 71 cm. Geography and Map Division, Library of Congress, Washington, D.C. *Probably the first geological map covering an entire state, this map classifies five groups of underlying rock strata, three organic substances, and four types of ore. Printed by the Pendleton lithographic firm, Boston, and published with Hitchcock's "Report on the geology of Massachusetts, examined under the direction of that State, during the years 1830 and 1831," in the 1832 issue of* American Journal of Science and Arts.

Aaron and continued the tradition of the Arrowsmith firm in preparing exemplary maps of North America based largely on data furnished by the Hudson's Bay Company. Ogden's information, gathered from six expeditions in the northwest and as far south as the Central Valley of California, allowed Arrowsmith to portray for the first time the relative positions of the Columbia and Snake rivers and their tributaries.

The year following Smith's tragic death, Lieutenant James Allen portrayed the first topographical and hydrographical delineations of the headwaters of the Mississippi River (*Plate 156*).

The map, based on compass bearings, was published by Congress at a scale of one inch to $5\frac{3}{4}$ miles, later reprinted at a smaller scale to embellish Henry Rowe Schoolcraft's *Narrative of an Expedition . . . to Itasca Lake*, published in 1834. Schoolcraft, who had first explored the region in 1820 with General Lewis Cass, was in charge of the exploring party. His objective was the source of the Mississippi River, which he found to be the lake he named Itasca. Schoolcraft is best known for his monumental six-volume *Historical and Statistical Information Respecting the . . . Indian Tribes of the United States*, published in 1851–57.

In 1834 William Norris, the locomotive designer, graphically illustrated the status of internal improvements with his "Map of the Railroads and Canals Finished, Unfinished and in Contemplation in the United States," which was drawn and engraved for D. K. Minor, editor of the *Railroad Journal* (*Plate 157*).

Internal improvements coupled with the great Irish and German migrations beginning in 1827 led to the production of traveler's guides that depicted roads and their distances, steamboat and canal routes, and lengths of principal railroads. The genesis of these guides can be traced to Christopher Colles and his strip maps of 1789 (*see Plate 130*). Mathew Carey's pocket atlas, first published in 1796, served a similar purpose (see page 212). Henry S. Tanner printed a pocket atlas in 1828 showing "the roads and distances, designed for the use of travellers." By 1834 this map, retitled "The Traveller's Guide, or, Map of the Roads, Canals, and Railroads of the United States," appeared in his *The American Traveller*. In 1832 Samuel Augustus Mitchell first issued his "Traveller's Guide through the United States" and complemented it two years later with "Tourist Pocket Maps" of different states (*Plate 158*). These early works and their multitudinous progeny over the next fifty years laid the foundation for the road maps of today.

As science became more specialized during the nineteenth century, Americans made important contributions to the fields of geology, meteorology, ethnology, and oceanography. Their contributions were often portrayed graphically in map form, thereby providing new conceptual images of the United States. Several pioneering maps devoted to special scientific subjects or themes were compiled and printed during the 1830s. State geological surveys, first initiated during this decade, resulted in a new type of state map emphasizing underlying rather than surface features. Edward Hitchcock, State Geologist of Massachusetts, completed probably the first geological map covering an entire state when he published his preliminary map in the *American Journal of Science and Arts* in 1832 (*Plate 159*). The final copy was printed in 1841 and consisted of five colors, eighteen patterns, and nine symbols to show rock formations and ore strata. Official state geological maps prepared during this period and included in scientific reports were Maine (1836), Tennessee (1839), and New Jersey (1839).

Albert Gallatin, the Swiss immigrant who became Secretary of the Treasury under Jefferson and Madison, produced in 1836 the earliest American publication of an ethnographic map which

Scenes of westward migration

PLATE 160: John Mackay and Jacob E. Blake, Captain and Lieutenant, respectively, U.S. Topographical Engineers. "Map of the Seat of War in Florida compiled by order of Bvt. Brig^r. Genl. Z. Taylor, principally from the surveys & reconnaissances of the Officers of the U.S. Army." 1839. Manuscript, pen and ink; 101.5 × 75 cm. Records of the Office of the Chief of Engineers, National Archives, Washington, D.C. *Military map depicting roads, trails, army posts, drainage, and battle sites during the Second Seminole War in Florida, 1835 to 1842.*

(opposite) PLATE 161: Joseph Goldsborough Bruff. "Map Exhibiting the position of the Lands occupied by Indian Tribes in Amity with the United States; and also The Lands Ceded to the United States by Treaty with various Indian Tribes." 1839. Pen and ink additions over engraved map; 123 × 200 cm. Records of the U.S. Senate, National Archives, Washington, D.C. *Lands ceded by and occupied by Indian tribes, here outlined on a copy of Henry S. Tanner's 1839* "United States of America" *and keyed to legends at the left that list the tribes alphabetically, the treaties relating to specific areas, and the occupied lands.*

he entitled "Map of the Indian Tribes of North America about 1600 A.D. along the Atlantic; and about 800 A.D. westwardly." This map, which classified North American Indians by linguistic families, was lithographed in Boston by Pendleton and was published in the *Transactions* of the American Antiquarian Society in 1836, along with Gallatin's article on the same subject. This work and subsequent essays by Gallatin earned him the appellation of "father of American ethnology." In addition to the contribution made to the field of ethnology, Gallatin's map is important also for its graphic expression of the geographical ideas of Jedediah Smith. On this map the Great Basin is portrayed as a "Sandy Desert" with no outlets to the Pacific Ocean. In the south, Gallatin's map depicts "J. S. Smith's route 1826," the first map printed in the United States to show the route of that intrepid fur trapper.

Smith's image of the west was corroborated by two important maps by Major Benjamin L. E. Bonneville in 1837. One was a reasonably accurate portrayal of the sources of the Colorado, Missouri, and Snake rivers; the other portrayed the territory west of the Rocky Mountains. Bonneville was an army officer on leave of absence to engage in the fur trade. From his trappers he acquired a knowledge of the general geography of the Great Basin.

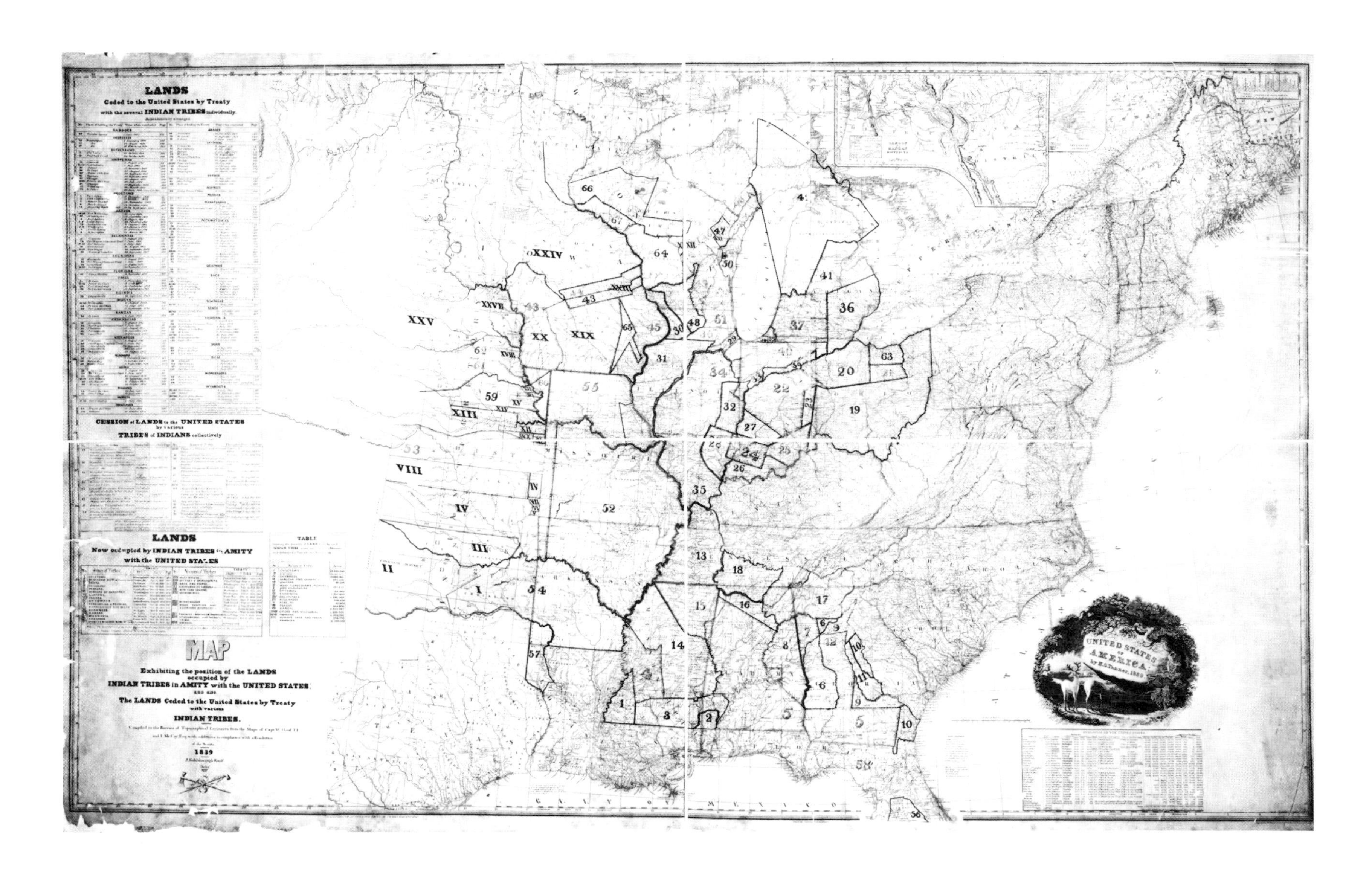

One of these trappers was Joseph Walker, who discovered a pass in the Sierra Nevada Range that was to become the main route for immigrant parties passing through the Basin in the 1840s. In addition to showing a basin with an interior drainage pattern, Bonneville reveals for the first time the Mary, or Ogden, River (Humboldt), named after Peter Skene Ogden, the Hudson's Bay Company trapper who discovered it. Bonneville's maps are significant because, unlike Gallatin's map, they received wide publicity through the writings of Washington Irving, the leading American literary figure of the period. Irving published the maps in 1837 along with his own *The Rocky Mountains; or, Scenes, Incidents, and Adventures in the Far West*, based on Bonneville's journal.

In the same year that Gallatin prepared his ethnographic map, Elias Loomis published his first work on the variations of the magnetic needle, using data gathered while still a student at Yale College. Two years later, in 1838, Loomis published in the *American Journal of Science and Arts* a map of the United States showing lines of equal declination and dip of the magnetic needle. It was based on observation furnished by hundreds of contributors scattered throughout the United States, and it represents one of the earliest maps based on extensive scientific data generalized for graphic presentation.

The second Seminole campaign in Florida, which resulted in the removal, between 1835 and 1842, of most of the Seminole Indians to beyond the Mississippi River, spurred the production of a number of topographic maps of the Florida peninsula. In 1837 "A Map of the Seat of War in Florida" was prepared by Captain Washington Hood from existing data in the Bureau of Topographical Engineers. Hood's map included an order by General Alex Macomb, Commander in Chief of the Army, "that officers who shall receive copies of it, may make such additions there to as they may . . . obtain as to the Topography of the Country and send the map, thus added to, to the Adjutant General, that, from the general information thus obtained, a correct map of the Seat of War in Florida, may be drawn for the use of the War Department." Based on numerous corrected maps received from the field, Hood's map was revised in 1839 by Captain John Mackay and Lieutenant J. E. Blake (*Plate 160*), and finally in 1843 by Captain John McClellan and Lieutenant Andrew A. Humphreys. Hood, a gifted artist and West Point graduate, died during a survey of Indian lands west of the Mississippi in 1840. Blake was later killed during the Mexican War in the Battle of Palo Alto, while Humphreys eventually advanced to command the U.S. Army Corps of Engineers from 1866 to 1879.

Joe Walker and his squaw, *watercolor by Alfred Jacob Miller, c. 1859–60*

The Saukie and Fox Indians, *watercolor by Karl Bodmer, 1833–34*

PLATE 162: David H. Burr. "Map of the United States of North America With Parts of the Adjacent Countries" (portion). 1839. Engraving, hand colored; entire dimensions 97 × 128 cm. Records of the Post Office Department, National Archives, Washington, D.C. *Northwest quadrant of one of the first maps to show the great interior basin of Nevada and Utah with no outlets to the Pacific Ocean. Depicts the routes of Jedediah Smith and Peter Skene Ogden, explorers and fur traders, whose geographical knowledge perhaps found expression in this map through information furnished by William H. Ashley, Missouri's Representative in Washington from 1831 to 1837, to David Burr, Geographer to the House of Representatives. Published by John Arrowsmith, London, in Burr's* The American Atlas Exhibiting the Post Offices, Railroads, Canals, and the Physical and Political Divisions of the United States of America . . .

Hood compiled another important map illustrating the defenses of the United States as proposed by Charles Gratiot in 1837. It shows the placement of proposed military forts in the Indian country along the Mississippi River from the Gulf of Mexico north to the forty-fifth parallel of latitude. A table of distances is included. Cartographic variations of this proposal were submitted also by Joel R. Poinsett, Secretary of War, and Major General Edmund P. Gaines, the latter proposal drawn by David H. Burr in 1838.

Hood also compiled a topographic map of the Territory of Oregon in 1838 to illustrate Senator Lewis Linn's bill authorizing the President to occupy that territory. Copied almost directly from Arrowsmith's map of 1832, it adds little new information except for the delineation of the northern boundary of Oregon Territory along the forty-ninth parallel of latitude. A new representation of the interior of Oregon Territory based upon personal observation is found in Samuel Parker's map of the territory, also dated in 1838. Engraved and printed in Utica, New

"A bivouack in safety or Florida troops preventing a surprise," an 1840 New York newspaper cartoon on the Seminole War in Florida

Fort Clark on the Missouri, *1834, lithograph after painting by Karl Bodmer*

York, Parker's map was widely circulated just prior to the great movement of immigrants to settle in the Oregon Territory in the 1840s.

The final year of the decade produced two important cartographic works. At the request of the U.S. Senate, the Corps of Topographical Engineers annotated Henry S. Tanner's 1839 map of the United States to show the locations of all "Lands occupied by Indian Tribes in Amity with the U.S. and also The Lands Ceded . . . by Treaty with various . . . Tribes" (*Plate 161*). This map contains a detailed list of tribes keyed to the map; tables listing acres held by each tribe; and a census providing by tribe the number of Indians who emigrated west of the Mississippi River, the number of tribes within striking distance of the western frontier, and the estimated number of warriors. Twelve copies of this map were produced, four of which are now in the Library of Congress and the National Archives. These maps were prepared by J. Goldsborough Bruff, an architect and mapmaker. It is interesting to note that Bruff had an indirect association with another architect-turned-cartographer, Robert Mills: objecting to Mills's design of about 1836 for the Washington Monument in the District of Columbia, Bruff submitted a revised design in 1876, when construction of the monument was resumed following the Civil War. Bruff's drawing closely resembles the monument as it appears today.

The final contribution of 1839 was David H. Burr's exquisite atlas of postal maps which was engraved by the Arrowsmith firm in London. Burr was an accomplished mapmaker as well as a publisher. Under the direction of his mentor, Simeon DeWitt, he compiled the second earliest state atlas (New York) in 1829. He served as Topographer of the Post Office in the 1830s, and at the time of his 1839 publication held the position of Geographer of the House of Representatives of the United States. His rare and valuable atlas, which measures 38 by 51 inches, consists of a map of the United States and twelve maps of one or more groups of states or territories designed to show every post office, with the distances between them (*Plate 162*). Four classes of post roads are shown, ranging from one- to four-horse roads. Burr's map of the United States, which portrays the entire country from coast to coast, was the most complete national map to appear up to that time. The Far West portion of the map fully expresses the geographical concepts of Jedediah Smith, and this has led Carl Wheat to speculate that Burr's map was probably based directly on a copy of Smith's map. Smith was killed in 1831, but his partner, William H. Ashley, served for Missouri in the House of Representatives from 1831 to 1837 and could have provided Burr with a copy at that time. Burr's set of maps sold for $75.00, colored and mounted on cloth in a portfolio; separate sheets sold for $5.00 each. Despite the fact that these maps were prepared under the direction of the Postmaster General, each postmaster had to buy his own maps since they were privately produced and Congress had not authorized their purchase.

9. Emergence of Scientific and Thematic Maps

We were not yet at work on the map. There was a mass of astronomical and other observations to be calculated and discussed before a beginning on this could be made. Indeed, the making of such a map is an interesting process. It must be exact. First, the foundations must be laid in observations made in the field; then the reduction of these observations to latitude and longitude; afterward the projection of the map, and the laying down upon it of positions fixed by the observations; then the tracing from the sketch-books of the lines of the rivers, the forms of the lakes, the contours of the hills. Specially is it interesting to those who have laid in the field these various foundations to see them all brought into final shape—fixing on a small sheet the results of laborious travel over waste regions, and giving to them an enduring place on the world's surface.

John Charles Frémont
Report of the Exploring Expedition to the Rocky Mountains (1845)

1840-1900

BURR'S ATLAS brought to a close the formative period of American cartography. With the 1840s a new era of cartographic expression of the United States unfolded to set the stage for the development of modern mapping. During the next sixty years there was an explosive expansion in the production of maps, as faster and cheaper printing technologies were devised. Also, there was a gradual shift from the preparation of individual maps to the production of maps in sets or series based on systematic surveys and mapping programs. Finally, a thematic mapping tradition emerged from the specialization of science, creating new visual map images of the United States.

Several important geological and mineralogical maps were introduced in the fifth decade. In 1840 Scottish-born David Dale Owen compiled a composite map of a large portion of the 11,000 square miles of mineral lands he surveyed in Iowa, Wisconsin, and Illinois for the General Land Office in 1839–40, in preparation of their sale to the public (*Plate 163*). This map, now in the National Archives and described by Herman Friis, was based on 270 township plats annotated to show settlements, mines, and diggings as well as mineral deposits. The author of the map was the son of Robert Owen, the British social reformer who established the collectivist community of New Harmony, Indiana, in the 1820s. It was at New Harmony that David worked with William Maclure, the geologist who had prepared the first geological map of the eastern United States in 1809 (see page 225). Owen's map was the earliest geological map based on a systematic survey of a large area. The initial field survey, which took two months, required a force of 139 men, including "several experienced lead miners."

Also in 1840, John Alexander compiled his pioneering topographic and geological map of Maryland, the first detailed contour map of an entire state. It was based on connected surveys undertaken from 1834 to 1840 by Alexander, who was State Topographical Engineer, and Julius T. Ducatel, State Geologist. Alexander's original manuscript map has never been published; it measured 79 by 41 inches as described by Edward Bennett Mathews in his *Maps and Map-Makers of Maryland* in 1898, when it still belonged to the Alexander family. A reduced copy on tracing linen, made by the U.S. Coast Survey for the War Department, is in the National Archives. Surface configuration was portrayed by contours, or lines of equal elevation, determined in part from relief profiles Alexander had prepared for the many canals, turnpikes, and railroads built in the state during this period.

In 1841 William Barton Rogers, director of the Geological Survey of Virginia from 1835 to 1848 and later the first president of Massachusetts Institute of Technology, devised a classification scheme for the underlying rock structures which he applied to the nine-sheet Böyë map of Virginia (see page 249), modified to show natural drainage patterns. Separate colors were used to illustrate lithology. The map was not published until 1875, however, because of the difficulty and cost of printing in color, a process that required a separate lithographic stone for each hue. In that year it was recompiled for printing by Jedediah Hotchkiss, a distinguished surveyor and mapmaker who mapped much of Virginia for the Confederacy during the Civil War.

The year 1841 also witnessed the issuance of the earliest official chart of a portion of the West Coast. It resulted from a U.S. Navy survey of the Pacific northwest coast by the U.S. Exploring Expedition, commanded by Lieutenant Charles Wilkes. The chart is titled "Map of the Oregon Territory" and its portrayal of the coastal region from Cape Mendocino north to Queen Charlotte Islands was the most accurate delineation until the U.S. Coast Survey entered the region a decade later. It is best known for its inset map of the Columbia River based on a survey as far east

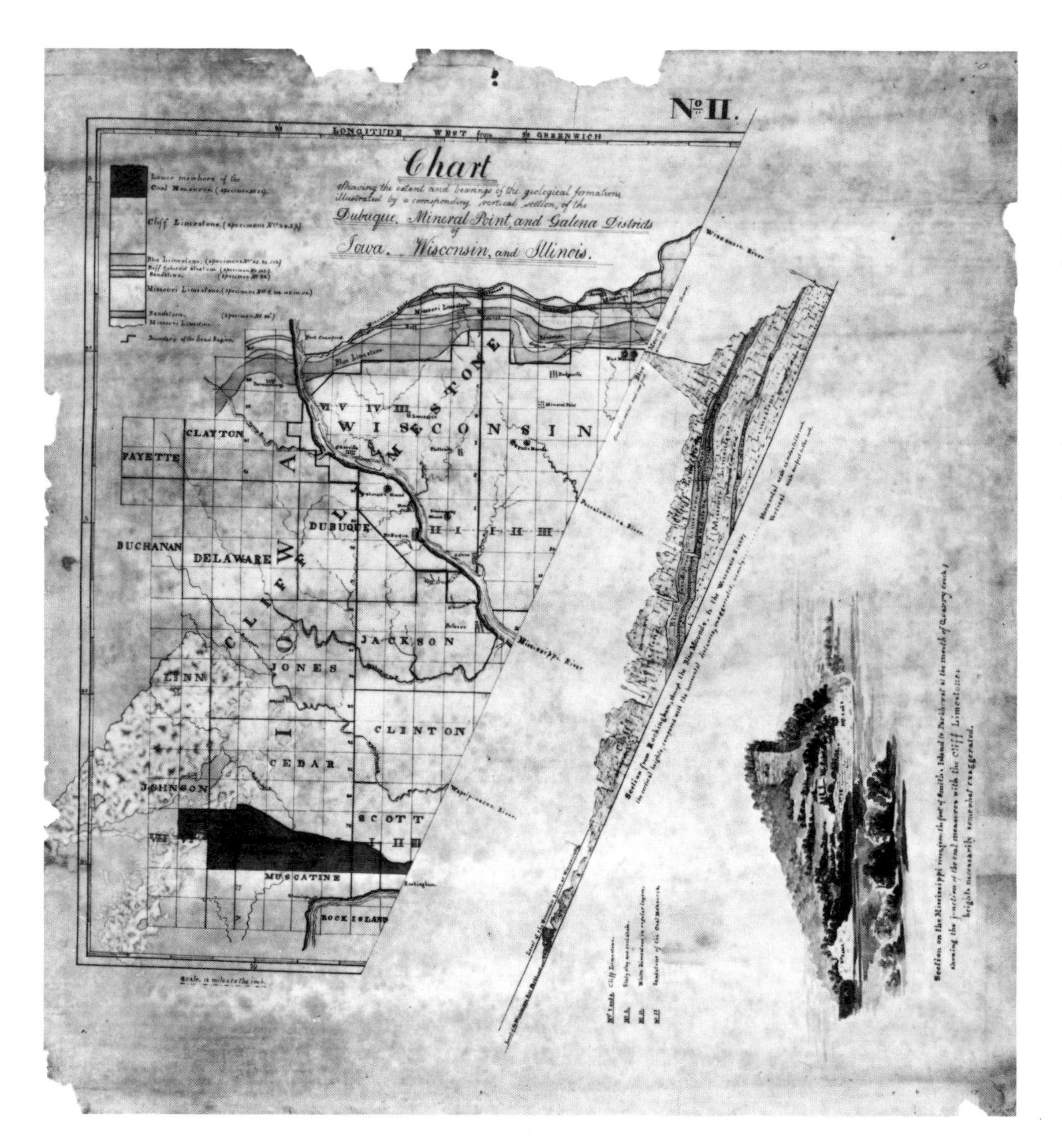

PLATE 163: David Dale Owen. "Chart Showing the extent and bearings of the geological formations, illustrated by a corresponding vertical section, of the Dubuque, Mineral Point, and Galena Districts of Iowa, Wisconsin, and Illinois." c. 1839–40. Manuscript, pen and ink with watercolor; 45.5 × 43 cm. Records of the U.S. Senate, National Archives, Washington, D.C. *One of several maps by Owen based on the first systematic geological and mineral survey of a large region. Prepared to accompany Owen's official* Report of a Geological Exploration of part of Iowa, Wisconsin, and Illinois, made . . . in the Year 1839 . . ., *which was published by the U.S. Senate.*

as Walla Walla. The Columbia River survey established an accurate and independent base line that was later used as a control point for Frémont's trans-Mississippi survey in 1843–44.

Geographic representation of the southwestern frontier also was advanced in 1841, when the Arrowsmith firm engraved an excellent map of Texas showing the counties, Indian tribes, and wagon roads. This map supported Texas land claims by depicting its western boundary as extending to the Rio Grande and including Santa Fe. Arrowsmith's map was copied and added to by Lieutenant William H. Emory for the State Department in 1844 and retitled "Texas and the Counties Adjacent." On Emory's version, the Texas panhandle was expanded northward to the forty-second parallel of north latitude.

Technological advances in the 1840s contributed to the tre-

The rough seas off Cape Horn

mendous expansion of map production during the remainder of the century, particularly after the Civil War. The introduction of low-cost wood-pulp paper in 1840, and the development of wax engraving by Sidney Edwards Morse, culminated in Morse and Breese's *Cerographic Atlas of the United States*, which was issued in parts between 1842 and 1845 (*Plate 164*). Cerography or wax engraving was a major technological breakthrough that greatly influenced American commercial map and atlas production in the United States. David Woodward, in his study of the wax-engraving process entitled appropriately *The All-American Map*, has estimated that nearly three-fourths of all commercially published atlases in the United States from 1842 to 1950 used this technique. In wax engraving, the initial image is etched on wax rather than on copper or stone. The engraved wax serves as a mold from which a duplicate printing surface in the form of a thin metal plate in relief is made by a process of electrodepositing. The result, notes Woodward, is "a relief-printing plate that could be printed on letterpress printing machines, a property that accounted in large measure for the versatility of the process in the nineteenth and early twentieth centuries." The use of this engraving medium also allows the engraver to insert metal letterpress type in the wax instead of laboriously engraving by hand each letter or figure. While this procedure speeded up the entire printing process, it contributed to a standardization of lettering that can only be described as dull and uninspired. Erwin Raisz, in his *General Cartography*, concluded that wax engraving encouraged overlettering—the excessive use of words and the inappropriate choice of type size and style—which became a major characteristic of American commercial maps. Morse was the son of Jedidiah Morse, whose geographical gazetteers and atlases taught generations of Americans the rudiments of geography, and the younger brother of Samuel Finley Breese Morse, noted artist and inventor.

In response to the needs of the second Seminole War in Florida and the rapidly expanded western military frontier, Congress increased the size of the Army and enlarged the Bureau of Topographical Engineers to corps status in 1838. Under the leadership of Colonel John J. Abert, the Corps of Topographical Engineers undertook the mapping of the trans-Mississippi West until 1863, when its consolidation with the Corps of Engineers was effected.

Joseph N. Nicollet, a noted French scientist and topographer, was chosen to lead the first exploring party sponsored by the newly reorganized Corps of Topographical Engineers. His objective was to explore and map the upper watershed of the Mississippi River, a portion of which Nicollet had explored independently in 1836 and 1837. The only civilian to lead an Army surveying

Sailing Ship Bound for California, *pencil drawing with ink notes*

PLATE 164: Sidney Edwards Morse and Samuel Breese. "Indiana." 1843. Wax engraving, 35 × 28 cm. Reference Collection, National Archives, Washington, D.C. *Plate from Morse and Breese's* Cerographic Atlas of the United States, *issued between 1842 and 1845. Morse introduced to cartography the wax engraving technique; this major technological breakthrough significantly influenced commercial map and atlas production in the United States during the second half of the nineteenth century, but it gave a characteristic mechanical appearance to American maps.*

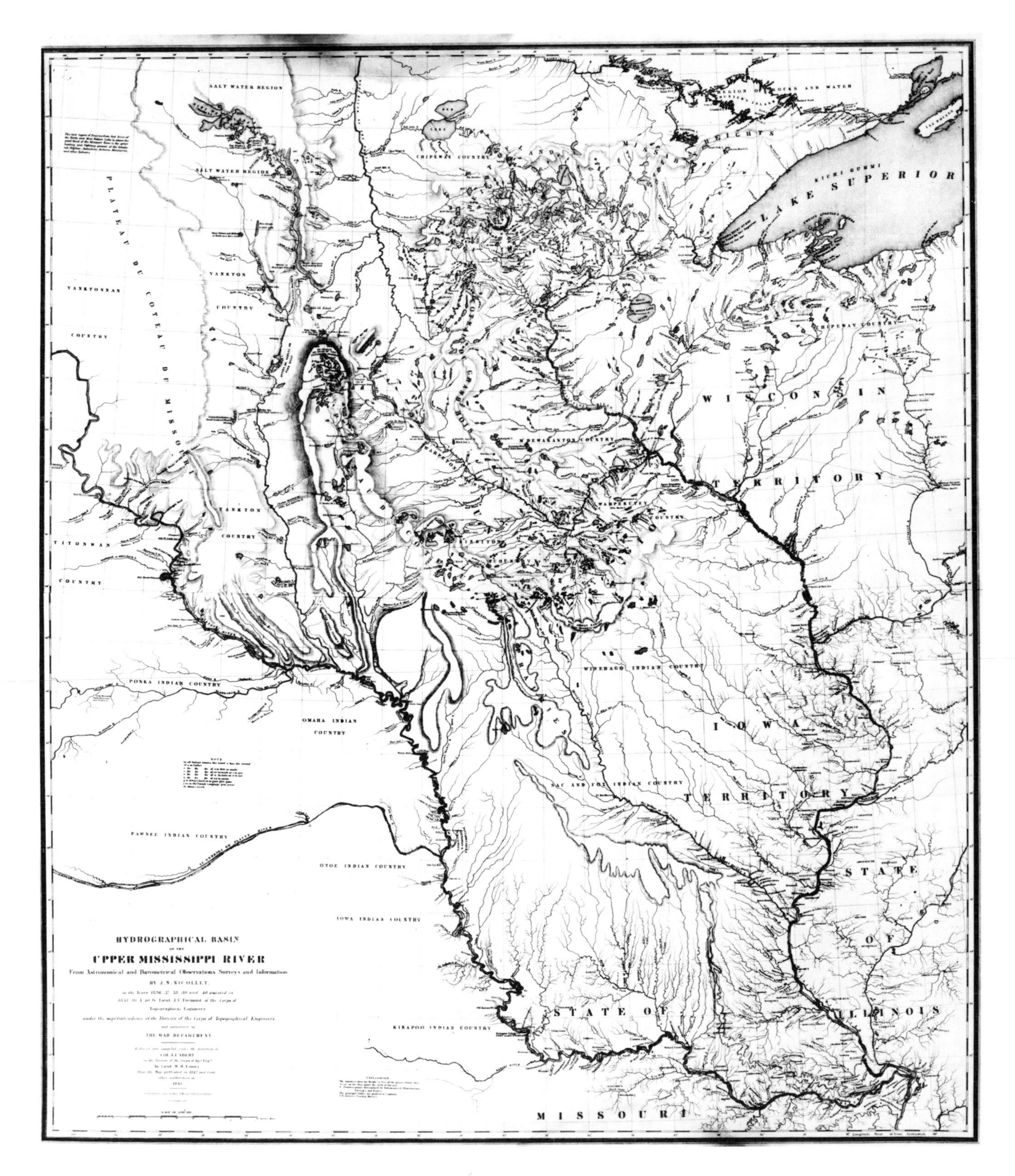

PLATE 165: Joseph N. Nicollet and William H. Emory, Lieutenant, Corps of Topographical Engineers. "Hydrographical Basin of the Upper Mississippi River From Astronomical and Barometrical Observations Surveys and Information." 1843. Engraving, 94 × 78 cm. Records of the U.S. House of Representatives, National Archives, Washington, D.C. *Earliest accurate map of the interior, from St. Louis north to the international boundary, and west to present central South Dakota. Based on systematic instrument surveys undertaken by the French mathematician and astronomer between 1836 and 1840. Nicollet's map, which was engraved by William J. Stone, Washington, D.C., and published separately by order of both the U.S. Houses of Congress, initiated the scientific mapping of the trans-Mississippi West by the War Department.*

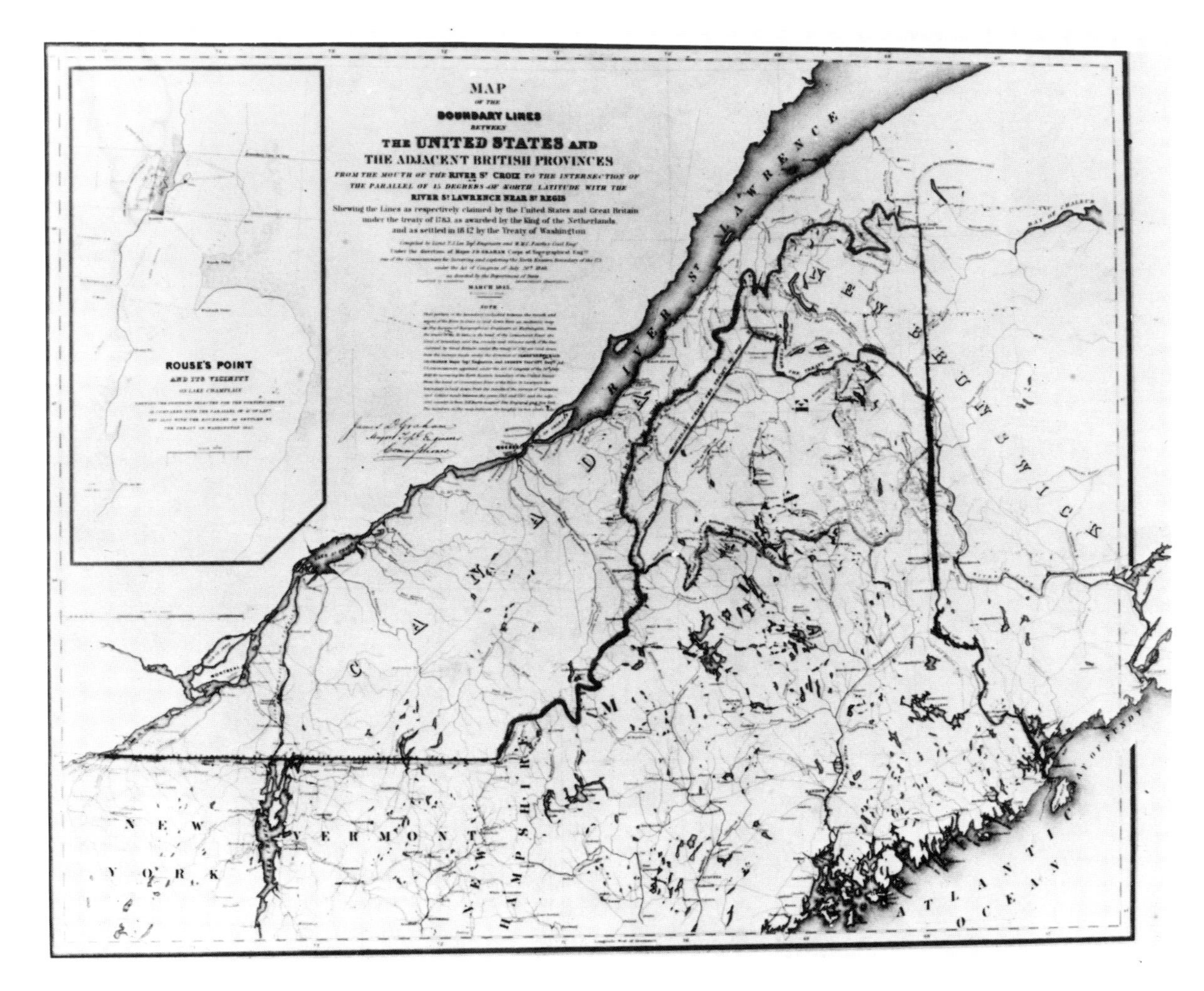

PLATE 166: James D. Graham, Major, Corps of Topographical Engineers. "Map of the Boundary Lines Between the United States and the Adjacent British Provinces . . ." 1843. Engraving, hand colored; 68 × 80 cm. Records of the Office of the Chief of Engineers, National Archives, Washington, D.C. *Delineates the northeast boundary line of the United States as claimed by the United States and by Great Britain under the Treaty of Paris of 1783, and the final boundary line as determined by the Webster-Ashburton Treaty of Washington, 1842. Inset map, "Rouse's Point and its Vicinity on Lake Champlain" (at northeast tip of lake). Prepared under the direction of the Department of State and printed by order of the U.S. Senate; engraved by William J. Stone, Washington, D.C.*

(opposite) PLATE 167: U.S. Coast Survey. "Map of New-York Bay and Harbor and the Environs" (Sheet No. 1 of six sheets). 1844. Engraving, entire dimensions 165 × 162 cm. Records of the Coast and Geodetic Survey, National Archives, Washington, D.C. *Title quadrant of the first copperplate engraving of a nautical chart issued by the Coast Survey, which set the standard for official nineteenth-century topographic and hydrographic mapping. For several decades following 1844, skilled engravers were brought from Europe to undertake this delicate work and to train American craftsmen.*

party until the 1870s, Nicollet undertook during 1838 and 1839 the first truly scientific topographic survey of the interior of North America. He was assisted by John C. Frémont, a young but ambitious lieutenant in the Corps of Topographical Engineers. Nicollet's portentous map of the "Hydrographical Basin of the Upper Mississippi River," which covers a region larger than half of Europe, was printed for distribution to the Senate in 1842 at a scale of ten miles to the inch. A reduced copy—at a scale of approximately twenty miles to the inch—was compiled by Lieutenant William H. Emory (*Plate 165*). It was published with Nicollet's report just a few months after the scientist's death in 1843 and appeared in Senate Document 237 (26th Congress) and House Document 52 (28th Congress). A contemporary Army explorer and mapmaker, Lieutenant Gouverneur K. Warren, believed that Nicollet's "map was one of the greatest contributions ever made to American geography" (see Bibliography). Surface relief was conveyed by hachures (short parallel lines that depict degree of slope) and spot heights (elevation figures) based on hundreds of barometric readings taken by Nicollet and Frémont. Nicollet, noted Warren, "was the first explorer who made much use of the barometer for obtaining the elevation of our great interior country above the sea." The French savant was also one of the first cartographers to incorporate placenames on maps based on systematic analysis of Indian and French place-

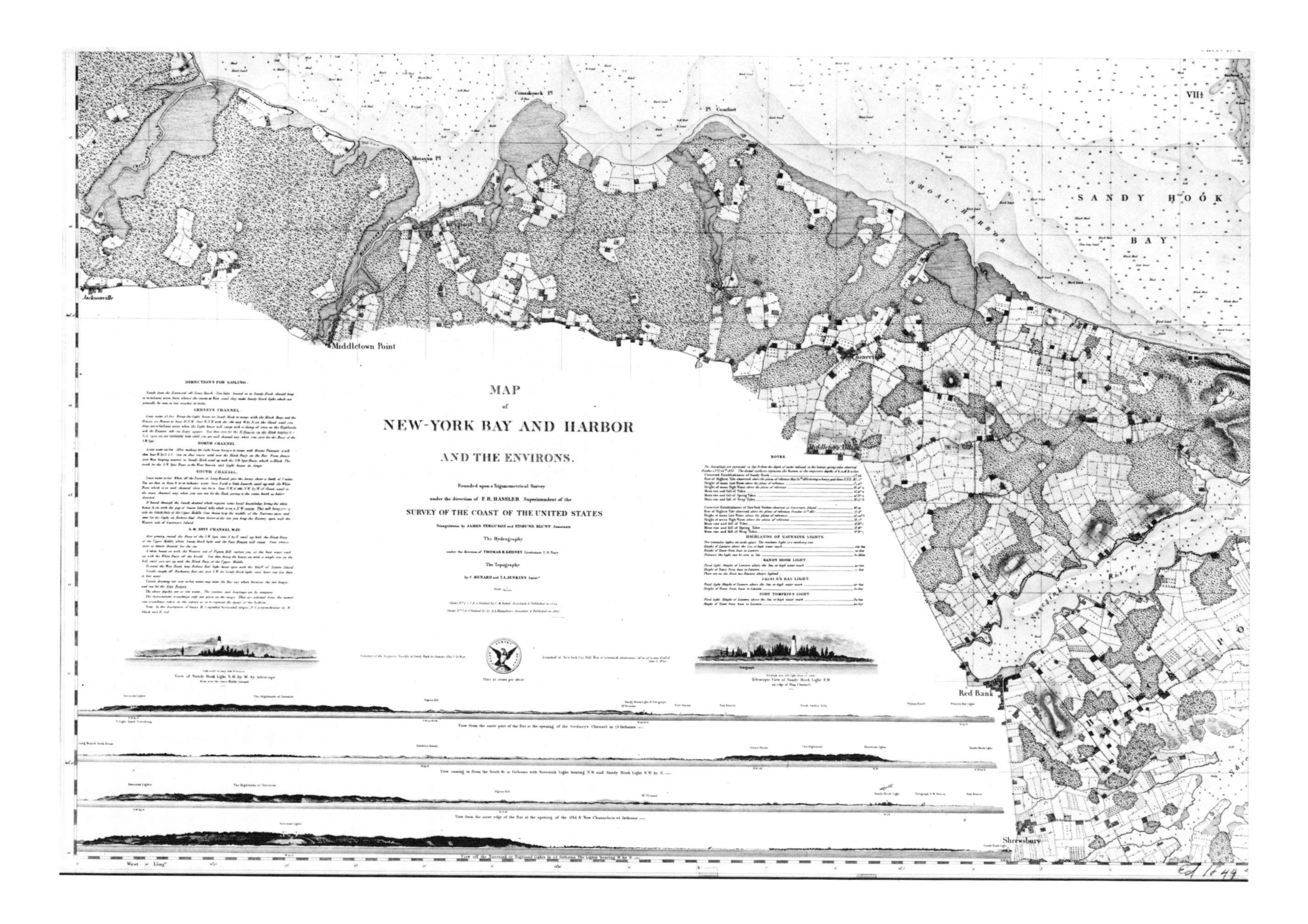

names. Through Frémont and Emory, Nicollet stamped his scientific imprint on subsequent War Department expeditions.

Also in 1843 and by order of the Senate was published an important map of the northeastern boundary of the United States, prepared under the direction of Major James D. Graham of the Corps of Topographical Engineers (*Plate 166*). It depicts both the British and United States boundary claims in the disputed highlands of Maine and adjacent British provinces, as well as the line agreed upon by the Webster-Ashburton Treaty of 1842. This dispute, which brought the two countries close to war in 1838, arose from the vagueness of the 1755 Mitchell map of North America (*see Plate 96*), upon which the original boundary line had been drawn.

Pioneering meteorological maps of the eastern United States were developed in 1843 by Elias Loomis, professor of mathematics and natural philosophy at Ohio Western Reserve College and

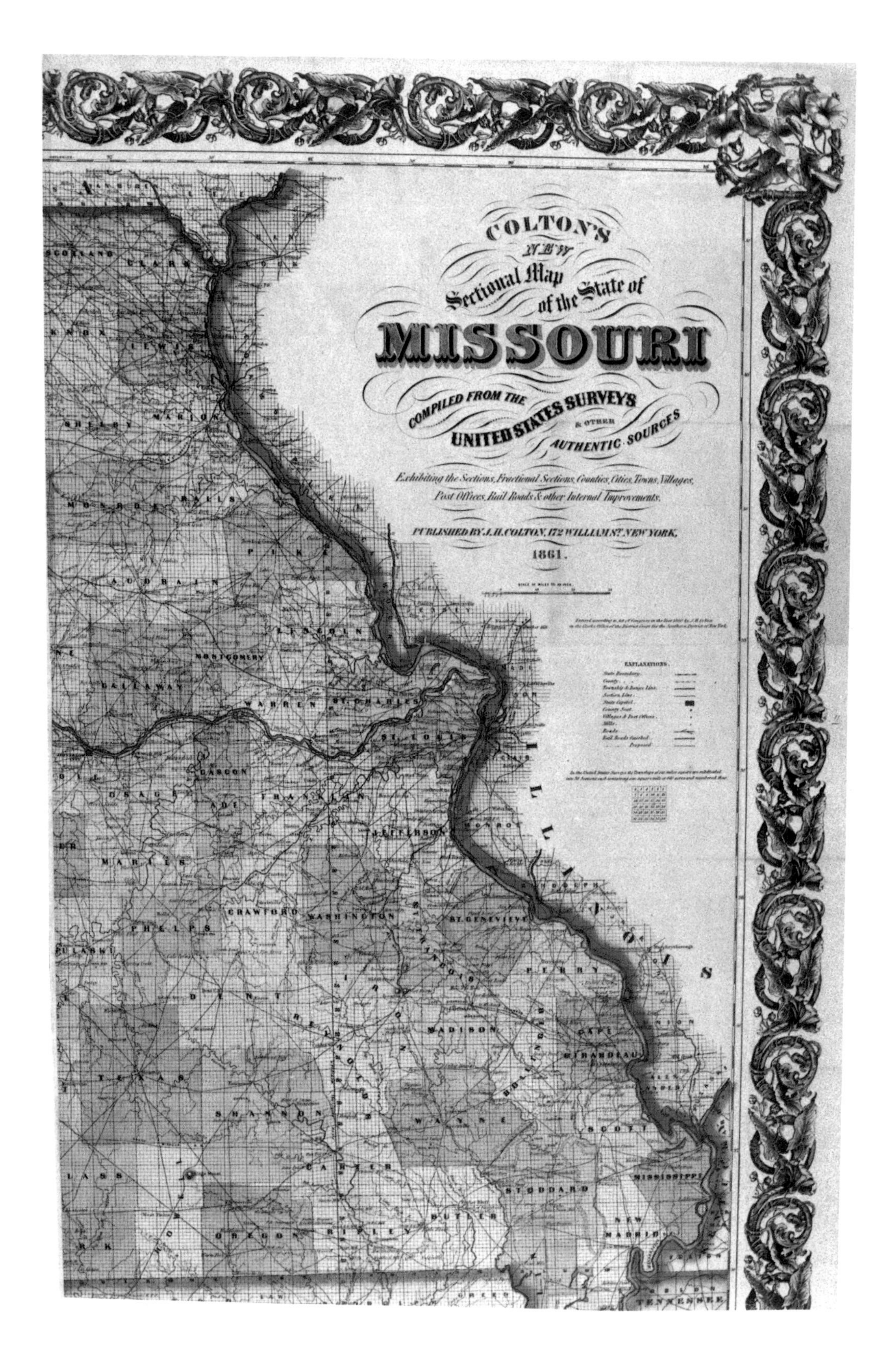

PLATE 168: Joseph H. Colton. "Colton's New Sectional Map of the State of Missouri . . . Exhibiting the Sections, Fractional Sections, Counties, Cities, Towns, Villages, Post Offices, Rail Roads & other Internal Improvement" (portion). 1861. Engraving, hand colored; entire dimensions 95 × 106 cm. Reference Collection, National Archives, Washington, D.C. *Eastern half of typical state wall map, published by J. H. Colton, New York City, one of the leading private map-publishing firms in the United States during the latter half of the nineteenth century. With the rise of literacy and mobility after the Civil War, wall maps such as this one increased in popularity.*

later at Yale. Loomis published his fundamental paper on storm atmospheric conditions in the *Transactions* of the American Philosophical Society in 1846. His paper was accompanied by a series of twelve maps showing variations of atmospheric conditions defined by lines of equal temperatures (isotherms) and equal barometric pressure (isobars). Wind direction and force were represented by the direction and length of arrows. In addition, precipitation was depicted by color hues applied manually. These charts, which traced the movement of storms on a daily basis, were compiled from data provided by sixty-eight observers scattered throughout the eastern half of the United States. They represent the earliest synoptic weather maps published and are essentially the same as weather maps produced today.

Systematic scientific charting of the American coasts is represented by the nautical charts produced by the Coast Survey, which was revived under Ferdinand R. Hassler in 1832 within the Treasury Department. The first nautical chart was printed in 1839, a lithograph of New York Bay. Alexander Dallas Bache, great-grandson of Benjamin Franklin, succeeded Hassler in 1843 and issued the first copperplate engraved chart in 1844 (*Plate 167*). It was a detailed six-plate engraving of New York Harbor and vicinity, and it already symbolized the artistic and elegant character of the charts produced by the Coast Survey. From 1844 to 1905 all "finished" charts were printed from engraved copperplates, while "preliminary" charts, those brought out as quickly as possible following a survey to meet the urgent needs of navigators, were either engraved or, after photolithography was developed, printed in that process. To maintain the high quality of technical craftsmanship, the Coast Survey imported chart paper and copperplates from Europe and, from 1842 to 1854, master engravers as well, who trained American apprentices. These included James McNeill Whistler, Lieutenant George Washington Whistler's artistic and temperamental son, who worked for the Survey for three months during 1854 and 1855 before being dismissed for poor attendance.

With Frémont was initiated the topographic mapping of the Far West based on field reconnaissance. Sponsored and influenced by his father-in-law, Thomas Hart Benton, the powerful senator from Missouri, Frémont undertook three principal expeditions that charted the route to Oregon and California and stimulated popular interest in the region. His influential "Map of an Exploring Expedition to the Rocky Mountains in the Year 1842 and to Oregon and North California in the Years 1843–1844" presented for the first time, in the words of Herman R. Friis, "a connected view" of the continent from Kansas City to the Pacific coast, where Frémont's survey intersected the Wilkes survey of 1841. Donald Jackson, editor of the Frémont papers and a noted scholar of western cartography, cites this map as "one of the brightest documents in a veritable welter of maps appearing during Frémont's generation." Based on personal observation and constructed according to the most advanced surveying and mapping principles of the period, it soon became "a base map which others used to expand the boundaries of cartographic knowledge." Large areas of the map were left blank in the absence of direct knowledge and Great Salt Lake and Utah Lake were depicted as a single body of water, but the map confirmed that the Great Basin had no exterior drainage system.

Both Frémont's journal and map were lithographed in 1845 by E. Weber and Company, a Baltimore firm that later, under the name of August Hoen and Company, became one of the principal publishers of government reports and maps. Edward Weber and his cousin, August Hoen, were both natives of Germany who had emigrated to the United States in the 1830s. Weber had studied lithography in Munich under the watchful eye of its originator, Aloys Senefelder.

Shortly after the publication of Frémont's 1845 map, the

Shipcard for New York–San Francisco Clipper Ship Line, c. 1851

PLATE 169: Robert Pearsall Smith. "Map of Schoharie Co. New York From actual Surveys by E. Wenig & W. Lorey." 1856. Wax engraving, with watercolor tints; 142 × 96 cm. Geography and Map Division, Library of Congress, Washington, D.C. *Published by R. P. Smith in Philadelphia. Representative county map with colored boundaries of townships. In addition to topographical features map shows roads, names of residences, plans of principal towns, and views of prominent public buildings.*

San Francisco in 1849, watercolor "to India, much love from Tom"

Senate ordered 10,000 copies of a large map of the Oregon Trail which was rapidly becoming the main route for the "great migration" to the Oregon country. Charles Preuss, the German cartographer who had compiled Frémont's earlier maps based on his own and the explorer's journal and field notes, prepared a large-scale, seven-section topographical road map of the trail. Information on Indians, buffaloes, and climatic conditions were included on the map sections. It, too, was printed by the Weber firm.

Geological mapping advanced in 1845 with the publication of Charles Lyell's map of the United States east of the Rocky Mountains. Lyell was an English geologist whose three-volume work, *The Principles of Geology*, published in 1830–33, contributed to the establishing of geology as an organized body of knowledge. The map accompanied his 1845 popular account, *Travels in North America*, and relied heavily upon David Dale Owen's map of the Upper Mississippi Valley (*see Plate 163*) and James Hall's map of the United States prepared in 1843. Lyell's hand-colored map introduced a modern classification scheme which clearly defined four physiographic divisions: the Atlantic and Gulf coastal plains; the Appalachian Mountain system; the Appalachian, Michigan, and Illinois coalfields; and the Laurentian Peneplain, or Canadian Shield, a vast area of ancient rock covering eastern Canada and part of the northeastern United States.

A resurgence of atlas production during the 1840s and 1850s reflected an emerging mass market fueled by increased prosperity and mobility. Samuel Augustus Mitchell's *New Universal Atlas* was first published in 1846 and issued periodically until 1893. A native of Scotland, Mitchell became a prolific publisher of geographical works. Walter W. Ristow notes that Mitchell employed as many as 250 persons in his Philadelphia establishment, which he took over from Henry S. Tanner in the mid-nineteenth century, and sold over 400,000 copies of his atlases (see Bibliography, *Maps for an Emerging Nation*).

Rivaling Mitchell's was the Colton firm in New York City. Beginning with large wall maps of the United States in 1847, Joseph H. and George W. Colton expanded their operations to include gazetteers and atlases. The latter were published from 1855 to 1884. Colton's maps are characterized by borders embellished with interweaving vines, marking them as products of the Victorian period (*Plate 168*). Like Tanner, both Colton and Mitchell continued to rely upon copperplate or steel engraving for atlases rather than the faster and less expensive lithography, to keep their publications in competition with the high-quality copperplate atlases produced in Europe.

Together with the increased popularity of national and world

Encounter with an enormous "she bear" in the Sierra Nevada Mts., 1863

atlases there also arose a demand for detailed town and county maps, which was not met by official agencies at the state or Federal level. These maps took the form of county wall maps, first introduced by Charles Varlé in 1808–9 (see page 238) and prepared in the 1820s for Pennsylvania and Virginia as a result of state legislative action directed toward the publication of state maps. By the mid-1840s, however, the production of cadastral county wall maps showing land ownership had become commercially profitable. In his check list of county maps in the Library of Congress, Richard W. Stephenson lists more than 1400 county maps representing some 1,041 counties—approximately one third of all counties in the United States—which were "concentrated mainly in the Northeast and North Central States, and in Virginia, California, and Texas" (see Bibliography). Most of these county maps were issued after 1846; the 1850s was the most productive decade, with some 330 county maps issued.

(opposite) PLATE 170: John Disturnell. "Mapa de los Estados Unidos de Méjico." 1847. Engraving, hand colored; 78 × 108 cm. General Records of the U.S. Government, National Archives, Washington, D.C. *Published by John Disturnell, New York City. Embraces Mexico and its provinces, including present California and New Mexico. This map was attached to the 1848 Treaty of Guadalupe Hidalgo, which ended the two-year Mexican War and subsequently added California, New Mexico, Arizona, Nevada, and Utah to the United States.*

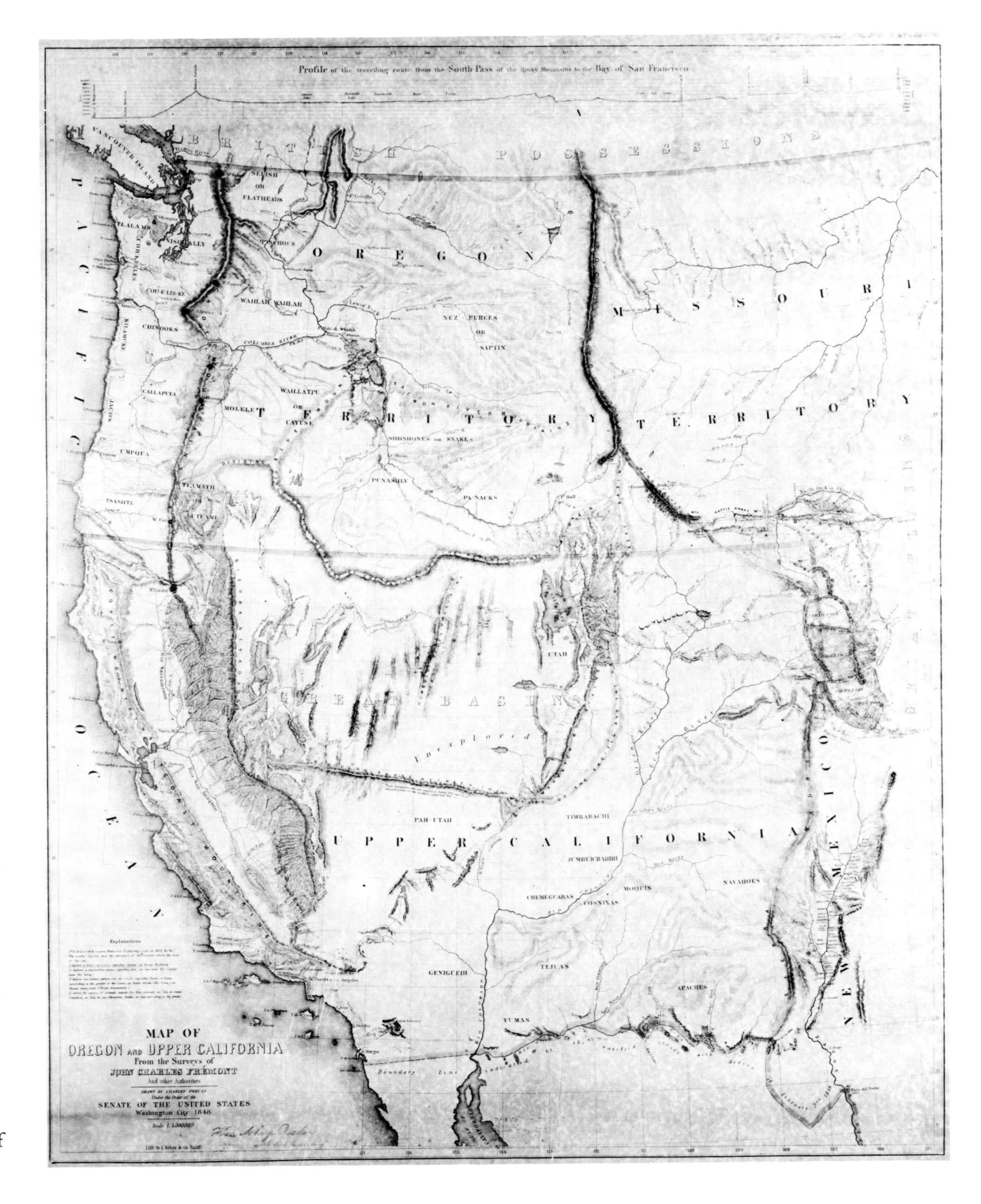

PLATE 171: Charles Preuss. "Map of Oregon and Upper California From the Surveys of John Charles Frémont And other Authorities." 1848. Lithograph, 69 × 87 cm. Records of the U.S. Senate, National Archives, Washington, D.C. *Most accurate general map of the Far West for its time. The German cartographer Charles Preuss incorporated geographical information obtained by Frémont between 1842 and 1847. Conveys the incorrect impression that the interior basin of present-day Nevada was encircled by ranges of mountains. Lithographed by E. Weber and Company, Baltimore, and published by order of the U.S. Senate in Frémont's comprehensive* Geographical Memoir Upon Upper California in Illustration of His Map of Oregon and California.

Steubenville, Ohio, lithograph from North American Scenery, *1846*

Two of the more prodigious producers of county maps were Robert Pearsall Smith and Henry F. Walling, whose combined output numbered more than 580 county maps. Smith's firm was located in Philadelphia, Walling's in Boston and later in New York City. Together with other publishers they mapped in detail the Northeast and parts of Ohio and Michigan before the Civil War. These maps varied in size but generally ranged from five to six feet square (*Plate 169*). The basic surveying information was obtained from traveling along existing roads; direction was determined by the surveyor's compass and distance by the odometer wheel. In addition to showing various cultural and physical features, these maps also depicted individual buildings and gave the names of residents. Each map included ornate cartouches and borders as well as inset plans of villages and views of selected public buildings, factories, and farms.

While detailed mapping of the Northeast was being initiated in 1846, two important maps of the West appeared in 1847. Mitchell's "A New Map of Texas, Oregon and California with the regions adjoining" depicted the western political situation on the eve of the Mexican War. A composite map, it judiciously incorporated the recent work of Nicollet, Wilkes, Frémont, and Emory. Both the Oregon Trail and the "Caravan route to Santa Fe" are included.

In the same year John Disturnell first printed his "Mapa de los Estados Unidos de Méjico," which passed through twenty-three editions between 1846 and 1858. Lawrence Martin traces the origin of this map to Henry S. Tanner's 1825 map of Mexico, which in turn had been copied and published in Spanish by the New York firm of White, Gallaher, and White in 1828 (see Bibliography). Disturnell reprinted the 1828 copy in 1846, changing the title, date, and name of publisher; other changes were made on the face of the map, particularly in the Great Basin region. The boundary of the United States is depicted as the Rio Grande in the east and the parallel of 32° 15′ north latitude in the west. This caused San Diego, which lies just north of this line, to be included in the California territory claimed by the United States. In 1848 the seventh state of the 1847 edition of this map was attached to the American copy of the Treaty of Guadalupe Hidalgo which brought to a close the two-year war with Mexico, and added New Mexico, Arizona, Nevada, California, and Utah to the United States (*Plate 170*).

Both of these maps by Mitchell and Disturnell were basically political maps stimulated by the Mexican War. During the war itself, which lasted from May 13, 1846, to February 2, 1848, Army topographical engineers prepared numerous reconnaissance and operations maps and order-of-dattle maps. Many of these were published for general distribution; the order-of-battle maps represented the first extensive use of this type of map by the Federal government.

A military campaign map of considerable significance dating from the same period is entitled "Military Reconnaissance of the Arkansas, Rio del Norte and Rio Gila." It was drawn by Joseph Welch under the direction of Lieutenant William H. Emory of the Corps of Topographical Engineers. Lithographed by E. Weber and Company in 1847, it depicts the route of Brigadier General Stephen W. Kearny's Army of the West from Fort Leavenworth to San Diego. Emory's map was based on the first accurate traverse of the southwest, and when connected with the traverses of Frémont and Wilkes, it provided a basis for a more accurate map of the trans-Mississippi West.

In 1847 the New York firm of Harper and Brothers published a large wall map of the United States and Canada showing the status of canals, railroads, and stage routes. Compiled by Samuel Breese and printed by the cerographic method for Sidney Edwards Morse, it represents the earliest known wall map printed by wax engraving.

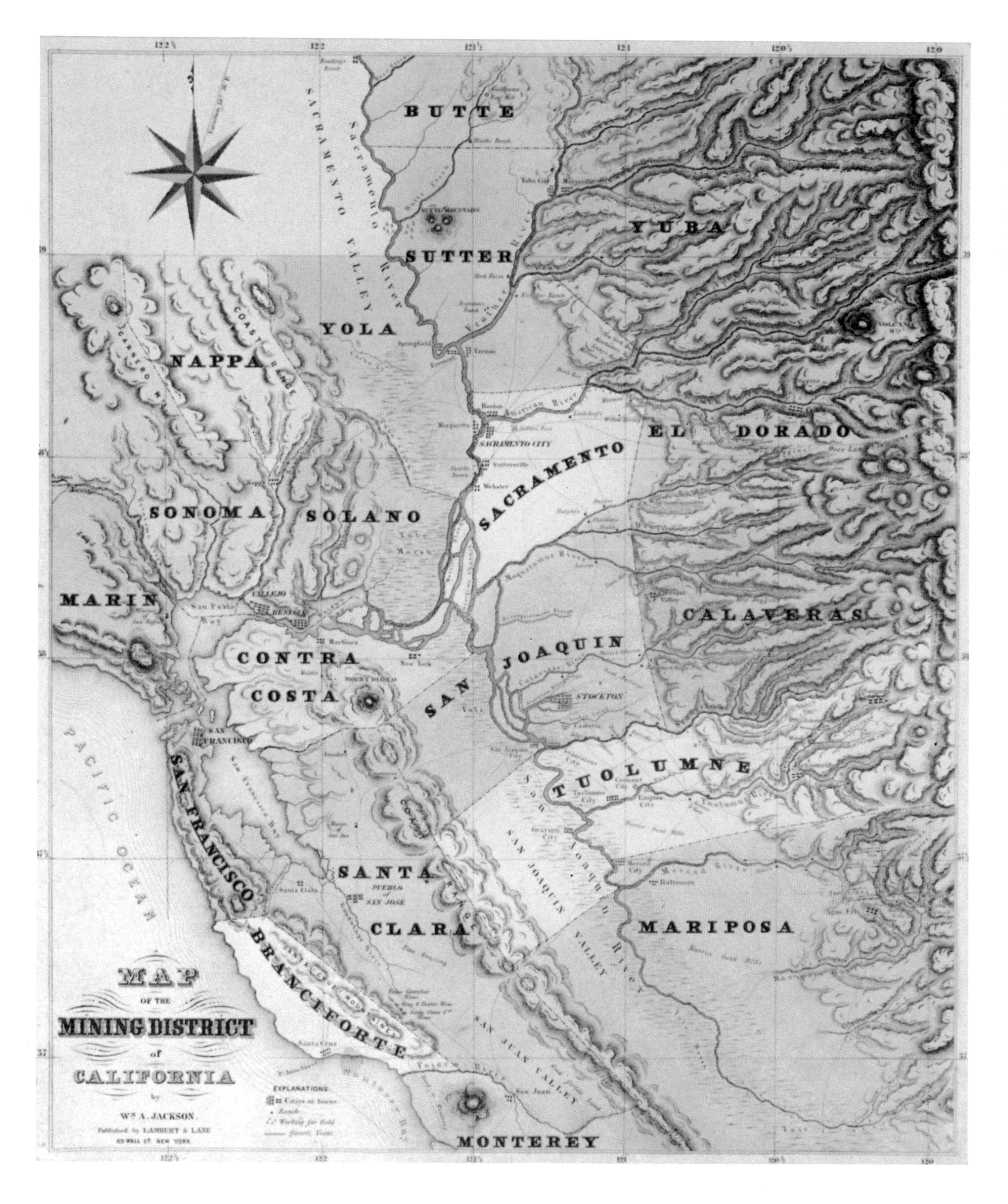

PLATE 172: William A. Jackson. "Map of the Mining District of California." 1851. Lithograph, with watercolor wash; 59 × 50 cm. Geography and Map Division, Library of Congress, Washington, D.C. *Published by Lambert & Lane, New York City. One of the earliest printed maps to depict the California gold mines in operation in 1849 and 1850.*

Town Hall, Northampton, Mass., from Gleason's Pictorial Drawing-room Companion, *1853–55*

Matthew Fontaine Maury produced in 1847 his unprecedented *Wind and Current Chart of the North Atlantic.* As Superintendent of the U.S. Navy Depot of Charts and Instruments (later the U.S. Naval Observatory), Maury developed a series of wind and current charts for ocean navigation based on data contained initially in old ships' logbooks, but supplemented after 1843 by data filled in on blank charts by ships' captains during their voyages. The force and direction of the winds and currents were shown by directional arrows. It has been estimated that Maury's charts could reduce the length of the average voyage between east and west coast ports from 180 to 133 days.

Frémont's epochal map of Oregon and Upper California appeared the following year (*Plate 171*). Drawn by Charles Preuss, it was prepared at the request of Congress through the efforts of Senator Benton, after Frémont had been court-martialed and had voluntarily resigned from the Army for his dubious role in the conquest of California in 1846. This map synthesized the works of earlier cartographers with observations from Frémont's third expedition, 1845–46, and, to quote his own words, it is "the earliest map that shows the structure and configuration of the interior of Upper California." On the eastern shore of Great Salt Lake the Mormon settlements are depicted. Two hypothetical mountain ranges are introduced into Western cartographic lore: these border the Great Basin on the north and the south, and are identified as the dividing ranges "between the waters of the Pacific and the waters of the Great Basin." Frémont's map added many new placenames to the geographical nomenclature of the West, including the Humboldt River, Lake, and Range in present-day Nevada (all named for the great German scientist whose map of 1811 had first portrayed this region; *see Plate 139*), and San Francisco's "Chrysopylae or Golden Gate" (named after the Chrysoceros, the Golden Horn of Constantinople, through whose narrows passed many riches of the Mediterranean world). Erwin Gudde also points out that three foreign geographic terms entered common usage through Frémont's maps of the West: butte, fourche, and canyon (see Bibliography). Finally, on both the south fork of the American River and the upper course of the Feather River, Preuss added the phrase "El Dorado or Gold Regions," one of the earliest graphic announcements of the discovery of gold in California. Some 50,000 copies of the Frémont-Preuss map were printed by order of the U.S. Senate and were widely distributed.

Discovery of gold at Sutter's sawmill in January 1848 spurred the production of western maps as did no other single event, particularly after President James Polk confirmed the discovery in his annual message to Congress on December 5. Frémont's map served as the basic source for subsequent commercial maps of the goldfields published in New York, Philadelphia, London, Paris, and Berlin. While many of the local maps and guides were of

First view of the Southwest, *lithograph after drawing by John Mix Stanley, from W. H. Emory's* Notes of a Military Reconnaissance, *1848*

dubious value, a "Topographical Sketch of the Gold and Quicksilver District of California" merits recognition. Dated July 25, 1848, it was prepared by Lieutenant Edward O. C. Ord of the U.S. Army and published to accompany Polk's message to Congress. Ord's map was copied by J. T. Lawson and sold through advertisements in the *New York Tribune*, beginning January 9, 1849. The important diggings of 1849 and 1850 were depicted on William A. Jackson's "Map of the Mining District of California," lithographed with a color wash in 1851 (*Plate 172*).

Among the valuable natural resources extracted from the ground, gold was not the only one that stimulated map production. An expanding railroad system, the introduction of steam power in manufacturing, and a rapidly advancing iron industry resulted in greater demands for Pennsylvania coal. In 1848 the Dauphin and Susquehanna Coal Company published a map illustrating the coal trade in Pennsylvania. Various anthracite and bituminous coalfields are depicted, along with railroads, canals, and navigable waters. A year later W. F. Robert prepared a much larger map of the anthracite regions and the Montour iron ore range. It was lithographed by P. S. Duval on a newly installed rotary steam press, the first in the United States. Duval, a native of France who settled in Philadelphia, had also undertaken experiments in color lithography as early as 1843.

At mid-century the U.S. Corps of Topographical Engineers published a composite map of the trans-Mississippi West which graphically summarized their geographical knowledge of the region. While those areas which had been politically active during the 1840s were portrayed rather accurately, many blank spots remained on the map of the West, noted only by the terse and tantalizing word "unexplored."

One of those "unexplored" regions was quickly filled in by maps prepared by two brothers, Edward and Richard Kern. Edward Kern's 1849 map recording Colonel John M. Washington's campaign against the Navajo Indians provided new topographic details of the region directly west of New Mexico. It was lithographed on Duval's rotary steam press and forms part of Lieutenant James H. Simpson's *Report* which was published by the Senate in 1850. Richard Kern also had accompanied the Navajo expedition and prepared a number of views that were "printed in color" by Duval, among the earliest chromolithographs to appear in a government report. In 1851 Richard drew a comprehensive "Map of the Territory of New Mexico" which

Co-Co-Pas Indians, lithograph from Report on the United States-Mexican Boundary Survey, *1850–53*

incorporated Edward's work on the Navajo region. Richard and the eldest brother, Benjamin, met tragic deaths in the West, Benjamin murdered in 1849 by angered Utes and Richard slain in 1853 by a group of Paiute Indians while on the ill-starred survey party led by Captain John W. Gunnison.

In the East the demand for more graphic detail found one form of expression in large-scale fire insurance maps of urban areas; these have been described by Walter W. Ristow in an excellent article with that title (see Bibliography). William Perris compiled one of the earliest series of fire insurance maps in the United States at the request of the Jefferson Insurance Company, New York City. This series consisted of large-scale map sheets of New York City, issued between 1852 and 1855. Designed to aid insurance underwriters in computing fire risks on individual buildings, these maps depicted the location and dimensions of all buildings and designated by watercolor tints and symbols the structural materials of which these were composed. Certain high-value commercial, industrial, and public buildings were identified by name. Perris also prepared fire insurance maps for Brooklyn, New York, and for Newark, New Jersey. The Aetna Fire Insurance Company began publishing fire insurance maps in 1855 but it was not until after the Civil War that production really expanded, particularly with the establishing of the Sanborn Map and Publishing Company in 1867 (*Plate 173*). The latter came to

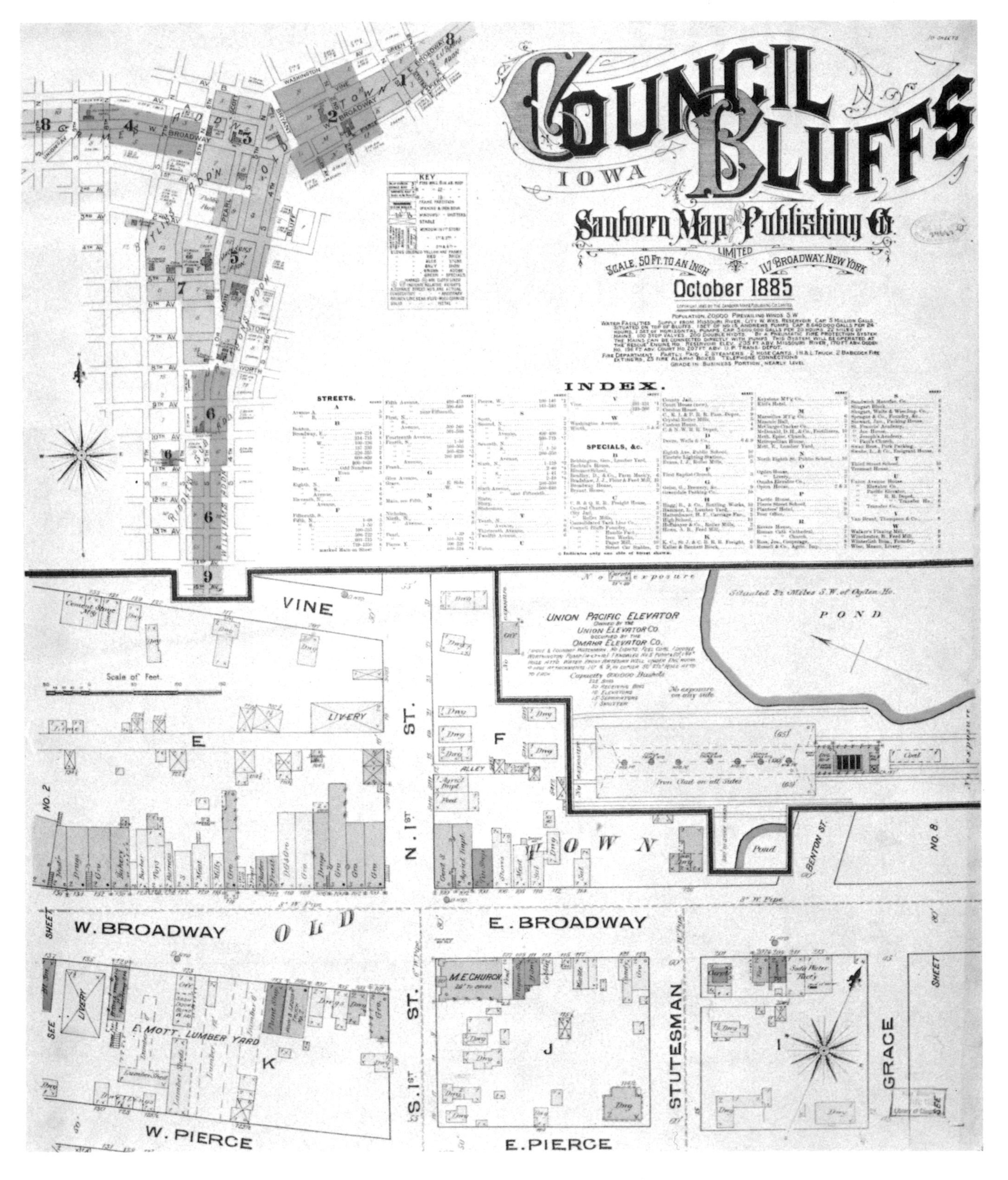

PLATE 173: Sanborn Map and Publishing Company, Limited. "Council Bluffs, Iowa" (portion). 1885. Lithograph, hand colored; each sheet 64 × 54 cm. Geography and Map Division, Library of Congress, Washington, D.C. *Title plate of representative ten-sheet fire insurance map, a unique form of large-scale urban map. Between about 1852 and 1961 these maps provided detailed information on individual buildings in thousands of American towns and cities.*

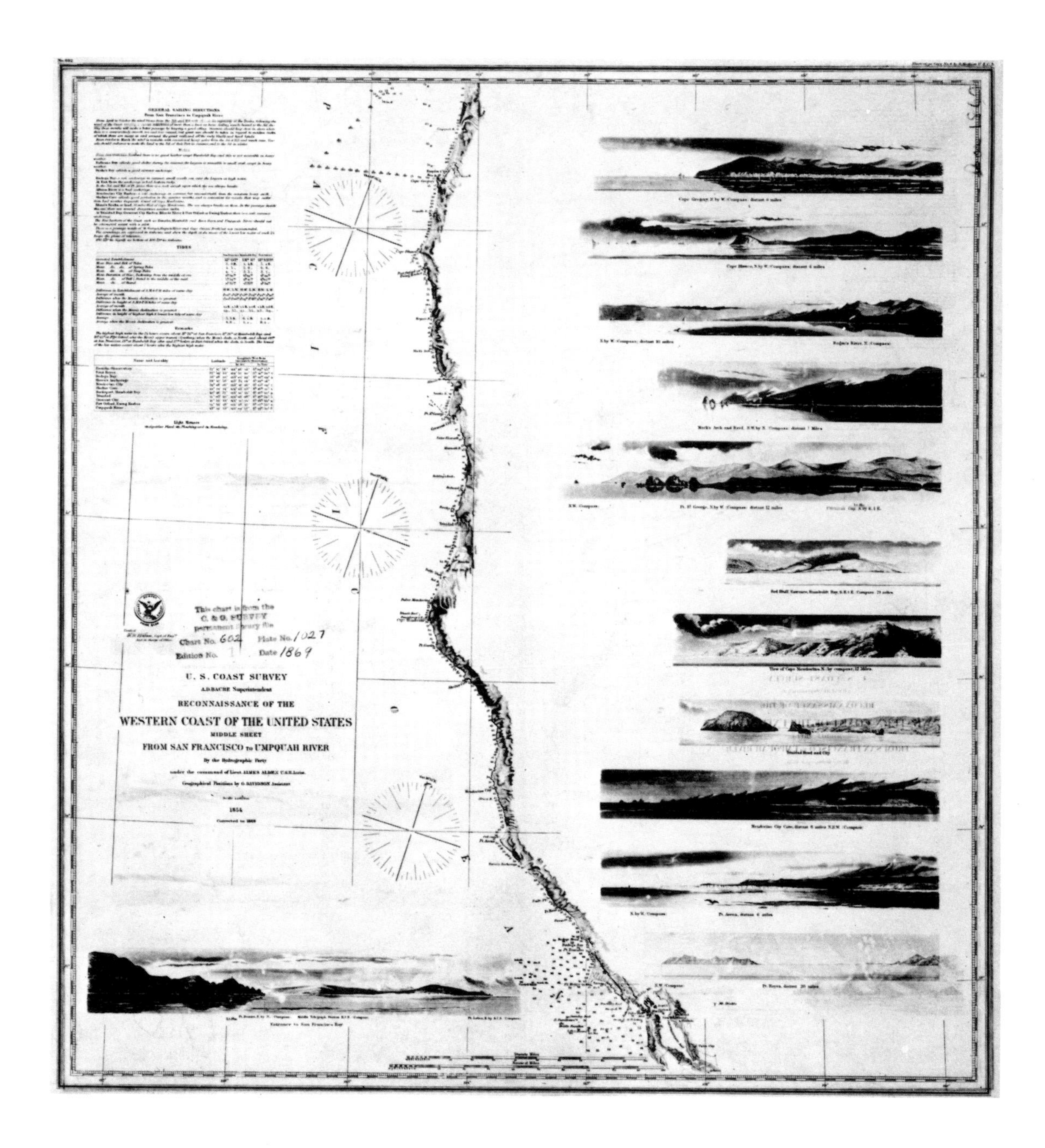

PLATE 174: U.S. Coast Survey. "Reconnaissance of the Western Coast of the United States. Middle Sheet. From San Francisco to Umpquah River . . . under the command of Lieut. James Alden U.S.N. Assist." (1 of three sheets). 1854 (corrected to 1869). Electrotype engraving, 61.5 × 56.5 cm. Records of the Coast and Geodetic Survey, National Archives, Washington, D.C. *Drawn by W. B. McMurtrie; reduced for engraving by A. Lindenkohl; engraved by G. McCoy, J. Knight, J. L. Hazzard, and G. B. Metzeroth. One of a set of three sheets, presenting the first official scientific reconnaissance charts of the Pacific coast of the United States. Outlines the coastal littoral, depicts dangerous reefs and shoals, and provides offshore bathymetric shoal soundings. Prominent headlands are illustrated as seen from the sea, with compass bearings.*

dominate this unique and specialized form of cartographic representation until 1961, when it discontinued the fire insurance atlas series. At the height of its commercial success, in 1939, Sanborn provided map coverage for almost 13,000 urban areas.

Charting of the coastal perimeter of the United States was expanded during the 1850s to include the Great Lakes and the Pacific coast. Official charts of the Great Lakes were prepared by the U.S. Lake Survey, established in 1841 under the aegis of the Corps of Topographical Engineers to survey and chart these waters. The charts began to be issued in 1852 when black-and-white harbor charts of Lake Erie were printed for distribution. Army engineers had surveyed parts of the "northern and north-western lakes," as the Great Lakes were then called, as early as 1816, but the real impetus for charting them was the opening of

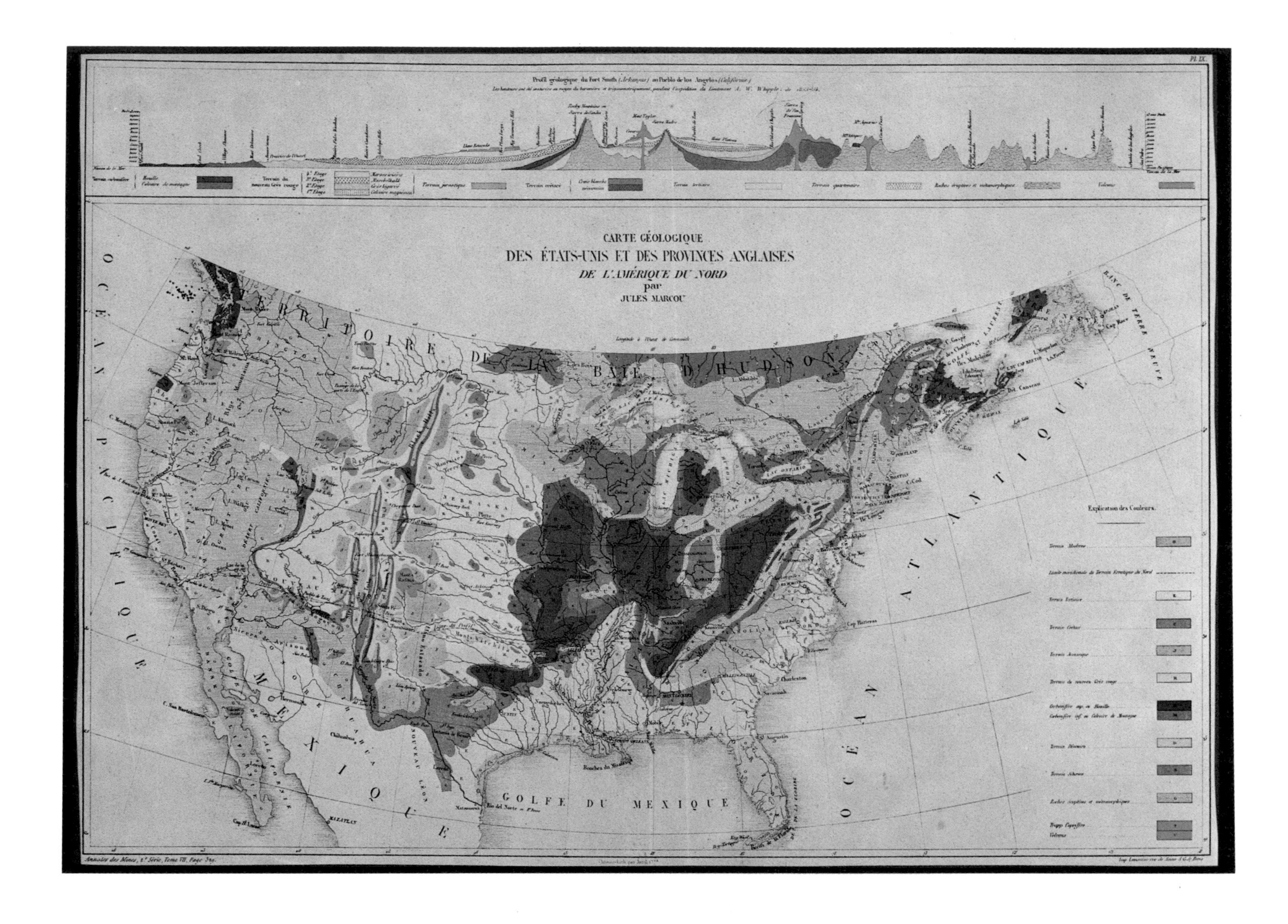

the Erie Canal in 1825, which provided an inexpensive mode of transporting surplus commodities from the interior. By 1841 shipping on the lakes had increased to the extent that navigational aids seemed desirable. As a result, the entire Great Lakes system was surveyed and charted between 1841 and 1881 and a series of seventy-nine charts were issued; these varied in scale from harbor charts to sailing charts. A three-sheet chart of Lake Superior, issued from 1870 to 1873, is the earliest of the sailing charts. Soundings were shown in feet and carried generally only to sixteen feet of depth; near the shoreline, depths were also represented by bathymetric or submarine contours. Like U.S. Coast Survey charts, a fringe of shoreline topography was also included, which varied with the scale of the chart. Surface relief was depicted by hachures. By the end of the century charts were being issued in two colors, depth represented by graduated blue tints and surface relief by a combination of brownish tint, oblique shading, and (*opposite*) PLATE 175: Jules Marcou. "Carte Géologique des Etats-Unis et des Provinces Anglaises de L'Amérique du Nord." 1855. Color lithograph, 41.5 × 58.5 cm. Geography and Map Division, Library of Congress, Washington, D.C. *Early color lithographic map depicting the geology of the United States from coast to coast. The geological profile of a line from Fort Smith, Arkansas, to "Pueblo de" Los Angeles, California, was based on barometric and trigonometric surveys undertaken by Lieutenant Amiel Weeks Whipple during the Pacific Railroad Surveys, 1853–55. Marcou's map was published in Paris in the* Annales des Mines.

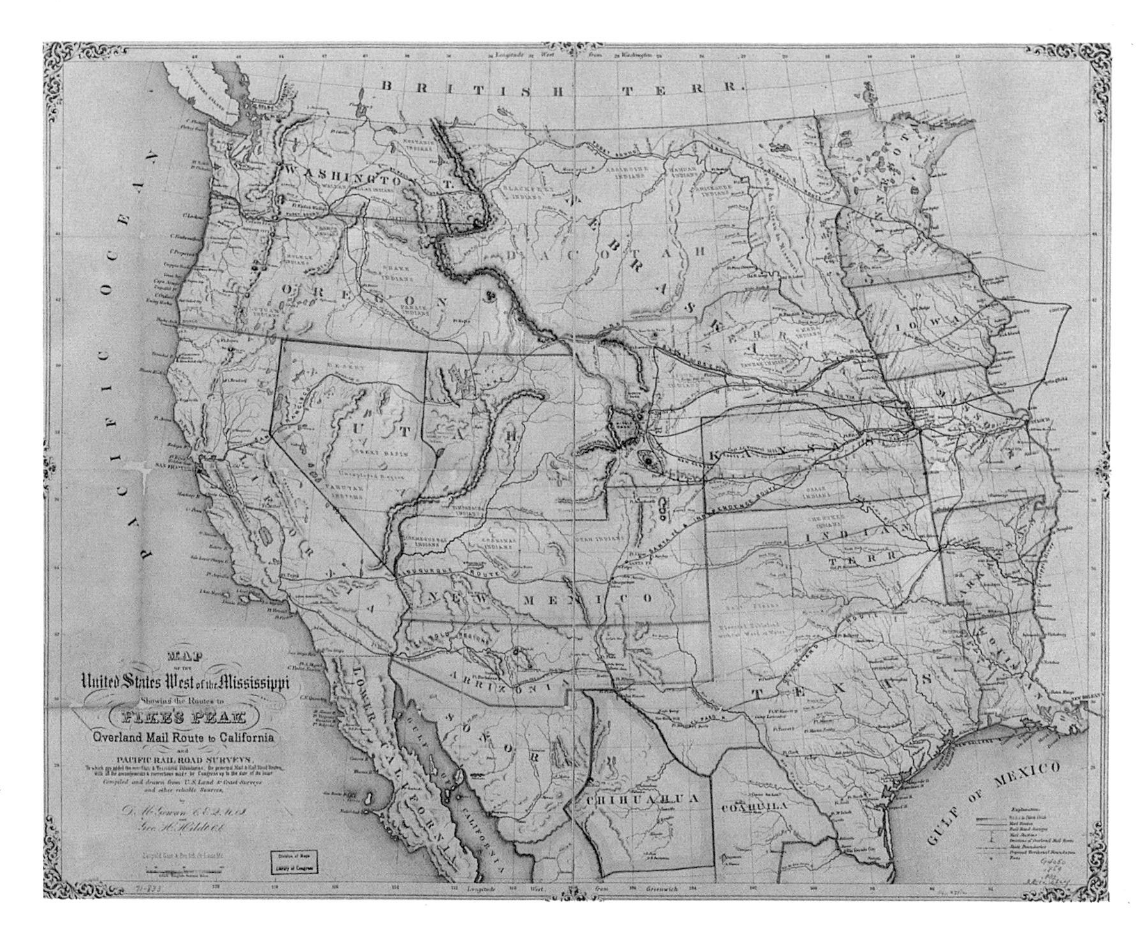

PLATE 176: D. McGowan and George H. Hildt. "Map of the United States West of the Mississippi Showing the Routes to Pike's Peak [,] Overland Mail Route to California[,] and Pacific Rail Road Surveys . . . ." 1859. Lithograph, hand colored; 58 × 72 cm. Geography and Map Division, Library of Congress, Washington, D.C. *Early commercial map lithographed by Leopold Gast and Brother, St. Louis; it depicts the four major routes of the Pacific Railroad Surveys, which were undertaken by the War Department from 1853 to 1855 in an effort to determine the most suitable route between the Mississippi Valley and the Pacific coast. One of the first maps to show gold regions near Denver and along the Gila River.*

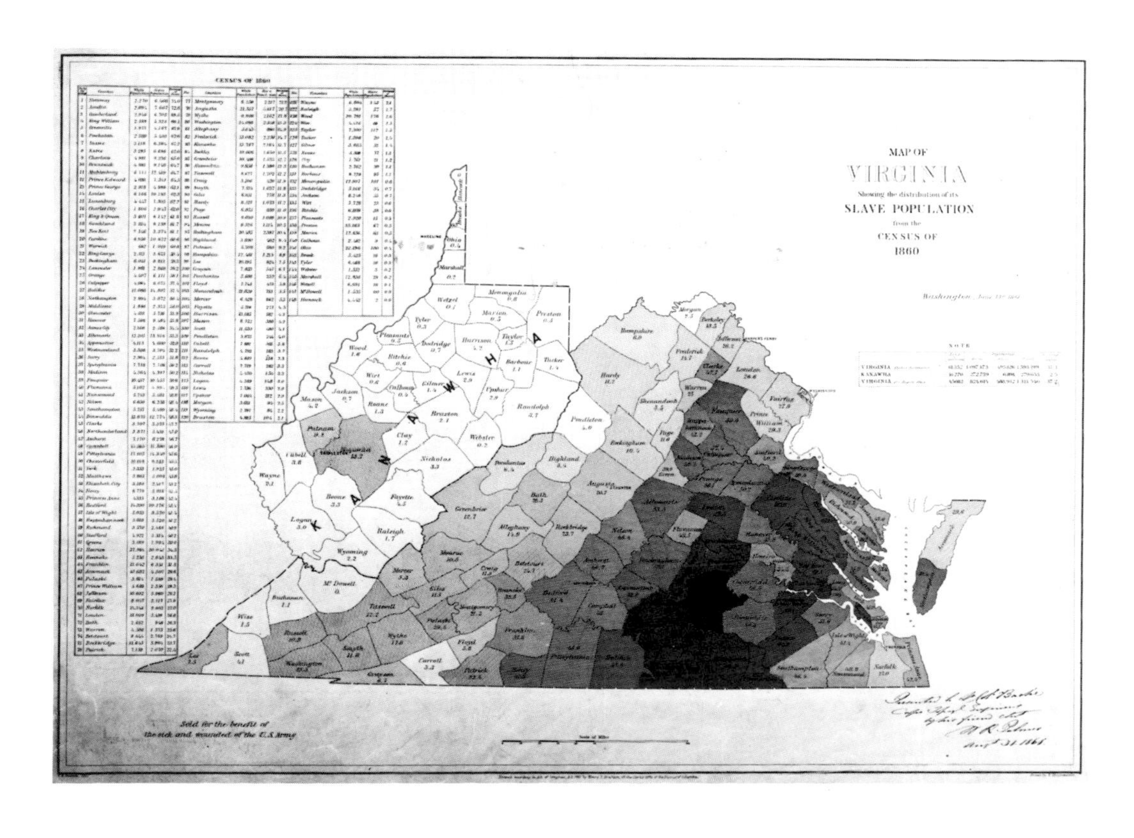

PLATE 177: E. Hergesheimer. "Map of Virginia Showing the distribution of its Slave Population from the Census of 1860." 1861. Lithograph, 51 × 76 cm. Records of the Office of the Chief of Engineers, National Archives, Washington, D.C. *Published by C. B. Graham, Washington, D.C. One of several maps prepared to illustrate one of the causes of the American Civil War and sold to aid sick and wounded Northern soldiers. An early example of statistical mapping, utilizing tonal tints and patterns to show quantitative distribution derived from data obtained through the decennial census. On September 9, 1861, this map was certified as accurate by Joseph C. G. Kennedy, Superintendent of the Eighth Census of the United States.*

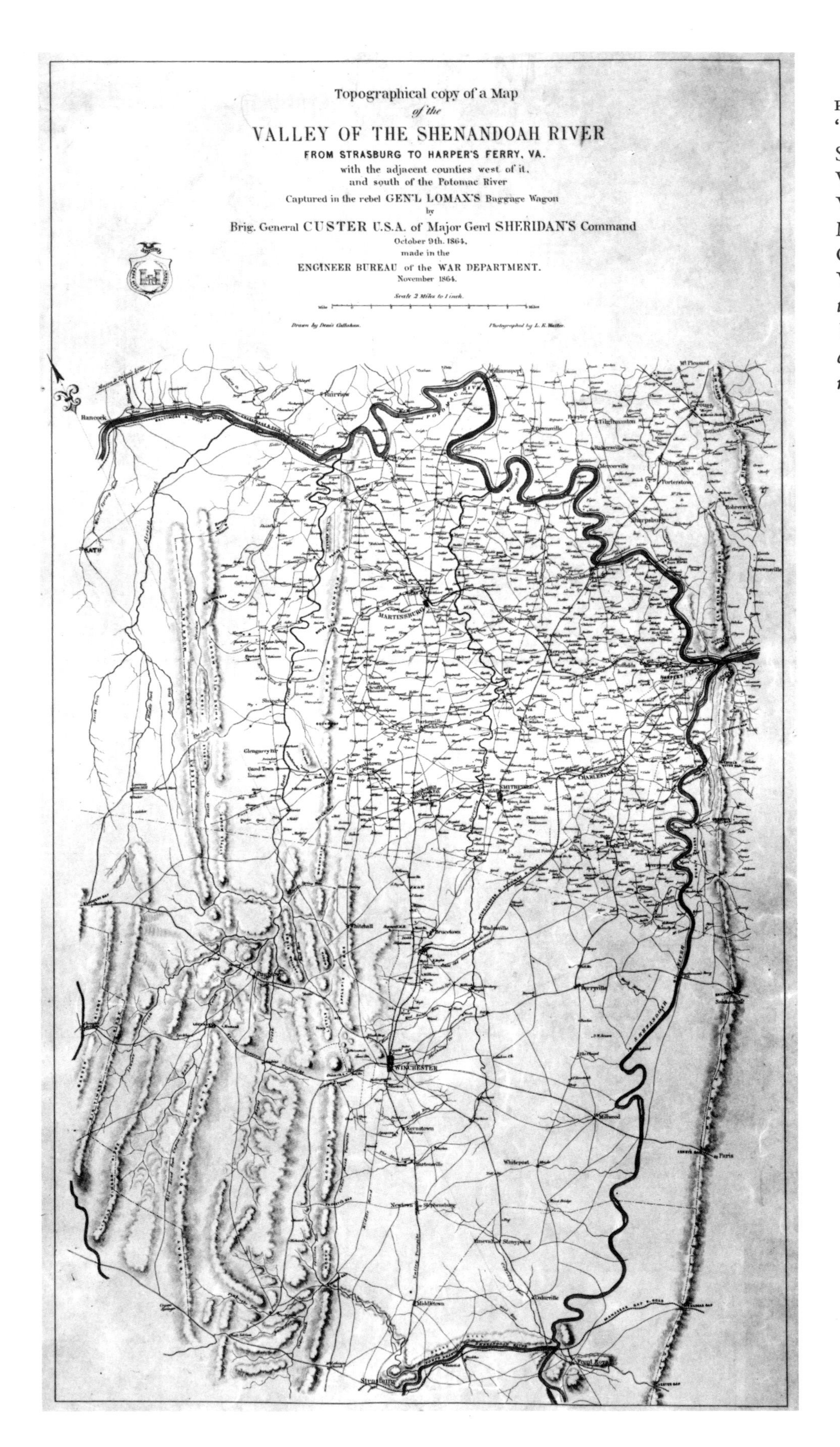

PLATE 178: Army of Northern Virginia (Confederate). "Topographical copy of a Map of the Valley of the Shenandoah River From Strasburg to Harper's Ferry, Va. . . . Captured in the rebel Gen'l Lomax's Baggage Wagon by Brig. General Custer U.S.A. . . ." 1864. Manuscript, pen and ink; 84.5 × 47 cm. Records of the Office of the Chief of Engineers, National Archives, Washington, D.C. *Manuscript copy of a Confederate map of the northern half of the economically important Shenandoah Valley, captured by General George Armstrong Custer's cavalry unit. This map was photographed in multiple copies for rapid distribution to Union commanders.*

(opposite) PLATE 179: J. R. Gilliss. "Map Showing Defences of Cincinnati Covington & Newport." 1862. Manuscript, pen and ink with watercolor wash; 62 × 92.5 cm. Records of the Office of the Chief of Engineers, National Archives, Washington, D.C. *Detailed military map of a strategic river port on the Ohio River at the beginning of the Civil War. Prepared under the direction of Major James H. Simpson and Captain William E. Merrill, Topographical Engineers, Military Department of the Ohio. Depicts the location of military fortifications, batteries, rifle pits, roads, and such military obstructions as felled timber, orchards, and buildings.*

contours. All charts were printed from copperplate engravings, and their quality compared favorably with that of the U.S. Coast Survey charts.

Surveying of the Pacific coast by the U.S. Coast Survey began in 1849 but the first relatively accurate reconnaissance chart of the coast was not issued until 1854 (*Plate 174*). It was prepared in three sheets under the direction of Lieutenant James Alden. Shore features were depicted by carefully sketched headlands.

Disturnell's 1853 political map of the West entitled "New Map of California, Oregon, Washington, Utah and New Mexico" portrayed numerous counties and towns, particularly in California, Utah, and the recently organized Washington Territory. Most dramatic was the depiction of the counties of Utah that extend from the front ranges of the Rocky Mountains on the east to the crests of the Sierra Nevada on the west, in an effort by the Mormon legislature to gain political control over their large, uninhabited Territory.

Mission of San José, Texas, drawing by John R. Bartlett, 1850

Mission of San Diego, Calif., sketch by Henry C. Pratt, 1852

A strip of Mexican land south of the Gila River, known as the Gadsden Purchase, was first added to the map of the United States by Herman Ehrenberg in 1854, shortly after it was obtained by James Gadsden, United States Minister to Mexico. A native of Germany, Ehrenberg participated in the Texas Revolution and was active in the southwest as a surveyor, mining engineer, and cartographer for some three decades prior to his death at the hands of Indians in 1866. Ehrenberg's "Map of the Gadsden Purchase, Sonora and portions of New Mexico, Chihuahua and California" shows the "Probable Route" of a southern railroad passing through this strip of territory, the main reason for securing the land and altering the boundary line. The map was lithographed in San Francisco by Alexander Zakreski, a former Polish Army officer, and it is, according to Carl Wheat, one of the earliest maps to be published in the Far West.

Color printing of maps was introduced to America in the mid-1850s. Early claimants for this honor include a geological map of the Pennsylvania coalfields compiled by R. C. Taylor and published by Bowen and Company in Philadelphia in 1854, and a "Map of Alabama" prepared by J. H. Colton and Son of New York City in 1855. More significant is Dr. Jules Marcou's chromolithograph of a geological map portraying the entire United States from coast to coast (*Plate 175*). The latter was based on data obtained during his duties as U.S. geologist to one of the U.S. Pacific Railroad expeditions. Marcou, a Frenchman and protégé of the scientist Louis Agassiz, had come to America in 1848 and had published a geological map of the United States and the British provinces of North America in 1853. This map, which extended as far west as Denver, Colorado, was colored by hand. In the spring of 1853 Marcou joined Lieutenant Amiel Weeks Whipple's exploration of a railroad route near the thirty-fifth parallel of latitude which took him from Fort Smith, Arkansas, to the Pacific coast. Back in Washington, D.C., the following year, the geologist was taken ill; he returned to Europe to regain his strength and prepare a report and map based on data gathered by the Whipple expedition. Secretary of War Jefferson Davis, however, insisting that the report be completed in the United States, had Marcou's official notebooks seized upon his arrival in Paris. The result, writes H. Andrew Ireland, was that Marcou's account of the trip and his geological map of the United States were published initially in French rather than English, and that both were "made from memory, personal notes, and use of his map of 1853." Editions of this map in German and English were printed in 1855 and 1858, respectively.

Marcou's map displays twelve geological patterns obtained by using eight colors in combination with ruled lines and dots. A colored cross section at the top of the map shows subsurface features along a line stretching from Fort Smith to Los Angeles.

While it has inaccuracies, Ireland claims that "it was the first United States map showing the geology to the Pacific Coast."

In 1855 Secretary of War Davis issued a preliminary map by the Office of Pacific Railroad Surveys showing four proposed routes for a trans-Mississippi railroad. These railroad surveys were conducted by the War Department from 1853 to 1855, during which time each of the four principal routes was examined in detail. The result was a mass of scientific and topographic data collected and distilled in thirteen volumes and culminating in Lieutenant Gouverneur K. Warren's fundamental master map of the trans-Mississippi West. Published in Volume XI of the *Pacific Railroad Reports* in 1857, Warren's map represents the first adequate topographic treatment of the entire West based on field reconnaissance surveys. Compiled by Edward Freyhold and Baron F. W. Egloffstein, a Prussian artist and cartographer, this map was accompanied by a detailed essay that enumerated and evaluated some seventy western maps, accumulated by the War Department over nearly fifty years. Warren's map was printed by Julius Bien, a German-born lithographer who had persuaded Secretary of War Davis that he could improve the generally low standards of map typography in the United States. Following his work on this map and the accompanying illustrations, Bien became a major publisher of geographical and geological reports and maps

California gold diggers on the Sacramento River, lithograph

prepared by the Federal government until his death in 1909. "During his long career," observed W. L. G. Joerg, "Bien did more than any other to create and establish scientific standards in American cartography" (see Bibliography). Warren's work remained the standard map of the West for twenty-five years. Revisions made in 1868 and 1879 incorporated later War Department explorations of the headwaters of the Missouri and Yellowstone rivers, the Great Basin, and the Colorado River.

The tumultuous twin issues of slavery and abolition found cartographic expression and illustration in 1856 in William C. Reynold's "Political Map of the United States, Designed to Exhibit the Comparative Area of the Free and Slave States, and the Territory open to Slavery or freedom by the repeal of the Missouri Compromise." Reynold's map also included a statistical table comparing the free and slave states from the census of 1850.

Another map dealing with the distribution of ethnic groups was prepared by William H. Carlton in 1857 to show the areas occupied by Indian tribes in the Pacific Northwest. Compiled under the direction of Isaac I. Stevens, Governor of Washington Territory and Superintendent of Indian Affairs, this manuscript map, now in the National Archives, also contained a tabular census of the Indian population.

A beautiful hand-colored lithograph portraying the West in 1859 is entitled "Map of the United States West of the Mississippi Showing the Routes to Pike's Peak, Overland Mail Route to California, and Pacific Rail Road Surveys" (*Plate 176*). One of the earliest commercial maps depicting the Pacific railroad routes and the Butterfield Overland Mail route from St. Louis to the Pacific Coast, it was prepared by McGowan and Hildt and published in St. Louis. The state and territorial boundaries as delineated reveal a West in political transition: particularly noteworthy is the territory of "Arrizonia," which is shown as a separate political entity, divided horizontally from the southern boundary of New Mexico. The newly discovered goldfields along the Gila River and in the vicinity of Pikes Peak are also labeled.

Matthew F. Maury's impressive and remarkable wall map of the United States was first issued in 1860, on the eve of the Civil War. Measuring 65 inches square, it is embellished with patriotic views of such national symbols as the White House, Mount Vernon, and the projected Washington Monument. An ornately detailed border contains portraits of previous presidents. A number of inset maps are devoted to special themes and display the

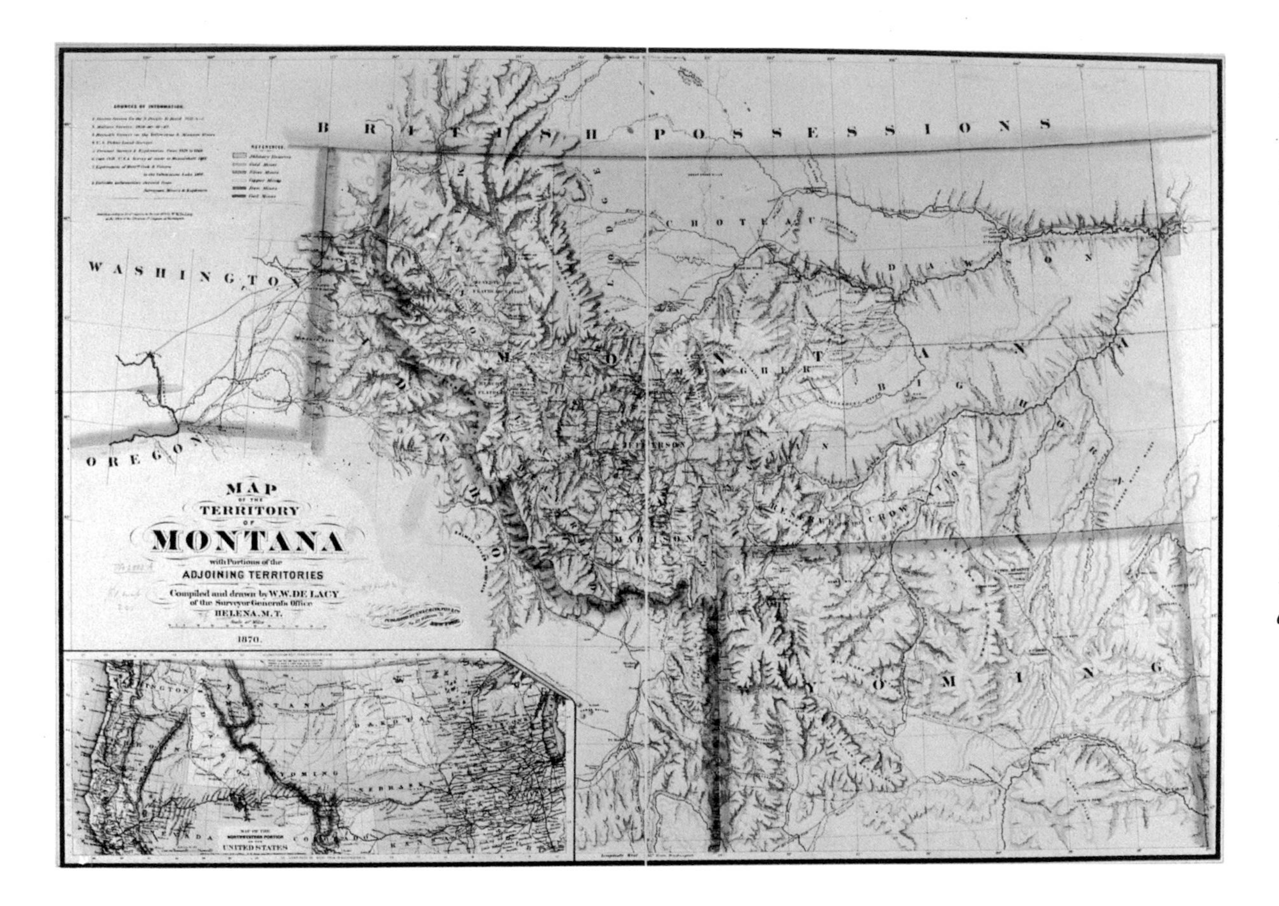

PLATE 180: Walter W. De Lacy. "Map of the Territory of Montana with Portions of the Adjoining Territories." 1870. Wax engraving, hand colored; 74 × 105.5 cm. Geography and Map Division, Library of Congress, Washington, D.C. *Published by G. W. & C. B. Colton and Company, New York City. At the request of the first legislature of the new Territory of Montana, De Lacy prepared a map of Montana in 1865 based on official military and civilian surveys, which was used to lay out the counties. Revised in 1870, De Lacy's new map incorporated for the first time the general geography of the Yellowstone region as provided by C. W. Cook and David E. Folsom from their expedition of 1869. A large inset map of the Northwest shows the proposed route of the Northern Pacific Railroad, which was chartered in 1864 but not completed until 1883.*

distribution of such subjects as agricultural staples, geological strata, climate, and animals. Maury's national map was reprinted in subsequent years, but his name was deleted after the 1861 edition because of his service as commander in the Confederate Navy. The map was published in Washington, D.C., by H. G. Bond and engraved by W. H. Holmes.

The Civil War focused cartographic attention on the Southeast. Thousands of military campaign and reconnaissance maps were produced by the Union and Confederate forces during the four-year conflict from 1861 to 1865. What resulted was some of the most accurate large-scale topographic coverage for parts of this region until well into the twentieth century.

An intriguing series of maps that vividly reveal one of the major causes of the war was published shortly after hostilities commenced. Based on the 1860 census, these maps show the distribution of the slave population in individual southern states and for the region as a whole (*Plate 177*). The maps were published privately in Washington, D.C., and "Sold for the benefit of the sick and wounded of the U.S. Army." In addition to graphically documenting one of the underlying social and economic reasons for the war, these statistical maps represent probably the first attempt to display U.S. Census data in cartographic format.

At the beginning of the war neither side had adequate maps of the critical theaters of operation. Confederate Brigadier General Richard Taylor wrote in 1862, regarding the Peninsular Campaign, that "Confederate commanders know no more of the topography than they did about central Africa." Guides, noted the historian H. V. Canan, substituted for maps for the Confederate forces until General Robert E. Lee appointed Albert H. Campbell as Chief Topographer for the Army of Northern Virginia (see Bibliography). Campbell established an office in Richmond in June 1862 which served as the map bureau for the entire

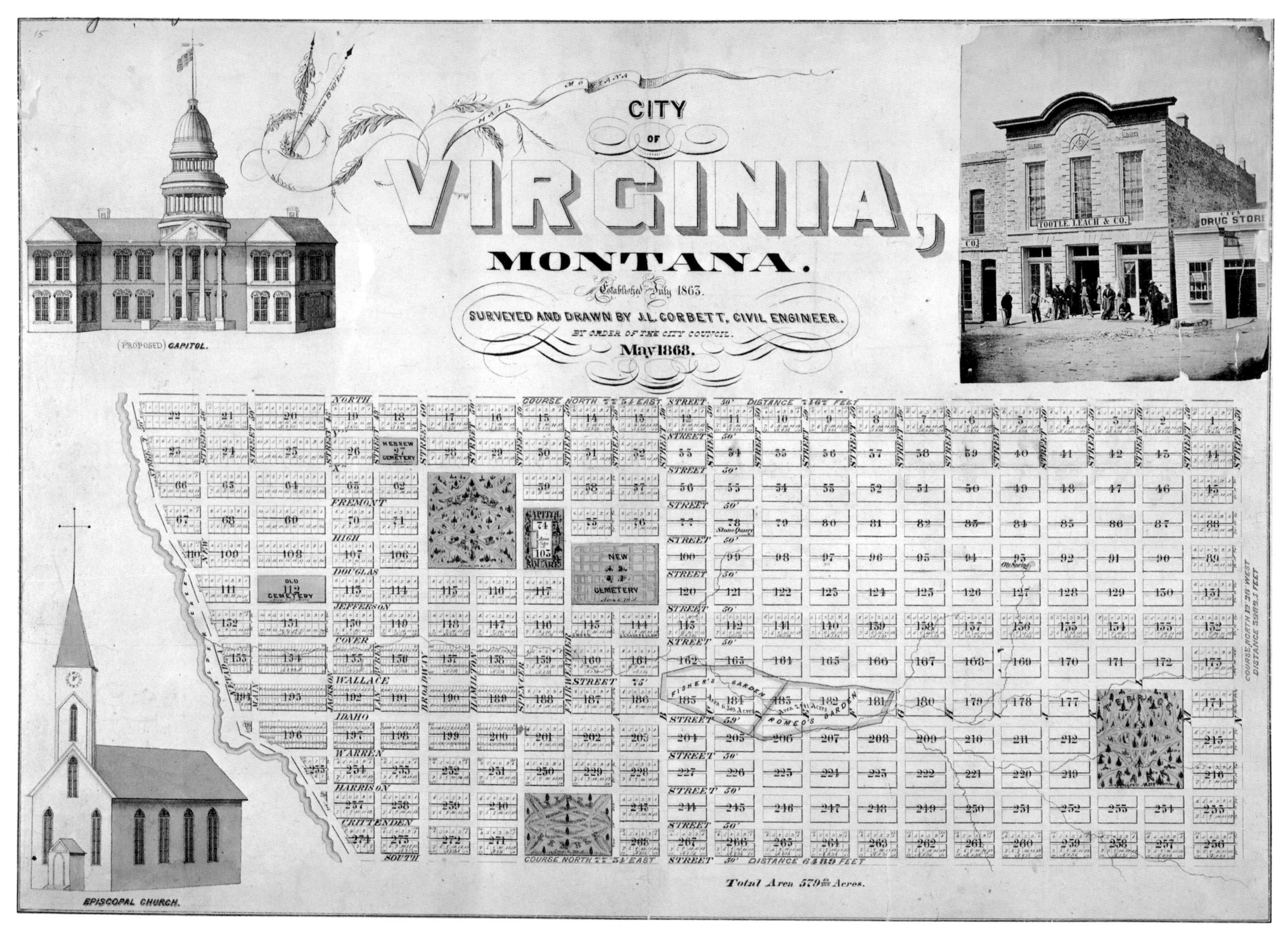

PLATE 181: J. L. Corbett. "City of Virginia, Montana." 1868. Manuscript, pen and ink with color and photographic inset; 55.5 × 77.5 cm. Records of the Bureau of Land Management, National Archives, Washington, D.C. *Townsite plat of Virginia City, shortly after the town was established in July 1863. Prepared by order of the City Council for the General Land Office, to aid in the disposition of Federal land. Three city parks reveal the influence of the eastern states in their landscape design.*

Confederacy. Although Campbell lacked instruments, tracing linen, paper, inks, and pens, he issued a lithographic map of the "Seat of the War" near the end of that year. It was based on data furnished by field parties. More significant was the preparation of a series of large-scale detailed county maps of Virginia that showed farmhouses and the names of residents, public buildings, roads, railroads, drainage patterns, and general topography (*Plate 178*). Restricted to key commanders in order to prevent their falling into the hands of Union troops, these maps were never widely distributed.

Most notable of the topographers assigned to the various Confederate corps was Major Jedediah Hotchkiss, who served on the staff of General Stonewall Jackson. Many of his detailed maps of Northern Virginia, Maryland, and Pennsylvania have survived and are now in the Hotchkiss Collection at the Library of Congress (see Bibliography, Legear).

Although the South developed a map bureau and topographers were attached to some field armies, the Confederacy never overcame its cartographic deficiencies, either through lack of supplies or absence of trust. Few maps were reproduced in multiple copies and distribution remained greatly circumscribed throughout the war. Union mapping, on the other hand, improved rapidly, particularly after 1863, when field mapping techniques and field reproduction methods were developed, principally by Nathaniel Michler, Chief of Topographical Engineers, Army of the Cumberland and later Army of the Potomac. Michler was succeeded by William E. Merrill, another extremely able topographer (*Plate 179*). Under Michler and Merrill, the Army of the Cumberland devised new photographic procedures so that maps could be quickly updated, copied, and distributed. Civilian members of the Coast Survey charted coastal regions, harbors, and interior waterways.

Immediately after the war, maps were drawn of the various military campaigns and battlefields, to record these events graphically for posterity. The War Department issued these maps both singly and in atlas format. One example entitled "Military Maps illustrating the Operations of the Armies of the Potomac and James, May 4th, 1864 to April 9th, 1865 . . ." depicts in great detail the major battles leading to the siege of Petersburg and Richmond, which ended the war. The maps in this atlas were drawn by John E. Weyss under the direction of Michler and show battle lines, roads, railroads, houses, names of residents, fences, drainage, and vegetation, and relief by hachures. Even more careful treatment of particular features is revealed in the "Map of the Battle Field of Gettysburg" surveyed and drawn under the watchful eye of Army topographer Gouverneur K. Warren, who not only participated in the historic three-day battle but played a central role in this pivotal campaign of the war. Compiled at a scale of 1 inch to 200 feet, this map measures 154 by 152 inches. It was used as the base map for compiling a set of three

"The cradle and manner of using it," Orientals engaged in gold mining, wood engraving from The Miners Own Book, *San Francisco, 1858*

smaller maps showing the respective troop positions on July 1st, 2nd, and 3rd, 1863, which were published in 1876, 1883, and 1912.

Work on the order-of-battle maps culminated in the publication of the *Atlas to Accompany Official Records of the Union and Confederate Armies* in 1891–95, issued in 37 parts. This cartographic catalog of the war consists of 175 plates, each containing five or six smaller maps, and illustrating in all some 350 battles, engagements, actions, and skirmishes fought during the four-year conflict. The plates were printed in color by the New York firm of Julius Bien.

Cartographic activities in the West continued unabated during this postwar period, spurred by the redrawing of the political boundaries of interior states and territories, and the discovery of gold in Nevada, Idaho, and Montana (Kansas had been admitted to the Union in 1861, Nevada in 1864; Arizona, Colorado, Dakota, Idaho, and Montana were organized as territories during the war years). Like their eastern counterparts three decades earlier, nearly all of these new states and territories had their own cartographers who prepared state and territorial maps for administrative purposes, often at the request of state and territorial legislatures (*Plate 180*). These cartographers included Henry DeGroot, Nevada; William Gilpin, Colorado; Richard Gird,

Arizona; B. A. M. Froiseth, Utah; Walter W. De Lacy, Montana; and Charles de LaBaume, Idaho.

Numerous maps of the regions of gold and silver mines, and of the towns which sprang up to service them, were also prepared during the 1860s. One of the most visually appealing is a townsite plat of Virginia City, a mining camp established in 1863 during the Montana gold rush which has come to epitomize the mining frontier (*Plate 181*). Townsite plats of western towns were prepared to aid city officials in the sale of town lots and were generally posted at the local Land Office. They show blocks, lots, streets, and alleys, usually partitioned in the traditional rectangular grid pattern common to nineteenth-century American towns and cities. The plat of Virginia City is notable for depicting landscaped parks in a formal manner which contrasts sharply with the conventional image of western towns as primitive and unplanned.

"A fortune made," from "Tipos Californianos," lithograph series

The most significant general map of this period devoted to the West was "Bancroft's Map of the Pacific States." Compiled by William H. Knight, it was published in San Francisco in 1863 by H. H. Bancroft, the publisher-turned-historian who later prepared the distinguished 39-volume work on the *History of the Pacific States of North America*. Knight's map incorporates the latest available information for the region west of the continental divide, and he is credited with first assigning the Indian name of Tahoe to that lake in the California Sierras.

Mapping activities in both East and West expanded dramatically after the Civil War as the emphasis shifted from individual maps to the preparation of map sets or series, often bound in atlas or folio format. One of the first map series to be produced by the Federal government consisted of postal route maps devised especially to aid the newly established free-carrier mail service and railroad mail service, both inaugurated in 1863–64. Between 1866 and 1894 postal route maps were prepared and revised for all the regions of the United States (*Plate 182*). After 1894 the format for this map series was changed from coverage of two or more states to coverage of individual states. Varying in size and scale, postal route maps depicted all post offices and distances between them, mail-carrying railroads, frequency of service, county boundaries, and principal drainage features. They were designed by W. L. Nicholson, a civilian cartographer with the U.S. Coast Survey during the Civil War. Initially colored and tinted manually, after 1883 they were printed by chromolithography—one of the earliest map series issued in this printing technique by the Federal government.

Maps delineating the northwest boundary of the United States from the Strait of Georgia on the Pacific to the summit of the Rocky Mountains were prepared in 1866, thereby completing the cartographic record of the major nineteenth-century boundary negotiations. The set consisted of two general maps and ten detailed maps showing the boundary line as it was surveyed and marked in 1857–61 by the United States Commission led by Commissioner Archibald Campbell and the Chief Astronomer and Surveyor Lieutenant John G. Parke of the U.S. Corps of Topographical Engineers. The detailed maps were drawn and compiled by Lemuel D. Williams, Theodor Kolecki, and Ed-

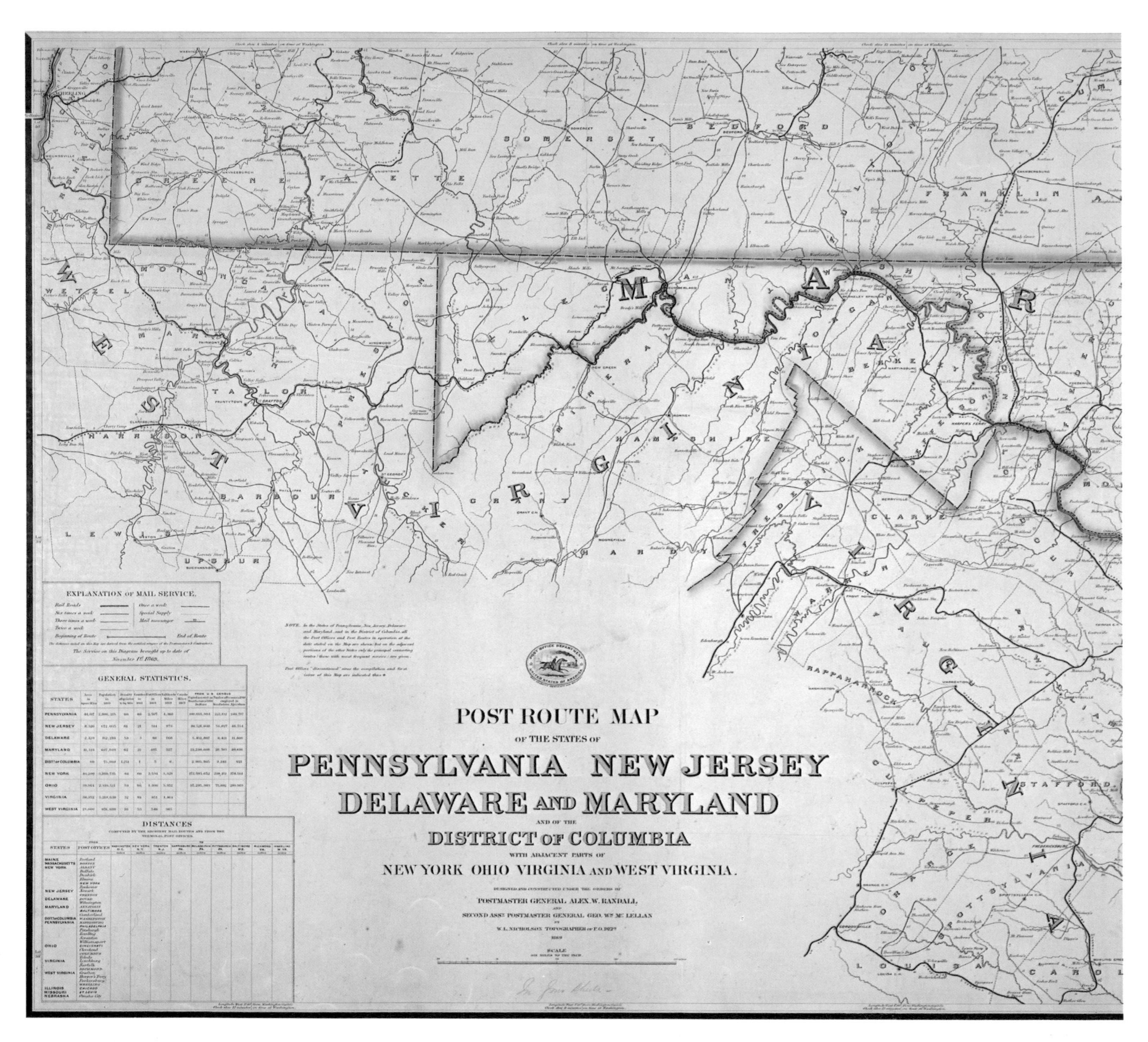

PLATE 182: W. L. Nicholson. "Post Route Map of The States of Pennsylvania[,] New Jersey[,] Delaware and Maryland and of the District of Columbia . . ." (1 of four sheets: "South-West Quarter"). 1869. Engraving, hand colored; 77 × 88 cm. Records of the Post Office Department, National Archives, Washington, D.C. *Presentation copy of title sheet of representative postal route map. This map series was initiated in 1866 to aid the newly established free-carrier mail service and railroad mail service. Depicts and designates post offices, mail routes of all types, frequency of mail delivery, distance between post offices, drainage; and state and county boundaries.*

ward Freyhold, and show all cultural and physical features along the line of survey. The two general maps of the western and eastern sections cover a much greater area, as far south as the mouth of the Columbia River, and incorporate new topographic details and Indian placenames. These maps were accompanied by a series of striking landscape sketches in watercolor drawn by a talented civilian named James Alden, nephew of Lieutenant James Alden of the U.S. Coast Survey who had charted the Pacific coast during the 1850s (*see Plate 174*).

County maps continued to be produced by commercial publishers after the Civil War, notably in Texas and California. But as the market for these detailed land-ownership maps became saturated in the northeastern and north central states, they were supplanted by two other distinctively American cartographic formats—illustrated county and state atlases.

A typical illustrated county atlas consists of detailed township plats, each depicting the same general ownership information found on county maps (*Plate 183A, B*). In addition, however, these atlases contain biographical sketches and lithographic portraits of local landowners, business leaders, and politicians as well as fanciful views of private, public, and commercial buildings. The story of the county atlas is told by Norman J. W. Thrower (see Bibliography). Based on General Land Office surveys and county records, county atlases were sold on a subscription basis for about $10.00 each by salesmen who canvassed the county. The inclusion of the subscriber's own biography, portrait, or view cost him an additional sum ranging from $10.00 to $50.00. Some 750 county atlases were published during the last half of the nineteenth century and, like county maps, their coverage was limited primarily to the rural northeast and midwest. When viewed together, the county atlases are evocative of a prosperous, pastoral landscape that is associated with the life of the period.

Closely related to the county atlas in format and style was the illustrated state atlas. Beginning with Simon J. Martenet's 1866 *Atlas of Maryland*, atlases were produced for some twenty states during the next twenty-five year period. Prominent publishers included Henry Francis Walling of Boston and Alfred T. Andreas of Chicago. Walling, the most prolific producer of state atlases, added thematic or special subject maps to his 1868 *Atlas of the State of Ohio*, a practice soon followed by other publishers. These topical maps generally showed meteorology, geology, and railroads. Andreas is credited by Walter W. Ristow with introducing the concept of illuminating state atlases with portraits and views (see Bibliography). His *Illustrated Historical Atlas of the State of Minnesota*, published in 1874, is a notable example.

You-Pel-Lay, or The Green Corn Dance of the Jémez Indians, *watercolor by Edward Kern, 1849*

Tucson, Arizona, pencil and wash drawing by John R. Bartlett, 1850

The atlas format also was utilized in 1867 by the Sanborn Map and Publishing Company for issuing fire insurance maps, as described above (*see Plate 173*). In the same year Matthew Dripps published a real estate atlas of New York City which included such detailed information as lot and block numbers, dimensions of streets, and locations of buildings. Other real estate atlas pub-

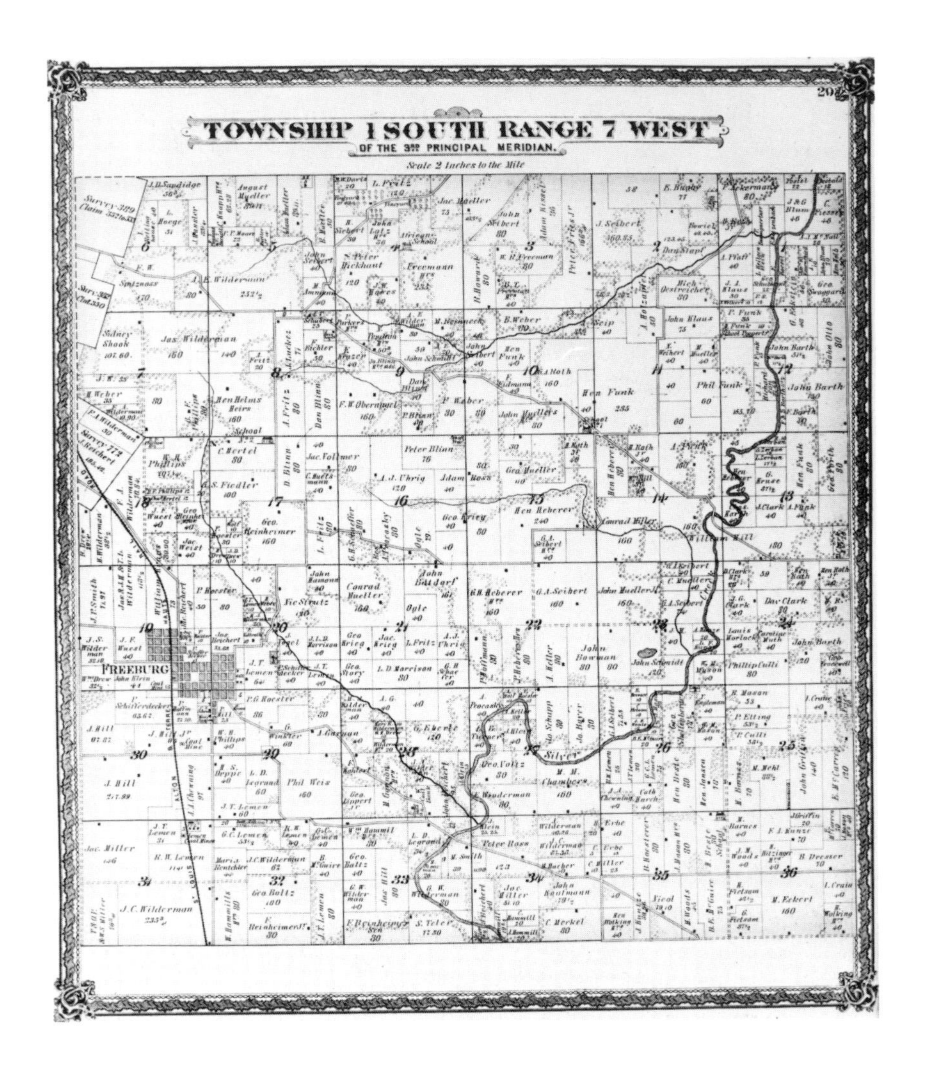

lishers soon followed, including the G. M. Hopkins Company and W. G. Baist Company, both in Philadelphia.

Gouverneur Warren's 1857 general map of the West was revised and redrawn eleven years later for the Corps of Topographical Engineers in 1868 by Edward Freyhold, incorporating the War Department explorations and surveys from 1858 to 1863 of the headwaters of the Missouri River, the Great Basin, and the Colorado River. As Carl Wheat observes in his *Mapping the Transmississippi West*, Freyhold's 1868 map "is the first recognizably modern map of the West, with nearly all the Western States locked into place, like a jigsaw puzzle properly fitted together." Alaska, ceded by Russia to the United States by treaty in 1867, and the Wyoming Territory, organized in 1868, are also shown. Yet patches of "unexplored country" remain, to be filled in by later expeditions, some of these taking place simultaneously with the issuance of this map.

One of these unexplored regions was the headwaters of the Yellowstone River and associated thermal springs, the existence of which was known only from Indian and fur-trapper lore. This region remained unmapped until after 1869, when David Folsom and C. W. Cook of Helena, Montana, visited the Grand Canyon, the falls of the Yellowstone River, Yellowstone Lake, and the Lower Geyser Basin on the Madison River. Their observations were first recorded in 1870 on Walter W. De Lacy's "Map of the Territory of Montana with Portions of the Adjoining Territories" (*see Plate 180*), engraved and printed by Colton. De *(opposite)* PLATE 183 A, B: Warner & Beers. "An Illustrated Historical Atlas of St. Clair Co. Illinois Compiled Drawn & Published from Personal Examinations & Surveys . . ." (2 sheets). 1874. Lithograph, with color wash; each sheet 44.5 × 36.5 cm. Geography and Map Division, Library of Congress, Washington, D.C. *Township plat from representative county atlas, published by Warner & Beers, Chicago. Shows names of landowners, property boundaries and acreage, roads and railroads, churches and schools. On separate page are views of two large farms and residences located in two sections of township.*

PLATE 184: Albert Ruger. "Bird's Eye View of the City of Council Bluffs. Pottawattamie Co. Iowa." 1868. Lithograph, 56 × 70 cm. Geography and Map Division, Library of Congress, Washington, D.C. *Representative panoramic map of a small midwestern city; printed by Merchant's Lithographing Company, Chicago. This characteristically American type of map was used to depict American cities and towns from 1870 to 1920, particularly in the East and Midwest.*

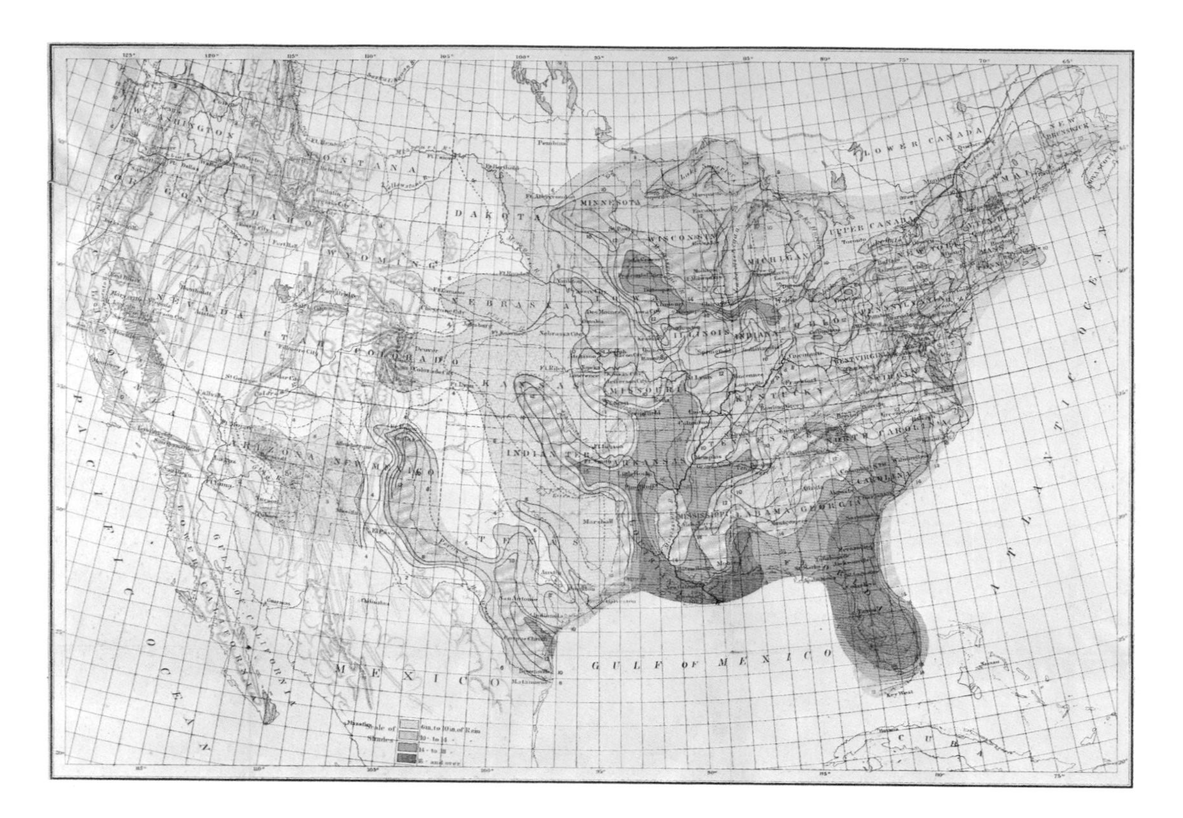

PLATE 185: Joseph Henry. "Rain-Chart of the United States . . ." 1872 (2nd edition, corrected from 1870). Chromolithograph, 43.5 × 57.5 cm. Records of the Office of the Chief of Engineers, National Archives, Washington, D.C. *Weather chart illustrating the average precipitation for the summer months by isohyetal lines (lines of equal precipitation), and color tints and patterns. Prepared under the direction of Professor Joseph Henry, Secretary of the Smithsonian Institution, from meteorological data telegraphed in by recording stations throughout the eastern United States. Base chart engraved by H. Lindenkohl; lithograph published by J. F. Gedney, Washington, D.C.*

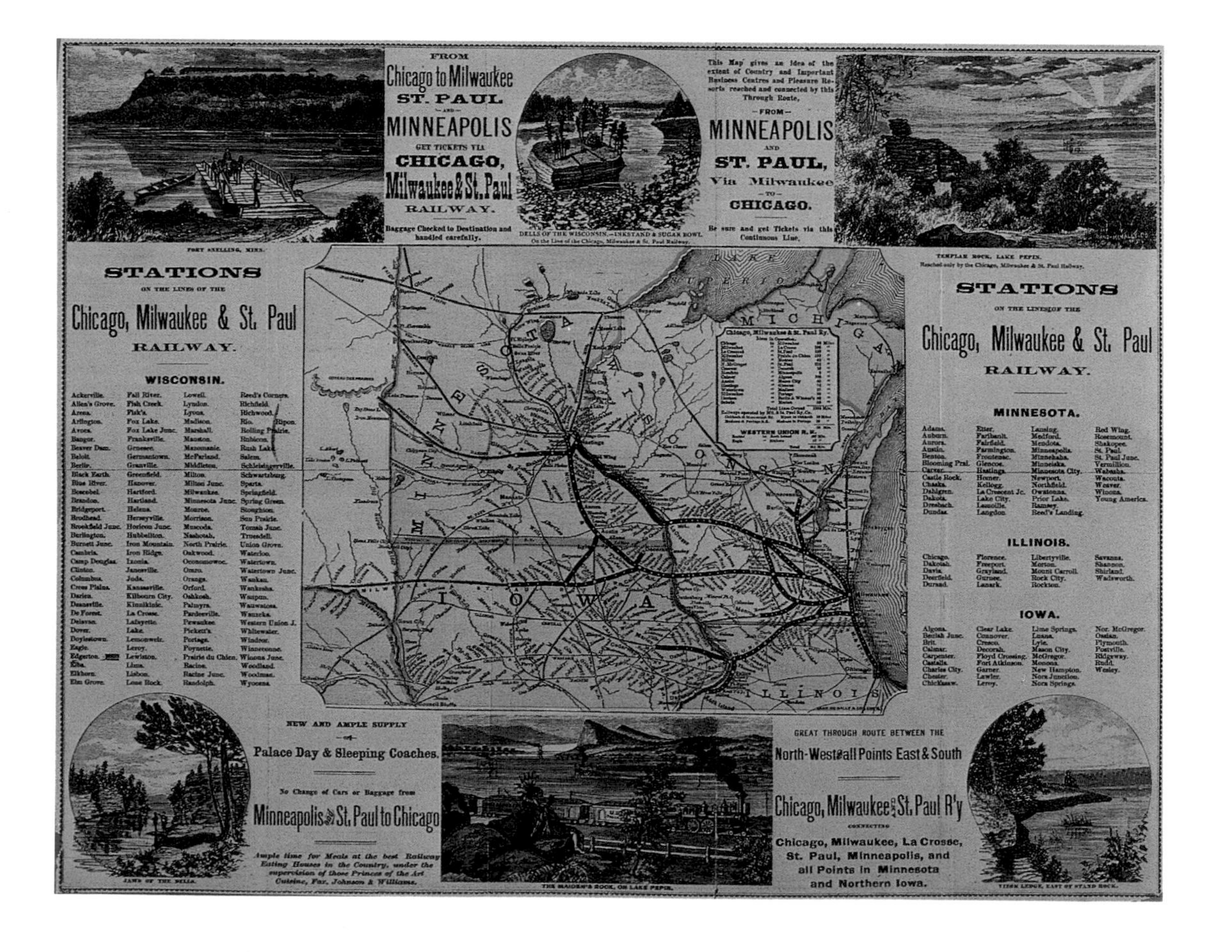

PLATE 186: Rand McNally and Company. "Map of the Chicago, Milwaukee & St. Paul Railroad." 1874. Wax engraving, 35 × 45 cm. Geography and Map Division, Library of Congress, Washington, D.C. *Promotional map depicting railroad lines in north central states. Published in Chicago by Rand McNally (now one of the world's leading commercial mapmakers) shortly after they began to print maps in 1872. Scenic views of the region border the map, and lists of stations and affiliated railways, with mileages. Maps such as this were circulated among immigrant groups by railroad companies to encourage settlement along their lines.*

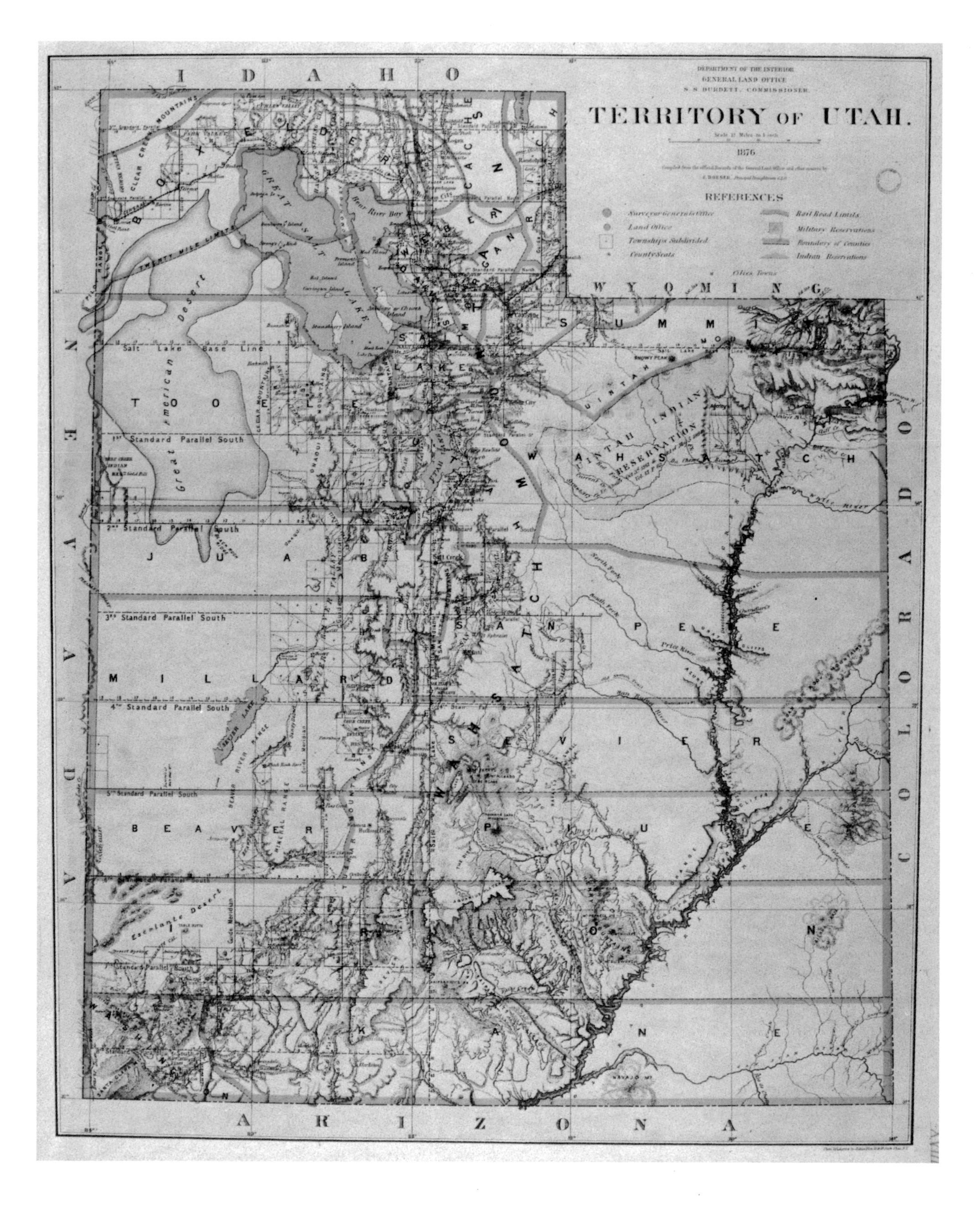

PLATE 187: C. Roeser. "Territory of Utah." 1876. Photolithograph in color, 68.5 × 81.5 cm. Records of the Bureau of Land Management, National Archives, Washington, D.C. *Published by Julius Bien, New York City, for the U.S. General Land Office. A typical territorial map issued by the General Land Office to show the disposition of Federal land in the public domain. Depicts the extent of public land surveys, limits of land-grant railroads, county boundaries, and Indian and military reservations. The "Great American Desert," the term Major Stephen H. Long used in 1820 to describe the West (see Plate 148), is portrayed on this map as a small, localized area southwest of Great Salt Lake. From the General Land Office's centennial atlas entitled* Geographical and Political Atlas of the States and Territories of the United States of America in which the Public Land Surveys are now in operation.

Volunteer fire brigade racing to fire, Philadelphia, 1840s, lithograph

Lacy was a draftsman in the U.S. Surveyor General's office in Helena, Montana. Later that year Lieutenant Gustavus C. Doane prepared "a general map of the country" from a personal reconnaissance of the region. Doane's manuscript map, now in the National Archives, provides the earliest detailed portrayal of the area destined to become America's first national park, established just two years later in 1872.

In response to the major epidemics that swept both northern and southern cities after the Civil War, medical doctors used cartographic-statistical techniques to portray the geographical distribution of the different diseases. As early as 1849 English medical doctors had published crude statistical maps showing deaths from cholera, notes Norman J. W. Thrower (see Bibliography). In the United States Dr. Edward H. Barton, using 1850 census returns, illustrated the association of sanitary conditions and epidemics in Louisiana, Mississippi, Arkansas, and Texas. In this work, which was published in 1852, each state map used the county unit to show the mortality of epidemics per 1,000 persons. It was not until after the Civil War, however, that regional maps showing distribution of diseases came into general use. Dr. Joseph M. Toner, a prominent Washington, D.C., physician, prepared one such map of the eastern United States that depicted the sites of occurrence of yellow fever since 1668. The elevation in feet above sea level for each site was included in an effort to reveal the connection of surface relief with incidence of the dreaded disease. In 1874 Dr. S. H. Carney of New York City issued his series of five large "medical charts" showing the geographical distribution of pulmonary tuberculosis, malaria, pneumonia, rheumatism, and typhoid fever, based on "information furnished by the highest medical authorities in each state." Each disease was shown on a separate Colton map of the eastern half of the United States and identified by a different color. An inset included a large map of California and Nevada.

A characteristically American cartographic form was the panoramic or bird's-eye-view map, which introduced a new graphic method of transmitting geographical information (*Plate 184*). Panoramic maps are perspective drawings of towns and cities that show street and railroad patterns, individual buildings, and physical landscape features. Dating from about 1868 to the 1920s, they provide unique and distinctive views of the urban landscape. Like illustrated atlases, panoramic maps were often adorned with insets of enlarged perspective views of individual buildings or building complexes. They were marketed through door-to-door sales campaigns and newspaper advertisements, and were extremely popular with individuals as wall hangings and as promotional aids for real estate agents and chambers of commerce. The largest collection of panoramic maps is in the Library of Congress, and is described by John R. Hébert (see Bibliography). The most productive panoramic artists and publishers were concentrated in the more urbanized midwest and northeast and included Albert Ruger, Thaddeus Mortimer Fowler, Henry Wellge, Oakley H. Bailey, and Joseph J. Stoner.

Under the direction of Cleveland Abbe of the U.S. Army Signal Corps, the first daily weather charts were issued in 1871. Based on meteorological data obtained via telegraph (a system devised by Joseph Henry, Secretary of the Smithsonian Institution, during the 1850s), these synoptic charts provided a systematic portrayal of weather patterns over the United States including temperature, barometric pressure, precipitation, and the location of storm centers. Daily weather maps were posted in public places throughout the country. By the late 1880s, according to Donald R. Whitnah in his *History of the U.S. Weather Bureau,* more than 175,000 weather maps were issued yearly. In order to reduce the number of maps being distributed, abbreviated copies began to appear in daily newspapers beginning in 1879. Weather charts summarizing meteorological conditions for longer periods of time were also prepared in the 1870s (*Plate 185*).

Log cabin, Salt Lake, Utah, photograph by A.J. Russell

Scientific illustrations from the Pacific Railroad Reports, *1853–59*

The year 1872 witnessed a notable addition to the cartographic fraternity when the commercial printing firm of Rand McNally added small strip maps to its *Railway Guide* in order to illustrate better the different railroad routes. A product of the railroad era, Rand McNally and Company was established in 1856 in Chicago, the future hub of the railroad network in the United States, to print railroad timetables. By 1869 the Union Pacific joined the Central Pacific to form the first of the transcontinental railroads, complete from Omaha to San Francisco, and the demand arose for railroad maps of the West. These maps, generally financed by the railroad companies through the advertisements adorning their borders, were freely distributed to promote settlement along the routes in anticipation that new settlements would increase rail-

PLATE 188: Francis Amasa Walker. "Map Showing the Proportion of Deaths from Malarial Diseases to Deaths from all Causes compiled from the Returns of Mortality at the Ninth Census of the United States 1870." 1874. Chromolithograph, 50 × 37.5 cm. Records of the Census Bureau, National Archives, Washington, D.C. *Statistical map published by Julius Bien, New York City, for the U.S. Census Bureau, illustrating the number of deaths from malaria in the eastern United States for each square mile having a population density greater than two persons. Plate 42 in Walker's* Statistical Atlas of the United States . . ., *the first statistical atlas published in this country.*

(opposite) PLATE 189: G. W. Peek. "Peek's Historical and Pictorial Charts of the United States: 1805–1843." 1895. Lithograph, hand colored; 91 × 119 cm. Geography and Map Division, Library of Congress, Washington, D.C. *Retrospective educational wall map from Peek's atlas, published by State Printing and Publishing Company, Olympia, Washington. Depicts the growth of the United States between 1805 and 1843, and the expeditions of Lewis and Clark, Zebulon M. Pike, and Stephen H. Long. Two vignettes illustrate heroic scenes from the War of 1812: Perry at Lake Erie, and the Battle of New Orleans.*

road traffic (*Plate 186*). Each map included the appropriate timetables. Railroad maps were printed in several different languages to entice foreign immigrants. It has been suggested by Duncan Fitchet that the maps printed in Swedish and Norwegian were responsible in part for the large concentration of Scandinavian immigrants in Minnesota and Wisconsin (see Bibliography). Because the changes resulting from new routes and new towns came so rapidly, Rand McNally relied solely upon the wax-engraving process which permitted correction patches to be inserted easily in the printing plate. By 1875 Rand McNally had broadened its mapping activities to include pocket guide maps, such as *Guide Map of Chicago* and *New Map and Guide to the Black Hills of Dakota*.

From 1873 to 1944 the U.S. General Land Office published intermittently but generally yearly an official map of the United States based on their field surveys. This standard map measuring

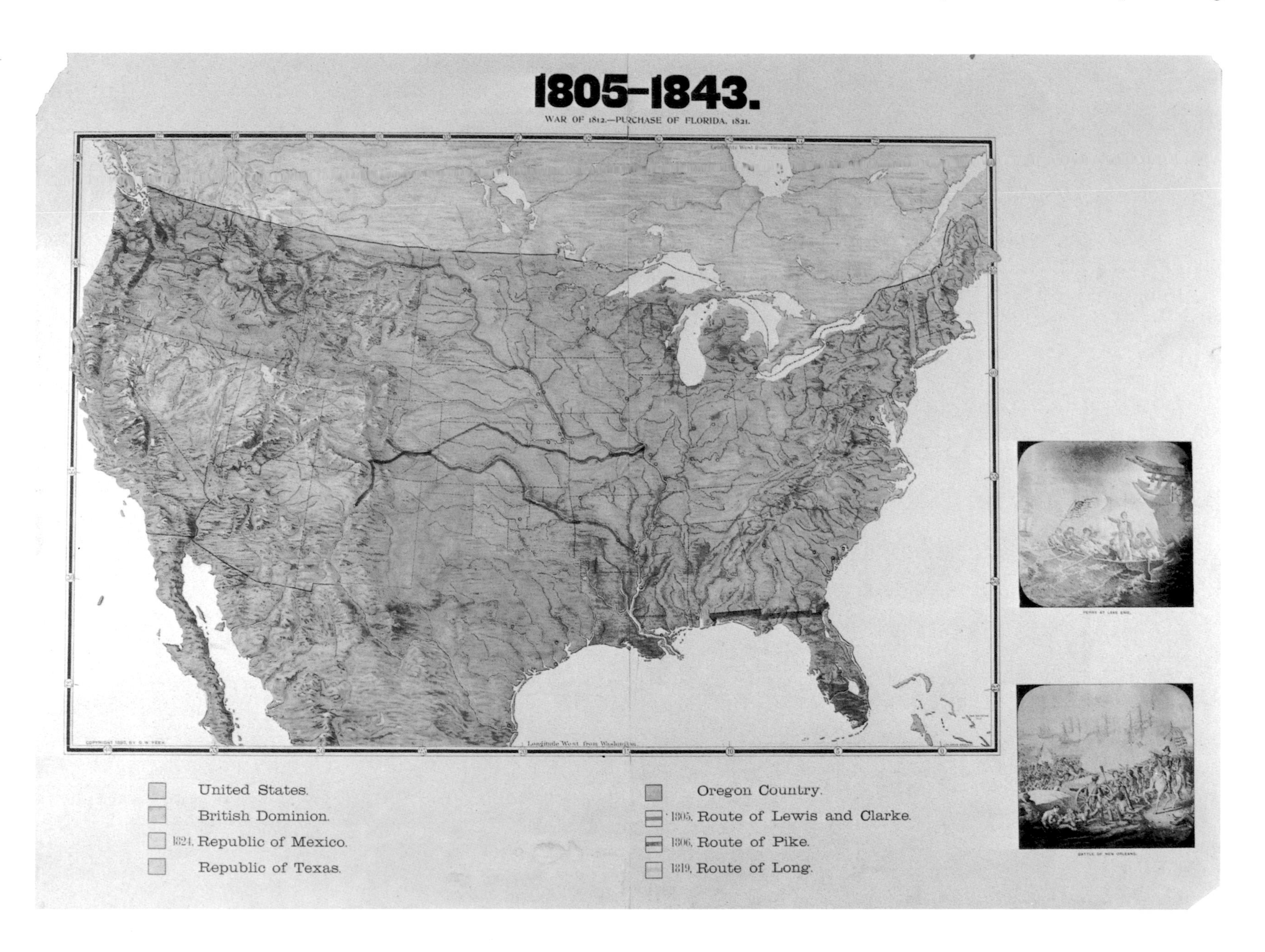

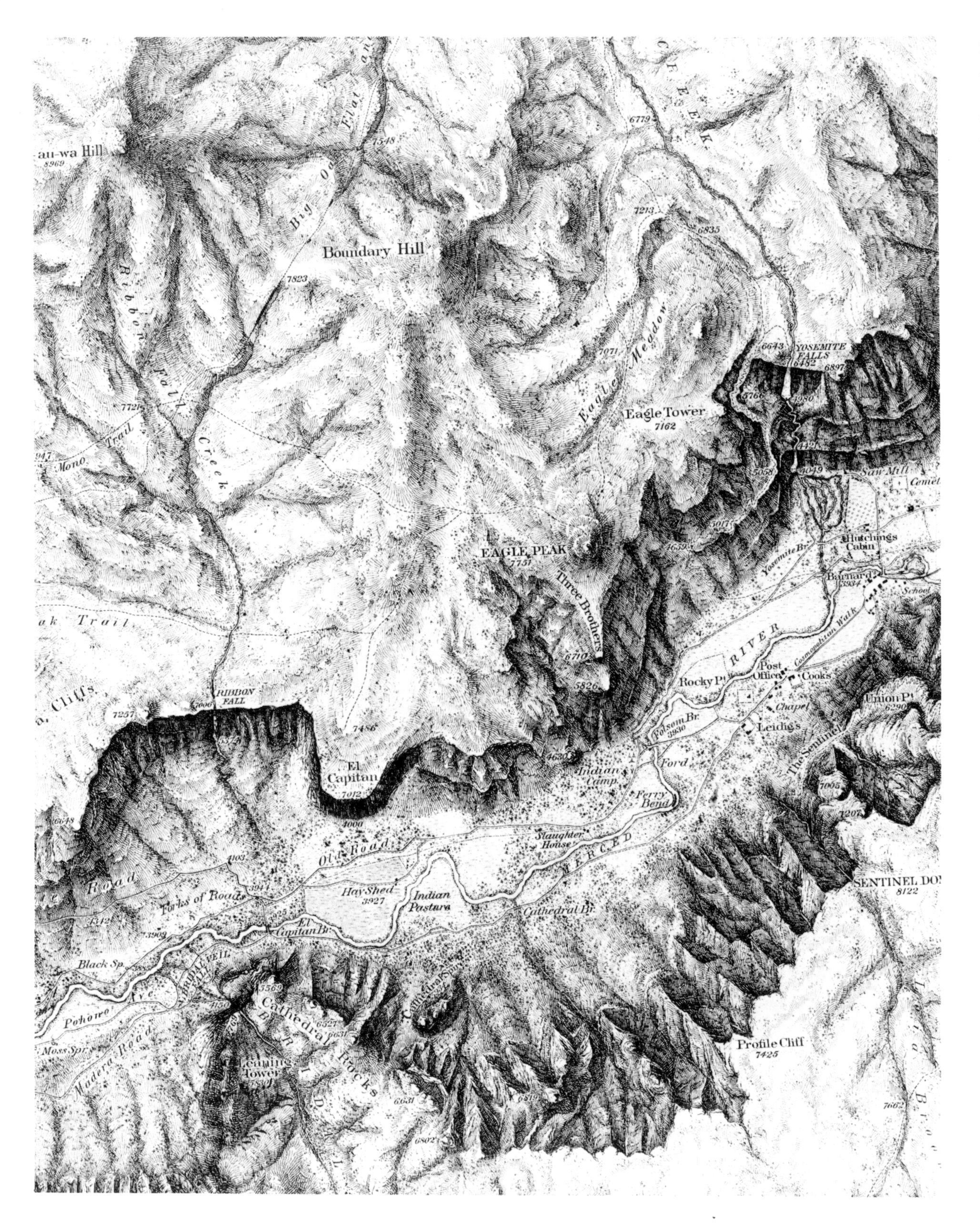

PLATE 190: John E. Weyss. "Topographical Map of the Yosemite Valley and Vicinity" (detail). 1883. Manuscript, pen and ink; entire dimensions 59 × 74 cm. Records of the Office of the Chief of Engineers, National Archives, Washington, D.C. *Detail of Yosemite Valley and Yosemite Falls. Reveals Weyss's skill in depicting surface relief by the standard nineteenth-century technique of hachures, which became replaced during the 1880s by the more scientific contour technique. Prepared from a topographical plat by Lieutenant J. N. Macomb under the direction of Captain George M. Wheeler, in the course of government-sponsored scientific surveys of the West. This manuscript map was photo-lithographed and issued as a printed "Preliminary Edition" by Julius Bien, New York City.*

(*opposite*) PLATE 191: Edward Freyhold. "Cordilleras." 1876. Lithograph, 70 × 55 cm. Records of the U.S. Geological Survey, National Archives, Washington, D.C. *Index sheet from Clarence King's* Geological and Topographical Atlas Accompanying the Report of the Geological Exploration of the Fortieth Parallel, *published by Julius Bien, New York City, for the War Department. Surface relief of the western mountain ranges is portrayed by the "plastic shading" technique, rather than by hachuring* about 62 by 82 inches depicted in a fairly uniform format the extent of public land surveys, railroad lines, land offices, cities and towns, Indian and military reservations, and national parks, monuments, and forests. At irregular intervals beginning in 1876, the General Land Office also published maps of individual states and territories in the public domain (*Plate 187*). Initially these were published as atlases but later the maps were made available in separate sheets. State maps portrayed county boundaries in addition to the information listed above for national maps.

Thematic maps were presented in atlas format in 1874 with the publication of the first statistical atlas of the United States. Prepared under the direction of Francis Amasa Walker, Superintendent of the Ninth Decennial Census, it was entitled *Statistical Atlas of the United States Based on the Result of the Ninth Census, 1870, With Contributions from Many Eminent Men of Science and Several Departments of the Government.* Printed in color by Julius Bien, the Walker atlas contained fifty-four plates and provided a variety of new, fresh images of the physical, economic, and social geography of the United States, including maps of topography, population, agriculture, and vital statistics (*Plate 188*). Of special interest are the maps showing population density by county of the settled areas of the United States for each decennial census from 1790 to 1870, and those portraying the percentages of black and foreign-born populations. This pioneering work was the first atlas of analytical maps that showed patterns of association and it greatly influenced the development of thematic mapping in the United States. It was followed in 1882 by a more sophisticated atlas by Fletcher W. Hewes and Henry Gannett derived from the tenth decennial census and published commercially by Charles Scribner's, New York City.

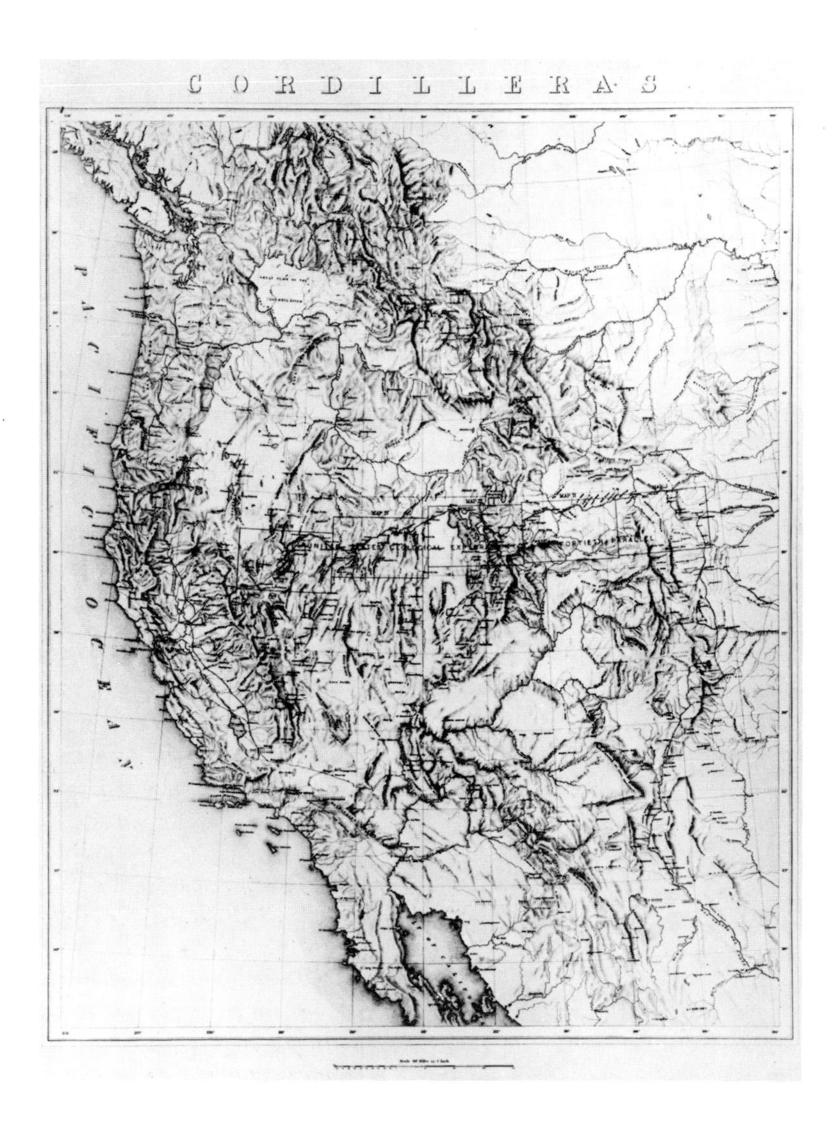

America's centennial was commemorated with the issuance of a number of significant cartographic works. Rand McNally chose 1876 to publish its large wax-engraved wall map which was titled "New Railroad and County Map of the United States and Canada, Compiled from the latest Government Surveys and Drawn to an Accurate Scale." When sectionalized and bound, this map formed the basis of Rand McNally's *Business Atlas of the Great Mississippi Valley and Pacific Slope* as well as its series of pocket maps of individual states and territories. The business atlas, as its full title revealed, showed "in detail the entire railroad system, the express company doing business over each road, and accurately locating counties, parishes, islands, lakes, rivers, mountains, etc., etc., together with all post offices, railroad stations and villages, and latest official census or estimated population of each." It was printed in color and indexed. Rand McNally's *Business Atlas* evolved into their celebrated *Commercial Atlas and Marketing Guide*, which has appeared annually ever since its inception in 1876.

Rufus Blanchard's educational wall map of significant historical events was also issued in 1876 and provides a unique graphic expression of American commercialism and chauvinism. The intriguing genre that Blanchard's wall map represents evolved from earlier descriptive wall charts that provided teachers and students with simple, chronological resumés of political and

military activities. Blanchard's large work, measuring almost five feet square, consists of a map of the eastern half of the United States showing early Spanish, French, and English discoveries and routes of exploration as well as military forts, towns, and battlefields of historic interest. Five large facsimile insets of significant earlier maps are reproduced, including the 1783 treaty map and a 1684 French map of North America. By the 1890s these graphic displays of American history had expanded into large, cumbersome folios consisting of twenty or more maps, often accompanied by views of patriotic battles and places. Examples are "Peek's Historical and Pictorial Charts of the United States (1895)" (*Plate 189*) and "Robertson's Geographic-Historical Series Illustrating the History of America and the United States from 1492 to the Present Time (1898)."

The first of the memorable atlases prepared by the Federal government's four Western geographical and geological surveys during the post-Civil War period was also appropriately issued during the centennial year, symbolizing the scientific conquest of America's last great natural frontier. These independent though related surveys of the Far West, which were carried out from 1867 to 1879, are generally known as the Hayden, King, Powell, or Wheeler Survey, after the man who led them. Based on such modern survey techniques as triangulation, they produced a profusion of maps published in atlas and loose-leaf form that laid *(opposite)* PLATE 192: William H. Holmes. "Panorama From Point Sublime." 1882. Chromolithograph, 51 × 82 cm. Records of the U.S. Geological Survey, National Archives, Washington, D.C. *Awe-inspiring views such as this one of a portion of the Kaibab division of the Grand Canyon were drawn by topographic artists accompanying many of the Federally sponsored western expeditions from the 1850s onward. Holmes, perhaps the most talented of these surveyor-artists, later became director of the National Gallery (now the National Collection of Fine Arts) at the Smithsonian Institution. The drawing for this lithographic view was prepared during surveys undertaken by Captain Clarence E. Dutton, U.S. Army, and published in his* Atlas to Accompany the Monograph on the Tertiary Report of the Grand Cañon District.

PLATE 193: Emil Mahlo. "Political Map of the United States Showing by Congressional Districts the Geographical Distribution of the Political Parties, . . ." 1877. Chromolithograph, 50.5 × 68 cm. Geography and Map Division, Library of Congress, Washington, D.C. *Utilizes colored patterns—green for Democrats, red for Republicans—to show the geographical distribution of the political parties by Congressional districts. Based on the election results for the forty-fifth U.S. Congress (1877–79). Published by Edward W. Welcke and Brothers, New York City.*

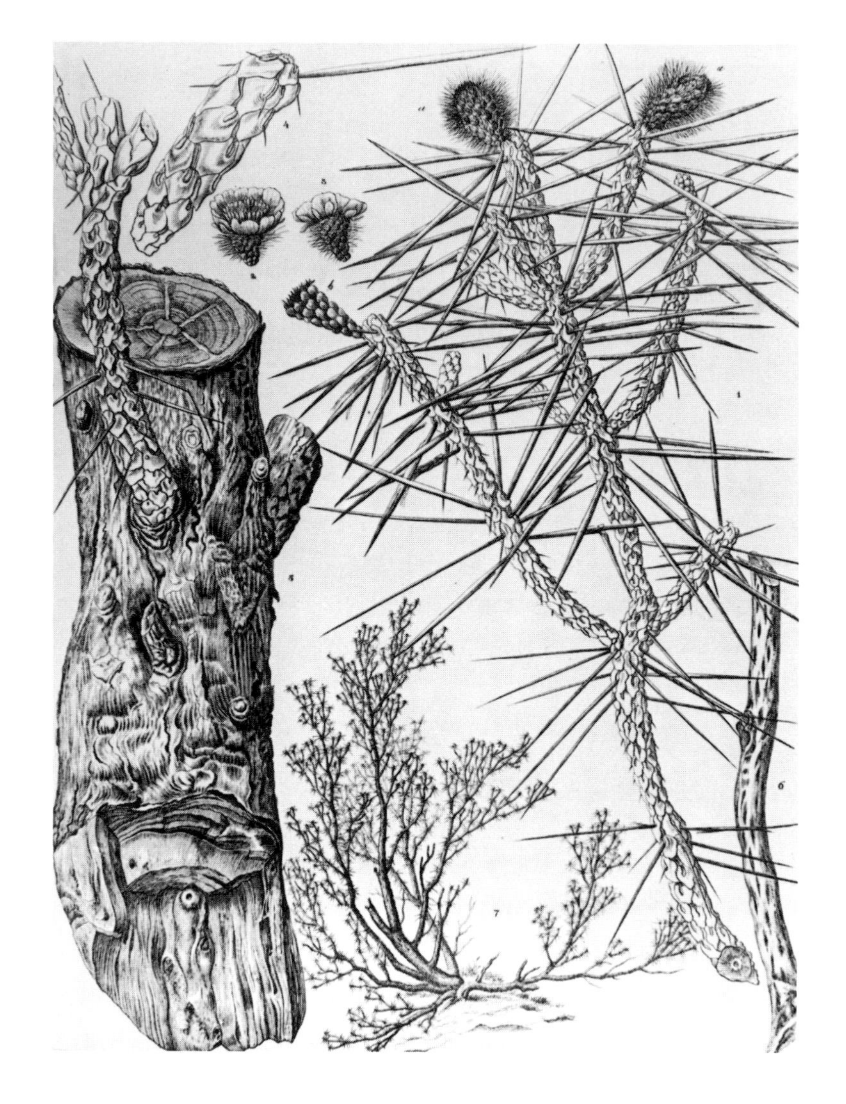

Scientific illustrations from the Pacific Railroad Reports, *1853–59*

Scientific illustrations from the Pacific Railroad Reports, *1853–59*

the scientific foundation of American geological, topographic, and land classification mapping. The surveys are also noted for introducing the works of such notable topographic artists as William H. Holmes, whose pictorially vivid and descriptive perspective views of geographical features convey a unique impression of western landscape (*see Plate 192*).

Lieutenant George Montague Wheeler undertook the most ambitious of these four surveys. Representing the U.S. Army Corps of Engineers, Wheeler surveyed some 361,000 square miles of the southwest between 1869 and 1879. The resultant geographical and geological field data were condensed in seven printed volumes titled *Report Upon United States Geographical Surveys West of the One Hundredth Meridian*, which was accompanied by geological and topographical maps issued individually from 1876 to 1883. Wheeler's primary objective was to prepare a detailed topographic map of the West. In pursuit of this goal he divided the area of the West into ninety-five "principal" rectangles, each rectangle comprising 2°45′ of longitude and 1°40′ of latitude, to be covered in four atlas sheets. Fifty-five of these atlas sheets were completed before the survey was halted prematurely with

Prairie dog, from the Pacific Railroad Reports, *1853–59*

the establishment of the U.S. Geological Survey in 1879. The final manuscript sheets, now in the National Archives, are works of delicate craftsmanship. Separate delineators were responsible for certain phases of compilation: map construction, lettering and line work, and hill-depiction. John E. Weyss, the skilled Civil War cartographer, was in charge of depicting relief by hachures (*Plate 190*). His work, according to W. L. G. Joerg, "represents a degree of technical excellence . . . not surpassed in this country before or since" (see Bibliography). The manuscript sheets were published at a reduced scale by the Graphic Company, New York City, using photolithography. Many of these maps were over-printed to show either geological or land-classification data, the latter differentiating agricultural lands, timbered tracts, grazing areas, and wastes or barrens.

More innovative was the work of Yale graduate Clarence King, a civilian who nonetheless led the second War Department survey party. King surveyed and mapped the geology and mineral resources of a 100-mile-wide strip of land along the recently conjoined Union Pacific and Central Pacific railroads which closely followed the fortieth parallel of latitude. King's atlas was published under the authority of the War Department by Julius Bien in 1876 and contained five topographic and five geologic map sheets covering some 87,000 square miles at a scale of four miles to one inch. Edward Freyhold, who had assisted in the drafting of Warren's map of 1857, prepared the topographical sheets. The depiction of surface features such as mountains and valleys on these sheets was accomplished by brush shading rather than the conventional technique of hachuring (*Plate 191*). The result is a strikingly realistic impression of spatial relief conveyed through the use of highlights and shadows. Subsequently known as "plastic shading," this technique, which was first used by the State Geological Survey of California in 1874, was made possible by the development of halftone lithography. The geological map sheets in King's atlas, constructed by S. G. Emmons and Arnold Hague, were more complex than those prepared by the Wheeler Survey, and defined as many as twenty-seven underlying rock formations by a combination of symbols and colors.

The two remaining surveys, patterned after King's, were undertaken by Ferdinand V. Hayden and John Wesley Powell, civilian scientists sponsored by the Interior Department, and resulted in such classic works as Hayden's *Geological and Geographical Atlas of Colorado* (1877), and Powell's *Atlas Accompanying the Report on the Geology of a Portion of the Uinta Mountains and a Region of Country adjacent thereto* (1876). Many of these and other reports were also published by the New York firm of Julius Bien. Hayden's atlas is particularly noteworthy for introducing to the public the topographic work of Henry Gannett and the panoramic views and geological and land-classification maps of William H. Holmes (*Plate 192*). The latter also had general responsibility for the publication of the *Atlas of Colorado*, one of the most artistic and beautiful American atlases ever issued. In recognition of his scientific and artistic ability, Holmes was appointed the first director of the Smithsonian's National Gallery of Art in 1906.

PLATE 194: George W. Howell and C. C. Vermeule. "A Topographical Map of a Part of Northern New Jersey . . ." (portion). 1882. Chromolithograph, entire dimensions 89.5 × 90 cm. Geography and Map Division, Library of Congress, Washington, D.C. *Lithographed by Julius Bien, New York City, for the Geological Survey of New Jersey. First printed map by a state agency to show surface relief by contours (lines of equal elevation). The contour technique was later adopted by the U.S. Geological Survey for its Topographic Atlas of the United States.*

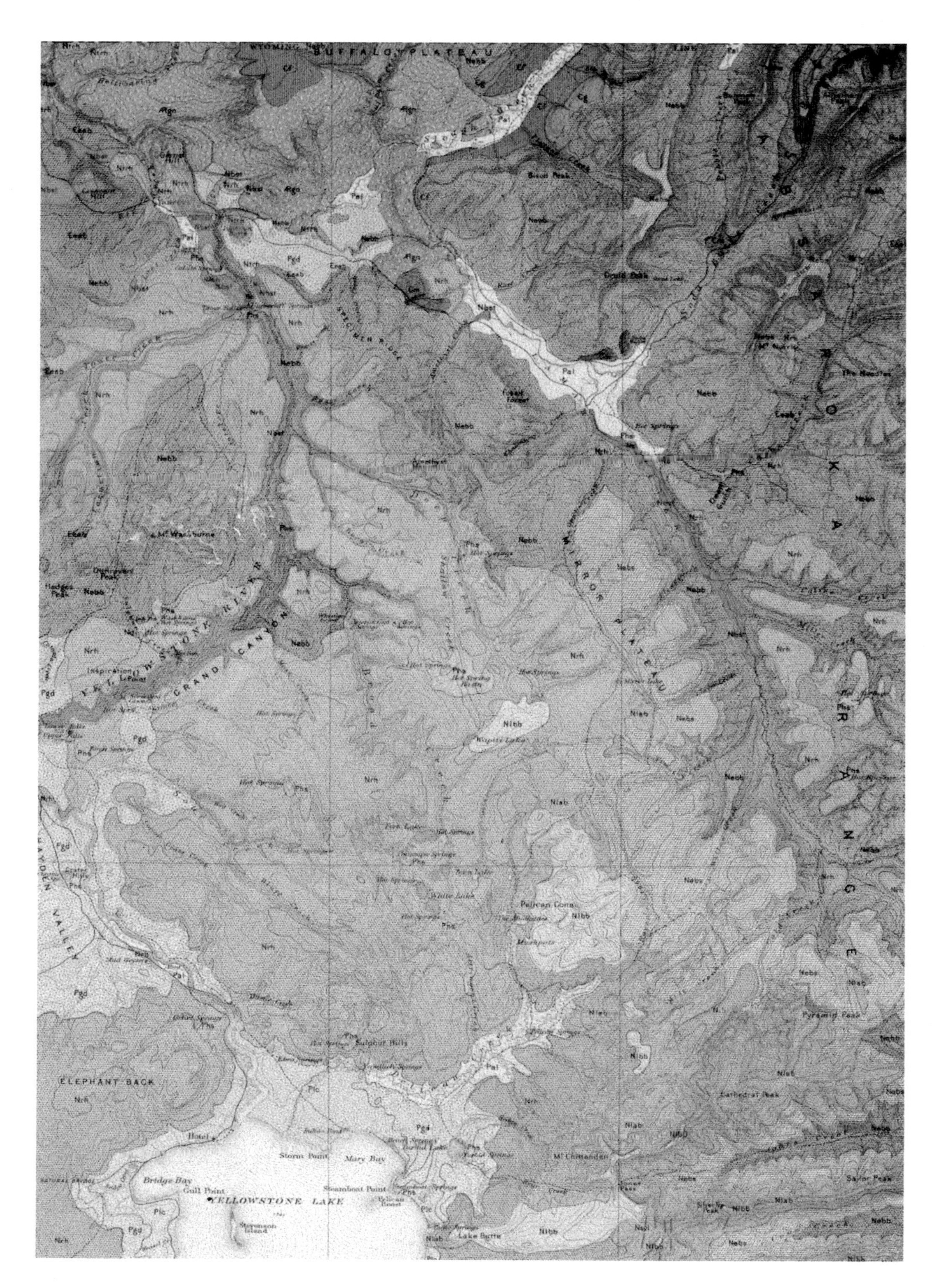

PLATE 195: Arnold Hague. "Areal Geology. Yellowstone National Park. Canyon Sheet." 1896. Chromolithograph, 55.5 × 47 cm. Records of the U.S. Geological Survey, National Archives, Washington, D.C. *Engraved by S. J. Kubel, Geological Survey; edited by Bailey Willis, Geological Survey; printed by the U.S. Geological Survey. A typical plate from the* Geological Atlas of the United States, *issued in folio format from 1894 to 1945. This sheet, showing the northwest corner of the state of Wyoming, indicates the distribution of rock formations by a combination of colored tints and patterns. Numerous hot springs, which had stirred the imagination of western explorers and travelers since early in the nineteenth century, are depicted north of Yellowstone Lake.*

Franklin Valley, from the Humboldt Mts., *engraving after sketch by F. W. Egloffstein, 1853–59*

A fifth major survey of the west was undertaken privately by the Northern Pacific Railroad Company from 1881 to 1884 to ascertain and exploit the mineral, agricultural, and forest resources of the immense region it served, which stretched from Lake Superior to Portland, Oregon. Known as the Northern Transcontinental Survey, it was directed by Raphael Pumpelly and included such prominent scientists as Bailey Willis, William Morris Davis, and Charles S. Sargent. Pumpelly's intention "was to make the record of the results of the survey essentially cartographic [and] to show upon the maps in a general form all the physical facts that have an important bearing on the prosperity of the region." To this end were published three map bulletins consisting of three to ten map sheets each, to show surface features by contour lines, distribution of forage plants, the locations of geological formations, and outcroppings of coal.

While selected physical features of the West were being studied and mapped for the first time by trained scientists, the War Department was executing a series of military campaigns against various Indian tribes that resulted in additional maps of the region. These included reconnaissance maps such as Sergeant James E. Wilson's map of Brigadier General A. H. Terry's 1876 expedition against the hostile Sioux near Little Big Horn, Montana, following General George Custer's defeat and massacre; and Lieutenant Robert H. Fletcher's "Map of the Nez Percé Indian Campaign," which depicts the routes of major military units and the location of battles fought with Chief Joseph and his tribe throughout the Pacific Northwest during the latter's unsuccessful attempt to reach Canada and freedom in 1877. Views of the six principal battles are also found on this map.

In the last quarter of the century thematic mapping, stimulated by the widespread success of Walker's *Statistical Atlas of the United States* of 1874 (*see Plate 188*), was used to portray a broader range of social and political data. In 1877 Emil Mahlo compiled a political map of the United States showing the geographical distribution of political parties by congressional districts for the forty-fifth Congress (*Plate 193*). Six years later Fletcher W. Hewes used modern cartographic techniques for displaying political issues in his *Citizen's Atlas of American Politics 1789–1883*. Coauthor with Henry Gannett of Scribner's *Statistical Atlas of the United States* for the 1880 census, Hewes devised graphs and maps to analyze the popular vote by state for each presidential election from 1824 to 1880, and by county for the 1880 election. By adopting the choropleth symbol, a simple cartographic technique used to depict quantitative data by tinting administrative units such as counties or states with graded lines and color patterns, Hewes was able to portray by county or state the percentage of votes cast for the two leading candidates. The Hewes atlas was revised in 1888, 1889, and 1892.

A map having important legal significance was prepared by Paul Brodie in 1879 from official records of the Bureau of Indian Affairs to show "the Original Cessions of Lands made to the United States by Treaty or Agreement with the Indian Tribes of the United States and Territories from the formation of the Government to the present time." This original map, now in the National Archives, measures 48 by 76 inches and is accompanied by an index containing copious notes and explanatory references keyed to the map. A smaller map by Brodie showing "Indian Reservations in the United States" was published in 1883.

On the eve of the 1880s began the modern era of topographic and geologic mapping. In 1877 New Jersey commenced the earliest state topographic and geologic survey controlled by triangulation. The topographic work was undertaken with the aid of the plane-table (portable drafting table), and elevations were measured by spirit level and vertical angles. The results of this survey were issued in 1882 as "A Topographical Map of a Part of Northern New Jersey From Surveys and Levelings made and

Isaac I. Stevens survey party meeting with Assiniboin Indians near Fort Union, lithograph after drawing by John Mix Stanley, 1853

View of Uncompahgre Mountain, Colo., advertisement for the Overland Mail Co. stage line

Local Surveys corrected" (*Plate 194*). The map was compiled by George W. Howell and C. C. Vermeule, and lithographed by Julius Bien. Reflecting modern advances, surface relief was depicted by contours or lines of equal elevation.

In the same year that New Jersey issued its topographic map, the U.S. Geological Survey, established in 1879 in an effort to consolidate the western geographical and geological surveys, initiated the Topographic Atlas of the United States (now the National Topographic Map Series). Described by J. Paul Goode as "the greatest national venture in mapping ever undertaken" (see Bibliography), the Topographic Atlas was conceived of as a set of map sheets, issued separately, which would be conjoined to provide a map of the entire United States. The plan adopted by the Survey for the atlas consisted of dividing and mapping the entire country by quadrilateral tracts bounded by parallels of latitude and meridians of longitude, similar to the plan devised by Wheeler for his Survey west of the one hundredth meridian (see page 306). These tracts were represented by map sheets at various scales, called quadrangles, and were identified by their scale and thereafter by the name of the most important town, city, or natural feature within the area represented.

Several quadrangle map series evolved and are designated

Building a "corduroy" road in the woods, Virginia

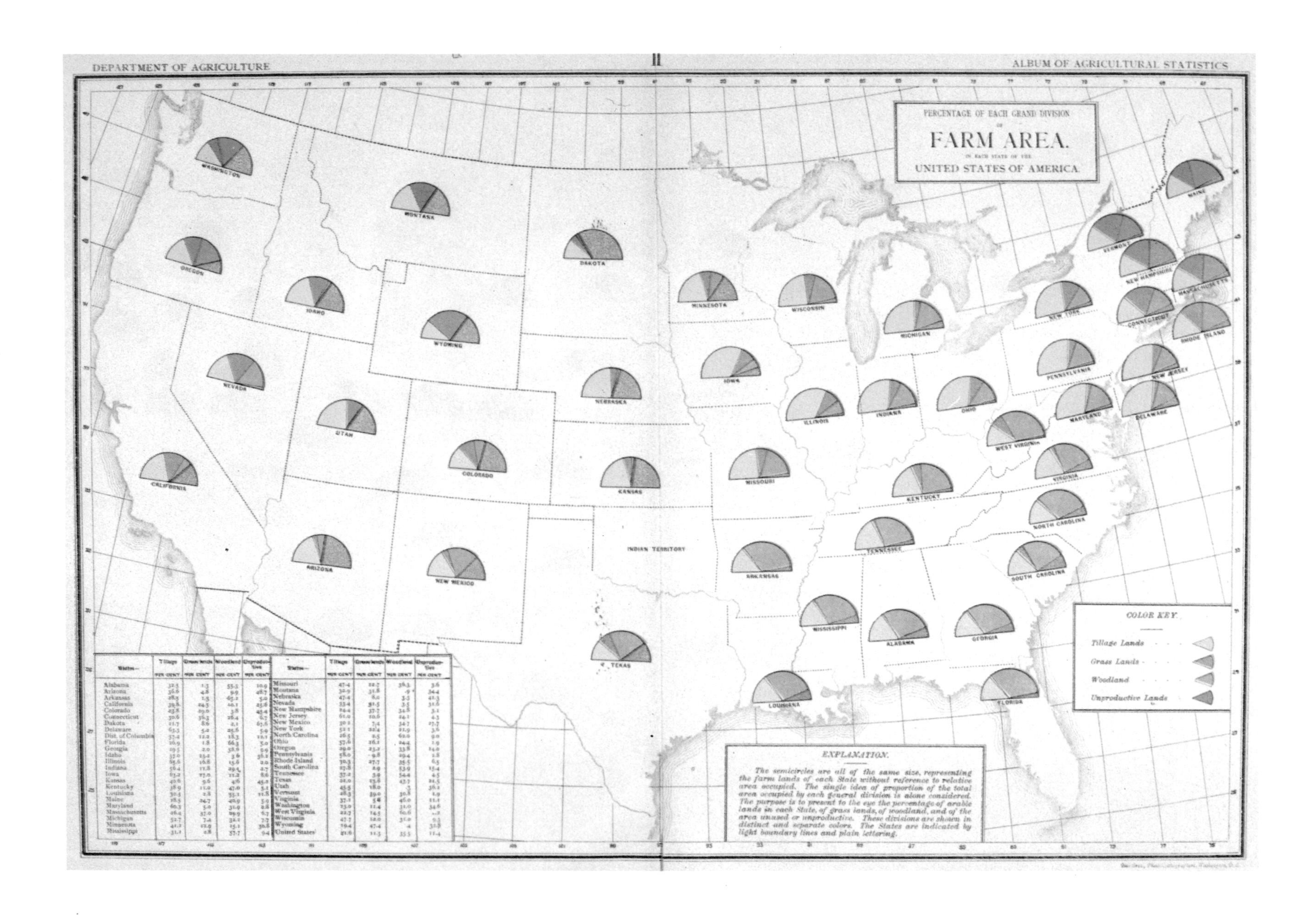

either by quadrangle size (e.g., "15-minute series") or by scale (e.g., 1 : 62,500). The initial quadrangle map series was compiled in a 1-degree format at a scale of one inch to approximately four miles (1 : 250,000), the same map scale used by the western surveys in 1869–79. Each map sheet in the 1-degree format series covers one degree square of the earth's surface, or approximately 3,100 to 4,100 square miles depending on whether the degree square was located in the north or south, respectively, of the United States. When the U.S. Geological Survey initiated cooperative surveys with individual states, starting with Massachusetts in 1884, it was found, however, that the densely settled regions of the East necessitated a more detailed quadrangle compiled at a larger scale. Thereafter, the survey issued three additional quadrangle sizes at scales governed by the following considerations: population density, economic importance, complexity of geologic phenomena, and intensity of topographic features.

In addition to the 1-degree format, other quadrangle series

(*opposite*) PLATE 196: U.S. Department of Agriculture. "Percentage of Each Grand Division of Farm Area. In Each State of the United States of America." 1889. Photolithograph in color, 31 × 46 cm. Records of the Office of the Secretary of Agriculture, National Archives, Washington, D.C. *Statistical agricultural map of the United States depicting percentages of land classified as tillage, grass, woodland, and unproductive. Early example of the pie-graph technique, whereby circles are divided proportionately according to the values they represent. From* Album of Agricultural Statistics of the United States, *lithographed by Bell Brothers, Washington, D.C.*

PLATE 197: Arnold Guyot. "Wall-Atlas" (North America). 1865. Lithograph, hand colored; 77 × 66 cm. Geography and Map Division, Library of Congress, Washington, D.C. *Reduction of Guyot's 1863 map, one of the first maps depicting surface relief by generalized hachures and watercolor washes to be prepared by a trained scientist. Guyot, a native of Switzerland, was a student of the celebrated German geographers Alexander von Humboldt and Karl Ritter. He introduced geography to the United States as an academic discipline at Princeton, where he taught from 1854 to 1884. Lithographed by Charles Scribner and Company, New York City.*

A Virginia farm of 1846, wood engraving

produced by the Geological Survey are: 30-minute, 15-minute, and 7.5-minute. The 1-degree format was retained until about 1940 for large, uninhabited desert or mountainous regions such as parts of the Far West and Alaska. The 30-minute format represents about 780 to 1,030 square miles at a scale of one inch to approximately two miles (1 : 125,000); this was selected as the standard quadrangle size and scale for the general map of the United States. It was the most popular quadrangle issued between 1884 and 1910, but thereafter lost ground to the 15-minute quadrangle as increased population and construction raised the demand for more detailed information. The 15-minute format covers an average of 196 to 258 square miles at different scales in the one inch to approximately one mile range (1 : 48,000; 1 : 62,500; 1 : 63,360), and was chosen for densely populated areas on the Atlantic coast, in parts of the midwest, and on the Pacific coast. The 7.5-minute format, which covers approximately 49 to 64 square miles at a scale of one inch to about one-half mile (1 : 24,000; 1 : 25,000; 1 : 31,680), was not introduced until the first decade of the twentieth century. Since World War II, almost all new mapping undertaken by the survey has been issued in the 7.5-minute format.

Standard symbols, colors, and placenames were adopted to simplify map interpretation and to encourage map reading by the general public. Features of topography and culture were depicted by three colors: black for cultural or manmade features, such as cities, roads, buildings, placenames, and boundary lines; blue for hydrography or drainage features, such as ponds, streams, lakes, and swamps; and brown for hypsography or surface features, such as hills, valleys, and plains. The location of local political boundaries and the determination of local placenames were ascertained by consulting town and county maps and through correspondence with postmasters, local officials, and railroad officials. In an effort to standardize domestic geographic placenames, the United States Board on Geographic Names was created by an executive order of President William H. Harrison on September 4, 1890, to insure that "Uniform usage in regard to geographic nomenclature and orthography obtain throughout the Executive Departments of the Government, and particularly upon the maps and charts issued by the various departments and bureaus." Perhaps the most innovative aspect of the topographic mapping program was the decision to depict surface features by contour lines, the first time this was done for an entire country on a uniform series of maps.

The Topographic Atlas of the United States was undertaken in part to provide an accurate base map for depicting geological data. Following the Civil War, state as well as Federal agencies strove to inventory natural resources in response to the demands of commercial and national interests. Guided by James Dwight Dana's *Manual of Geology* (1862), which provided the framework for classifying geological formations, geologists either initiated or resumed twenty-two state geological surveys. The result was a new generation of geological state maps, more detailed and accurate than those before that war. Representative of this type are Thomas C. Chamberlain's geological atlas of Wisconsin (1876) and South Carolina's geological map produced by the South Carolina Department of Agriculture, lithographed and hand colored by the Colton firm (1883).

A great advance in geological mapping was made in 1883, according to W. L. G. Joerg, the year in which August Hoen and Company devised a method of combining colors with patterns of lines, dots, and circles that enabled geologists to depict a greater

"Veteran troops moving up the Ohio River to Louisville and Cincinnati," wood engraving

number of geological formations than previous printing techniques had allowed (see Bibliography). First applied by Hoen to maps appearing in R. D. Irving's *The Copper-Bearing Rocks of Lake Superior*, a U.S. Geological Survey monograph published in 1885, this technique was soon adopted by most publishers of geological and thematic maps. Also furthering the growth of geological mapping was the approval by a conference of geologists in 1889 of a set of rules standardizing geologic nomenclature and a system of classification for geological formations. Both of these developments were utilized by the Geological Survey to produce the monumental *Geological Atlas of the United States* from 1894 to 1945 (*Plate 195*). Issued in a folio format of uniform style and size, the atlas was designed to cover the United States in 227 folios. Each folio consisted of a brief descriptive text and maps depicting the area's topography, geological formations, deposits of economic value, and the underground structure of the rocks. More than fifty design patterns were used on the geological maps to identify the various classes of sedimentary, igneous, and metamorphic rocks within the United States.

An important set of sixteen forest maps of North America was prepared by Harry King under the direction of Charles S. Sargent for the U.S. Census Bureau in 1883. Three general maps show the distribution of forest, prairie, and treeless regions while the remaining thirteen maps portray the extent of individual tree species by color tint overprints of topographic maps.

Applying the newly developed statistical techniques to a cartographic format, the Department of Agriculture issued the *Album of Agricultural Statistics of the United States* in 1889 (*Plate 196*). Designed to popularize the use of illustrated statistics as an instructional aid for educational societies and schools, the authors used choropleth (a depiction of quantitative data in terms of administrative units) and pie-graph techniques to portray rural population, farm tenure, the distribution of farm land, production of selected grains, yields per acre, and average value of selected farm animals and land.

Almost thirty years of commercial and Federal topographic mapping culminated in 1890 with the first reasonably accurate topographic wall map of the United States. The genealogy of the United States topographic wall map is difficult to trace, but one of the earliest was prepared by Arnold Guyot in 1863. A native of Switzerland and student of the renowned German geographers Alexander von Humboldt and Karl Ritter, Guyot taught geography and geology at Princeton from 1854 until his death in 1884. His educational wall map, an attractive and descriptive hand-colored lithograph measuring 56 by 42 inches, depicted surface

Grand Army of the U.S. crossing the Potomac at 2 A.M., May 24, 1861

PLATE 198: John Wesley Powell. "Linguistic Stocks of American Indians North of Mexico." 1891. Chromolithograph, 56 × 48 cm. National Anthropological Archives, Smithsonian Institution, Washington, D.C. *Thematic map published by Sackett and Wilhelms, New York City, for the U.S. Bureau of Ethnology. It depicts the geographical distribution of fifty-eight Indian tribes, based on a careful analysis of Indian linguistic families. Powell, leader of the first expedition to descend the Colorado River in 1869, also had an important role in systematizing the study of the Amerindian language, as founder of the U.S. Bureau of Ethnology in 1879 and its director until 1902. He also served as director of the U.S. Geological Survey from 1880 to 1894, and was instrumental in developing the Topographical and the Geographical atlases of the United States.*

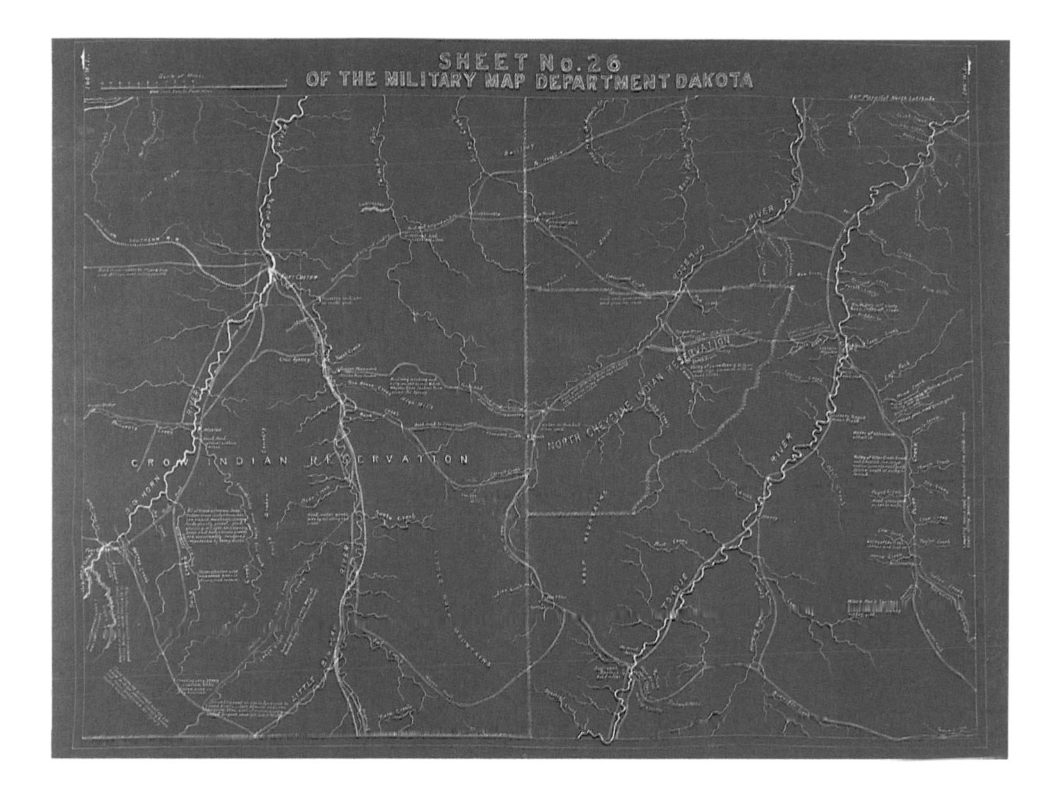

PLATE 199: H. C. Hale, Lieutenant, Department of the Dakota, U.S. Army. "Sheet No. 26 of the Military Map Department Dakota." 1895. Blueprint on cloth, 54 × 74 cm. War Department Map Collection, National Archives, Washington, D.C. *Map in thirty-one sheets and an index sheet of the sprawling Military Department of the Dakota (present-day Minnesota, Montana, North Dakota, and South Dakota) at the close of the Indian wars. The durability of cloth maps, such as this one, made them useful to cavalry officers during the Civil War and Indian wars.*

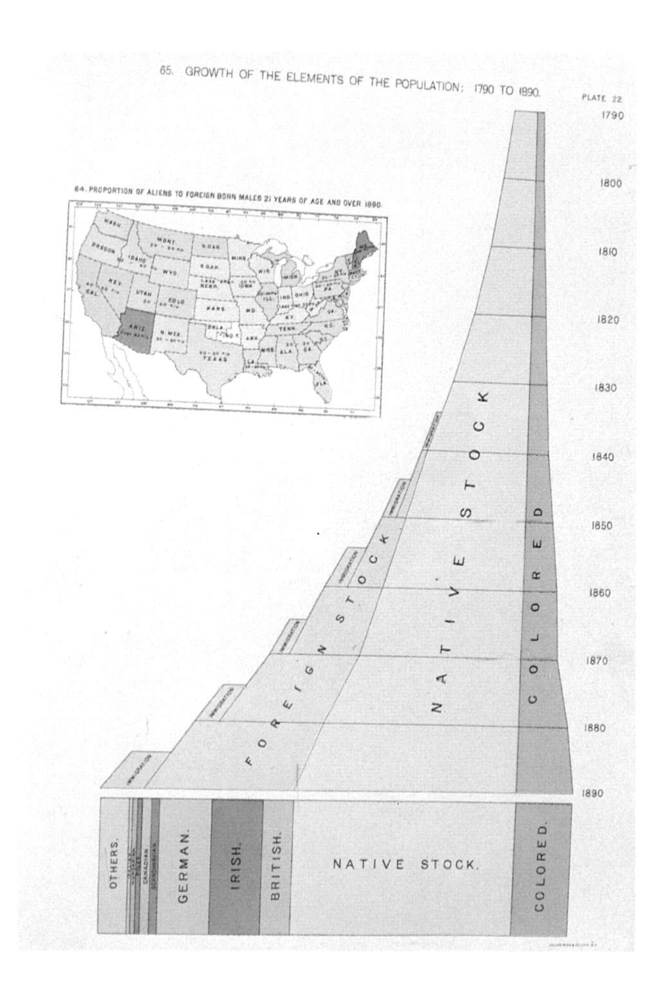

PLATE 200: Henry Gannett. "Growth of the Elements of the Population: 1790 to 1880." 1898. Chromolithograph, 53 × 41 cm. Records of the Census Bureau, National Archives, Washington, D.C. *Map and diagram illustrating the spatial and temporal structure of ethnic groups and native-born Americans comprising the population of the United States during the first hundred years of the census. These are figures 64 and 65 of Plate 22 from the* Statistical Atlas of the United States Based Upon the Results of the Eleventh Census (1890)*; lithographed by Julius Bien and Company, New York City, for the U.S. Census Bureau.*

Immigrants arriving, illustration by W. T. Benda

relief in a generalized manner by using a combination of hachures and color tints. A greatly reduced version of this map appeared in 1865 (*Plate 197*). In 1879 another important but smaller topographic map was prepared by Private R. Meston of the Office of the Chief Signal Officer, U.S. Army. It represents one of the first topographic maps of the United States to express surface relief by the use of a graduated color scheme that combines contour lines with altitude tints. These and other works set the stage for the large topographic map issued by the U.S. Geological Survey in 1890. Compiled and drawn by Harry King under the direction of Henry Gannett, Chief Topographer, surface relief is shown by contour lines based on spot heights furnished by railroad, national, and state topographic surveys. This map, which measures $48\frac{1}{2}$ by $76\frac{1}{2}$ inches, has served as the principal base map for many government agencies and has been reprinted periodically since it first became available. A smaller version of the relief map was issued by the U.S. Geological Survey in 1896, also in the format of contours and altitude tints.

John Wesley Powell, contributor to topographical and geological mapping as leader of the Survey of the Rocky Mountain Region in the 1870s and as director of the U.S. Geological Survey from 1880 to 1894, enlarged the field of thematic mapping with his map of *Linguistic Stocks of American Indians* in 1891 (*Plate 198*). Published in the *7th Annual Report* of the Bureau of Ethnology, the organization Powell founded and directed (later the Bureau of American Ethnology), this map depicted the distribution of fifty-eight Indian tribes based on language. Although Powell's map represented progress over Gallatin's 1836 map of Indian tribes (see page 257), it perpetuated the ethnocentricity common to maps of this type. Because the boundaries of Indian nations continued to be based upon those occupied by the Indians at the time of their first contact with white explorers or officials, the map showed the distribution of tribes in the East as this had been in the seventeenth century and the distribution of some tribes in the West as situated in the nineteenth century. Powell's map,

Scene at the Union Pacific Railroad Depot, Omaha City, Nebraska, 1868

The Last of His Race, *by Charles M. Russell, 1899*

revised and reprinted in 1906 and 1915, was followed by C. F. and F. M. Voegelin's *Map of North American Indian Languages*, which was prepared for the American Ethnological Society in 1941.

Maps relating to American Indians also continued to absorb the cartographic activities of the War Department during this period. The Indian campaigns which followed the Civil War from about 1865 to the 1890s required up-to-date strategic maps for planning purposes. Army regulations of 1873 required each military department which represented a geographical area to keep "in course of preparation a map of the territory comprised within the command, upon which will be embodied all geographical or other information useful in military operations." One of the more interesting Army departmental maps is the detailed military map of the Dakota Territory prepared by the Engineers Office of the Department of Dakota in 1895 (*Plate 199*). Printed on cloth for durability, it consisted of one index sheet and thirty-one map sheets showing Indian reservations, military posts, and wagon roads and trails; numerous notes described pertinent physical features.

Minerals maps have a long tradition in the United States dating from the work of David Dale Owen in 1840 (*see Plate 163*). With the advent of national and state geological surveys, a natural by-product was the maps that showed the location and distribution of mineral deposits. One such map was compiled in 1895 by Frederick J. H. Merrill, director of the New York State Museum in Albany. Using nonquantitative colored symbols of various shapes and designs, it depicts the location of portland cement, shale deposits, graphite, gypsum, gas fields, and other minerals. An expanded revision in 1904 showed the location of thirty-seven different substances.

Closing out the 1890s was a dramatic work that provides a graphic summation of nineteenth-century cartography as well as a preface to twentieth-century mapping. Entitled *Statistical Atlas of the United States, Based Upon the Results of the Eleventh Census*, it was compiled under the direction of Henry Gannett, Geographer to both the U.S. Census Bureau and the Geological Survey, and published by Julius Bien in 1898. In addition to introducing economic maps of manufacturing and mining and of the valuation of real and personal property, the 1898 *Statistical Atlas* represents the most comprehensive and imaginative use of graphs and analytical maps for depicting population, vital statistics, agricultural, medical, economic, and physiographic data until the 1930s (*Plate 200*). A large number of plates showing population distribution by ethnic group reflects an incipient national provincialism as the tide of immigration shifted in the 1880s from persons of English and northwest European stock to persons from southern and eastern Europe and Asia. Subsequent decennial atlases were prepared by the U.S. Census Bureau through 1920, but they lack the cartographic creativity of the 1898 work.

10. *Mapping an Industrialized United States*

The modern age in American cartography is characterized by a more scientific trend, and by the enormously widespread application of maps, not only in the scientific field, but also in the everyday life of people.

ERWIN RAISZ
General Cartography (1938)

SINCE 1900

THE WORK of the last three decades of the nineteenth century laid the foundation for the modern mapping of the United States. Scientific mapping and charting techniques, represented most explicitly by the U.S. Geological Survey and the U.S. Coast and Geodetic Survey, were well established by 1900, and little new activity was undertaken in topographic and hydrographic mapping until the 1950s. In sum, the general surface features of the United States had been delineated by the turn of the century. The major cartographic challenges and developments during the present century lay in the field of thematic or special purpose mapping. Influenced by new social and technological forces, both private and official mapmaking establishments responded with novel and innovative mapping techniques and map types which have provided a kaleidoscope of new cartographic images of the United States.

An appropriate and representative map with which to usher in the new century is the "Chautauqua Agricultural and Industrial Map of the United States and Possessions." Chautauqua, a national adult-education movement that was popular during the late nineteenth and early twentieth centuries, consisted of a program of courses and lectures in arts, science, humanities, and religion. This particular map was overprinted with tabular statistical accounts of agricultural crops and mining activities by state, and it illustrates an early attempt to depict statistical data in map format designed to be readily understood by the general public.

During this period industrial corporations also began to issue their own maps to advertise their products and their growth. A typical map by the United States Steel Corporation in 1903 shows the location of properties, railroad and steamship lines, smelters, iron ranges, and coal and gas fields controlled by the giant corporation (*Plate 201*). Created in 1901, the U.S. Steel Corporation signaled the emergence of the modern corporate unit in this country.

National inventories of soil and forest resources were based on systematic field observation made during this decade to complement the inventory of geological resources already underway. As bold and ambitious as the topographic and geological surveys undertaken by the U.S. Geological Survey, the county soil survey was designed by the Department of Agriculture to provide a national soil inventory as well as practical data to aid farmers in managing their farms. The product of these surveys was a succession of county maps that showed the boundaries of individual soil types by symbols and color tints. Each map was supplemented by a soil report which described the climate, physiography, geology, drainage, and land use of the area, together with a classification of the soil and predictions of crop yields under different systems of farm management. The first map was issued in 1899, but the program got underway only in the first decades of the twentieth century. By 1940 some 1,600 soil maps of counties and regions had been published. This cartographic data bank was systematized and condensed by Curtis F. Marbut and Francis J. Marschner in the form of a twelve-sheet "Soil Map of the United States." Published by August Hoen and Company in 1935, the first national soil map contained some 250 colored symbols denoting soil groups and types (*Plate 202*). An inset map specified the reliability of the survey data, indicating that detailed soil surveys were completed in the agricultural belt of the north central states, the coastal states of the South and East, and California. The mountainous sections of the country and the western portion of the Great Plains remained blank, signifying that these regions, even at that date, had not yet been fully surveyed and mapped.

The first comprehensive attempt to inventory forests on a

national basis was undertaken by Henry Gannett and the Division of Geography and Forestry of the U.S. Geological Survey between 1897 and 1903, when a series of land-classification maps of individual forests were prepared to show forest, cutover, and burntover areas, as well as irrigable and pasture lands. With the establishment of the U.S. Forest Service in 1905 and the growth of the conservation movement spurred by Theodore Roosevelt and Gifford Pinchot, Chief Forester of the Department of Agriculture, a series of thematic maps devoted to forestry was issued. Between 1908 and 1910 a large wall map of the United States was prepared that depicted the distribution of national forests and provided related information on principal watersheds and precipitation. Beginning also in 1908, the *Atlas of National Forests* was issued in folio format and depicted in detail such economic data for individual national forests as stands of commercial timber, grazing regions, mining areas and claims, and species of trees. The latter was compiled under the direction of A. C. Roberts and incorporated the work of the U.S. Geological Survey, the General Land Office, and the Hayden, Transcontinental, and Wheeler surveys.

Commercial cartography was revitalized during this decade by meeting the developing need for the automobile road map. In his article on oil-company road maps, Walter W. Ristow traces the evolution of this "uniquely American" contribution to cartography, from the scarce and rather crude guidebooks and maps of bicycle roads of the 1880s to the pervasive and sophisticated promotional road maps offered free by oil companies in the 1960s (see Bibliography). Although the early motorists preferred descriptive guidebooks, separate automobile road maps began to appear shortly after the turn of the century. These early road maps were either in the form of small-scale regional maps depicting unmarked roads in the proximity of large cities, such as Rand McNally's 1904 *New Automobile Road Map of New York City and Vicinity*, or in the form of small black-and-white strip maps that showed a single road and the location of important motoring and navigational aids along the route such as cafes, garages, hotels, schools, churches, and public buildings. Representative of the latter type was G. S. Chapin's series of "Photo Auto Maps," including one, dated 1907, of the road between Chicago and New York City, supplemented by photographic views and descriptions of interesting features (*Plate 203*), and F. S. Blanchard and Company's sectional road map of New England and the Hudson District, issued in 1908 and 1909.

Although most of the carto-statistical techniques in use today had already been developed in Europe by 1865, they were adopted slowly by American cartographers, whose focus was less on statistical maps and more on topographic, geologic, and transportation maps. An exception was the U.S. Census Bureau, which used the choropleth technique as early as 1870 to show statistical distribution by county or state units. As interest in thematic mapping increased, however, European methods for depicting economic and social data were gradually introduced. One such technique was the use of dots of uniform size to illustrate density of distribution. Devised in England in the late 1840s for medical maps, this technique was already adopted by the Commissioners of the District of Columbia by 1876 on maps of small areas to show the distribution of diseases. But it was the Department of Agriculture that first made extensive use of dot maps in this country. About 1905 W. J. Spillman compiled a series of dot maps of the United States based on the 1900 census showing the distribution of individual grasses and forage crops. Thirteen of these maps were published in Spillman's *Farm Grasses of the United States* in 1905; the twelve remaining manuscript maps now repose in the National Archives. From 1905 onward, dot maps were utilized to depict a wide variety of agricultural data. Many of these are described by William Heynen in his *Cartographic Records of the Bureau of Agricultural Economics* (see Bibliography). Particularly notable was the work of Henry C. Taylor, pioneer agricultural economist at the University of Wisconsin and the Department of Agriculture. From 1909 to 1912 Taylor prepared a series of some 100 dot maps of crops, livestock, farms, and rural population, based on the decennial censuses from 1840 (the date of the first agricultural census) to 1900, in order to analyze the historical and geographical expansion of American agriculture throughout that period.

Although the United States was still predominantly an agrarian nation in 1900, the urban network as it exists today was in essence established and it began to attract the attention of scholars interested in the analysis and interpretation of the modern city. An early contribution to urban studies was the pioneering attempt by the newly created Association of American Geographers to portray graphically the distribution and size of American towns and cities in 1910. Using a variety of nonquantitative symbols, eleven classes of urban centers were depicted, ranging in size of population from one thousand to five million, with the heaviest concentration located in the northeast and midwest regions of the country.

The cartographic treatment of the geographical distribution of plants dates from the elementary land classification maps of the Western surveys of the 1870s and from Sargent's forest atlas of 1883 (see page 315), but these early maps were limited to individual forest or prairie species. It was at the urging of a German publishing firm in Leipzig that John W. Harshberger, professor of botany at the University of Pennsylvania, prepared in 1911 the first comprehensive work on the vegetation of North America. Harshberger's *Phytogeographic Survey of North America* was accompanied by a striking wall map of the vegetation of North America which illustrated twenty-nine plant communities by a combination of color tints and pattern symbols. This distinctive achievement was followed by Forest Shreve's 1917 map of vegetation areas of the United States, published by the American Geographical Society, and H. L. Shantz and R. Zon's map of natural vegetation, published as part of the *Atlas of American Agriculture* in 1924 (see page 328).

An international program of unprecedented scope was initiated in 1908 to map topographically the entire land surface of the earth, at a standardized scale of one inch to approximately sixteen miles (1 : 1,000,000) and in a uniform style. Entitled the *International Map of the World*, it was first suggested by the German geographer Albrecht Penck at the International Geographical Congress at Berne in 1891, and adopted at the congress at Geneva in 1908. From 1913 to 1953 this project was administered by an international committee headquartered at the British Ordnance Survey, Southampton, and since 1953 by the Cartographic Section of the Department of Economic and Social Affairs at the United Nations in New York. Penck's formal proposal, according to the cartographic historian Norman J. W. Thrower, began the modern period of cartography (see Bibliography).

Thirty-five countries initially participated in the map program; eventually it will consist of 1,500 sheets, each covering an area of four degrees of latitude and six degrees of longitude or approximately 73,700 to 122,000 square miles, depending on location. The continental United States will be contained in forty-two sheets prepared by the U.S. Geological Survey. The first three sheets were issued between 1912 and 1915: they cover the regions around Boston, San Francisco (*Plate 204*), and Point Conception, California. Little additional progress was made until after World War II. Twenty-two sheets have now been completed, covering primarily the coastal regions; these are complemented by twenty sheets of the World Aeronautical Chart series, issued initially by the Army Air Force and more recently by the U.S. Defense Mapping Agency Aerospace Center in St. Louis, Missouri. The latter series is designed primarily for navigation. Also compiled at the scale of 1 : 1,000,000, the World Aeronautical Chart series has been adopted as the standard world aeronautical chart by the International Civil Aviation Organization. Together, these two series provide complete coverage of the United States at the intermediate scale of one inch to approximately sixteen miles. Designed for general and scientific purposes, each sheet depicts principal cities and towns, railroads, political boundaries, roads, and water and topographic features. Because of the extreme variety of topographic features over the earth, surface relief is illustrated by variable contour intervals; these reduce contour crowding in mountainous regions and increase contours in lowland areas, for better visual effect. Reflecting their heritage, recent issues are bilingual (French and English) and contain standardized international symbols so that they can be read anywhere in the world, regardless of differences in language.

About the same time commercial publishers began issuing automobile road maps of individual states. Otto G. Lindberg, trained at the Technical University of Helsingfors, Finland, and founder of the General Drafting Company in 1909, prepared a road map of Vermont in 1912 for the fledgling Automobile Association of America. By 1914, the year in which the first drive-in gasoline service station appeared, banks and oil companies were distributing by mail and through service stations free automobile road maps of high quality as part of their promotional campaigns.

Major publishers of automobile road maps during the second and third decades were Rand McNally, General Drafting, and H. M. Gousha. In his history of Rand McNally, Duncan M. Fitchet credits that venerable map-producing company with conceiving the idea of marking roads and highways for easier identification by the motorist (see Bibliography). Names, symbols, and marks were stenciled on telephone and electric power poles along principal routes, notes Fitchet, enabling the map publisher to identify these routes by corresponding map symbols.

PLATE 201: White and Kemble. "Map Showing the Properties of The United States Steel Corporation." 1903. Chromolithograph, 48.5 × 61 cm. Geography and Map Division, Library of Congress, Washington, D.C. *Promotional industrial map depicting the concentration of economic power of U.S. Steel, the first billion-dollar holding company, organized in 1901 by a group of Chicago and New York financiers. Lithographed by Edward Aberle, New York City; color symbols and tints illustrate the location of companies, railroads, steamship lines, and mineral and ore deposits controlled by the corporation in the Midwest and Northeast.*

(opposite) PLATE 202: Curtis F. Marbut and Francis J. Marschner. "Soil Map of the United States." 1935. Photolithograph, each sheet 50 × 72.5 cm. Records of the Bureau of Agricultural Economics, National Archives, Washington, D.C. *Title sheet of first synoptic soil map of the entire country, in twelve sheets. Based on thirty-six years of soil research, the map contains some 250 different colored patterns denoting soil groups and types, lithographed by August Hoen and Company, Baltimore, for the U.S. Department of Agriculture. From O. E. Baker's* Atlas of American Agriculture, *issued in eight parts from 1917 to 1935, and as a bound volume in 1936 by the U.S. Bureau of Agricultural Economics.*

A series of sectional maps known as "Auto Trails Maps" was issued by Rand McNally to illustrate these marked highways (*Plate 205*), and by 1922 this series covered the entire United States. Rand McNally also developed the concept of numbering highways, which was first implemented on a statewide basis in Wisconsin in 1917. Six years later General Drafting published the earliest road map in two colors by offset lithography, a new printing process which was cheaper and faster than conventional lithography and particularly suited for the constant updating that automobile road maps required. The first road map to be published by this process was a map of New Jersey. Principal routes were shown in red. Some 280,000 copies of this map were distributed by the Standard Oil Company of New Jersey. (Walter W. Ristow has estimated that by the 1960s more than 200 million oil-company road maps were being dispensed annually in an effort "to stimulate travel and promote the use of petroleum products";

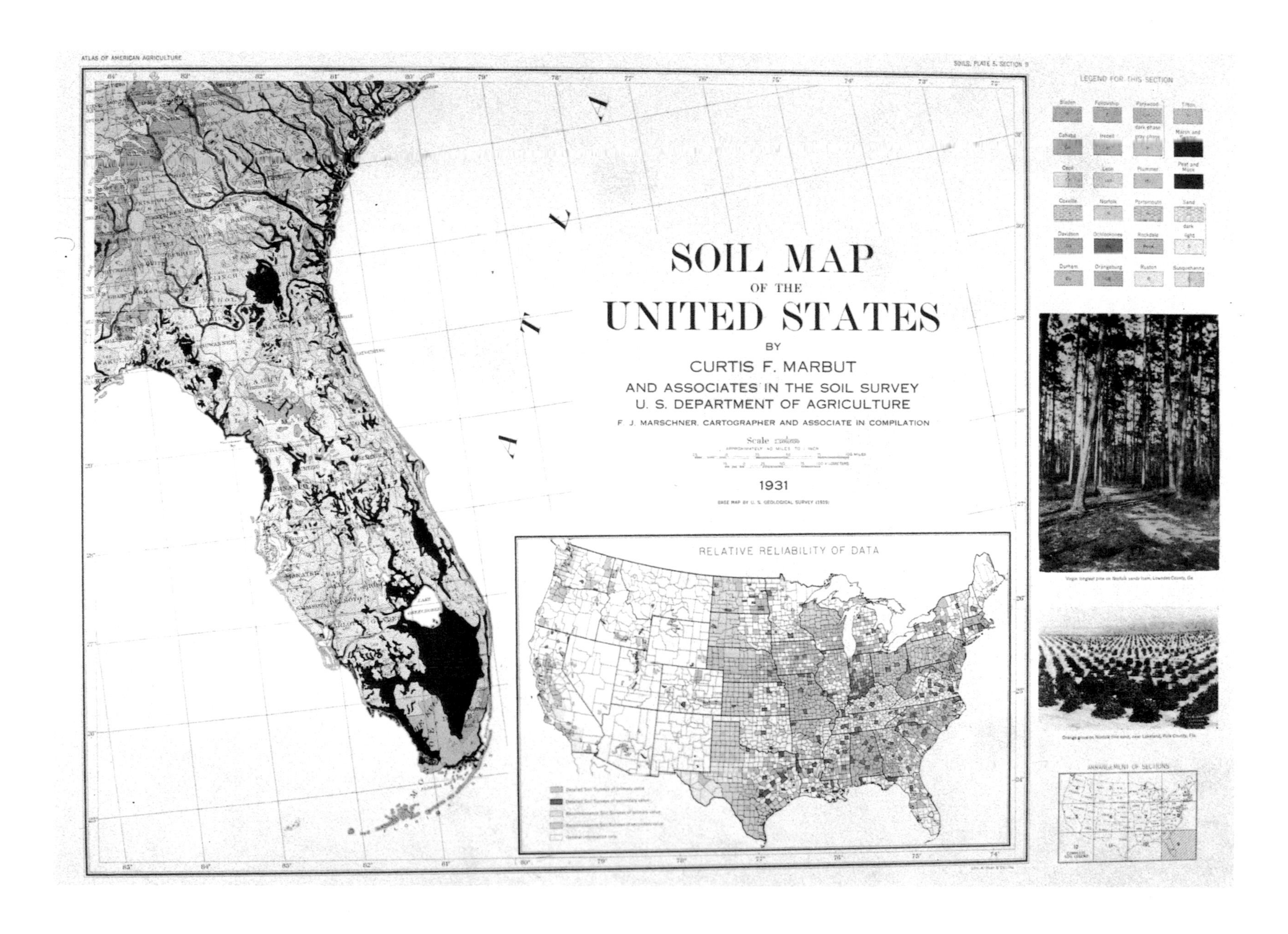

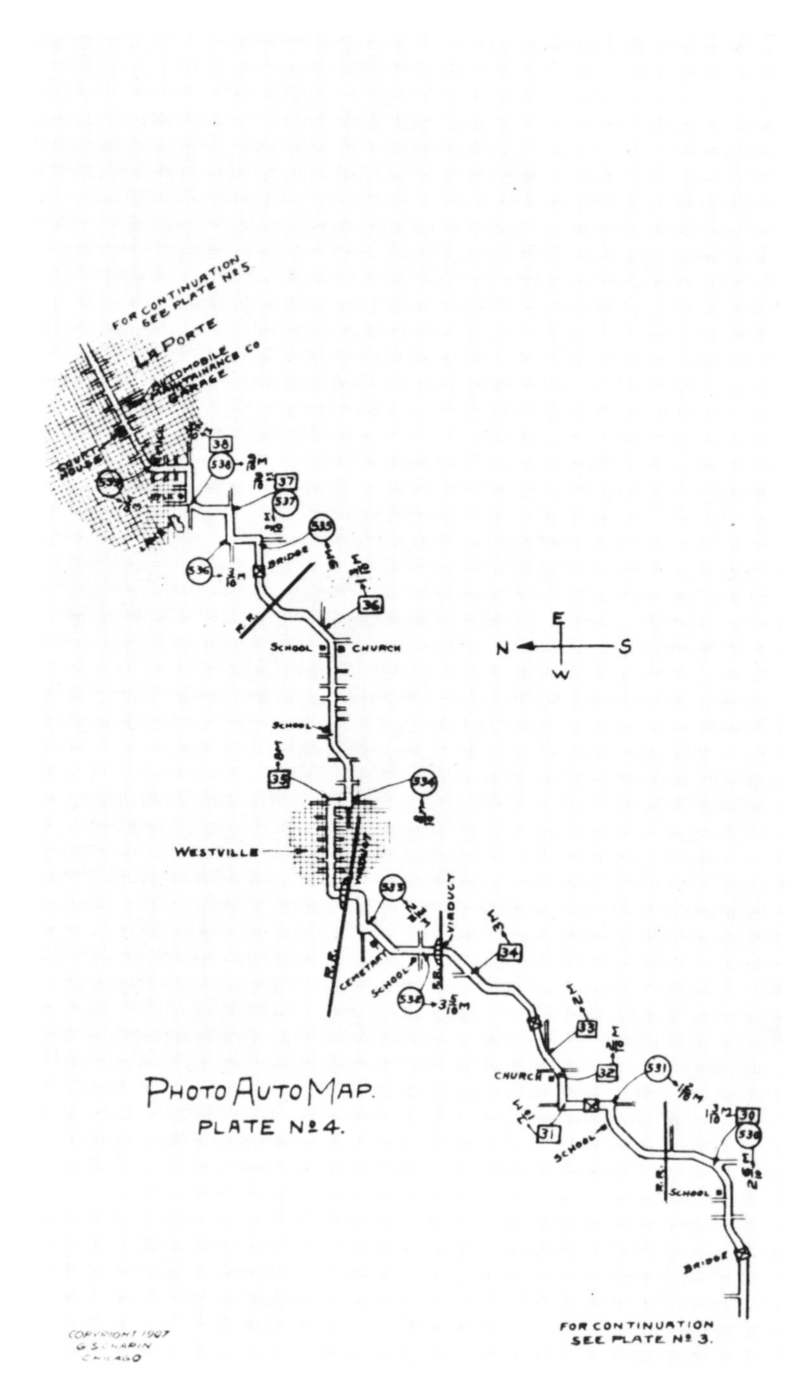

PLATE 203: G. S. Chapin. "Photo Auto Map. Plate No. 4." 1907. Lithograph, 19 × 10.5 cm. Geography and Map Division, Library of Congress, Washington, D.C. *A typical sheet from a series of early road maps showing a stretch in Indiana with mileages, bridges, viaducts, railroad crossings, location of important service centers, and directional aids such as ice houses, garages, hotels, cemeteries, schools, churches, and public buildings.*

"Why! Good Afternoon! Yes it is a shame, he should have fixed that before we came."

see Bibliography.) The availability of inexpensive government state maps and free automobile road maps caused the commercial publishers to discontinue the sale of individual state maps by the 1920s.

Until about 1913–14, American educators relied heavily upon European firms for good educational wall maps of the United States. These were characterized by bold lettering and generalized features which conveyed essential information at a distance, indispensable qualities for wall maps. A striking example of the dramatic workmanship of European wall maps is illustrated by R. Barmm's industrial map of the United States, published by Georg Westermann of Braunschweig, Germany, in 1914 (*Plate 206*). Enhanced by large, strikingly colored symbols, this map vividly shows the relationship of water and rail transportation to the resources of the United States; ranks the major industrial centers by size; depicts the geographical distribution of coalfields in Appalachia and Illinois, the iron and steel industry extending from New York to Milwaukee, and the textile industry stretching from Portland, Maine, to Durham, North Carolina; and reveals the value and tonnage of imports and exports at major ports.

Pedagogical advances in American methods of teaching during

this decade, however, led to improved educational wall maps by American publishers. Between 1914 and 1924 some 170 wall maps were issued, beginning with J. Paul Goode's political map series published by Rand McNally. Many of these wall maps were reviewed in the American Geographical Society's *Geographical Review*, notably by the cartographic scholar W. L. G. Joerg (see Bibliography). While continuing to rely upon European maps and atlases as sources for their maps of ancient and European history, American commercial mapmakers made a distinctive contribution in their American historical maps, since in this field there were no foreign models to emulate. Most notable was the Hart American History Series, published in Chicago by Denoyer-Geppert Company, 1918–21 (*Plate 207*). This series of historical maps reflected Professor James Harvey Robinson's *The New History*, published in 1912, which emphasized "totality" in approaching the study of all social facts; it dealt with such subjects as exploration and colonization, military campaigns, and economic developments in agriculture, industry, and transportation in addition to the traditional topics of politics and territorial gain. Equally

An early gas station, New York

as significant was Vernon C. Finch's *Commercial Geography of the United States Series*, brought out in 1919 by another Chicago map-publishing firm, A. J. Nystrom and Company. Finch utilized the dot method to illustrate the distribution of agricultural and manufacturing products and industries.

The portrayal of surface topography on maps so that it can be easily visualized remains one of the major challenges facing cartographers. By 1914 the scientific community had generally come to accept the contour technique for illustrating surface relief on maps, but cartographers continued to experiment with new ways of expressing topographic features for nonscientists. One result of these efforts was a series of shaded relief maps prepared initially by John H. Renshawe of the U.S. Geological Survey. Beginning in 1914, Renshawe devised a technique in which a system of graduated shading replaced contours for representing highlands and lowlands (*Plate 208*). At first restricted to maps of national parks, the Renshawe technique was soon utilized for state maps of wall-size dimensions, overprinting them to show drainage patterns, railroads, county boundaries, and names of principal towns. The production of this series ceased in the 1930s but was resumed after World War II, when the use of tools such as the airbrush allowed the cartographic artist to achieve a wider range of tonal gradation than was possible by hand.

More effective and dramatic in its visual impact, however, was the innovative work of Arnim K. Lobeck. A trained geomorphologist and gifted artist, Lobeck perfected the physiographic or landform map. This entirely new method of depicting relief, whose origin can be traced to the work of the noted geomorphologist and physical geographer William Morris Davis, emphasized the geomorphological structure of landforms through exaggerated perspective views rather than mere depiction of elevation. Lobeck's first "Physiographic Diagram of the United States" was printed by August Hoen and Company and published by A. J. Nystrom and Company in 1921, when the author was a young assistant professor of geology at the University of Wisconsin. Lobeck's map divided the United States into seventeen physiographic units, and provided for the first time a vivid and realistic impression of the rugged character of the mountains, plains, and plateaus that comprise much of the United States. The physiographic technique was further elaborated and systematized by Erwin J. Raisz who classified and standardized physiographic symbols (see Bibliography). His map of the landforms of the

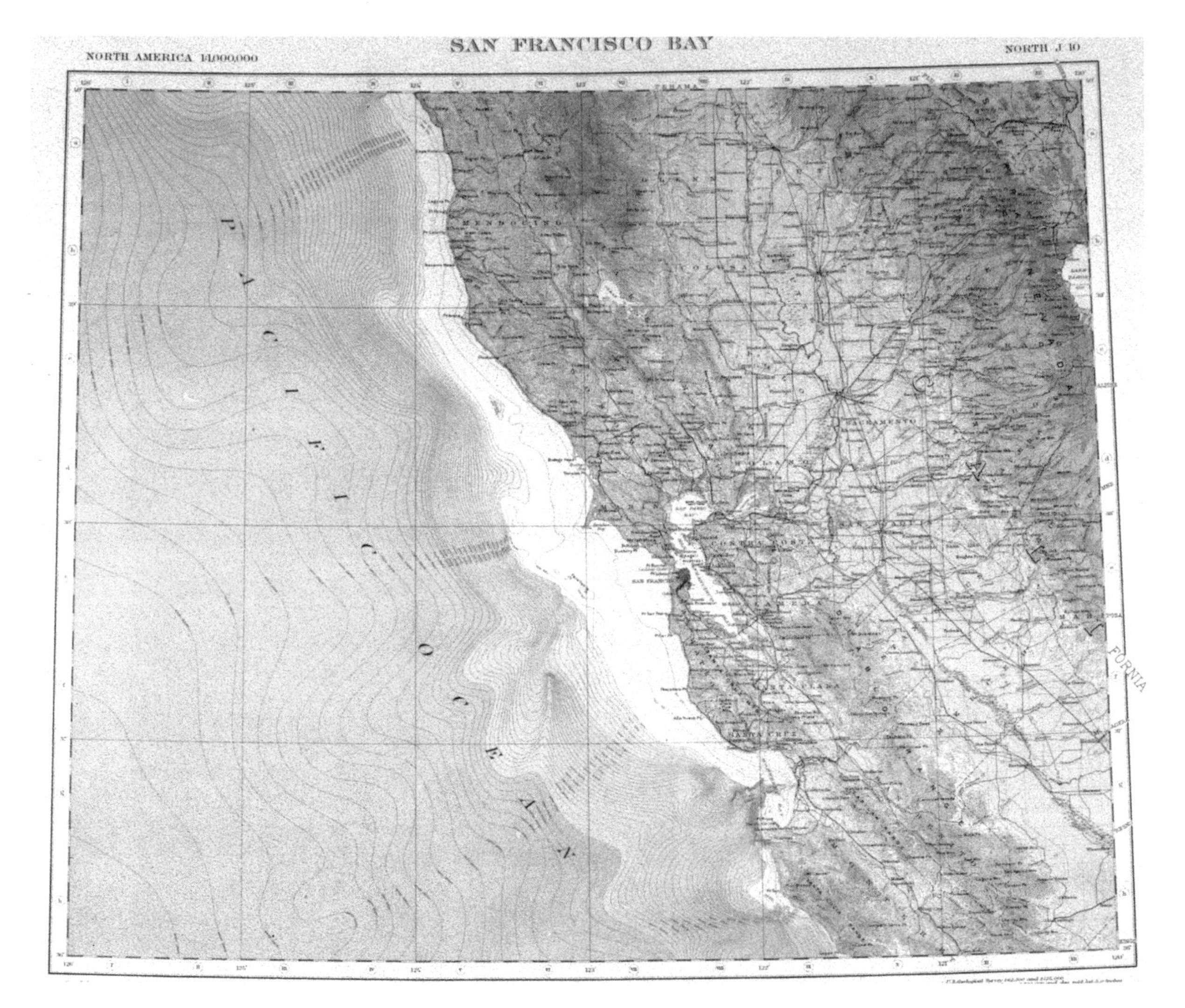

PLATE 204: A. F. Hassan. "San Francisco Bay." 1914. Color engraving, 61 × 63 cm. Records of the U.S. Geological Survey, National Archives, Washington, D.C. *A sheet from the United States contribution, by the U.S. Geological Survey, to the* International Map of the World, *the first international effort to map systematically the entire world at an intermediate scale using a standardized format. Graduated color tints and contour lines depict surface relief and bathymetric depth.*

(opposite) PLATE 205: Rand McNally and Company. "Auto Trails Map. Southern Wisconsin. Northern Illinois." 1917. Wax engraving, 85.5 × 50.5 cm. Geography and Map Division, Library of Congress, Washington, D.C. *One of the first numbered highway maps showing the road system between Chicago and Milwaukee. Roads are differentiated by width, the larger ones identified by separate numbers and symbols. Road maps such as this one came to dominate commercial mapmaking during the twentieth century.*

United States, first prepared in 1939 to accompany Wallace W. Atwood's *Physiographic Provinces of North America*, remains a standard work for students of geology and geography (*Plate 209*).

The final cartographic contribution of the second decade was the commencement of the remarkable *Atlas of American Agriculture* in 1917. It was prepared by the Department of Agriculture under the direction of O. E. Baker, a former student of Henry C. Taylor at the University of Wisconsin; Baker used a historical-geographical approach to illustrate graphically the physical and economic forces that shaped the development of American agriculture. Sections of the atlas appeared in folio format from 1917 through 1935, as soon as they were completed; these included separate folios on annual precipitation, frost, rural population, cotton, precipitation and humidity, natural vegetation, temperature, and soils. The eight folios were bound and reprinted as a single volume in 1936.

One of the major impacts upon cartography during the 1920s was the airplane. This provided a new and cheaper method for gathering topographic data in the form of the aerial photograph and, alternatively, stimulated the production of maps as aids to air navigation. Aerial photography had received its initial impetus during World War I, and it was tested extensively during the 1920s for mapping purposes by both private firms and government agencies. Although large areas were not mapped by aerial

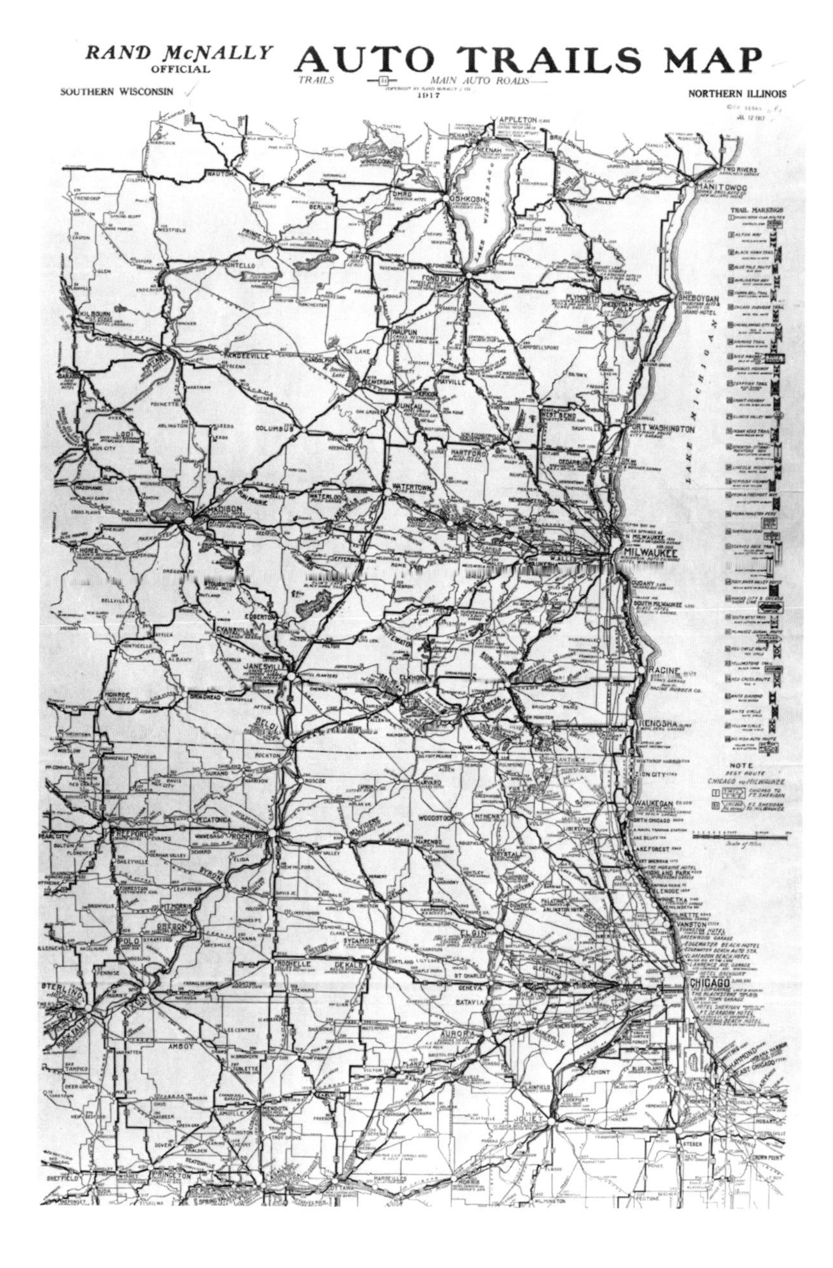

photography until the 1930s, the first topographic map made in the United States by aerial photogrammetric techniques was the "Schoolcraft, Michigan," quadrangle map prepared by the U.S. Geological Survey in 1921. The photographs used for the compilation of this map were taken with a single-lens aerial camera by the Army Air Service; three years later the Fairchild Aerial Camera Corporation photographed and mapped some 625 square miles of New York City.

The aircraft era also required maps as navigational aids. Early aviators relied upon existing general maps, particularly those depicting railroad lines: railroads, given favorable weather, could easily be seen from open cockpits and followed to their destinations. But these maps soon proved less than suitable as air speeds and altitudes increased and air distances expanded. The Army Air Service, introduced to French and Italian air navigational charts during World War I, authorized in 1923 the production of air navigation strip maps which showed prominent features along Army air routes between principal cities in the continental United States (*Plate 210*). The Air Service strip map series consisted of fifty-two maps, when completed in 1927. Significant features important to air safety and navigation were exaggerated on the charts to facilitate identification, such as airports, auxiliary landing fields, radio ranges, beacons, and high steel towers. As a result of the Air Commerce Act of 1926, the Coast and Geodetic Survey began to compile a new series of strip maps in 1927 which provided coverage for the civilian commercial routes then being established. These maps covered strips of territory about eight miles wide and included essentially the same information as the earlier Air Service maps.

Sectional maps for air navigation over the entire United States were introduced by Rand McNally in 1928. Known as "Air Trails Maps," this series consisted of standard state maps overprinted in red to show airport information and isogonic lines. When the cost became prohibitive for commercial publishing, the Coast and Geodetic Survey assumed responsibility in 1930 for preparing sectional air navigational charts. The Coast and Geodetic sectional charts were more sophisticated and detailed than the Air Trails Maps and were especially designed for general flying as well as navigation. A complete series of eighty-seven sectional charts at a scale of eight miles to the inch was ready in 1937. Each chart was flight-checked before final publication, and periodically thereafter for accuracy and new features.

Sten de Geer, a Swedish geographer whose work strongly influenced American statistical mapping in the areas of population and economics, prepared an influential map in 1927 showing the distribution and intensity of manufacturing in the United States. This pioneering attempt to present graphically the manufacturing region was published in *Geografiska Annaler* under the title, "The Manufacturing Belt of North America and its Cities

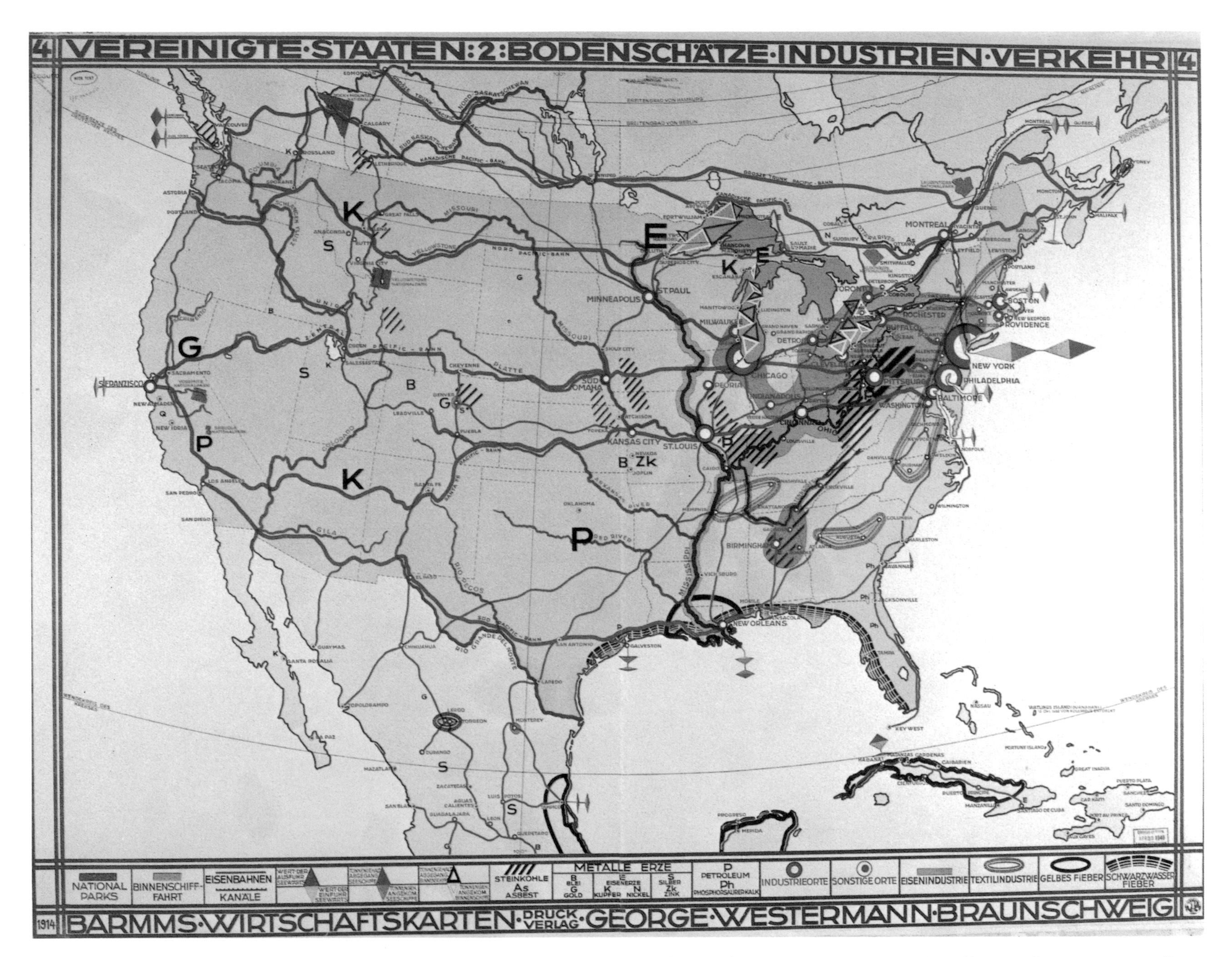

PLATE 206: R. Barmm. "Wirtschaftskarten (Industrial Map)." 1914. Chromolithograph, 89 × 118 cm. Geography and Map Division, Library of Congress, Washington, D.C. *A dramatic German-produced economic wall map of the United States, published by Georg Westermann, Braunschweig, Germany. Characterized by bold lettering and symbols. Issued on the eve of World War I in Europe, the map depicts the geographical distribution and intensity of mineral and industrial resources, transportation networks, and international trade—also dangerous fevers.* The Chicago Sunday Tribune *reproduced this map in full color with English translation, warning that its detailed portrayal of important industrial points provided a sinister enemy with the information needed to "paralyze the greatest manufacturing nation of the world."*

(opposite) PLATE 207: R. Baxter Blair. "Lines of Transportation." 1918. Chromolithograph, 79 × 113 cm. Geography and Map Division, Library of Congress, Washington, D.C. *Educational wall map in the Hart American History Series, published by Denoyer-Geppert Company, Chicago. An innovative series designed to incorporate recent advances in the study of history, which utilized social and economic data to a greater extent than before. Portrays major railroads and waterways in the United States at what was to be the peak of the railroad era.*

according to their Number of Wage-Earners in 1919." De Geer's work was followed by more thorough graphic treatments by American geographers in professional journals in the late 1930s, utilizing the 1930 census of manufacturing.

Business-oriented sales and investment maps became popular during the second and third decades. Prepared primarily for bankers, merchants, and investors, these special purpose maps provided businessmen with graphic aids for analyzing and interpreting domestic trade and investments. Two early producers of these "guide charts of commerce," as the geographer Helen M. Strong labeled them, were Roger W. Babson and Arthur T. Emery. Babson, a market analyst, issued his maps periodically from about 1912 to 1930 along with his "Reports on Fundamental [Economic] Conditions" (*Plate 211*).

Although the U.S. Census Bureau ceased to publish statistical atlases after the 1920 census, population and other statistical data from the decennial censuses has continued to stimulate the development of new cartographic products. The Census of Distri-

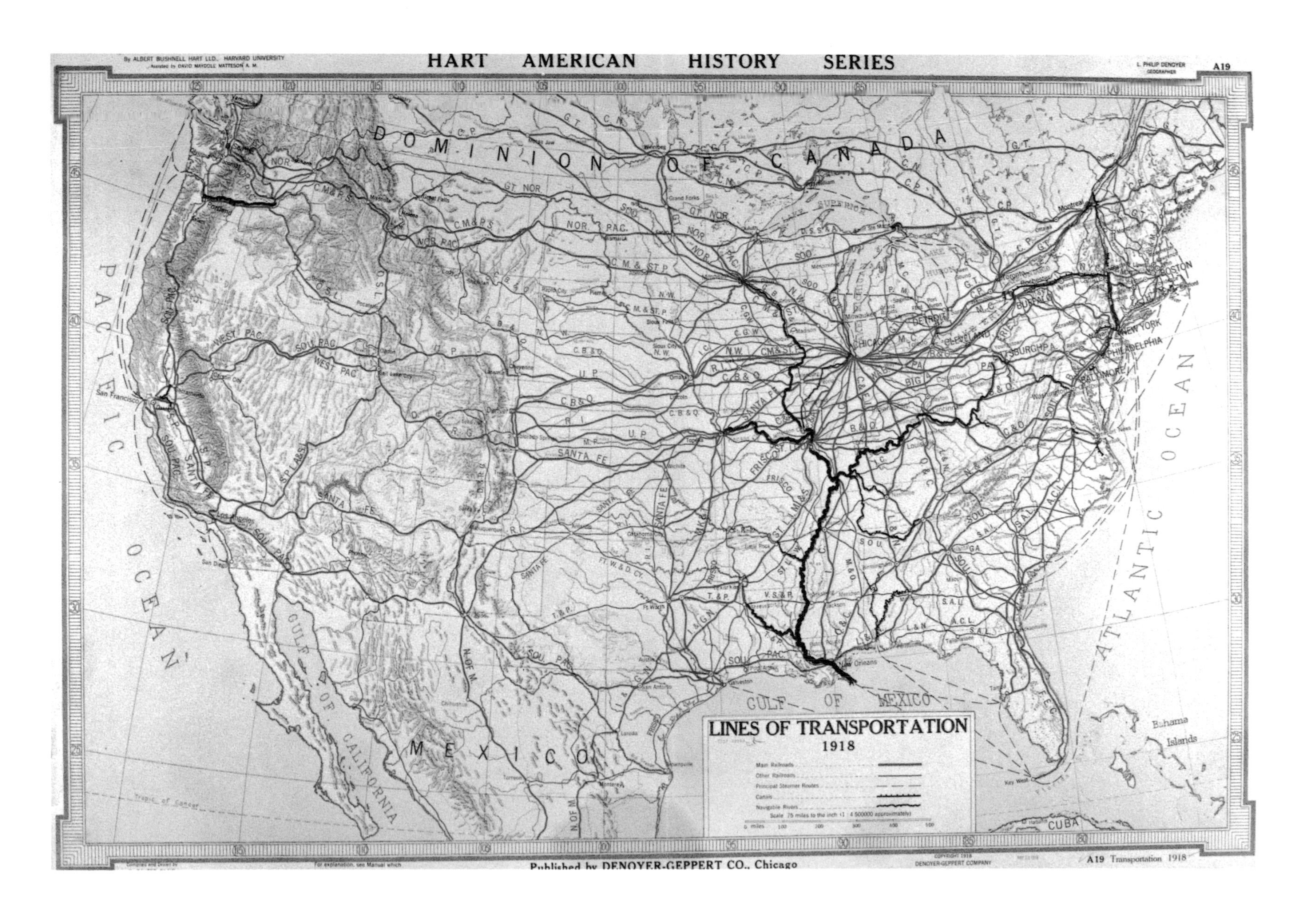

Boston Airport, seen from a Navy plane

bution of 1929, for example, provided detailed distributional data for mapping the trading areas and trading population of domestic commerce. Although a few production and marketing maps appeared as early as the turn of the century, it was not until the census of 1929 and later production and distribution censuses that the necessary statistics became available for reliable marketing maps that depicted business activities to be compiled on a national basis. One of the earliest was a general map of the United States delimiting 183 wholesale grocery marketing areas which accompanied the *Market Data Handbook of the United States*, published in 1929. Walter W. Ristow, in his list of marketing maps in the Library of Congress, describes some 150 different marketing maps and atlases produced during the 1930s (see Bibliography).

Subsequent decennial censuses of distribution resulted in a similar outpouring of marketing maps showing trading areas, industrial markets, retail sales, and distribution of income. Many of these maps were "distorted" to emphasize economic factors rather than geographic area (*Plate 212*).

The census of 1930 provided data for "A New Population Map of the United States," designed by Professor Floyd A. Stilgenbauer of the College of the City of Detroit (*Plate 213*). Stilgenbauer employed dots of uniform size to show the distribution of rural population, and proportional circles to classify urban areas. Large metropolitan areas of over 650,000 inhabitants were indicated by area symbols colored black. This map provided the first accurate impression of the population distribution of the United States, although the solid black symbols tended to magnify population density in the northeast. Eleven inset maps illustrated metropolitan areas that numbered over one million inhabitants. This map was published in black-and-white at wall-map size by Rand McNally and Company in 1932, and set the standard for later population maps.

A major publishing event in 1932 was the issuance of the *Atlas of the Historical Geography of the United States.* Compiled by C. O. Paullin between 1913 and 1927 and published jointly by the Carnegie Institution of Washington and the American Geographical Society of New York, it still provides, in the words of John K. Wright of the American Geographical Society, "a graphic concept of how the United States had gradually grown and changed and become more complex since the earliest settlement" (see Bibliography). Influenced by James Harvey Robinson's "new history," Paullin used some 620 maps to illustrate cartographically the natural environment, explorers' routes, Indian distribution and contact, land policies and practices, population density and settlement patterns, cultural and religious developments, political opinions and reform movements, economic and transportation growth, city plans, and military campaigns. This remarkable work remains, as Wright observed in 1932, "one of the most comprehensive historical atlases that has ever been produced for a single nation."

An unprecedented expansion of Federal cartographic activities took place during the remainder of the 1930s as President Franklin Roosevelt's New Deal, the broadest national planning program ever undertaken by the United States during peacetime, was inaugurated in 1933 in an effort to blunt the effects of the economic depression. An early focus of these Federal programs was agricultural and natural resources.

Two land-use maps issued by the United States Bureau of Agricultural Economics in 1933 graphically depict the problems confronting New Deal administrators in formulating a national agricultural policy for a nation characterized by enormous physical diversity. A map of the "Natural Land-Use Areas of the United States," compiled by C. P. Barnes and drawn by Francis

PLATE 208: John H. Renshawe. "Panoramic View of the Yosemite National Park, California." 1914. Photolithograph, 54.5 × 65 cm. Records of the U.S. Geological Survey, National Archives, Washington, D.C. *Renshawe devised this new technique, the shaded relief map, for the U.S. Geological Survey to convey to nonscientists the impression of surface relief. A typical example, printed by the U.S. Geological Survey. Initially restricted to maps of national parks, the Geological Survey adopted this technique in the 1920s for their series of state wall maps.*

J. Marschner, revealed 272 separate regions based on local environmental differences in climate, topography, soil, geological formations, natural vegetation, and drainage systems. An even greater variation of agricultural areas was revealed by F. F. Elliott's map of types of farming areas. Based on the 1930 census of agriculture, Elliott showed no fewer than 514 farming regions as determined by the relative proportion of gross income derived from agricultural products, such as grain, cotton, tobacco, soy beans, fruit, dairy, poultry, animals, and forests. By using the value of production as a measure of types of farming, Elliott introduced critical social and economic factors into the graphic classification of agricultural units.

Soil erosion conditions, aggravated by the droughts of the early 1930s, were surveyed nationwide by the Department of Agriculture on a county-by-county basis in 1934. The results were summarized on thirty-four reconnaissance erosion survey state maps and on the reconnaissance erosion survey map of the United States in 1935. The latter map was printed by August Hoen and Company, and utilized color tints and line pattern symbols to illustrate thirty categories of surface sheet and wind erosion.

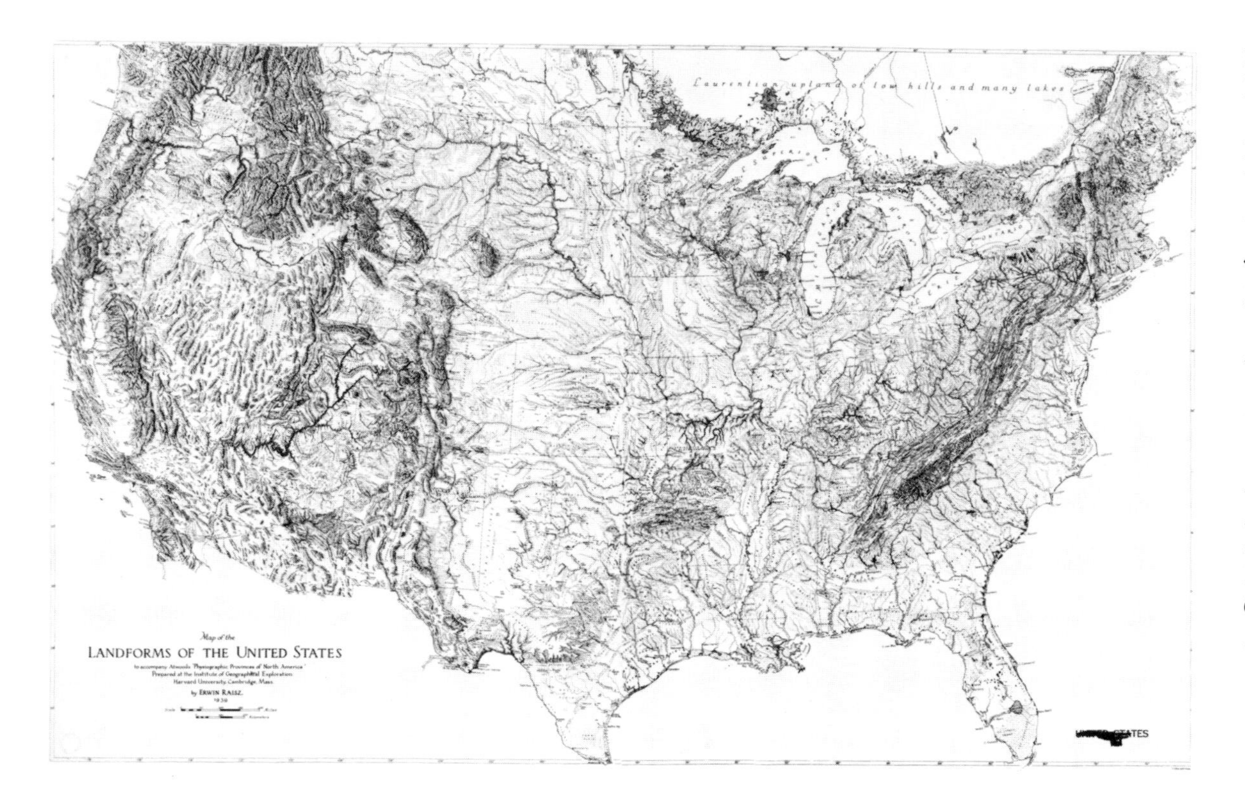

PLATE 209: Erwin J. Raisz. "Map of the Landforms of the United States . . ." 1939. Lithograph, 64 × 101 cm. Reference Collection, National Archives, Washington, D.C. *A physiographic map of the United States showing the geomorphological structure of landforms through exaggerated perspective views. This technique, uniquely American, was perfected by Arnim K. Lobeck of Columbia University, New York, and further elaborated and systematized by Erwin J. Raisz, who classified and standardized physiographic symbols. This map was first prepared to accompany Wallace W. Atwood's* Physiographic Provinces of North America *(published in 1939 by Ginn and Company, Boston), and it remains a standard work for students of geography and geomorphology.*

Similarly, soil productivity was depicted on Marbut and Marschner's national soil classification map of 1935 described above (*see Plate 202*). From 1933 onward, the year in which the Agricultural Adjustment Administration inaugurated the first nationwide aerial mapping program, soil survey maps were prepared with the aid of low-cost aerial photographs.

Recreational maps, a specialized type of land-use map, began to be produced in great numbers during this period in recognition of the ever-increasing urban concentration of the population, together with its increased mobility and leisure time. Representative works published by the National Resources Planning Board include a map of "The Geography of Recreation," which illustrated the relation between population distribution and national recreational areas, and a map of "Winter Sports in New England," which depicted a variety of winter activities by pictorial rather than geometrical symbols (*Plate 214*).

A wide assortment of population maps were prepared to show population density, movement, and economic conditions. The map designers of the New Deal era experimented with a wide assortment of sophisticated cartographic techniques in order to display this areal data. An interesting map of the Upper Mississippi region by the Mississippi Valley Committee of the National Resources Planning Board, for example, uses the isopleth method (lines on a map connecting points of equal density or value of any element to illustrate distribution) to show the relative social-economic status of the population (*Plate 215*). Each county in the six-state region was rated according to "level of well being," a quantitative assessment derived from a combined analysis of population density, farm abandonment, gross productivity, net income, and standard of living for the decade 1920–30. Francis J. Marschner of the Bureau of Agricultural Economics, on the other hand, used the dasymetric method (color or shading on a map to represent discrete, homogeneous areas without regard to statistical or administrative boundaries) to portray rural population density in the southern Appalachians, a region characterized by irregular population patterns because of the rough terrain.

One of the major national inventories undertaken by the

Roosevelt administration was the real property survey of some 370 towns and cities. Its objective was to identify and classify the availability and condition of urban housing. The data collected during these surveys by the Federal Housing Administration from 1934 to 1939 resulted in the preparation of large-scale cadastral-type maps of cities which listed for each block the average monthly rent, total number of dwelling units, number of structures used for business purposes, and percents of residential structures needing major repairs or unfit for use, of dwelling units without private toilet or bath, and of households of a race other than white (*Plate 216*). The Federal Housing Administration also prepared innovative analytical maps of the age and condition of structures; dynamic maps showing various aspects of the growth of individual cities; functional maps showing the locations of residential, commercial, and business areas; and housing-market analysis maps delineating the areas in which mortgage insurance could safely be provided. Taken together, these maps provided a unique portrait of American cities during the 1930s.

Finally, the New Deal spurred the production of general planning maps and atlases prepared by Federal, state, and local planning boards that had sprung up throughout the country. One of these boards prepared the earliest state atlas devoted entirely to thematic maps: entitled *List of State Planning Board Maps showing existing conditions in Maine*, it was compiled by Arthur H. Lewis and published by the State Planning Board of Maine. The atlas is copiously illustrated by fifty-two maps covering transportation, agriculture and land utilization, conservation, recreation, public utilities, sanitation, housing and living conditions, and labor and industry.

Night landing in the early days of flight, 1922

The unremitting growth of motor transportation and the rapid expansion and alteration of highway systems continued to stimulate the production of road maps. By 1930 some ten major oil companies were distributing their own free, up-to-date road maps to motorists through gasoline stations. Walter Ristow notes that many innovations were introduced by road-map publishers during this decade: inset maps of cities appeared about 1930, four-color offset lithography was developed in 1933, and distances between principal points and mileage tables were added to aid the motorist.

Federal aid for highway construction increased significantly during the 1930s. With the passage of the Federal-Aid Road Acts of 1916 and 1921, Federal and state governments once again became roadbuilders on a large scale, and since 1922 the Bureau of Public Roads has issued periodically a series of progress maps showing the improvement of the Federal-Aid Highway System. This series consists of 114 sheets covering the entire United States, and depicts principal highways, cities, railroads, rivers, state boundaries, and national forests. More detailed was the series of transportation maps inaugurated jointly in 1934 by the Bureau of Public Roads and the state highway departments. Printed in three colors at a scale of one inch to four miles on sheets of uniform size, measuring 26 by 36 inches, these maps show all important transportation facilities: roads, railroads, airways and airports, canals, and dredged channels. This series now covers the continental United States in 438 sheets.

Censuses of highway traffic were portrayed graphically during the 1930s by novel flow-line maps which gave the impression of movement by varying the width of traffic line symbols according to the volume of traffic. Beginning in 1934, the Bureau of Public Roads began issuing a series of these dynamic maps by state, showing the average and maximum volumes of traffic flow of passenger and commercial vehicles over a twenty-four-hour period (*Plate 217*).

The Linguistic Society of America proposed a systematic

survey in 1929 of the spoken languages in the United States, which found initial expression in Hans Kurath's preliminary and experimental *Linguistic Atlas of New England*, published in five volumes in 1939. Based on extensive field work carried out from 1931 to 1937, Kurath mapped the essential features of dialects and speech habits of representative social groups in a limited number of New England communities, to display both their numerical and geographic distributions. Although the Linguistic Society's ambitious objective has not yet been fulfilled, Kurath's efforts have been followed by local works, such as Carroll E. Reed's *Linguistic Atlas of Pennsylvania German* (1954) and Glenn G. Gilbert's *Linguistic Atlas of Texas German* (1972).

The areal distribution and intensity of American manufacturing was the focus of an atlas prepared by the Bureau of the Census in 1940, the first full cartographic treatment of this subject. Based on data from the 1937 Census of Manufactures, this folio consists of 117 small-scale maps of the United States showing the location by county of establishments, wage earners, and value added by manufacture of thirty-nine national industries. It provides a graphic summary of United States industrial strength on the eve of World War II.

A detailed and decorative series of regional maps of the United States was introduced by the National Geographic Society in 1940. The six-sheet series was completed in 1950 and provided a ten-color reference map of the country equivalent in size to four by seven feet. Containing a wealth of information, the series is valuable for inclusion of some 42,000 placenames, principal railroads and canals, natural features, important highways and roads, national parks, and other features of scenic and historic interest. The maps were drawn on the Albers conical equal area map projection, a basic system of parallels and meridians that minimizes areal distortion on a map.

One of the final cartographic contributions of the New Deal era was C. W. Thornthwaite's *Atlas of Climatic Types in the United States, 1900–1939*. Published by the Department of Agriculture in 1941, Thornthwaite's work summarizes forty years of climatological data in graphic format and reveals the intricate relationship between climatic type and natural vegetation.

For the remainder of the 1940s American cartographers and cartographic establishments were absorbed by the war effort and its aftermath. Few new maps of the United States were produced during these years. An interesting method of cartographic ex-

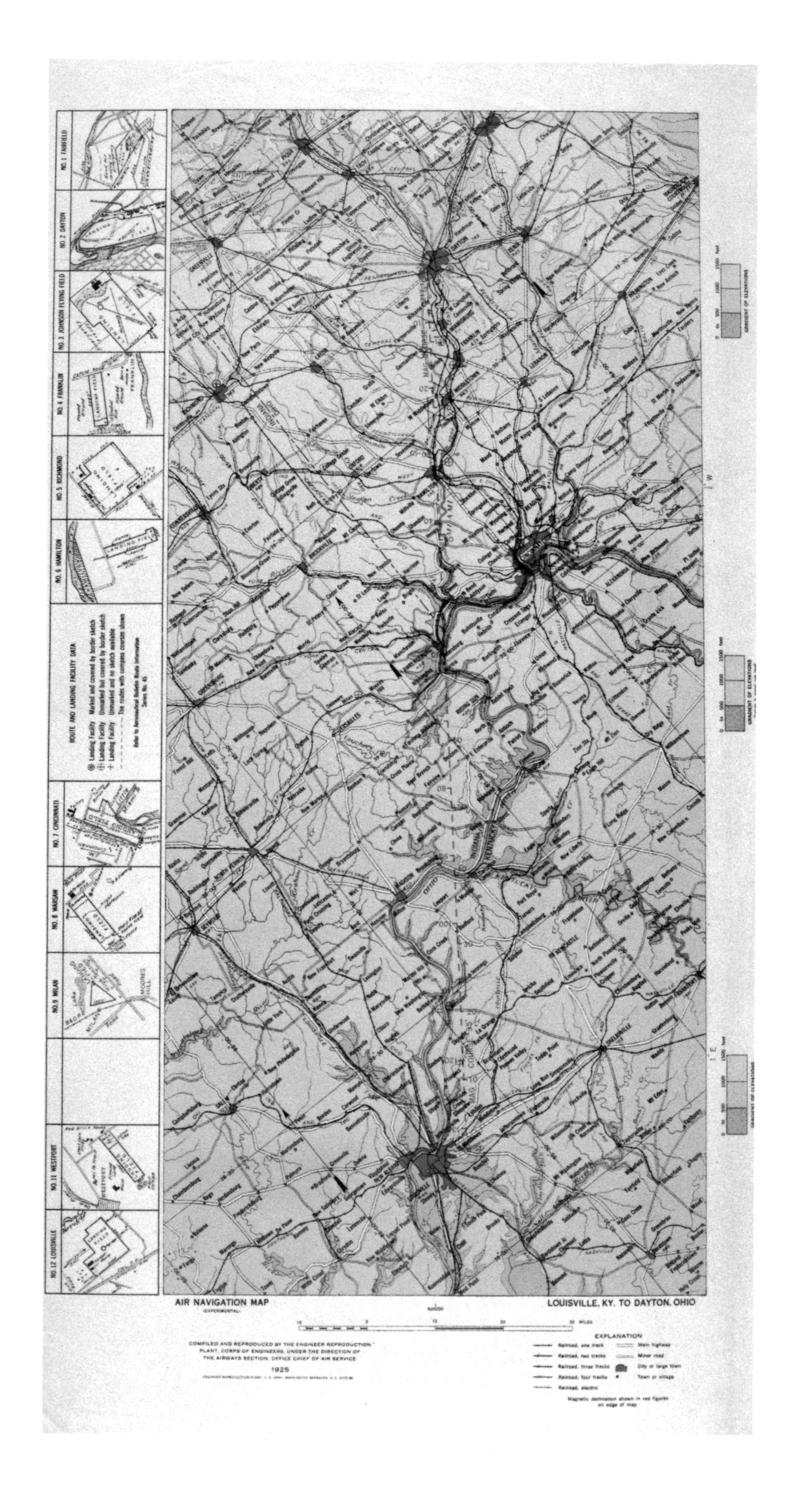

(*opposite*) PLATE 210: U.S. Army Air Service. "Air Navigation Map. Louisville, Ky., to Dayton, Ohio." 1925. Chromolithograph, 69 × 35.5 cm. Records of the Army Air Forces, National Archives, Washington, D.C. *Experimental navigational strip chart of route and landing facility data, with marginal plans of landing fields. Printed by the U.S. Corps of Engineers at their Engineer Reproduction Plant in Washington, D.C., this map is typical of the early navigational charts issued in the 1920s by the War Department which were little more than topographic maps overprinted with navigational aids as these became available.*

PLATE 211: Babson's Statistical Organization, Incorporated. "The Babson Sales and Credit Map—June, 1929." Chromolithograph, 34 × 57 cm. Geography and Map Division, Library of Congress, Washington, D.C. *Special purpose map prepared for bankers, merchants, and investors, revealing sales, construction activity, and building conditions by city and state on the eve of the Great Depression. Published monthly.*

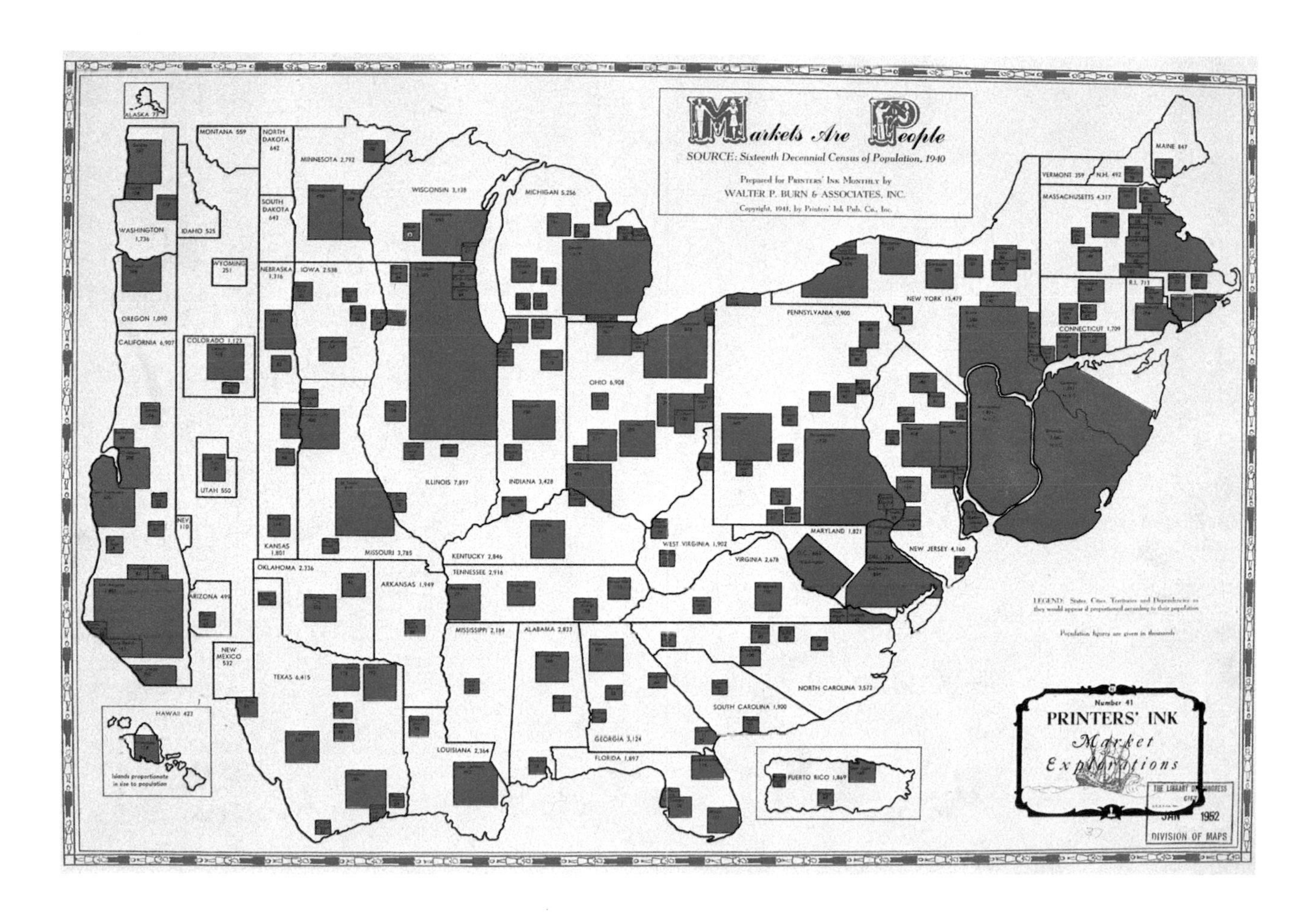

PLATE 212: Walter P. Burn and Associates, Incorporated. "Markets Are People." 1941. Two-color offset lithography, 36 × 50 cm. Geography and Map Division, Library of Congress, Washington, D.C. *Cartogram of the United States scaled in terms of population density rather than geographical distance. Based on the 1940 decennial census. Cartographic technique useful for highlighting a single phenomenon, and popular for propaganda and promotional purposes.*

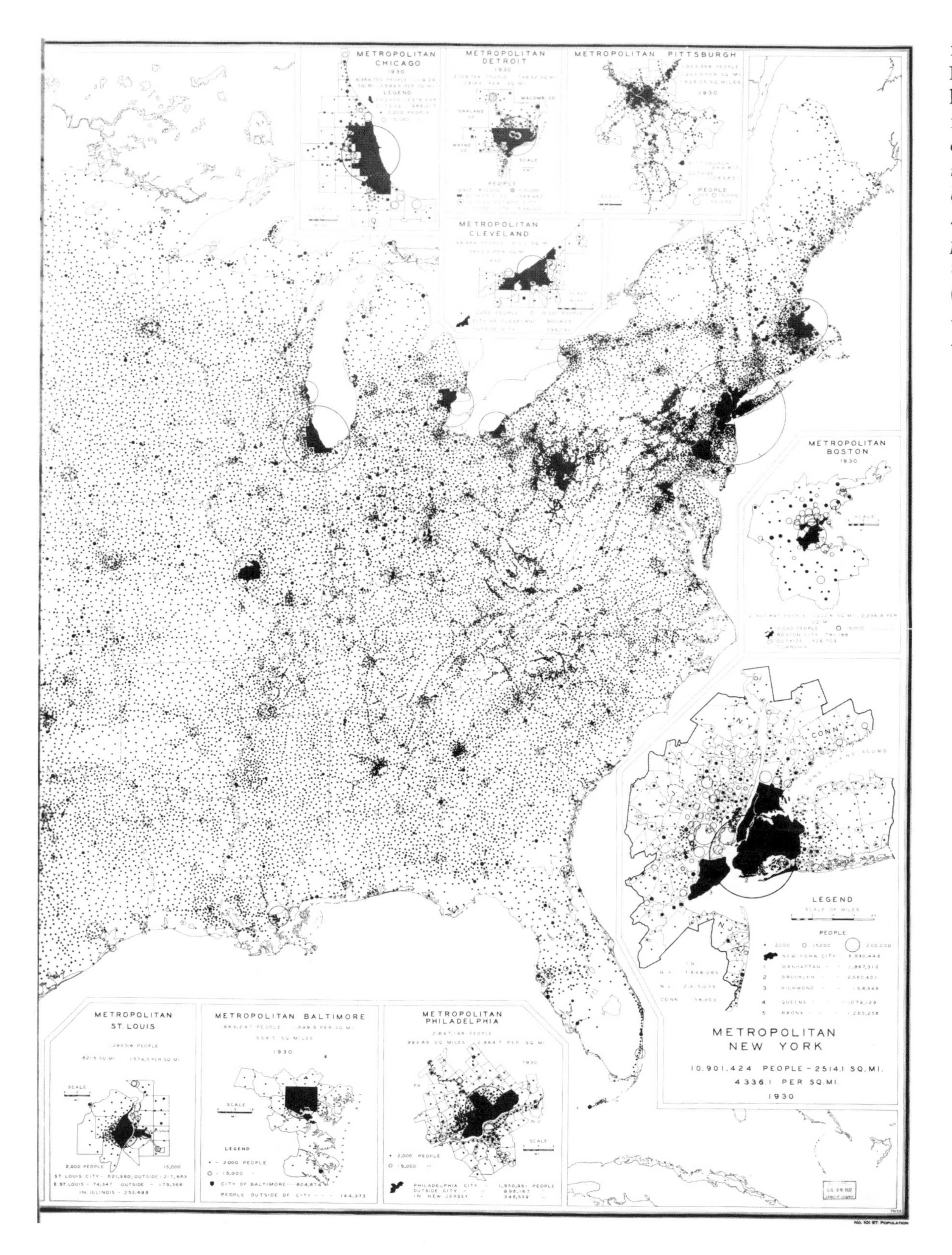

PLATE 213: Floyd A. Stilgenbauer. "A New Population Map of the United States" (eastern half). 1932. Lithograph, entire dimensions 109 × 159 cm. Geography and Map Division, Library of Congress, Washington, D.C. *Eastern half of map depicting population density of the United States by combining uniform dots with circles of graduated size. Based on the 1930 decennial census, and published by Rand McNally. Inset plans of major metropolitan areas show population by wards for (clockwise) Chicago, Detroit, Cleveland, Pittsburgh, Boston, New York, Philadelphia, Baltimore, and St. Louis.*

(opposite) PLATE 214: C. Mackinnon. "Winter Sports in New England." c. 1936. Manuscript, pen and ink on tracing cloth; 87.5 × 67 cm. Records of the National Resources Planning Board, National Archives, Washington, D.C. *A recreational map of New England prepared by the New England Regional Planning Commission to promote tourist trade in winter by pictorial rather than geometrical symbols. Maps such as this were relatively rare until after World War II, when the return of mobility and leisure time encouraged the establishment of new recreational sites, both private and public.*

pression that found favor during World War II was the innovative and interpretive work of Richard Edes Harrison. Combining the graphic landscape technique of Arnim K. Lobeck and the panoramic method of nineteenth-century topographic artists, Harrison prepared a series of perspective terrain maps of large segments of the earth on a global scale. These dramatic illustrations, prepared for *Fortune* magazine over a period of several years to show the major theaters of the war, presented unusual images of the United States (*Plate 218*). Harrison's work was collected and published in 1944 under the title *Look at the World: The Fortune Atlas for World Strategy.*

In 1945 Francis J. Marschner began work on his map of "Major Land Uses in the United States." The first authoritative medium-scale map of land use, it was based on aerial photographs taken by the Department of Agriculture in the late 1930s and early 1940s. Twelve categories of land and land use were depicted by different color symbols. This work was published in 1950 and represents the crowning achievement of Marschner's distinguished career with the Department of Agriculture, spanning more than five decades (*Plate 219*). Marschner, who was born in Austria and educated in Berlin at the Cartographic Institute of the Imperial Army, was cited for his meritorious contribution to the field of American geography by the Association of American Geographers in recognition of this important work.

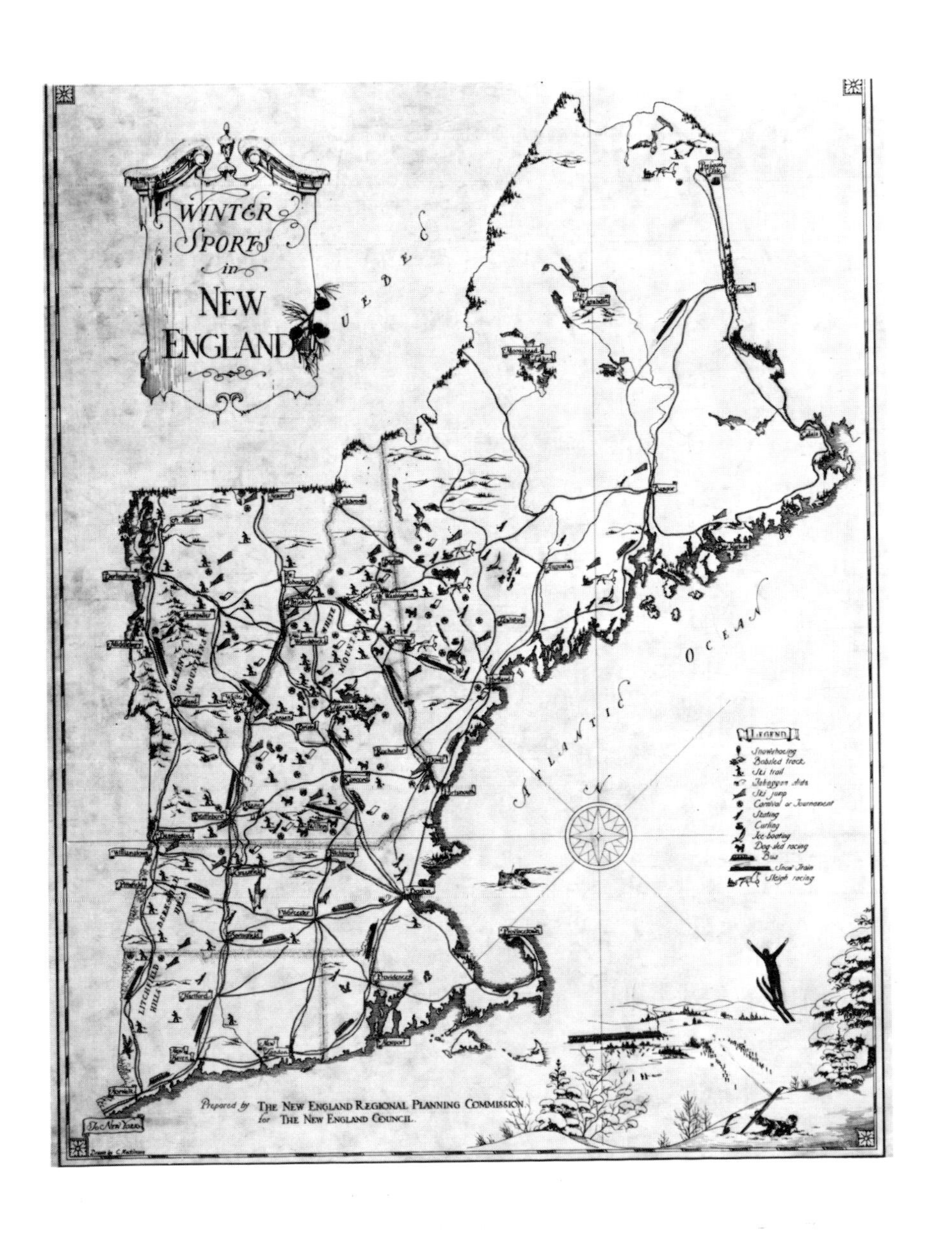

One of the first major mapping programs undertaken after the war was the metropolitan area map series, inaugurated by the U.S. Geological Survey in 1946. The objective was to map all of the large metropolitan areas at a scale of one inch to 2,000 feet; by now some fifty cities are included in this map series. These detailed area maps, each one composed of several quadrangle maps of the National Topographic Map Series (formerly the Topographic Atlas of the United States; see page 311), depict a city's business and residential sections, railroad yards, highways and streets, and public buildings and memorials. Surface relief is portrayed by contour lines which are highlighted by artistic shading.

Utilizing techniques developed during World War II, the Army Map Service (which, as the nation's principal military map production facility during the war, issued more than 500,000,000 map sheets) undertook a new Strategic Map of the United States at the medium scale of one inch to approximately four miles (1 : 250,000). Work on this series began in 1946; the first sheet, which covered Washington, D.C., and vicinity, was published in January 1947. Four hundred and sixty-five map sheets, each measuring 21 by 27 inches, cover the entire country. This ambitious series is based on aerial photographs, the first time that this method of gathering topographic data had been used so extensively for the preparation of medium-scale maps. The colors used (black for cultural features, gray for surface relief, blue for water, yellow for built-up areas, red for roads, and purple for military grid) were selected after thorough testing and their intensity is proportionate to the relative value of these features to the user. The representation of surface relief combines the pictorial qualities of hill shading with the topographic precision of

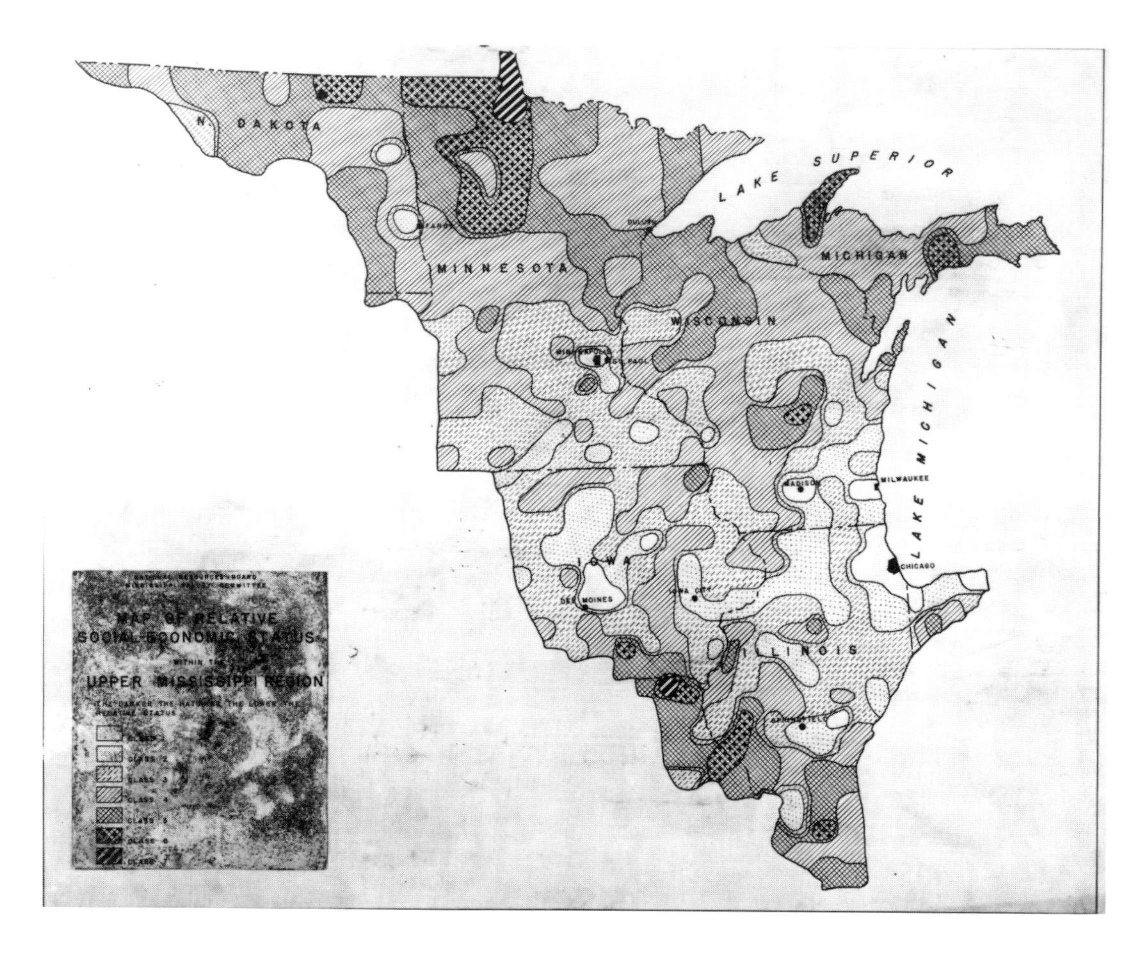

PLATE 215: U.S. National Resources Planning Board. "Map of Relative Social-Economic Status within the Upper Mississippi Region." 1934. Manuscript, pen and ink on tracing cloth; 54 × 65 cm. Records of the National Resources Planning Board, National Archives, Washington, D.C. *One of numerous maps prepared by this New Deal agency to portray social and economic conditions of people and regions. This map shows the standard of living in 1920–1930 based on an analysis of population density, farm abandonment, gross productivity, and net income. Published at a reduced scale in* Report of the Mississippi Valley Committee of the Public Works Administration, . . . to Harold L. Ickes, Administrator, Federal Emergency Administration of Public Works.

(opposite) PLATE 216: U.S. Federal Housing Administration. "Block Data Map. City of Hartford, Connecticut." 1939. Photoprocessed, with pen and ink and watercolor wash; 75.5 × 94 cm. Records of the Federal Housing Administration, National Archives, Washington, D.C. *Map prepared as part of a real property inventory of urban areas. Block data maps of some 370 cities during the Depression, illustrate graphically the social and economic conditions that prevailed.*

contour lines, to aid in rapid interpretation by mobile units and military engineers. The verso of each sheet contains large-scale diagrammatic plans of important towns that appear on the face of the map. This series replaced the eighty-seven-sheet Strategic Map of the United States prepared in 1938–39 at a scale of one inch to eight miles, which answered to the static strategies of World War I rather than the mobile techniques developed during World War II.

Mapping in the third quarter of the twentieth century resists a simple chronological narrative. It is a period characterized by extremely rapid development and innovation in the field of cartography; several new map forms have been introduced while more familiar map types have reached their full fruition during this twenty-five year span. Each of these map forms or map types will be treated in their approximate order of appearance.

One development of World War II mapmaking that proved productive during the 1950s and later was the raised relief or terrain model. Constructed of heavy plaster or rubber, these three-dimensional maps were used extensively during the war, for planning and operation purposes. Topographic models had been made sporadically in the United States since the late nineteenth century as palpable educational and planning aids, and in 1941 a huge relief map of the United States was completed on the campus of the Babson Institute of Business Administration, Wellesley Hills, Massachusetts; at a scale of four inches to the mile, it measures 65 feet in length and cost more than $150,000 to fabricate. With the development of durable, nonflammable vinyl plastic, however, the production of embossed relief models of the United States increased substantially. Because a cartographic image could be impressed on a plastic sheet by employing the same lithographic processes used for printing paper maps, it was much cheaper to produce a map on vinyl plastic than to paint the image by hand

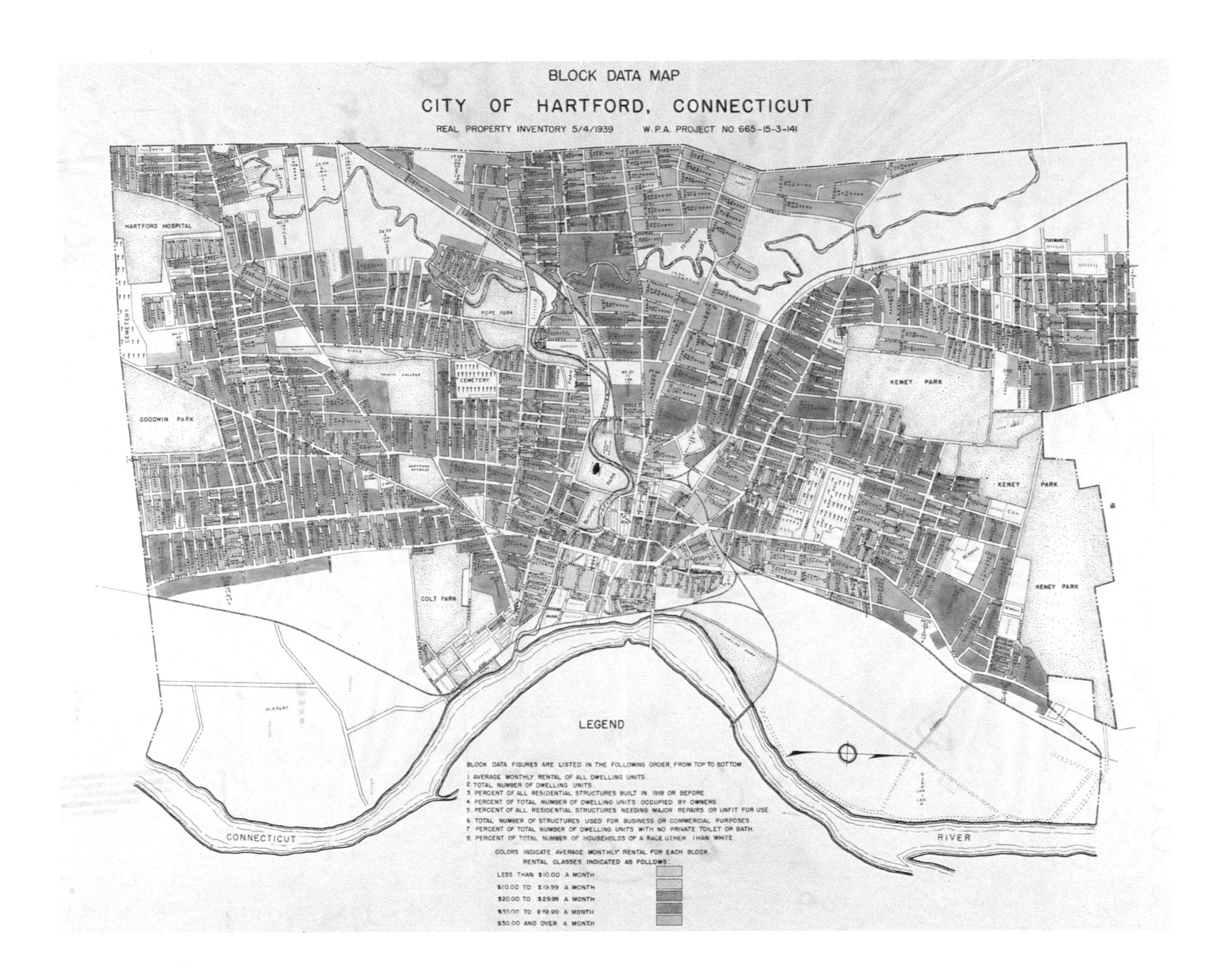

on a plaster or rubber base. One of the earliest companies to exploit this technique was the Aero Service Corporation of Philadelphia, which issued a large three-dimensional plastic relief map of the United States in 1950. Measuring 64 by 40 inches and weighing 2¼ pounds, this map was designed primarily to be a teaching aid. It was lithographed in eleven colors, including seven gradient tints to accentuate topographic features. With the success of embossed relief maps during the Korean War, the Army Map Service undertook a program to produce plastic relief maps of selected sheets of the 1938–39 Strategic Map of the United States.

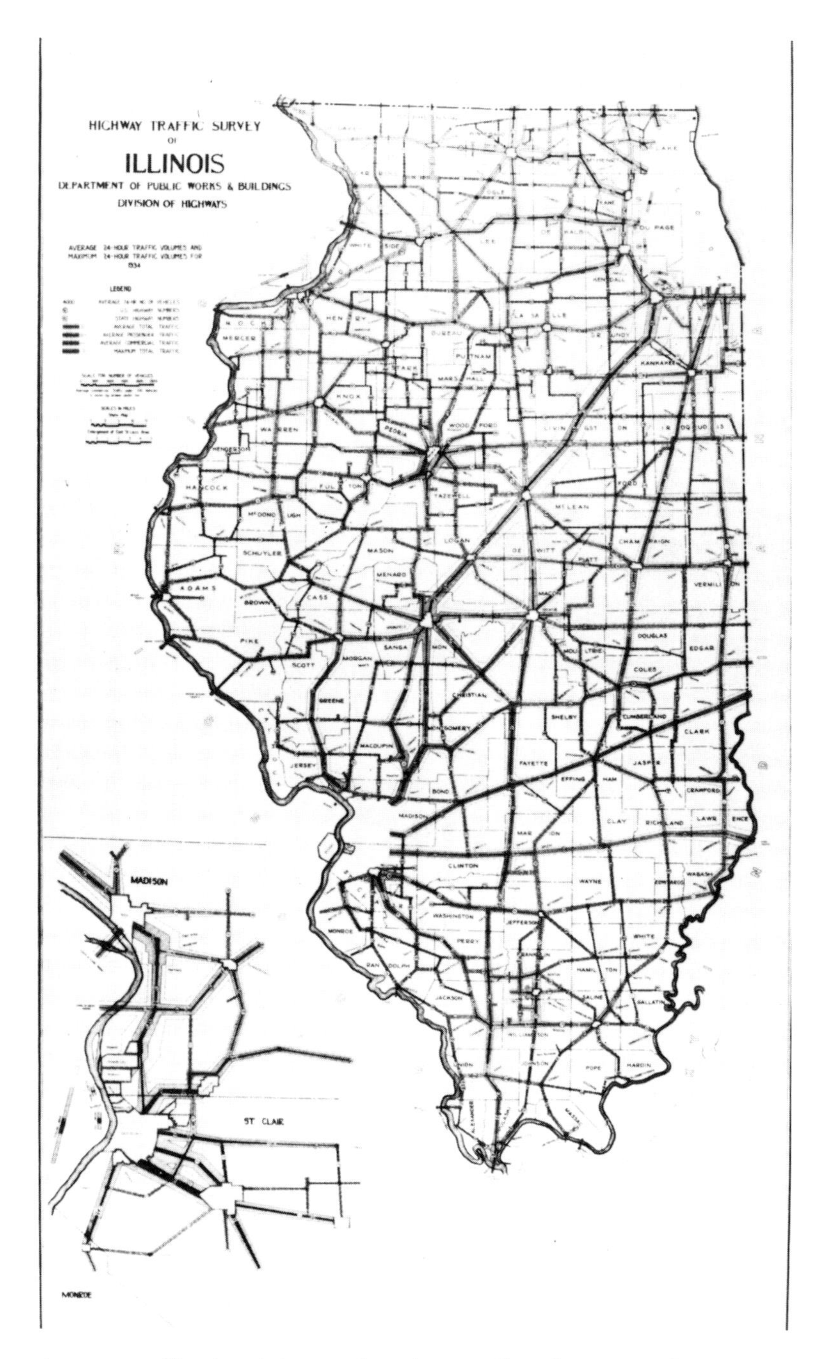

PLATE 217: Illinois Division of Highways. "Highway Traffic Survey of Illinois." 1934. Offset lithography, 100 × 58 cm. Records of the Bureau of Public Roads, National Archives, Washington, D.C.
A typical highway traffic-flow chart developed during the 1930s to aid in the planning and construction of highways. Reveals the average and the maximum traffic volume within twenty-four hours for one year.

Retrospective maps for both the general public and the specialist were produced in large numbers during this period. The National Geographic Society issued a wall-size ten-color historical map of the United States in 1953 to commemorate the 150th anniversary of the Louisiana Purchase. This map was the culmination of the society's "Rediscovering America" series of decorated regional maps, the first issued in 1941; it contained historical references and routes of exploration in addition to principal railroads, canals, highways, and placenames. Many historical maps of local and state interest were also published, such as the pictorial map of *Historic Massachusetts, A Travel Map to Help You Feel at Home in the Bay State.* Designed by the cartographic artist Ernest Dudley Chase, it was published in 1957 by the Massachusetts Department of Commerce to encourage tourism.

Both the Revolutionary and Civil wars were special subjects of the cartographer's pen. Richard Stephenson's list of Civil War maps in the Library of Congress describes eleven maps and atlases of the Southeast published between 1956 and 1965 to celebrate the Civil War centennial (see Bibliography). A number of these are pictorial road maps, such as Edwin Fulwider's "Battlefields and historic shrines, 1861–1865"; subtitled "A motorist's guide to historic sights in the South," Fulwider's map was published in 1961 by the Ford Motor Company and distributed by independent Ford automobile dealers. More accurate and thorough was Volume I of *The West Point Atlas of American Wars,* which contained 138 maps illustrating Civil War campaigns. This two-volume work, edited by Colonel Vincent J. Esposito of the Department of Military Art and Engineering, U.S. Military Academy, was issued to accompany the standard text used at West Point in teaching a course on the Civil War.

A high point of historical mapping was achieved with the publication of the scholarly and attractive *Atlas of Early American History: The Revolutionary Era, 1760–1790,* a joint venture of the Newberry Library in Chicago and the Institute of Early American History and Culture. Published in 1976 under the direction of historian Lester J. Cappon and cartographer Barbara Bartz Petchenik, this six-color atlas, containing some 285 maps and 80 pages of text, took five years to produce at a cost of $1,500,000. The thematic maps comprising this work are organized semichronologically according to cities, boundaries, population, economic activity, and cultural activity. It represents the first successful effort to reconstruct and formulate graphically

Skyline from Pier 10, Brooklyn, 1931, *etching by Reginald Marsh*

Gas, *painting by Edward Hopper, 1940*

PLATE 218: Richard Edes Harrison. "The U.S. from the Outside." 1944. Photolithograph, 35 × 27.5 cm. Reference Collection, National Archives, Washington, D.C. *Three perspective views of the United States on a global scale, made during World War II and illustrating the new vulnerability wrought by the development of the airplane. From Harrison's* Look at the World: The Fortune Atlas for World Strategy.

(opposite) PLATE 219: Francis J. Marschner. "Major Land Uses in the United States." 1950. Photolithograph in color, 62.5 × 98 cm. Records of the Bureau of Agricultural Economics, National Archives, Washington, D.C. *The first authoritative medium-scale map of America's utilization of its vast land resources. Based on analysis of thousands of aerial photographs taken by the U.S. Department of Agriculture in the late 1930s and early 1940s, and printed by the Government Printing Office, Washington, D.C. Twelve major categories of land and land use are depicted by color patterns and symbols.*

the colonial geography of the United States.

Advances in thematic cartography during the third quarter of the twentieth century have provided new spatial images of social and economic characteristics of the United States. Meyer, Broome, and Schweitzer, in their article on "Color Statistical Mapping by the U.S. Bureau of the Census" (see Bibliography), describe in detail the major statistical map series initiated during this period by the U.S. Census Bureau. Two series, for either wall display or desk use, have been prepared. The first, named GE–50 (Geography Series 50), was designed to depict the geographical distribution of census data in three different categories: economic; social, such as percent of population in poverty; and area boundaries of administrative or political interest, such as congressional districts. Sixty maps of this series were issued between 1960 and 1975, each measuring 42 by 30 inches. A second series, denoted GE–70, is more complex in its purpose, and can be used as both a descriptive and an analytical tool. The maps in this series use color to present two related sets of data, such as the number of workers commuting into a county and the percent of workers commuting out of the same county, thus conveying simultane-

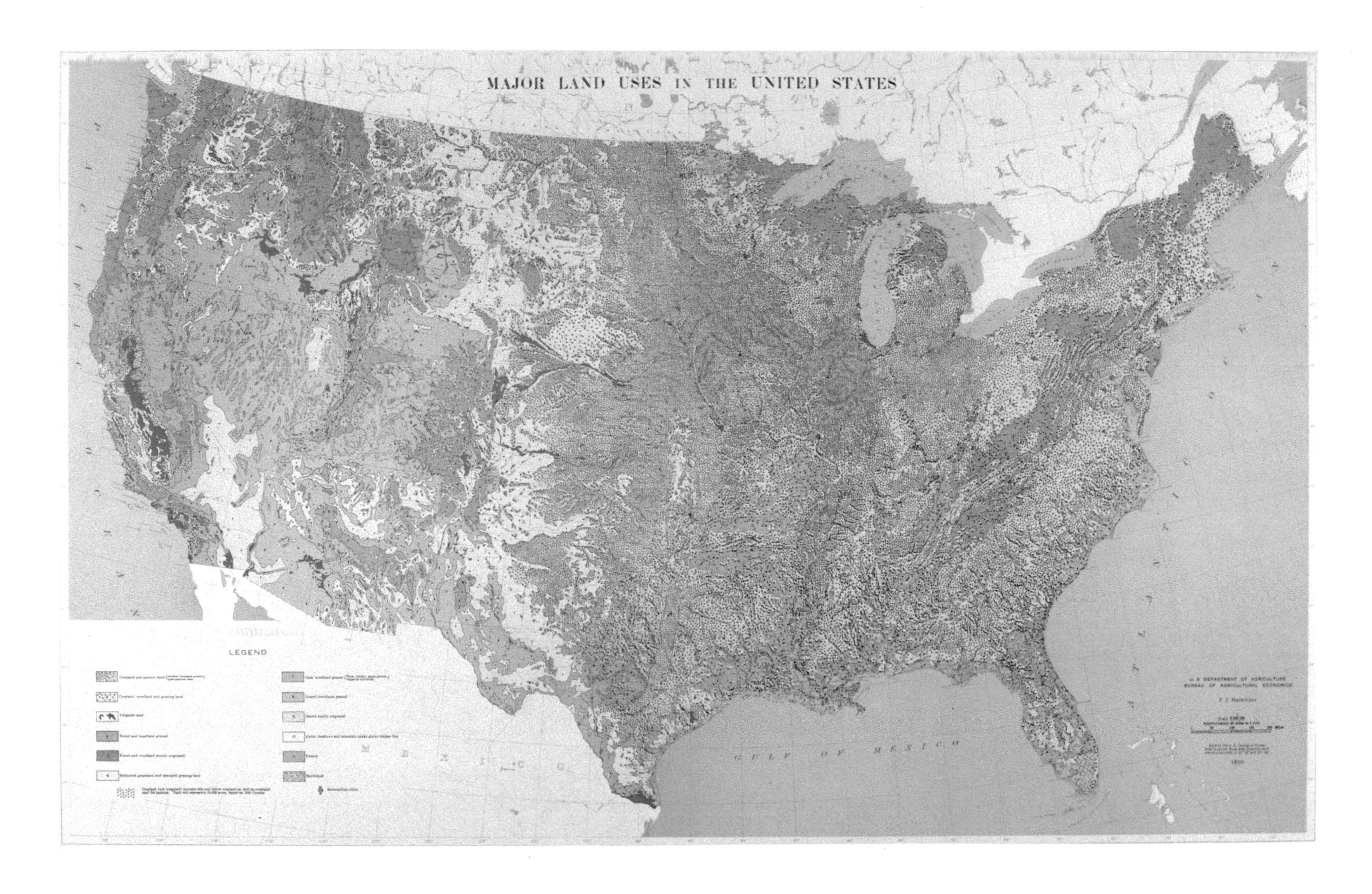

The amount of data used in compiling a coast and geodetic chart in the nineteenth century

ously the spatial distribution and the relationship of the two phenomena (*Plate 220*).

Thematic maps are the major class of maps in *The National Atlas of the United States of America*, our nation's first official public atlas. Published in 1970 under the direction of Arch C. Gerlach, Chief Geographer of the U.S. Geological Survey, this monumental and massive reference work—it weighs fourteen pounds—represents symbolically and artistically the culmination of two hundred years of traditional mapmaking by American cartographers and printers. The 765 maps, especially designed and compiled by cartographers from 84 government agencies, provide a unique and exquisite cartographic compendium of national characteristics ranging from the economic to the physical and socio-cultural. Twenty-five atlas sheets were also published separately for individual distribution, each measuring 19 by 28 inches.

Computer-generated maps, introduced in the 1950s, represent a new, rapid, and accurate method for providing a variety of graphic displays from the same data base. Although computers are still in an early stage of development as a mapmaking technique, they are currently used to collect and synthesize cartographic data and to portray this data in one of three modes: on paper, microfilm, or cathode-ray tubes. The latter provides a temporary image similar to that of a television picture tube.

A special focus of automated cartography during the 1970s has been on urban areas, reflecting both the explosion of urban

ERTS Satellite, illustration by NASA

Datagrid II: a computer-aid mapping system which can create digital information maps from aerial photographs, onto which additional information can be added. The map is stored in the computer and can be revised

statistical and geographical data and the urban character of contemporary America. One of the most ambitious and sophisticated computer-generated map programs is the Census Bureau's Urban Atlas Project, designed in 1974 to display selected census traits for the nation's sixty-five largest metropolitan regions, the traits derived from the 1970 decennial census. Computers are being used in all phases of this project, from digitizing the original census data to "drawing" the individual map images on cathode-ray tubes. These transitory, "CRT" map images are photographed onto 35-mm microfilm, from which printed maps are prepared by standard photographic processes. A separate atlas is published for each metropolitan area, with maps depicting the geographic distribution of population, education, income, occupation, housing value, rental cost, residential ownership, and age of housing unit. A standard legend for each map throughout the series facilitates comparative analysis.

Computer technology has allowed cartographers to generate new and exciting images that challenge contemporary visual concepts. Recent experimental work with nontraditional forms of map generalization has resulted in highly abstract, three-dimensional "surface" maps to depict social and cultural phenomena. Geoffrey Dutton of the Laboratory of Computer Graphics and Spatial Analysis at Harvard University has used this technique to trace the spread of settlement and the growth of cities in the conterminous United States from 1790 through 1970. The result is a series of maps showing the changing population surface by decennial years (*Plate 221*). Dutton's maps are reproduced in his 1975 work entitled *Manifested Destiny: A Graphic Account of the*

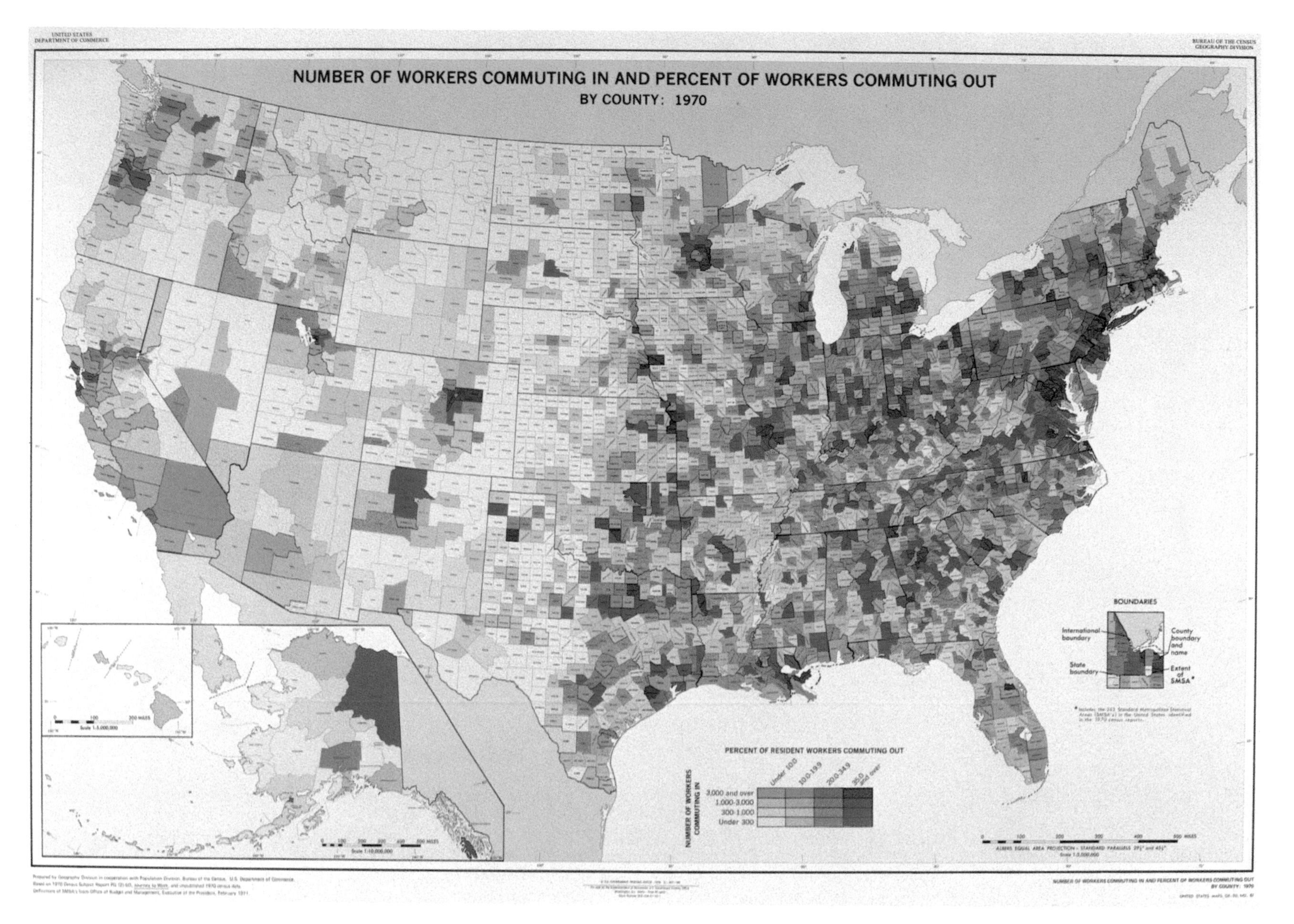

PLATE 220: U.S. Census Bureau. "Number of Workers Commuting In and Percent of Workers Commuting Out by County: 1970." 1975. Photolithograph, 76 × 107 cm. Records of the Census Bureau, National Archives, Washington, D.C. *Sophisticated statistical wall map of the United States from the Census Bureau showing two different but related commuting patterns on the same map. Published by the U.S. Government Printing Office. The development of statistical maps capable of simultaneously displaying the distribution of two variables provides a new graphic tool for analyzing social and economic conditions.*

(opposite) PLATE 221: Geoffrey Dutton. "Selected Maps of U.S. Population Density." 1975. Offset lithograph of cathode-ray tube display; 17.5 × 25 cm. Reproduced from *Lab-Log* (Laboratory for Computer Graphics and Spatial Analysis, Graduate School of Design, Harvard University, 1976). *Computer-produced maps displaying the spread of settlement in the United States for selected decennial censuses from 1790 to 1970, by oblique perspective of three-dimensional surfaces. Abstract thematic maps such as this are generated increasingly by physical and social scientists in the effort to illustrate and analyze complex physical and social processes that have generally defied traditional graphic representation. From Geoffrey Dutton,* Manifested Destiny: A Graphic Account of the Settlement and Growth of America 1790–1970 *(Harvard University, 1975).*

Settlement and Growth of America 1790–1970.

Finally, aerial photographs and maps were combined in the 1950s to produce a new form of map—the orthophotomap. This consists of an aerial photographic image, corrected for horizontal accuracy, that has been overprinted with conventionalized map symbols. It unites the speed and comprehensiveness of photography with the clarity of cartography. Since the late 1950s orthophotomaps have been produced by the U.S. Geological Survey for selected standard topographic maps at a scale of one inch to 2,000 feet, and at various experimental scales (*Plate 222*). The first photomap to cover a larger region was compiled in 1968 from twenty-seven space photographs taken by Gemini astronauts; it embraced some 270,000 square miles of the Southwest and revealed large geological faults and formations not previously visible in conventional aerial photographs.

Another dimension was added to cartography in the 1970s

GREAT WHITE HERON
NATIONAL WILDLIFE REFUGE
NORTHWEST CHANNEL
PEARL BASIN
KEY WEST
NATIONAL WILDLIFE REFUGE
Mule Key
Wisteria Island
Fleming Key
Salt Pond Keys
KEY WEST
KEY WEST INTERNATIONAL AIRPORT
INTRACOASTAL
WATERWAY
HAWK CHANNEL

(opposite) PLATE 222: U.S. Geological Survey. "State of Florida. Key West Quadrangle." 1971. Photolithograph, 68.5 × 60.5 cm. Records of the U.S. Geological Survey, National Archives, Washington, D.C. *Orthophotomap prepared from overprinting an aerial photographic image, corrected for horizontal accuracy, with standardized map symbols. The rapidity with which the orthophotomap can be produced has caused orthophoto procedures to be used increasingly by the U.S. Geological Survey in updating its comprehensive national topographic map series.*

PLATE 223: U.S. Geological Survey. "New Jersey." 1972. Photolithograph, 72.5 × 55 cm. Records of the U.S. Geological Survey, National Archives, Washington, D.C. *Satellite image mosaic from NASA's Earth Resources Technology Satellite (ERTS–I, now Landsat I). Consists of three images acquired from an altitude of 915 kilometers (569 miles), and covers approximately 68,450 square kilometers (over 26,000 square miles). On this "false color" mosaic, red represents vegetation in vigorous growth; dark blue is clear water; light blue depicts polluted water and the heavy concentrations of asphalt and concrete found in urban areas.*

when the U.S. National Aeronautics and Space Administration launched a high-altitude mapping satellite in 1972 designated as ERTS I (Earth Resources Technology Satellite); a second satellite was launched in 1975. These two satellites, renamed Landsat I and II, monitor every point on the earth's surface once every nine days. Two visible colors—red and green—and two frequencies of infrared radiation are recorded and relayed by electronic signals to NASA's Goddard Space Flight Center in Greenbelt, Maryland, where the data are converted to photographic images and computer-compatible tapes. At the U.S. Geological Survey the converted data are used to produce photoimage maps ranging in size from metropolitan areas (*Plate 223*) to the entire North American continent. For the first time Americans can view geographical features of the United States not as represented in one manner or another, but as they actually appear from space.

BIBLIOGRAPHY

Part I: 1500–1800

Andrews, Charles M. *The Colonial Period of American History*. 4 vols. New Haven: Yale University Press, 1934–38.

Atlas of Early American History: The Revolutionary Era, 1760–1790. Lester J. Cappon (editor in chief), Barbara Bartz Petchenik (cartography editor), et al. Published for the Newberry Library and the Institute of Early American History and Culture. Princeton: Princeton University Press, 1976.

Atlas of the American Revolution. Map selection and commentary by Kenneth Nebenzahl. Narrative text by Don Higginbotham. Chicago: Rand McNally and Company, 1974.

Bagrow, Leo. *History of Cartography*. Revised and enlarged by R. A. Skelton. Translated by D. L. Paisey. Cambridge, Mass.: Harvard University Press, 1964.

Berkeley, Edmund, and Berkeley, Dorothy Smith. *Dr. John Mitchell: The Man Who Made the Map of North America*. Chapel Hill: University of North Carolina Press, 1974.

Bricker, Charles. *Landmarks of Mapmaking: An Illustrated Survey of Maps and Mapmakers*. Maps chosen and displayed by R. V. Tooley. Preface by Gerald Roe Crone. Amsterdam: Elsevier, 1968. Reprint. New York: Thomas Y. Crowell Company, 1976.

Brown, Lloyd A. *Early Maps of the Ohio Valley: A Selection of Maps, Plans, and Views Made by Indians and Colonials from 1673 to 1783*. Pittsburgh: University of Pittsburgh Press, 1959.

———. *The Story of Maps*. Boston: Little, Brown and Company, 1949. Reprint. New York: Bonanza Books, 1969.

Burrus, Ernest J. *Kino and the Cartography of Northwestern New Spain*. Tucson: Arizona Pioneers' Historical Society, 1965.

Chiappelli, Fredi, ed. *First Images of America: The Impact of the New World on the Old*. Coedited by J. B. Allen and Robert L. Benson. 2 vols. Berkeley and Los Angeles: University of California Press, 1976.

Cumming, William P. *British Maps of Colonial America*. The Kenneth Nebenzahl, Jr., Lectures in the History of Cartography. Chicago: University of Chicago Press, 1974.

———. *The Southeast in Early Maps: With an Annotated Check List of Printed and Manuscript Regional and Local Maps of Southeastern North America During the Colonial Period*. Princeton: Princeton University Press, 1958.

Cumming, W. P.; Hillier, S. E.; Quinn, D. B.; and Williams, G. *The Exploration of North America, 1630–1776*. New York: G. P. Putnam's Sons, 1974.

Cumming, W. P.; Skelton, R. A.; and Quinn, D. B. *The Discovery of North America*. New York: American Heritage Press, 1972.

De Vorsey, Louis. "Pioneer Charting of the Gulf Stream: The Contributions of Benjamin and William Gerard De Brahm." *Imago Mundi* 28 (1976): 105–20.

Fite, Emerson D., and Freeman, Archibald, eds. *A Book of Old Maps Delineating American History from the Earliest Days Down to the Close of the Revolutionary War*. Cambridge, Mass.: Harvard University Press, 1926. Reprint. New York: Dover Publications, 1969.

Ganong, W. F. *Crucial Maps in the Early Cartography and Place-Nomenclature of the Atlantic Coast of Canada*. Introduction, commentary, and map notes by Theodore E. Layng. Toronto: University of Toronto Press/Royal Society of Canada, 1964.

Harley, J. B.; Petchenik, Barbara Bartz; and Towner, Lawrence W. *Mapping the American Revolutionary War*. The Kenneth Nebenzahl, Jr., Lectures in the History of Cartography. Chicago: University of Chicago Press, 1978.

Harrisse, Henry. *The Discovery of North America: A Critical, Documentary, and Historic Investigation, with an Essay on the Early Cartography of the New World*. London: H. Stevens, 1892. Reprint. Amsterdam: N. Israel, 1961.

LeGear, Clara Egli. "The New England Coasting Pilot of Cyprian Southack." *Imago Mundi* 11 (1954): 137–44.

Lowery, Woodbury. *The Lowery Collection: A Descriptive List of Maps of the Spanish Possessions Within the Present Limits of the United States, 1502–1820*. Edited with notes by Philip Lee Phillips. Washington, D. C.: Government Printing Office, 1912.

Lunny, Robert M. *Early Maps of North America*. Newark: New Jersey Historical Society, 1961.

Morison, Samuel Eliot. *The European Discovery of America*. Vol. 1: *The Northern Voyages, A.D. 500–1600*; Vol. 2: *The Southern Voyages, A.D. 1492–1616*. New York: Oxford University Press, 1971–74.

———. *The Oxford History of the American People*. New York: Oxford University Press, 1965.

———. *Samuel de Champlain: Father of New France*. Boston: Little, Brown and Company, 1972.

Morris, Richard B., ed. *Encyclopedia of Ameri-*

can History. New York: Harper and Brothers, 1953.

Nebenzahl, Kenneth. *A Bibliography of Printed Battle Plans of the American Revolution, 1775–1795*. Chicago: University of Chicago Press, 1975.

Nordenskiöld, A. E. *Facsimile-Atlas to the Early History of Cartography, with Reproductions of the Most Important Maps Printed in XV and XVI Centuries*. Translated by Johan Adolf Ekelöf and Clements R. Markham. Stockholm: P. A. Norstedt & Söner, 1889. Reprint, with corrections. New introduction by J. B. Post. New York: Dover Publications, 1973.

Paullin, Charles O. *Atlas of the Historical Geography of the United States*. Edited by John K. Wright. Carnegie Institution of Washington Publication No. 401. Washington, D.C.: Carnegie Institution; New York: American Geographical Society, 1932.

Phillips, P. Lee. *A List of Maps of America in the Library of Congress*. Preceded by a list of works relating to cartography. Washington, D.C.: Government Printing Office, 1901. Reprint. Amsterdam: Theatrum Orbis Terrarum, 1967.

Ristow, Walter W., ed. *A la Carte: Selected Papers on Maps and Atlases*. Washington, D.C.: Library of Congress, 1972.

Ristow, Walter W., and Skelton, R. A., eds. *Nautical Charts on Vellum in the Library of Congress*. Washington, D.C.: Library of Congress, 1977.

Skelton, R. A. *Explorers' Maps: Chapters in the Cartographic Record of Geographical Discovery*. New York: Frederick A. Praeger, 1958.

———. *Maps: A Historical Survey of Their Study and Collecting*. The Kenneth Nebenzahl, Jr., Lectures in the History of Cartography at the Newberry Library. Chicago: University of Chicago Press, 1972.

Skelton, R. A.; Marston, Thomas E.; and Painter, George D. *The Vinland Map and the Tartar Relation*. Foreword by Alexander O. Vietor. New Haven: Yale University Press, 1965.

Stevens, Henry N. *Lewis Evans, His Map of the Middle British Colonies in America: A Comparative Account of Eighteen Different Editions Published Between 1755 and 1814*. 2d ed. London: H. Stevens, Son, and Stiles, 1920. Reprint. New York: Arno Press, 1971.

Stevenson, Edward Luther, ed. *Maps Illustrating Early Discovery and Exploration in America, 1502–1530*. Reproduced by photography from the original manuscripts. New Brunswick, N. J.: n. p., 1903–6.

Stokes, I. N. Phelps. *The Iconography of Manhattan Island, 1498–1909*. 4 vols. New York: Robert H. Dodd, 1915–28. Reprint. New York: Arno Press, 1967.

Tooley, R. V. *Maps and Map-Makers*. 6th ed. New York: Crown Publishers, 1978.

Tucker, Sara Jones, ed. *Indian Villages of the Illinois Country*. 2 vols. Springfield: Illinois State Museum, 1942–58.

Verner, Coolie. "The First Maps of Virginia, 1590–1673." *The Virginia Magazine of History and Biography*. 58 (1950): 3–15.

———. *Maps of the Yorktown Campaign, 1780–1781: A Preliminary Checklist of Printed and Manuscript Maps Prior to 1800*. Map Collectors' Series No. 18. London: Map Collectors' Circle, 1965.

Wagner, Henry R. *The Cartography of the Northwest Coast of America to the Year 1800*. 2 vols. Berkeley: University of California Press, 1937.

Wheat, Carl I. *Mapping the Transmississippi West, 1540–1861*. Vol. 1. San Francisco: Institute of Historical Cartography, 1957.

Wheat, James Clements, and Brun, Christian F. *Maps and Charts Published in America Before 1800: A Bibliography*. New Haven: Yale University Press, 1969.

Winsor, Justin, ed. *Narrative and Critical History of America*. 8 vols. Boston: Houghton, Mifflin and Company, 1884–89.

Woodward, David, "The Foster Woodcut Map Controversy: A Further Examination of the Evidence." *Imago Mundi*, 21 (1967): 52–61.

World Encompassed, The. An exhibition of the history of maps held at the Baltimore Museum of Art, October 7 to November 23, 1952. Organized by the Peabody Institute Library, the Walters Art Gallery, and the John Work Garrett Library of Johns Hopkins University in cooperation with the Baltimore Museum of Art. Baltimore: Walters Art Gallery, 1952.

Wroth, Lawrence C. "An Unknown Champlain Map of 1616." *Imago Mundi* 11 (1954): 85–94.

———. *The Voyages of Giovanni Verrazzano, 1524–1528*. New Haven: Yale University Press for the Pierpont Morgan Library, 1970.

Part II: Since 1800

Allen, John Logan. *Passage Through the Garden: Lewis and Clark and the Image of the American Northwest*. Urbana: University of Illinois Press, 1975.

Burton, Alfred H. *Conquerors of the Airways: A Brief History of the USAF-ACIC and Aeronautical Charts*. St. Louis: U.S. Aeronautical Chart and Information Center, 1953.

Canan, H. V. "Maps for the Civil War." *Armor: The Magazine of Mobile Warfare* 65 (September–October 1956): 34–42.

Dictionary of American Biography, s.v. "Bien, Julius," by W. L. G. J[oerg].

Dictionary of American Biography, s.v. "Hoen, August," by W. L. G. J[oerg].

"Distinctive Recent Maps." *Surveying and Mapping*. Appeared regularly from 1945 to 1974, when it was transferred to the *Bulletin* of the American Congress of Surveying and Mapping.

Ehrenberg, Ralph E. *Geographical Exploration and Mapping in the 19th Century: A Survey of the Records in the National Archives*. National Archives, Reference Information Paper No. 66. Washington, D.C., 1973.

———. "Taking the Measure of the Land." *Prologue: The Journal of the National Archives* 9 (Fall 1977): 128–50.

Fitchet, Duncan M. "100 Years and Rand McNally." *Surveying and Mapping* 16 (1956): 126–32.

Foster, James W. "Fielding Lucas, Jr., Early 19th Century Publisher of Fine Books and Maps." *Proceedings of the American Antiquarian Society* 65 (1956): 161–212.

Friis, Herman R. "A Brief Review of the Development and Status of Geographical and Cartographical Activities of the United States Government: 1776–1818." *Imago Mundi* 19 (1965): 68–80.

———. "Cartographic and Geographic Activities of the Lewis and Clark Expedition." *Journal of the Washington Academy of Sciences* 44 (1954): 338–51.

———. "The David Dale Owen Map of Southwestern Wisconsin." *Prologue: The Journal of the National Archives* 1 (Spring 1969): 9–28.

———. "Highlights in the First Hundred Years of Surveying and Mapping and Geographical Exploration of the United States by the Federal Government 1775–1880." *Surveying and Mapping* 18 (1958): 186–206.

———. "Statistical Cartography in the United States Prior to 1870 and the Role of Joseph C. G. Kennedy and the U.S. Census Office." *The American Cartographer* 1 (1974): 131–57.

———. "Stephen H. Long's Unpublished Manuscript Map of the United States Compiled in 1820–1822 (?)." *The California Geographer* 8 (1967): 75–87.

Fuechsel, C. F. "Cartographic Activities of the U.S. Geological Survey." *Surveying and Mapping* 9 (1949): 174–82.

Gannett, Henry. "The Mother Maps of the United States." *The National Geographic Magazine* 4 (1892): 101–16.

Goode, J. Paul. "The Map As a Record of Progress in Geography." *Annals of the Association of American Geographers* 17 (1927): 1–14.

Gudde, Erwin G. "Frémont-Preuss and Western Names." *Names: Journal of the American Name Society* 5 (1957): 169–81.

Hargett, Janet L., comp. *List of Selected Maps of States and Territories.* National Archives, Special List No. 29. Washington, D.C., 1973.

Hébert, John R., comp. *Panoramic Maps of Anglo-American Cities: A Checklist of Maps in the Collections of the Library of Congress, Geography and Map Division.* Washington, D.C.: Library of Congress, 1974.

Heynen, William J., comp. *Cartographic Records of the Bureau of Agricultural Economics.* National Archives, Special List No. 28. Washington, D.C., 1971.

Ireland, H. Andrew. "History of the Development of Geological Maps." *Bulletin of the Geological Society of America* 54 (1943): 1227–80.

Joerg, W. L. G. "Recent American Wall Maps: A Review." *The Geographical Review* 14 (1924): 456–64.

Jones, Frank N. "Baltimore Mapmakers: An Account of an Exhibition at the Peabody Institute Library, July–August 1961." *Surveying and Mapping* 21 (1961): 487–91.

Kelsay, Laura E. *Cartographic Records in the National Archives of the United States Relating to American Indians.* National Archives, Reference Information Paper No. 71. Washington, D.C., 1974.

Landen, David. "History of Photogrammetry in the United States." *Photogrammetric Engineering* 18 (1952): 854–98.

Lee, Paul B. "General Drafting Celebrates 50 Years of Mapmaking." *Surveying and Mapping* 19 (1959): 71–73.

LeGear, Clara Egli. *The Hotchkiss Map Collection: A List of Manuscript Maps, Many of the Civil War Period, Prepared by Major Jed. Hotchkiss, and Other Manuscript and Annotated Maps in His Possession.* Washington, D.C.: Library of Congress, 1951.

——— comp. *United States Atlases: A List of National, State, County, City, and Regional Atlases in the Library of Congress.* 2 vols. Washington, D.C.: Library of Congress, 1950–53.

MacDonald, Thomas H. "Map Work of the Public Roads Administration." *The Military Engineer* 32 (1940): 37–38.

McLaughlin, Patrick D. *Transportation in Nineteenth-Century America: A Survey of the Cartographic Records in the National Archives of the United States.* National Archives, Reference Information Paper No. 65. Washington, D.C., 1973.

Martin, Lawrence. "Disturnell's Map." In *Treaties and Other International Acts of the United States of America,* edited by Hunter Miller, vol. 5, pp. 340–70. Publications of the Department of State No. 1017. Washington, D.C.: United States Government Printing Office, 1937.

Merrill, George, ed. and comp. *Contributions to a History of American State Geological and National History Survey.* Smithsonian Institution, United States National Museum, Bulletin 109. Washington, D.C.: Government Printing Office, 1920.

Meyer, Morton A.; Broome, Frederick R.; and Schweitzer, Richard H., Jr. "Color Statistical Mapping by the U.S. Bureau of the Census." *The American Cartographer* 2 (1975): 100–17.

Modelski, Andrew M., comp. *Railroad Maps of the United States: A Selective Annotated Bibliography of Original 19th-Century Maps in the Geography and Map Division of the Library of Congress.* Washington, D.C.: Library of Congress, 1975.

Muehrcke, Phillip C. "Trends in Cartography." In *Focus on Geography: Key Concepts and Teaching Strategies,* edited by Phillip Bacon, pp. 197–225. National Council for the Social Studies, 40th Yearbook. Washington, D.C., 1970.

Munchmeyer, Charlotte, comp. *Cartographic Records of the Federal Housing Administration.* National Archives, Preliminary Inventories No. 45. Washington, D.C., 1952.

Petchenik, Barbara Bartz. "Cartography and the Making of an Historical Atlas: A Memoir." *The American Cartographer* 4 (1977): 11–28.

Raisz, Erwin. *General Cartography.* 2d ed. New York and London: McGraw-Hill Book Company, 1948.

Ristow, Walter W. "A Half Century of Oil-Company Road Maps." *Surveying and Mapping* 24 (1964): 617–37.

———. "Alfred T. Andreas and His Minnesota Atlas." *Minnesota History* 40 (1966): 120–29.

———. "John Melish and His Map of the United States." *The Library of Congress Quarterly Journal of Current Acquisitions* 19 (1962): 159–78.

———. "Lithography and Maps, 1796–1850." In *Five Centuries of Map Printing,* edited by David Woodward, pp. 77–112. The Kenneth Nebenzahl, Jr., Lectures in the History of

Cartography at the Newberry Library. Chicago and London: University of Chicago Press, 1975.

———. "The Map Publishing Career of Robert Pearsall Smith." *The Quarterly Journal of the Library of Congress* 26 (1969): 170–96.

———. "Maps." *The Quarterly Journal of the Library of Congress* 23 (1966): 230–42.

———. *Maps for an Emerging Nation: Commercial Cartography in Nineteenth-Century America.* Washington, D.C.: Library of Congress, 1977.

———. "Nineteenth-Century Cadastral Maps in Ohio." *The Papers of the Bibliographical Society of America* 59 (1965): 306–15.

———. "State Maps of the Southeast to 1833." *The Southeastern Geographer* 16 (1966): 33–40.

———. "United States Fire Insurance and Underwriters Maps, 1852–1968." *The Quarterly Journal of the Library of Congress* 25 (1968): 194–218.

———, comp. *Marketing Maps of the United States: An Annotated Bibliography.* 3d rev. ed. Washington, D.C.: Library of Congress, 1958.

———, comp. *Three-Dimensional Maps: An Annotated List of References Relating to the Construction and Use of Terrain Models.* 2d ed., rev. and enl. Washington, D.C.: Library of Congress, 1964.

Robinson, Arthur H. "Book Reviews: The National Atlas of the United States of America." *Surveying and Mapping* 31 (1971): 330–38.

Robinson, Arthur H.; Morrison, Joel L.; and Muehrcke, Phillip C. "Cartography 1950–2000." *Institute of British Geographers, Transactions,* n.s. 2 (1977): 3–18.

Schweitzer, Richard H., Jr. "Mapping Urban America with Automated Cartography." *American Congress of Surveying and Mapping, Proceedings of the Annual Meeting* 33 (1973): 265–83.

Skop, Jacob. "The New 1:250,000 Scale Map of the Army Map Service." *Surveying and Mapping* 7 (1947): 161–64.

Stephenson, Richard W. "Charles Varlé: Nineteenth Century Cartographer." *American Congress of Surveying and Mapping, Proceeding of the Annual Meeting* 32 (1972): 189–98.

———, comp. *Civil War Maps: An Annotated Lists of Maps and Atlases in Map Collections of the Library of Congress.* Washington, D.C.: Library of Congress, 1961.

———, comp. *Land Ownership Maps: A Checklist of Nineteenth Century United States County Maps in the Library of Congress.* Washington, D.C.: Library of Congress, 1967.

Stephenson, Richard W., and Galneder, Mary. "Anglo-American State and Provincial Thematic Atlases: A Survey and Bibliography." *The Canadian Cartographer* 6 (1969): 15–45.

Thiele, Walter, under the direction of A. F. Kuhlman. *Official Map Publications: A Historical Sketch and a Bibliographical Handbook of Current Maps and Mapping Services in the United States, Canada, Latin America, France, Great Britain, Germany, and Certain Other Countries.* Chicago: American Library Association, 1938.

Thompson, Morris. *Maps for America: Cartographic Products of the U.S. Geological Survey and Others.* Washington, D.C.: Government Printing Office, 1979.

Thrower, Norman J. W. "The County Atlas of the United States." *Surveying and Mapping* 21 (1961): 365–73.

———. *Maps & Man: An Examination of Cartography in Relation to Culture and Civilization.* Englewood Cliffs, N.J.: Prentice-Hall, 1972.

Thrower, Norman J. W., and Jensen, John R. "The Orthophoto and Orthophotomap: Characteristics, Development and Application." *The American Cartographer* 3 (1976): 39–56.

United States, Department of the Interior, Geological Survey. *The United States Geological Survey: Its Origin, Development, Organization, and Operations.* Geological Survey Bulletin No. 227. Washington, D.C.: Government Printing Office, 1904.

United States, National Archives. *Civil War Maps in the National Archives.* National Archives Publication No. 64–12. Washington, D.C., 1964.

———. *Geographical Exploration and Topographic Mapping by the United States Government, 1777–1952 (Exhibition Catalog).* National Archives Publication No. 53-2. Washington, D.C., 1952.

———. *Guide to Cartographic Records in the National Archives.* National Archives Publication No. 71–16. Washington, D.C., 1971.

Warren, Gouverneur K. *Memoir to Accompany the Map of the Territory of the United States From the Mississippi River to the Pacific Ocean, Giving A Brief Account of Each of the Exploring Expeditions Since A.D. 1800 . . .,* Volume 11 of *Reports of Explorations and Surveys, to Ascertain the Most Practicable and Economical Route for a Railroad From the Mississippi River to the Pacific Ocean, Made Under the Direction of the Secretary of War, in 1853–56.* Senate Executive Document 78, 1861.

Wheat, Carl I. *Mapping the Transmississippi West 1540–1861.* Vols. 2–5. San Francisco: Institute of Historical Cartography, 1958–63.

Woodward, David. *The All-American Map: Wax Engraving and Its Influence on Cartography.* Chicago and London: University of Chicago Press, 1977.

———, ed. *Five Centuries of Map Printing.* The Kenneth Nebenzahl, Jr., Lectures in the History of Cartography at the Newberry Library. Chicago and London: University of Chicago Press, 1975.

Wright, John K. "Sections and National Growth: An Atlas of the Historical Geography of the United States." *The Geographical Review* 22 (1932): 353–60.

INDEX

PHOTOGRAPHIC CREDITS

The authors and publisher wish to thank the libraries and museums for permitting the reproduction in black-and-white of paintings, prints, and drawings in their collections. Photographs have been supplied by the owners or custodians of the works of art except for the following, whose courtesy is gratefully acknowledged:

Academy of Natural Sciences of Philadelphia: 293 top; American Philosophical Society, Philadelphia: 238, 239; Anschutz Collection (photo by Milmoe): 258 bottom; Bancroft Library, University of California, Berkeley: 33, 159 bottom, 198, 265, 273, 287, 291, 311 bottom, left; British Museum, London: 76, 79, 209 top; John Carter Brown Library, Brown University, Providence: 293 bottom; Buffalo Historical Society: 151; Amon Carter Museum, Fort Worth: 261; Culver Pictures, New York: 326, 327, 332, 335; Environmental Science Services Administration: 346 top; Thomas Gilcrease Institute, Tulsa: 121; Historical Society of Pennsylvania, Philadelphia: 211; Independence National Historical Park Collection, Philadelphia: 231; Metropolitan Museum of Art, New York: 185 top, 215 top, 235 bottom; Museum of Modern Art, New York: 343 bottom; Museum of the City of New York: 105, 113, 119, 245; NASA: 346 bottom; National Archives, Washington, D.C.: 249; Nebraska State Historical Society, Lincoln: 319; New-York Historical Society: 42, 89, 92 top, 108, 109, 135, 166, 179, 224 top, 234, 253, 260, 271, 276, 290; Peabody Museum, Harvard University, Cambridge: 139; Pennsylvania Academy of the Fine Arts, Philadelphia: 202; Pilgrim Society, Plymouth: 96; Private Collection: 343 top; Rare Book Division, New York Public Library: 49, 70, 126, 208; C. M. Russell Museum, Great Falls, Mont.: 319; Stokes Collection, New York Public Library: 144 bottom, 174, 185 bottom, 221; Summagraphics, Fairfield, Conn.: 347; University of Texas Library, Austin: 102, 278 bottom, 279, 299 top, 286, 306, 307, 310; Utah State Historical Society, Logan: 299 bottom; Walters Art Gallery, Baltimore: 258 top; Yale University Library, New Haven: 251, 311 top.